Business Mathematics and Applications

Central Washington University

Custom 7th Edition

Brechner | Bergeman

CENGAGE
Learning·

Australia • Brazil • Japan • Korea • Mexico • Singapore • Spain • United Kingdom • United States

Business Mathematics and Applications: Central Washington University

Contemporary Mathematics for Business and Consumers, Seventh Edition
Robert Brechner | George Bergeman

© 2015, 2012 Cengage Learning. All rights reserved.

For product information and technology assistance, contact us at
Cengage Learning Customer & Sales Support, 1-800-354-9706

For permission to use material from this text or product,
submit all requests online at **cengage.com/permissions**
Further permissions questions can be emailed to
permissionrequest@cengage.com

This book contains select works from existing Cengage Learning resources and was produced by Cengage Learning Custom Solutions for collegiate use. As such, those adopting and/or contributing to this work are responsible for editorial content accuracy, continuity and completeness.

Compilation © 2015 Cengage Learning

ISBN: 978-1-337-04707-4

WCN: 01-100-101

Cengage Learning
20 Channel Center Street
Boston, MA 02210
USA

Cengage Learning is a leading provider of customized learning solutions with office locations around the globe, including Singapore, the United Kingdom, Australia, Mexico, Brazil, and Japan. Locate your local office at:
www.international.cengage.com/region.

Cengage Learning products are represented in Canada by Nelson Education, Ltd.

For your lifelong learning solutions, visit **www.cengage.com/custom.**

Visit our corporate website at **www.cengage.com.**

BRIEF CONTENTS

CONTENTS

Percents and Their Applications in Business

PERFORMANCE OBJECTIVES

UNDERSTANDING AND CONVERTING PERCENTS

SECTION I

It takes only a glance at the business section of a newspaper or an annual report of a company to see how extensively percents are applied in business. Percents are the primary way of measuring change among business variables. For example, a business might report "revenue is up 6% this year" or "expenses have been cut by 2.3% this month." Interest rates, commissions, and many taxes are expressed in percent form. You may have heard phrases like these: "Sunnyside Bank charged 12% on the loan," "A real estate broker made 5% commission on the sale of the property," or "The state charges a $6\frac{1}{2}$% sales tax." Even price changes are frequently advertised as percents, "Sears Dishwasher Sale—All Models, 25% off!"

To this point, we have learned that fractions and decimals are ways of representing parts of a whole. Percents are another way of expressing quantity with relation to a whole. **Percent** means "per hundred" or "parts per hundred" and is represented by the **percent sign, %.**

Percents are numbers equal to a fraction with a denominator of 100. Five percent, for example, means five parts out of 100 and may be written in the following ways:

Percents are commonly used in retailing to advertise discounts.

5 percent	5%	5 hundredths	$\frac{5}{100}$	.05

Before performing any mathematical calculations with percents, they must be converted to either decimals or fractions. Although this function is performed automatically by the percent key on a calculator, Section I of this chapter covers the procedures for making these conversions manually. Sections II and III introduce you to some important applications of percents in business.

percent sign The symbol, %, used to represent percents. For example, 1 percent would be written 1%.

percent A way of representing the parts of a whole. Percent means "per hundred" or "parts per hundred."

CONVERTING PERCENTS TO DECIMALS AND DECIMALS TO PERCENTS

6-1

Because percents are numbers expressed as parts per 100, the percent sign, %, mean multiplication by $\frac{1}{100}$. Therefore, 25% means

$$25\% = 25 \times \frac{1}{100} = \frac{25}{100} = .25$$

STEPS FOR CONVERTING A PERCENT TO A DECIMAL

STEP 1. Remove the percent sign.

STEP 2. Divide by 100.

Note: If the percent is a fraction such as $\frac{3}{8}$% or a mixed number such as $4\frac{3}{4}$%, change the fraction to a decimal; then follow Steps 1 and 2 above.

$$\frac{3}{8}\% = .375\% = .00375 \qquad 4\frac{3}{4}\% = 4.75\% = .0475$$

Note: If the percent is a fraction such as $\frac{2}{3}$%, which converts to a repeating decimal, .66666, round the decimal to hundredths, .67; then follow Steps 1 and 2 above.

$$\frac{2}{3}\% = .67\% = .0067$$

> **Learning Tip**
>
> To divide a number by 100, move the decimal point two places to the left. Add zeros as needed.
>
> Remember, if there is no decimal point, it is understood to be to the right of the digit in the ones place. (24 = 24.)

EXAMPLE 1 — CONVERTING PERCENTS TO DECIMALS

Convert the following percents to decimals.

a. 44%   b. 233%   c. 56.4%   d. .68%   e. $18\frac{1}{4}$%   f. $\frac{1}{8}$%   g. $9\frac{1}{3}$%

▶ SOLUTIONSTRATEGY

Remove the percent sign and move the decimal point two places to the left.

a. 44% = .44   b. 233% = 2.33   c. 56.4% = .564   d. .68% = .0068

e. $18\frac{1}{4}\% = 18.25\% = .1825$ f. $\frac{1}{8}\% = .125\% = .00125$ g. $9\frac{1}{3}\% = 9.33\% = .0933$

▶ TRYITEXERCISE 1

Convert the following percents to decimals.

a. 27%   b. 472%   c. 93.7%   d. .81%   e. $12\frac{3}{4}\%$ f. $\frac{7}{8}\%$

CHECK YOUR ANSWERS WITH THE SOLUTIONS ON PAGE 182.

STEPS FOR CONVERTING A DECIMAL OR WHOLE NUMBER TO A PERCENT

STEP 1. Multiply by 100.

STEP 2. Write a percent sign after the number.

STEP 3. If there are fractions involved, such as $\frac{3}{4}$, convert them to decimals first; then proceed with Steps 1 and 2 above.

$$\frac{3}{4} = .75 = 75\%$$

Learning Tip

To multiply a number by 100, move the decimal point two places to the right. Add zeros as needed. As a "navigational aid" to the direction of the decimal point, consider the words *decimal* and *percent* as written alphabetically, with *decimal* preceding *percent*.

• When converting from decimal to percent, the decimal moves **right**

    decimal → percent

• When converting from percent to decimal, the decimal moves **left**

    decimal ← percent

EXAMPLE2   CONVERTING DECIMALS TO PERCENTS

Convert the following decimals or whole numbers to percents.

a. .5   b. 3.7   c. .044   d. $.09\frac{3}{5}$ e. 7   f. $6\frac{1}{2}$

▶ SOLUTIONSTRATEGY

Move the decimal point two places to the right and add a percent sign.

a. .5 = 50%   b. 3.7 = 370%   c. .044 = 4.4%

d. $.09\frac{3}{5} = .096 = 9.6\%$ e. 7 = 700%   f. $6\frac{1}{2} = 6.5 = 650\%$

▶ TRYITEXERCISE 2

Convert the following decimals or whole numbers to percents.

a. .8   b. 1.4   c. .0023   d. $.016\frac{2}{5}$ e. 19   f. $.57\frac{2}{3}$

CHECK YOUR ANSWERS WITH THE SOLUTIONS ON PAGE 182.

CONVERTING PERCENTS TO FRACTIONS AND FRACTIONS TO PERCENTS

6-2

STEPS FOR CONVERTING PERCENTS TO FRACTIONS

STEP 1. Remove the percent sign.

STEP 2. (*If the percent is a whole number*) Write a fraction with the percent as the numerator and 100 as the denominator. If that fraction is improper, change it to a mixed number. Reduce the fraction to lowest terms.

or

STEP 2. (*If the percent is a fraction*) Multiply the number by $\frac{1}{100}$ and reduce to lowest terms.

or

STEP 2. (*If the percent is a decimal*) Convert it to a fraction and multiply by $\frac{1}{100}$. Reduce to lowest terms.

Dollars AND Sense

If you have not already done so and your instructor allows it, this would be a good time to purchase a business calculator. There are many choices available today in the $10 to $40 price range. Popular brands include Hewlett-Packard and Texas Instruments. Calculators are also available from Canon, Sharp, Casio, and others.

To help you choose a calculator, go to www.shopzilla.com and enter *business calculators* in the "I'm Shopping for" box.

EXAMPLE3 CONVERTING PERCENTS TO FRACTIONS

Convert the following percents to reduced fractions, mixed numbers, or whole numbers.

a. 3%   b. 57%   c. $2\frac{1}{2}\%$ d. 150%   e. 4.5%   f. 600%

SOLUTIONSTRATEGY

a. $3\% = \frac{3}{100}$

b. $57\% = \frac{57}{100}$

c. $2\frac{1}{2}\% = \frac{5}{2} \times \frac{1}{100} = \frac{5}{200} = \frac{1}{40}$

d. $150\% = \frac{150}{100} = 1\frac{50}{100} = 1\frac{1}{2}$

e. $4.5\% = 4\frac{1}{2}\% = \frac{9}{2} \times \frac{1}{100} = \frac{9}{200}$

f. $600\% = \frac{600}{100} = 6$

TRYITEXERCISE 3

Convert the following percents to reduced fractions, mixed numbers, or whole numbers.

a. 9%   b. 23%   c. 75%   d. 225%   e. 8.7%   f. 1,000%

CHECK YOUR ANSWERS WITH THE SOLUTIONS ON PAGE 182.

STEPS FOR CONVERTING FRACTIONS TO PERCENTS

STEP 1. Change the fraction to a decimal by dividing the numerator by the denominator.

STEP 2. Multiply by 100. (Move the decimal point two places to the right. Add zeros as needed.)

STEP 3. Write a percent sign after the number.

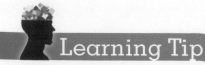

Learning Tip

Use the % key on your calculator to save the step of multiplying by 100.

For example: $\frac{44}{50} = .88 = 88\%$.

Calculator sequence:

$$44 \div 50 \; \boxed{\%} = 88$$

Note: Scientific and business calculators require pushing the $\boxed{=}$ button after the % key; common arithmetic calculators do not.

EXAMPLE 4 — CONVERTING FRACTIONS TO PERCENTS

Convert the following fractions or mixed numbers to percents.

a. $\frac{1}{10}$ b. $\frac{69}{100}$ c. $\frac{15}{4}$ d. $4\frac{3}{8}$ e. $\frac{18}{25}$ f. $13\frac{1}{2}$

SOLUTIONSTRATEGY

Change the fractions to decimals by dividing the denominator into the numerator; then move the decimal point two places to the right and add a percent sign.

a. $\frac{1}{10} = .10 = \underline{10\%}$ b. $\frac{69}{100} = .69 = \underline{69\%}$ c. $\frac{15}{4} = 3\frac{3}{4} = 3.75 = \underline{375\%}$

d. $4\frac{3}{8} = 4.375 = \underline{437.5\%}$ e. $\frac{18}{25} = .72 = \underline{72\%}$ f. $13\frac{1}{2} = 13.5 = \underline{1350\%}$

▶ TRYITEXERCISE 4

Convert the following fractions or mixed numbers to percents.

a. $\frac{1}{5}$ b. $\frac{70}{200}$ c. $\frac{23}{5}$ d. $6\frac{9}{10}$ e. $\frac{45}{54}$ f. $140\frac{1}{8}$

CHECK YOUR ANSWERS WITH THE SOLUTIONS ON PAGE 182.

SECTION I   **6**   REVIEW EXERCISES

Convert the following percents to decimals.

1. 28%
   .28

2. 76%

3. 13.4%

4. 121%

5. 42.68%

6. $6\frac{1}{2}\%$

7. .02%

8. $\frac{3}{5}\%$

9. $125\frac{1}{6}\%$

10. 2,000%

Convert the following decimals or whole numbers to percents.

11. 3.5
    350%

12. .11

13. 46

14. $.34\frac{1}{2}$

15. .00935

16. $.9\frac{3}{4}$

17. 164

18. .04

19. 5.33

20. $1.15\frac{5}{8}$

Convert the following percents to reduced fractions, mixed numbers, or whole numbers.

21. 5%
    $\frac{5}{100} = \frac{1}{20}$

22. 75%

23. 89%

24. 230%

25. 38%   26. 37.5%   27. $62\frac{1}{2}$%

28. 450%   29. 125%   30. .8%

Convert the following fractions or mixed numbers to percents.

31. $\frac{3}{4}$

.75 = 75%

32. $\frac{1}{8}$ 33. $\frac{12}{5}$ 34. $6\frac{3}{10}$

35. $\frac{125}{100}$ 36. $\frac{78}{24}$ 37. $\frac{3}{16}$ 38. $4\frac{1}{5}$

39. $\frac{35}{100}$ 40. $\frac{375}{1,000}$

Use the pie chart "What is Your Favorite Cookie?" to find the decimal and reduced fraction equivalent for Exercises 41–45.

	Type of Cookie	Decimal	Reduced Fraction
41.	Chocolate chip		
42.	Peanut butter		
43.	Oatmeal		
44.	Sugar/Shortbread		
45.	Other		

What is your favorite cookie?

Chocolate chip 53%
Peanut butter 16%
15% Oatmeal
11% Sugar/shortbread
5% Other

Source: Impulse Research for Downtown Cookie Co. survey of 1,033 adults

Anne R. Carey and Sam Ward, *USA Today*

BUSINESS DECISION: ENHANCING THE PIE

Disney Dollars

46. You have been asked to make a presentation about The Walt Disney Company. In your research, you locate the accompanying pie chart, which shows Disney revenue by segment expressed in billions of dollars.

To enhance your presentation, you have decided to convert the dollar amounts to percents and display both numbers.

a. What is the total revenue?

b. What percent (rounded to the nearest tenth percent) does each segment contribute to the total revenue?

    Media Networks   Parks and Resorts

    Consumer Products   Studio Entertainment

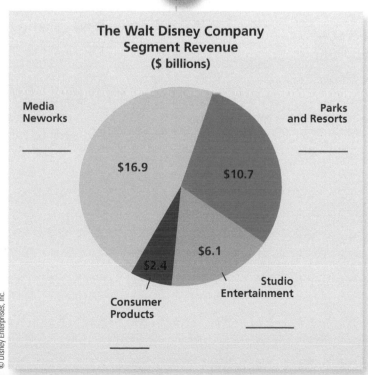

The Walt Disney Company Segment Revenue ($ billions)

Media Networks — $16.9

Parks and Resorts — $10.7

Studio Entertainment — $6.1

Consumer Products — $2.4

SECTION II | 6 | USING THE PERCENTAGE FORMULA TO SOLVE BUSINESS PROBLEMS

base The variable of the percentage formula that represents 100%, or the whole thing.

portion The variable of the percentage formula that represents a part of the base.

rate The variable of the percentage formula that defines how much or what part the portion is of the base. The rate is the number with the percent sign.

Now that we have learned to manipulate percents, let's look at some of their practical applications in business. Percent problems involve the use of equations known as the percentage formulas. These formulas have three variables: the **base**, the **portion**, and the **rate**. In business situations, two of the variables will be given and are the *knowns*; one of the variables will be the *unknown*.

Once the variables have been properly identified, the equations are simple to solve. The variables have the following characteristics, which should be used to help identify them:

BASE: The base is the number that represents 100%, or the *whole thing*. It is the starting point, the beginning, or total value of something. The base is often preceded by the word *of* in the written statement of the situation because it is multiplied by the rate.

PORTION: The portion is the number that represents a *part* of the base. The portion is always in the same terms as the base. For example, if the base is dollars, the portion is dollars; if the base is people, the portion is people; if the base is production units, the portion will be production units. The portion often has a "unique characteristic" that is being measured or compared with the base. For example, if the base is the total number of cars in a parking lot, the portion could be the part of the total cars that are convertibles (the unique characteristic).

RATE: The rate is easily identified. It is the number with the *percent sign* or the word *percent*. It defines what part the portion is of the base. If the rate is less than 100%, the portion is less than the base. If the rate is 100%, the portion is equal to the base. If the rate is more than 100%, the portion is greater than the base.

The following percentage formulas are used to solve percent problems:

Portion = Rate × Base	$P = R \times B$
Rate = $\dfrac{\textbf{Portion}}{\textbf{Base}}$	$R = \dfrac{P}{B}$
Base = $\dfrac{\textbf{Portion}}{\textbf{Rate}}$	$B = \dfrac{P}{R}$

STEPS FOR SOLVING PERCENTAGE PROBLEMS

STEP 1. Identify the two knowns and the unknown.

STEP 2. Choose the formula that solves for that unknown.

STEP 3. Solve the equation by substituting the known values for the letters in the formula.

Hint: By remembering the one basic formula, $P = R \times B$, you can derive the other two by using your knowledge of solving equations from Chapter 5. Because multiplication is indicated, we isolate the unknown by performing the inverse, or opposite, operation, division.

Learning Tip

Don't confuse the word *percentage* with the percent, or rate. The *percentage* means the portion, not the rate.

To solve for rate, R, divide both sides of the equation by B:

$$P = R \times B \longrightarrow \frac{P}{B} = \frac{R \times \cancel{B}}{\cancel{B}} \longrightarrow \frac{P}{B} = R$$

To solve for base, B, divide both sides of the equation by R:

$$P = R \times B \longrightarrow \frac{P}{R} = \frac{\cancel{R} \times B}{\cancel{R}} \longrightarrow \frac{P}{R} = B$$

Another method for remembering the percentage formulas is by using the Magic Triangle.

The Magic Triangle

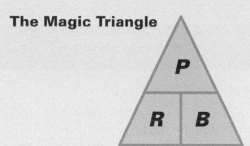

The triangle is divided into three sections representing the portion, rate, and base. By circling or covering the letter in the triangle that corresponds to the *unknown* of the problem, the triangle will "magically" reveal the correct formula to use.

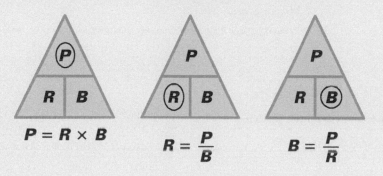

$$P = R \times B \qquad R = \frac{P}{B} \qquad B = \frac{P}{R}$$

SOLVING FOR THE PORTION

Remember, the portion is a part of the whole and will always be in the same terms as the base. It is found by multiplying the rate times the base: $P = R \times B$. The following examples will demonstrate solving for the portion.

EXAMPLE 5   SOLVING FOR THE PORTION

What is the portion if the base is \$400 and the rate is 12%?

▶ SOLUTIONSTRATEGY

Substitute the knowns for the letters in the formula Portion = Rate × Base. In this problem, 12% is the rate and \$400 is the base. Do not forget to convert the percent (rate) to a decimal by deleting the % sign and moving the decimal point two places to the left (12% = .12).

$$P = R \times B$$
$$P = 12\% \times 400 = .12 \times 400 = 48$$
$$\underline{\text{Portion} = \$48}$$

6-3

$$P = R \times B$$

Learning Tip

Shortcut
Remember to use the % key on your calculator.
$$12\,\boxed{\%}\,\boxed{\times}\,400\,\boxed{=}\,48$$

▶TRYITEXERCISE 5

Solve the following for the portion.

What is the portion if the base is 980 and the rate is 55%?

CHECK YOUR ANSWER WITH THE SOLUTION ON PAGE 182.

EXAMPLE6 USING THE PERCENTAGE FORMULA

What number is 43.5% of 250?

▶SOLUTIONSTRATEGY

In this problem, the rate is easily identified as the term with the % sign. The base, or whole amount, is preceded by the word *of*. We use the formula Portion = Rate × Base, substituting the knowns for the letters that represent them.

$$P = R \times B$$
$$P = 43.5\% \times 250 = .435 \times 250 = 108.75$$
$$\underline{108.75}$$

▶TRYITEXERCISE 6

Solve the following for the portion.

What number is 72% of 3,200?

CHECK YOUR ANSWER WITH THE SOLUTION ON PAGE 182.

EXAMPLE7 USING THE PERCENTAGE FORMULA

Republic Industries produced 6,000 stoves last week. If 2% of them were defective, how many defective stoves were produced?

▶SOLUTIONSTRATEGY

To solve this problem, we must first identify the variables. Because 2% has the percent sign, it is the rate. The terms are stoves; the total number of stoves (6,000) is the base. The unique characteristic of the portion, the unknown, is that they were defective.

$$P = R \times B$$
$$P = 2\% \times 6,000 = .02 \times 6,000 = 120$$
$$\underline{120 = \text{Number of defective stoves last week}}$$

►TRYITEXERCISE 7

Solve the following for the portion.

a. Premier Industries has 1,250 employees. 16% constitute the sales staff. How many employees are in sales?

b. Aventura Savings & Loan requires a 15% down payment on a mortgage loan. What is the down payment needed to finance a $148,500 home?

CHECK YOUR ANSWERS WITH THE SOLUTIONS ON PAGE 182.

SOLVING FOR THE RATE

6-4

The rate is the variable that describes what part of the base is represented by the portion. It is *always* the term with the percent sign. When solving for the rate, your answer will be a decimal. Be sure to convert the decimal to a percent by moving the decimal point two places to the right and adding a percent sign. We use the formula

$$\text{Rate} = \frac{\text{Portion}}{\text{Base}} \quad \text{or} \quad R = \frac{P}{B}$$

The following examples demonstrate solving for the rate.

$$R = \frac{P}{B}$$

EXAMPLE8 SOLVING FOR THE RATE

What is the rate if the base is 160 and the portion is 40?

►SOLUTIONSTRATEGY

Substitute the knowns for the letters in the formula.

$$\text{Rate} = \frac{\text{Portion}}{\text{Base}}$$

$$R = \frac{P}{B}$$

$$R = \frac{40}{160} = .25 = 25\%$$

$$\underline{\text{Rate} = 25\%}$$

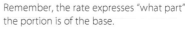

Learning Tip

Remember, the rate expresses "what part" the portion is of the base.
- When the rate is less than 100%, the portion is *less* than the base.
- When the rate is more than 100%, the portion is *more* than the base.
- When the rate is 100%, the portion *equals* the base.

►TRYITEXERCISE 8

Solve the following for the rate. Round to the nearest tenth when necessary.

What is the rate if the base is 21 and the portion is 9?

CHECK YOUR ANSWER WITH THE SOLUTION ON PAGE 182.

EXAMPLE9 USING THE PERCENTAGE FORMULA

What percent of 700 is 56?

▶SOLUTIONSTRATEGY

This problem asks what percent, indicating that the rate is the unknown. The 700 is preceded by the word *of* and is therefore the base. The 56 is part of the base and is therefore the portion. Once again we use the formula $R = P \div B$, substituting the knowns for the letters that represent them.

$$R = \frac{P}{B}$$

$$R = \frac{56}{700} = .08 = 8\%$$

$$\underline{\underline{8\%}}$$

▶TRYITEXERCISE 9

Solve the following for the rate. Round to the nearest tenth when necessary.

67 is what percent of 142?

CHECK YOUR ANSWER WITH THE SOLUTION ON PAGE 182.

EXAMPLE10 USING THE PERCENTAGE FORMULA

Pet Supermarket placed an order for 560 fish tanks. If only 490 tanks were delivered, what percent of the order was received?

▶SOLUTIONSTRATEGY

The first step in solving this problem is to identify the variables. The statement asks "what percent"; therefore, the rate is the unknown. Because 560 is the total order, it is the base; 490 is a part of the total and is therefore the portion. Note that the base and the portion are in the same terms, fish tanks; the unique characteristic of the portion is that 490 tanks *were delivered*.

$$R = \frac{P}{B}$$

$$R = \frac{490}{560} = .875 = 87.5\%$$

$$\underline{87.5\% = \text{Percent of the order received}}$$

Note: Because 560 is the total order, it is the base and therefore represents 100% of the order. If 87.5% of the tanks were received, then 12.5% of the tanks were not received.

$$100\% - 87.5\% = \underline{12.5\% \text{ not received}}$$

▶TRYITEXERCISE 10

Solve the following for the rate. Round to the nearest tenth when necessary.

a. A contract called for 18,000 square feet of tile to be installed in a shopping mall. In the first week, 5,400 feet of tile was completed.

What percent of the job has been completed?

What percent of the job remains?

b. During a recent sale, Sir John, a men's boutique, sold $5,518 in business suits. If total sales amounted to $8,900, what percent of the sales were suits?

CHECK YOUR ANSWERS WITH THE SOLUTIONS ON PAGE 182.

SOLVING FOR THE BASE

6-5

To solve business situations in which the whole or total amount is the unknown, we use the formula

$$\text{Base} = \frac{\text{Portion}}{\text{Rate}} \quad \text{or} \quad B = \frac{P}{R}$$

The following examples illustrate solving for the base.

$$B = \frac{P}{R}$$

EXAMPLE11 SOLVING FOR THE BASE

What is the base if the rate is 21% and the portion is 58.8?

►SOLUTIONSTRATEGY

In this basic problem, we simply substitute the known values for the letters in the formula. Remember, the rate must be converted from a percent to a decimal.

$$B = \frac{P}{R}$$

$$B = \frac{58.8}{21\%} = \frac{58.8}{.21} = 280$$

$$\underline{\text{Base} = 280}$$

►TRYITEXERCISE 11

Solve the following for the base. Round to hundredths or the nearest cent when necessary.

What is the base if the rate is 40% and the portion is 690?

CHECK YOUR ANSWER WITH THE SOLUTION ON PAGE 182.

> ### Learning Tip
>
> Percentage problems can also be solved by using proportion. Set up the proportion
>
> $$\frac{\text{Rate}}{100} = \frac{\text{Portion}}{\text{Base}}$$
>
> and cross-multiply to solve for the unknown.
>
> For example, at a Radio Shack store last week, 70 televisions were sold with built-in DVD players. If this represents 20% of all TVs sold, how many total TVs were sold?
>
> $$\frac{20}{100} = \frac{70}{\text{base (total TVs)}}$$
> $$20b = 100(70)$$
> $$20b = 7,000$$
> $$b = 350 \text{ Total TVs}$$

EXAMPLE12 USING THE PERCENTAGE FORMULA

75 is 15% of what number?

►SOLUTIONSTRATEGY

Remember, the base is usually identified as the value preceded by *of* in the statement. In this case, that value is the unknown. Because 15 has the percent sign, it is the rate, and 75 is the part of the whole, or the portion.

$$B = \frac{P}{R}$$

$$B = \frac{75}{15\%} = \frac{75}{.15} = 500$$

$$\underline{500}$$

▶ TRYITEXERCISE 12

Solve the following for the base. Round to hundredths or the nearest cent when necessary.

$550 is 88% of what amount?

CHECK YOUR ANSWER WITH THE SOLUTION ON PAGE 182.

EXAMPLE13 USING THE PERCENTAGE FORMULA

All Star Sporting Goods reports that 28% of total shoe sales are from Nike products. If last week's Nike sales were $15,400, what was the total amount of sales for the week?

▶ SOLUTIONSTRATEGY

In this problem, the total amount of sales, the base, is unknown. Because 28% has the percent sign, it is the rate and $15,400 is the portion. Note again, the portion is in the same terms as the base, dollar sales; however, the unique characteristic is that the portion represents Nike sales.

$$B = \frac{P}{R}$$

$$B = \frac{15,400}{28\%} = \frac{15,400}{.28} = 55,000$$

$$\underline{\$55,000 \text{ Total sales for the week}}$$

▶ TRYITEXERCISE 13

Solve the following for the base. Round to hundredths or the nearest cent when necessary.

a. In a machine shop, 35% of the motor repairs are for broken shafts. If 126 motors had broken shafts last month, how many total motors were repaired?

b. At Office Mart, 75% of the copy paper sold is letter size. If 3,420 reams of letter size were sold, how many total reams of copy paper were sold?

CHECK YOUR ANSWERS WITH THE SOLUTIONS ON PAGE 182.

SECTION II 6 REVIEW EXERCISES

Solve the following for the portion. Round to hundredths when necessary.

1. 15% of 380 is _____
   $P = R \times B = .15 \times 380 = \underline{57}$

2. 3.6% of 1,800 is _____

3. 200% of 45 is _____

4. $5\frac{1}{2}\%$ of $600 is _____

5. What is the portion if the base is 450 and the rate is 19%?

6. What is the portion if the base is 1,650 and the rate is 150%?

7. What number is 35.2% of 184?

 8. What number is .8% of 500?

9. What number is $15\frac{4}{5}$% of 360?   10. What number is 258% of 2,500?

Solve the following for the rate. Round to the nearest tenth of a percent when necessary.

11. 40 is _____ % of 125   12. _____ % of 50 is 23   13. 600 is _____ % of 240

$$R = \frac{P}{B} = \frac{40}{125} = .32 = \underline{\underline{32\%}}$$

14. What is the rate if the base is 288 and the portion is 50?

15. What is the rate if the portion is 21.6 and the base is 160?

16. What is the rate if the base is $3,450 and the portion is $290?

17. What percent of 77 is 23?   18. What percent of 1,600 is 1,900?

19. 68 is what percent of 262?   20. $7.80 is what percent of $58.60?

Solve the following for the base. Round to hundredths when necessary.

21. 69 is 15% of _____   22. 360 is 150% of _____   23. 6.45 is $18\frac{1}{2}$% of _____

$$B = \frac{P}{R} = \frac{69}{.15} = \underline{\underline{460}}$$

24. What is the base if the rate is 16.8% and the portion is 451?

25. What is the base if the portion is 10 and the rate is $2\frac{3}{4}$%?

26. What is the base if the portion is $4,530 and the rate is 35%?

27. 60 is 15% of what number?   28. 160 is 130% of what number?

29. $46.50 is $86\frac{2}{3}$% of what number?   30. .55 is 21.4% of what number?

Solve the following word problems for the portion, rate, or base.

31. Alicia Kirk owns 37% of a travel agency.

   a. If the total worth of the business is $160,000, how much is Alicia's share?

   b. Last month Alicia's agency booked $14,500 in airline fares on Orbit Airline. If Orbit pays agencies a commission of 4.1%, how much commission should the agency receive?

32. What is the sales tax rate in a state where the tax on a purchase of $464 is $25.52?

Travel Agent According to data from the U.S. Bureau of Labor Statistics, employment of travel agents is expected to grow 10% between 2010 and 2020. The job prospects are best for travel agents who specialize in either specific types of travelers, such as corporate travelers, or particular destinations. The median annual wage for a travel agent is roughly $2,000 less than the median wage for all occupations.

33. A recent report on a financial website noted that for the first time in more than a decade, the size of the average newly built American house had shrunk to 2,065 square feet, or 93% of its original size. What was the original size before the decline? Round to the nearest square foot.

34. According to *The Miami Herald*, a large retail book chain recently launched a textbook rental program for college students. The company said books would rent for 42.5% of their original price. If a chemistry textbook rents for $48, what was the original price of the text? Round to the nearest cent.

35. If Rob Winter, a real estate agent, earned $6\frac{1}{2}$% commission on the sale of property valued at $210,000, how much was Rob's commission?

Cities with the highest average monthly utility bills[1]

Baltimore $390.44
Houston $359.52
Dallas $346.46
Orlando $310.10
Las Vegas $300.03

1 - Including home phone, television, high-speed Internet, electricity, and natural gas as of the third quarter.

Source: WhiteFence.com

36. As part of a report you are writing that compares living expenses in various cities, use the chart "Cities with the highest average monthly utility bills" to calculate the following:

   a. What percent is the Baltimore utility bill of the Las Vegas bill? Round to the nearest whole percent.

   b. What percent is the Orlando utility bill of the Dallas bill? Round to the nearest tenth of a percent.

37. Thirty percent of the inventory of a Nine West shoe store is high heels. If the store has 846 pairs of high heels in stock, how many total pairs of shoes are in the inventory?

38. Municipal Auto Sales advertised a down payment of $1,200 on a Mustang valued at $14,700. What is the percent of the down payment? Round to the nearest tenth of a percent.

39. According to *The Miami Herald* for every dollar of tip left at South Florida restaurants, 74% went to the server, 5% went to the host, 6% went to the bartender, and 15% went to the busser. One night a large party spent $750 on dinner and left a 20% tip.

   a. How much tip was left?

   b. Use the research percents to distribute the tip between the server, the host, the bartender, and the busser.

40. A quality control process finds 17.2 defects for every 8,600 units of production. What percent of the production is defective?

41. The Parker Company employs 68 part-time workers. If this represents 4% of the total work force, how many individuals work for the company?

42. A medical insurance policy requires Ana to pay the first $100 of her hospital expense. The insurance company will then pay 80% of the remaining expense. Ana is expecting a short surgical stay in the hospital, for which she estimates the total bill to be about $4,500. How much will Ana's portion of the bill amount to?

43. A corporation earned $457,800 last year. If its tax rate is $13\frac{3}{8}\%$, how much tax was paid?

44. In June, the New York Yankees won 15 games and lost 9. What percent of the games did they win? (*Hint:* Use total games played as the base.)

Use the pie chart "Century Mutual Fund – Investments" for Exercises 45–46.

45. What is the total amount invested in the Century Mutual Fund?

46. What percent does each investment category represent? Round your answers to the nearest tenth of a percent.

Century Mutual Fund – Investments
($ billions)

Chemicals $3.4

Transportation $5.2

Financials $8.1

Manufacturing $15.6

Copyright © Cengage Learning®

47. Ford Motor Co. announced that it planned to sell a new police cruiser vehicle in the United States to replace its Crown Victoria "Police Interceptor." Ford sells about 45,000 police vehicles a year, or about 75% of all police vehicles sold in the United States. Based on this information, what is the total number of police vehicles sold in the United States each year?

48. Elwood Smith attends a college that charges $1,400 tuition per semester for 12 credit hours of classes. If tuition is raised by 9% next year:

   a. How much more will he pay for two semesters of classes with the same course load?

   b. If Elwood works at a car wash earning $8 per hour and pays 15% in taxes, how many extra hours must he work to make up for the tuition increase? Round to the nearest whole hour.

BUSINESS DECISION: THE PARTY PLANNER

49. You are the catering manager for the Imperial Palace Hotel. Last Saturday your staff catered a wedding reception in the main ballroom, during which 152 chicken dinners, 133 steak dinners, and 95 fish dinners were served. All dinners are the same price. The hotel charges "per person" for catered events.

   a. What percent of the total meals served was each type of dinner?

   b. If $13,300 was charged for all the meals, how much revenue did each type produce?

© Daxa Burns/Shutterstock.com

Nuptial Numbers According to the Bridal Association of America, in 2009, there were over 2.3 million weddings in the United States, with a market value of over $72 billion. The average cost of a wedding was almost $31,000, with 169 guests. The average engagement time was 17 months.

In 1960, an American bride was typically 20 years old and a groom was 23. Today the average age of wedding couples is 26 for the bride and 28 for the groom. Approximately 75 percent of all wedding receptions take place at a hotel, country club, or catering facility.

c. If a 20% price increase goes into effect next month, what will be the new price per meal?

d. When photographers, florists, DJs, bands, and other outside vendors are booked through your office for events at the hotel, a $5\frac{1}{2}$% "finder's fee" is charged. Last year $175,000 of such services were booked. How much did the hotel make on this service?

e. If your boss is expecting $11,000 in "finder's fee" revenue next year, what amount of these services must be booked?

SECTION III   **SOLVING OTHER BUSINESS PROBLEMS INVOLVING PERCENTS**

Learning Tip

It is important to remember when solving percentage problems that involve "change" from an original number to a new number, the original number is always the *base* and represents 100%.

In addition to the basic percentage formulas, percents are used in many other ways in business. Measuring increases and decreases, comparing results from one year with another, and reporting economic activity and trends are just a few of these applications.

The ability of managers to make correct decisions is fundamental to success in business. These decisions require accurate and up-to-date information. Measuring percent changes in business activity is an important source of this information. Percents often describe a situation in a more informative way than do the raw data alone.

For example, a company reports a profit of $50,000 for the year. Although the number $50,000 is correct, it does not give a perspective of whether that amount of profit is good or bad. A comparison to last year's figures using percents might reveal that profits are up 45% over last year or profits are down 66.8%. Significant news!

6-6   DETERMINING RATE OF INCREASE OR DECREASE

In calculating the rate of increase or decrease of something, we use the same percentage formula concepts as before. Rate of change means percent change; therefore, the *rate* is the unknown. Once again we use the formula $R = P \div B$. Rate of change situations contain an original amount of something, which either increases or decreases to a new amount.

In solving these problems, the original amount is always the base. The amount of change is the portion. The unknown, which describes the percent change between the two amounts, is the rate.

$$\text{Rate of change (Rate)} = \frac{\text{Amount of change (Portion)}}{\text{Original amount (Base)}}$$

STEPS FOR DETERMINING THE RATE OF INCREASE OR DECREASE

STEP 1. Identify the original and the new amounts and find the *difference* between them.

STEP 2. Using the rate formula $R = P \div B$, substitute the difference from Step 1 for the portion and the original amount for the base.

STEP 3. Solve the equation for R. Remember, your answer will be in decimal form, which must be converted to a percent.

Tropical Storm Force Wind Speed Probabilities
For the 120 hours (5 days) from 8am EDT Thu Aug 27 to 8am EDT Tue Sep 1

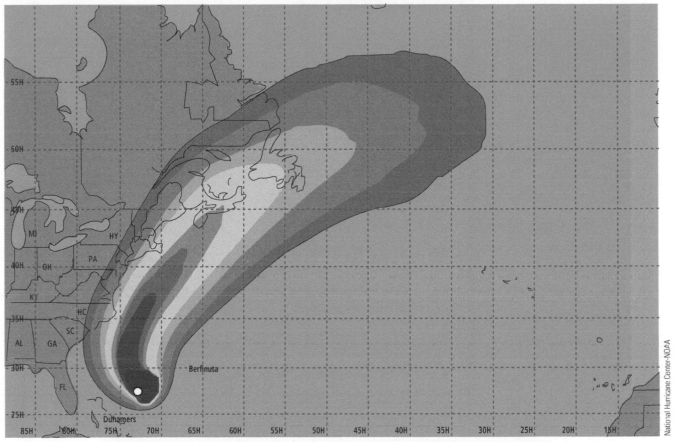

Probability of tropical storm force surface winds (1-minute average>=39mph) from all tropic cyclones
O indicates TROPICAL STORM DANNY center location at 8AM EDT Thu Aug 27 2009 (Forecast/Advisory 05)

| 5% | 10% | 20% | 30% | 40% | 50% | 60% | 70% | 80% | 90% | 100% |

Predicting the probability of an event occurring is often expressed as a percent. This graphic illustrates the probabilities of tropical storm force winds during Tropical Storm Danny in 2009.

EXAMPLE 14 FINDING THE RATE OF INCREASE

If a number increases from 60 to 75, what is the rate of increase?

▶ SOLUTIONSTRATEGY

In this basic situation, a number changes from 60 to 75 and we are looking for the percent change; in this case, it is an increase. The original amount is 60; the new amount is 75.

The portion is the difference between the amounts, $75 - 60 = 15$, and the base is the original amount, 60. We now substitute these values into the formula.

$$R = \frac{P}{B} = \frac{15}{60} = .25 = 25\%$$

Rate of increase = 25%

▶ TRYITEXERCISE 14

Solve the following problem for the rate of increase or decrease. Round to the nearest tenth of a percent when necessary.

If a number increases from 650 to 948, what is the rate of increase?

CHECK YOUR ANSWER WITH THE SOLUTION ON PAGE 182.

EXAMPLE15 FINDING THE RATE OF DECREASE

A number decreased from 120 to 80. What is the rate of decrease?

►SOLUTIONSTRATEGY

This problem illustrates a number decreasing in value. The unknown is the rate of decrease. We identify the original amount as 120 and the new amount as 80.

The difference between them is the portion: $120 - 80 = 40$. The original amount, 120, is the base. Now apply the rate formula.

$$R = \frac{P}{B} = \frac{40}{120} = .333 = 33.3\%$$

Rate of decrease = 33.3%

►TRYITEXERCISE 15

Solve the following problem for the rate of increase or decrease. Round to the nearest tenth of a percent when necessary.

If a number decreases from 21 to 15, what is the rate of decrease?

CHECK YOUR ANSWER WITH THE SOLUTION ON PAGE 182.

EXAMPLE16 FINDING THE RATE OF CHANGE

Last year Iberia Furniture had a work force of 360 employees. This year there are 504 employees. What is the rate of change in the number of employees?

►SOLUTIONSTRATEGY

The key to solving this problem is to properly identify the variables. The problem asks "what is the rate?"; therefore, the rate is the unknown. The original amount, 360 employees, is the base. The difference between the two amounts, $504 - 360 = 144$, is the portion. Now apply the rate formula.

$$R = \frac{P}{B} = \frac{144}{360} = .4 = 40\%$$

40% Increase in employees

►TRYITEXERCISE 16

Solve the following problem for the rate of increase or decrease. Round to the nearest tenth of a percent when necessary.

When Mike Veteramo was promoted from supervisor to manager, he received a salary increase from $450 to $540 per week. What was the percent change in his salary?

CHECK YOUR ANSWER WITH THE SOLUTION ON PAGE 182.

EXAMPLE17 FINDING THE RATE OF CHANGE

Over-the-Top Roofing had revenue of $122,300 in May and $103,955 in June. What is the percent change in revenue from May to June?

►SOLUTIONSTRATEGY

In this problem, the rate of change, the unknown, is a decrease. The original amount, $122,300, is the base. The difference between the two amounts, $122,300 − $103,955 = $18,345, is the portion. Now apply the rate formula.

$$R = \frac{P}{B} = \frac{18,345}{122,300} = .15 = 15\%$$

15% Decrease in revenue

►TRYITEXERCISE 17

Solve the following problem for the rate of increase or decrease. Round to the nearest tenth of a percent when necessary.

You are the production manager for the Berkshire Corporation. After starting a quality control program on the production line, the number of defects per day dropped from 60 to 12. Top management was very pleased with your results but wanted to know what percent decrease this change represented. Calculate the percent change in the number of defects per day.

CHECK YOUR ANSWER WITH THE SOLUTION ON PAGE 182.

DETERMINING AMOUNTS IN INCREASE OR DECREASE SITUATIONS

6-7

FINDING THE NEW AMOUNT AFTER A PERCENT CHANGE

Sometimes the original amount of something and the rate of change will be known and the new amount, after the change, will be the unknown. For example, if a store sold $5,000 in merchandise on Tuesday and 8% more on Wednesday, what are Wednesday's sales?

Keep in mind that the original amount, or beginning point, is always the base and represents 100%. Because the new amount is the total of the original amount, 100%, and the amount of increase, 8%, the rate of the new amount is 108% (100% + 8%). If the rate of change had been a decrease instead of an increase, the rate would have been 8% less than the base, or 92% (100% − 8%).

The unknown in this situation, the new amount, is the portion; therefore, we use the formula Portion = Rate × Base.

Learning Tip

Remember
- If the rate of change is an increase, *add* that rate to 100%.
- If the rate of change is a decrease, *subtract* that rate from 100%.

STEPS FOR DETERMINING THE NEW AMOUNT AFTER A PERCENT CHANGE

STEP 1. In the formula Portion = Rate × Base, substitute the original amount, or starting point, for the base.

STEP 2. If the rate of change is an increase, add that rate to 100% to get the rate.

or

STEP 2. If the rate of change is a decrease, subtract that rate from 100% to get the rate.

STEP 3. Solve the equation for the portion.

EXAMPLE18 FINDING THE NEW AMOUNT AFTER A PERCENT CHANGE

Affiliated Insurance estimated that the number of claims on homeowner's insurance would increase by 15% this year. If the company received 1,240 claims last year, how many can it expect this year?

▶SOLUTIONSTRATEGY

Last year's claims, the original amount, is the base. Because the rate of change is an increase, we find the rate by adding that change to 100% (100% + 15% = 115%). Now substitute these values in the portion formula.

$$P = R \times B$$
$$P = 115\% \times 1,240 = 1.15 \times 1,240 = 1,426$$
$$\underline{1,426 \text{ Homeowners' claims expected this year}}$$

▶TRYITEXERCISE 18

Solve the following business situation for the new amount after a percent change.

Worldwide Imports had a computer with a 525 gigabyte hard drive. If it was replaced with a new model containing 60% more capacity, how many gigabytes would the new hard drive have?

CHECK YOUR ANSWER WITH THE SOLUTION ON PAGE 183.

EXAMPLE19 FINDING THE NEW AMOUNT AFTER A PERCENT CHANGE

Mel's Drive-in Restaurant sold 25% fewer milk shakes this week than last week. If the drive-in sold 380 shakes last week, how many did it sell this week?

▶SOLUTIONSTRATEGY

Because this situation represents a percent decrease, the rate is determined by subtracting the rate of decrease from 100% (100% − 25% = 75%). As usual, the base is the original amount.

$$P = R \times B$$
$$P = 75\% \times 380 = .75 \times 380 = 285$$
$$\underline{285 \text{ Milk shakes sold this week}}$$

▶TRYITEXERCISE 19

Solve the following business situation for the new amount after a percent change.

Overland Express has delivery trucks that cover 20% fewer miles per week during the winter snow season. If the trucks average 650 miles per week during the summer, how many miles can be expected per week during the winter?

CHECK YOUR ANSWER WITH THE SOLUTION ON PAGE 183.

FINDING THE ORIGINAL AMOUNT BEFORE A PERCENT CHANGE

In another business situation involving percent change, the new amount is known and the original amount, the base, is unknown. For example, a car dealer sold 42 cars today. If this represents a 20% increase from yesterday, how many cars were sold yesterday? Solving for the original amount is a base problem; therefore, we use the formula

$$\text{Base} = \frac{\text{Portion}}{\text{Rate}}$$

STEPS FOR DETERMINING THE ORIGINAL AMOUNT BEFORE A PERCENT CHANGE

STEP 1. In the formula Base = Portion ÷ Rate, substitute the new amount for the portion.

STEP 2. If the rate of change is an increase, add that rate to 100% to get the rate.

or

STEP 2. If the rate of change is a decrease, subtract that rate from 100% to get the rate.

STEP 3. Solve the equation for the base.

EXAMPLE20 FINDING THE ORIGINAL AMOUNT

At Costco, the price of a Sony HD camcorder dropped by 15% to $425. What was the original price?

►SOLUTIONSTRATEGY

Because this situation represents a percent decrease, the rate is determined by subtracting the rate of decrease from 100%. 100% − 15% = 85%. The portion is the new amount, $425. The original price, the base, is the unknown. Using the formula for the base,

$$R = \frac{P}{R}$$

$$B = \frac{425}{85\%} = \frac{425}{.85} = 500$$

$$\underline{\$500}$$

►TRYITEXERCISE 20

Solve the following business situation for the original amount before a percent change.

The water level in a large holding tank decreased to 12 feet. If it is down 40% from last week, what was last week's level?

CHECK YOUR ANSWER WITH THE SOLUTION ON PAGE 183.

Christopher Griffin/Alamy

Costco Wholesale Corporation operates an international chain of membership warehouses, mainly under the "Costco Wholesale" name, that carry brand name merchandise at substantially lower prices than are typically found at conventional wholesale or retail sources.

Costco has over 400 stores in more than 40 states and in Puerto Rico. Typical annual revenues exceed $70 billion.

EXAMPLE21 FINDING THE ORIGINAL AMOUNT

Viking Technologies found that after an advertising campaign, business in April increased 12% over March. If April sales were $53,760, how much were the sales in March?

►SOLUTIONSTRATEGY

April's sales, the new amount, is the portion. Because the rate of change is an increase, we find the rate by adding that change to 100%. 100% + 12% = 112%.

$$B = \frac{P}{R}$$

$$B = \frac{53,760}{112\%} = \frac{53,760}{1.12} = 48,000$$

$$\underline{\$48,000}$$

▶ **TRYITEXERCISE 21**

Solve the following business situation for the original amount before a percent change.

A John Deere harvester can cover 90 acres per day with a new direct-drive system. If this represents an increase of 20% over the conventional chain-drive system, how many acres per day were covered with the old chain-drive?

CHECK YOUR ANSWER WITH THE SOLUTION ON PAGE 183.

6-8 UNDERSTANDING AND SOLVING PROBLEMS INVOLVING PERCENTAGE POINTS

percentage points A way of expressing a change from an original amount to a new amount without using a percent sign.

Learning Tip

Calculating percentage points is an application of the rate formula, Rate = Portion ÷ Base, with the change in percentage points as the *portion* and the original percentage points as the *base*.

Percentage points are a way of expressing a change from an original amount to a new amount without using a percent sign. When percentage points are used, it is assumed that the original amount of percentage points is the base amount, or the whole to which the change is compared. For example, if a company's market share increased from 40 to 44 percent of a total market, this is expressed as an increase of 4 percentage points.

The actual percent change in business, however, is calculated by using the formula

$$\text{Rate of change} = \frac{\text{Change in percentage points}}{\text{Original amount of percentage points}}$$

In this illustration, the change in percentage points is 4 and the original amount of percentage points is 40; therefore,

$$\text{Rate of change} = \frac{4}{40} = .10 = \underline{\underline{10\% \text{ increase in market share}}}$$

EXAMPLE22 SOLVING A PERCENTAGE POINTS PROBLEM

When a competitor built a better mouse trap, a company's market share dropped from 55 to 44 percent of the total market, a drop of 11 percentage points. What percent decrease in market share did this represent?

▶ SOLUTIONSTRATEGY

In this problem, the change in percentage points is 11 and the original market share is 55. Using the formula to find rate of change:

$$\text{Rate of change} = \frac{\text{Change in percentage points}}{\text{Original amount of percentage points}}$$

$$\text{Rate of change} = \frac{11}{55} = .2 = 20\%$$

$$\underline{20\% \text{ Decrease in market share}}$$

▶ TRYITEXERCISE 22

Prior to an election, a political research firm announced that a candidate for mayor had gained 8 percentage points in the polls that month, from 20 to 28 percent of the total registered voters. What is the candidate's actual percent increase in voters?

CHECK YOUR ANSWER WITH THE SOLUTION ON PAGE 183.

REVIEW EXERCISES

6 SECTION III

Solve the following increase or decrease problems for the unknown. Round decimals to hundredths and percents to the nearest tenth.

1. If a number increases from 320 to 440, what is the rate of increase?

    Portion = Increase = 440 − 320 = 120
    Base = Original number = 320 $R = \dfrac{P}{B} = \dfrac{120}{320} = .375 = \underline{\underline{37.5\%}}$

2. If a number decreases from 56 to 49, what is the rate of decrease?

3. What is the rate of change if the price of an item rises from \$123 to \$154?

4. What is the rate of change if the number of employees in a company decreases from 133 to 89?

5. 50 increased by 20% = _____

    Rate = 100% + 20% = 120%
    Base = Original number = 50
    $P = R \times B = 1.2 \times 50 = \underline{\underline{60}}$

6. 750 increased by 60% = _____

7. 25 decreased by 40% = _____

8. 3,400 decreased by 18.2% = _____

9. 2,500 increased by 300% = _____

10. \$46 decreased by $10\frac{1}{2}$% = _____

11. Over a two-month period, the number of weekly visitors to a city-sponsored art museum dropped from 2,340 per week to 1,083 per week. What was the percent decrease?

12. Sunshine Honda sold 112 cars this month. If that is 40% greater than last month, how many cars were sold last month?

13. At a Sports King store, 850 tennis racquets were sold last season.
    a. If racquet sales are predicted to be 30% higher this season, how many racquets should be ordered from the distributor?

b. If racquet sales break down into 40% metal alloy and 60% graphite, how many of each type should be ordered?

Supermarket Revenues In 2012, for the first time in history, each of the 75 companies in *Supermarket News'* list of Top 75 Food Retailers in North America had annual sales exceeding $1 billion.
Source: Based on Supermarket News

14. At a Safeway Supermarket, the price of yellow onions dropped from $0.59 per pound to $0.45 per pound.

a. What is the percent decrease in the price of onions?

b. Tomatoes are expected to undergo the same percent decrease in price. If they currently sell for $1.09 per pound, what will be the new price of tomatoes?

15. According to the American Association of Retired Persons, AARP, without healthcare reform, the number of people in the United States without healthcare insurance would have reached 61 million in 2020. This represents a 24.5% increase from 2010. How many people were uninsured in 2010? Round to the nearest million.

16. Housing prices in the Brighton area of Webster County have increased 37.5% over the price of houses five years ago.

a. If $160,000 was the average price of a house five years ago, what is the average price of a house today?

b. Economists predict that next year housing prices will drop by 4% in this area. Based on your answer from part **a**, what will the average price of a house be next year?

17. At Camper's Paradise, sales have increased 15%, 20%, and 10% over the past three years; that is, 15% three years ago, 20% two years ago, and 10% one year ago. If sales this year are $1,000,000, how much were sales three years ago? Round each year's sales to the nearest dollar.

18. According to the U.S. Census Bureau, in 1950, 39.3 million families had a child under 18 at home. A recent study found that number had decreased by 9.4 percent. How many families had a child under 18 at home according to this study? Round the number of millions to the nearest tenth.

19. After a vigorous promotion campaign, Crunchy Flakes Cereal increased its market share from 5.4% to 8.1%, a rise of 2.7 percentage points. What percent increase in sales does this represent?

20. The chart "Chip Rivalry" illustrates the global market share of Intel and AMD processing chips shipped to PC makers in the years before tablet computers became very popular. Use this chart to answer the following questions:

    a. From 2004 to 2009, Intel's market share dropped by 2.3 percentage points. What percent decrease in market share does this represent?

    b. From 2004 to 2009, AMD's market share increased by 4.7 percentage points. What percent increase in market share does this represent?

21. Economic reports indicate that during a recent manufacturing slowdown, unemployment in River Valley increased from 7.4% to 9.8%, an increase of 2.4 percentage points.

    a. What percent increase does this represent? Round to the nearest tenth of a percent.

    b. As manufacturing picked up, unemployment dropped from 9.8% to 8.1%, a decrease of 1.7 percentage points. What percent decrease does this represent? Round to the nearest hundredth of a percent.

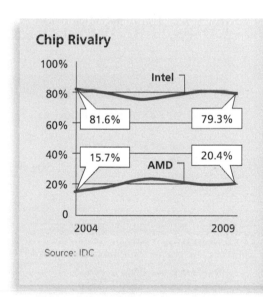

Chip Rivalry

Source: IDC

BUSINESS DECISION: CREATING AN ECONOMIC SNAPSHOT

22. You are the editor of your school newspaper. For the next edition, you are writing a story about inflation. You have located the following chart listing various consumer purchases and their costs in 2008 and 2012, as well as the percentage change based on the 2008 prices. Unfortunately, portions of the chart are missing.

23. Fill in the blank spaces to complete the chart for your story. Round percent answers to the nearest tenth of a percent. Round dollar amount answers to the nearest whole dollar.

	Consumer Purchase	**2008**	**2012**	**Percent Change**
	Single-Family Home Median resale price (month of July)	$237,300	$224,200	_____
	Toyota Camry MSRP for the LE – manual transmission	$20,600	_____	+9.7%
	Pair of Jeans Gap's Easy Fit, stonewashed	$44.50	$59.95	_____
	McDonald's Big Mac Average price at company-owned restaurants	$2.97	$3.57	_____
	A Year in College In-state including room and board and fees, typical state university undergraduate	$21,030	_____	+28.1%

CHAPTER 6

CHAPTER FORMULAS

The Percentage Formula

Portion = Rate × Base
Rate = Portion ÷ Base
Base = Portion ÷ Rate

Rate of Change

$$\text{Rate of change (Rate)} = \frac{\text{Amount of change (Portion)}}{\text{Original amount (Base)}}$$

Percentage Points

$$\text{Rate of change} = \frac{\text{Change in percentage points}}{\text{Original amount of percentage points}}$$

CHAPTER SUMMARY

Section I: Understanding and Converting Percents

Topic	Important Concepts	Illustrative Examples
Converting a Percent to a Decimal **Performance Objective 6-1, Page 155**	1. Remove the percent sign. 2. Move the decimal point two places to the left. *Note:* If the percent is a fraction such as $\frac{4}{5}\%$ or a mixed number such as $9\frac{1}{2}\%$, change the fraction part to a decimal; then follow Steps 1 and 2.	$28\% = .28$　　$\frac{4}{5}\% = .8\% = .008$ $159\% = 1.59$　$9\frac{1}{2}\% = 9.5\% = .095$ $.37\% = .0037$
Converting a Decimal or Whole Number to a Percent **Performance Objective 6-1, Page 156**	1. Move the decimal point two places to the right. 　　2. Write a percent sign after the number. *Note:* If there are fractions involved, convert them to decimals first; then proceed with Steps 1 and 2.	$.8 = 80\%$　　$3 = 300\%$ $2.9 = 290\%$　$\frac{1}{2} = .5 = 50\%$ $.075 = 7.5\%$
Converting a Percent to a Fraction **Performance Objective 6-2, Page 157**	1. Remove the percent sign. 2. *(If the percent is a whole number)* Write a fraction with the percent as the numerator and 100 as the denominator. Reduce to lowest terms. 　or 2. *(If the percent is a fraction)* Multiply the number by $\frac{1}{100}$ and reduce to lowest terms. 　or 2. *(If the percent is a decimal)* Convert it to a fraction and multiply by $\frac{1}{100}$. Reduce to lowest terms.	$7\% = \frac{7}{100}$ $60\% = \frac{60}{100} = \frac{3}{5}$ $400\% = \frac{400}{100} = 4$ $2.1\% = 2\frac{1}{10}\% = \frac{21}{10} \times \frac{1}{100} = \frac{21}{1,000}$ $5\frac{3}{4}\% = \frac{23}{4} \times \frac{1}{100} = \frac{23}{400}$
Converting a Fraction or Mixed Number to a Percent **Performance Objective 6-2, Page 157**	1. Change the fraction to a decimal by dividing the numerator by the denominator. 2. Move the decimal point two places to the right. 3. Write a percent sign after the number.	$\frac{1}{8} = .125 = 12.5\%$ $\frac{16}{3} = 5.333 = 533.3\%$ $12\frac{3}{4} = 12.75 = 1,275\%$

Section II: Using the Percentage Formula to Solve Business Problems

Topic	Important Concepts	Illustrative Examples
Solving for the Portion **Performance Objective 6-3, Page 161**	The portion is the number that represents a part of the base. To solve for portion, use the formula $$\text{Portion} = \text{Rate} \times \text{Base}$$	15% of Kwik-Mix Concrete employees got raises this year. If 1,800 individuals work for the company, how many got raises? $$P = .15 \times 1{,}800 = 270$$ <u>270 employees got raises this year.</u>
Solving for the Rate **Performance Objective 6-4, Page 163**	The rate is the variable that describes what part of the base is represented by the portion. It is always the term with the percent sign. To solve for rate, use the formula $$\text{Rate} = \frac{\text{Portion}}{\text{Base}}$$	28 out of 32 warehouses owned by Metro Distributors passed safety inspection. What percent of the warehouses passed? $$\text{Rate} = \frac{28}{32} = .875 = 87.5\%$$ <u>87.5% passed inspection.</u>
Solving for the Base **Performance Objective 6-5, Page 165**	Base is the variable that represents 100%, the starting point, or the whole thing. To solve for base, use the formula $$\text{Base} = \frac{\text{Portion}}{\text{Rate}}$$	34.3% of Thrifty Tile's sales are from customers west of the Mississippi River. If those sales last year were $154,350, what are the company's total sales? $$\text{Base} = \frac{154{,}350}{.343} = \$450{,}000$$ <u>Total sales = $450,000.</u>

Section III: Solving Other Business Problems Involving Percents

Topic	Important Concepts	Illustrative Examples
Determining Rate of Increase or Decrease **Performance Objective 6-6, Page 170**	1. Identify the original and the new amounts and find the difference between them. 2. Using the rate formula $R = P \div B$, substitute the difference from Step 1 for the portion and the original amount for the base. 3. Solve the equation for R. $$\text{Rate of change } (R) = \frac{\text{Amount of change } (P)}{\text{Original amount } (B)}$$	A price rises from $45 to $71. What is the rate of increase? $$\text{Portion} = 71 - 45 = 26$$ $$\text{Rate} = \frac{P}{B} = \frac{26}{45} = .5778 = \underline{57.8\%}$$ What is the rate of decrease from 152 to 34? $$\text{Portion} = 152 - 34 = 118$$ $$\text{Rate} = \frac{P}{B} = \frac{118}{152} = .776 = \underline{77.6\%}$$
Determining New Amount after a Percent Change **Performance Objective 6-7, Page 173**	Solving for the new amount is a portion problem; therefore, we use the formula $$\text{Portion} = \text{Rate} \times \text{Base}$$ 1. Substitute the original amount for the base. 2. If the rate of change is an increase, add that rate to 100%. or 2. If the rate of change is a decrease, subtract that rate from 100%.	Prestige Plastics projects a 24% increase in sales for next year. If sales this year were $172,500, what sales can be expected next year? $$\text{Rate} = 100\% + 24\% = 124\%$$ $$P = R \times B = 1.24 \times 172{,}500$$ $$P = 213{,}900$$ <u>Projected sales = $213,900</u>
Determining Original Amount before a Percent Change **Performance Objective 6-7, Page 175**	Solving for the original amount is a base problem; therefore, we use the formula $$\text{Base} = \frac{\text{Portion}}{\text{Rate}}$$ 1. Substitute the new amount for the portion. 2. If the rate of change is an increase, add that rate to 100%. or 2. If the rate of change is a decrease, subtract that rate from 100%.	If a DVD was marked down by 30% to $16.80, what was the original price? $$\text{Portion} = 100\% - 30\% = 70\%$$ $$\text{Base} = \frac{P}{R} = \frac{16.80}{.7} = 24$$ <u>Original price = $24</u>

Section III (continued)

Topic	Important Concepts	Illustrative Examples
Solving Problems Involving Percentage Points **Performance Objective 6-8, Page 176**	Percentage points are a way of expressing a change from an original amount to a new amount without using the percent sign. When percentage points are used, it is assumed that the base amount, 100%, stays constant. The actual percent change in business, however, is calculated by using the formula $$\text{Rate of change} = \frac{\text{Change in percentage points}}{\text{Original percentage points}}$$	After an intensive advertising campaign, General Industries' market share increased from 21 to 27%, an increase of 6 percentage points. What percent increase in business does this represent? $$\% \text{ change} = \frac{6}{21} = .2857 = 28.6\%$$ % increase in business = 28.6%

TRY IT: EXERCISE SOLUTIONS FOR CHAPTER 6

1a. $27\% = .27$

1b. $472\% = 4.72$

1c. $93.7\% = .937$

1d. $.81\% = .0081$

1e. $12\frac{3}{4}\% = 12.75\% = .1275$

1f. $\frac{7}{8}\% = .875\% = .00875$

2a. $.8 = 80\%$

2b. $1.4 = 140\%$

2c. $.0023 = .23\%$

2d. $.016\frac{2}{5} = .0164 = 1.64\%$

2e. $19 = 1,900\%$

2f. $.57\frac{2}{3} = .5767 = 57.67\%$

3a. $9\% = \frac{9}{100}$

3b. $23\% = \frac{23}{100}$

3c. $75\% = \frac{75}{100} = \frac{3}{4}$

3d. $225\% = \frac{225}{100} = 2\frac{25}{100} = 2\frac{1}{4}$

3e. $8.7\% = 8\frac{7}{10}\% = \frac{87}{10} \times \frac{1}{100} = \frac{87}{1,000}$

3f. $1,000\% = \frac{1,000}{100} = 10$

4a. $\frac{1}{5} = .2 = 20\%$

4b. $\frac{70}{200} = .35 = 35\%$

4c. $\frac{23}{5} = 4\frac{3}{5} = 4.6 = 460\%$

4d. $6\frac{9}{10} = 6.9 = 690\%$

4e. $\frac{45}{54} = .8333 = 83.33\%$

4f. $140\frac{1}{8} = 140.125 = 14,012.5\%$

5. $P = R \times B = .55 \times 980 = 539$

6. $P = R \times B = .72 \times 3,200 = 2,304$

7a. $P = R \times B = .16 \times 1,250 = 200$ Salespeople

7b. $P = R \times B = .15 \times 148,500 = \$22,275$ Down payment

8. $R = \frac{P}{B} = \frac{9}{21} = .4285 = 42.9\%$

9. $R = \frac{P}{B} = \frac{67}{142} = .4718 = 47.2\%$

10a. $R = \frac{P}{B} = \frac{5,400}{18,000} = .3 = 30\%$ Completed

$100\% - 30\% = 70\%$ Remains

10b. $R = \frac{P}{B} = \frac{5,518}{8,900} = .62 = 62\%$ Suits

11. $B = \frac{P}{R} = \frac{690}{.4} = 1,725$

12. $B = \frac{P}{R} = \frac{550}{.88} = \$625$

13a. $B = \frac{P}{R} = \frac{126}{.35} = 360$ Motors

13b. $B = \frac{P}{R} = \frac{3,420}{.75} = 4,560$ Reams of paper

14. Portion = Increase = $948 - 650 = 298$

Base = Original number = 650

$R = \frac{P}{B} = \frac{298}{650} = .45846 = 45.8\%$ Increase

15. Portion = Decrease = $21 - 15 = 6$

Base = Original number = 21

$R = \frac{P}{B} = \frac{6}{21} = .2857 = 28.6\%$ Decrease

16. Portion = Increase = $\$540 - \$450 = \$90$

Base = Original number = $450

$R = \frac{P}{B} = \frac{90}{450} = .2 = 20\%$ Increase

17. Portion = Decrease = $60 - 12 = 48$

Base = Original number = 60

$R = \frac{P}{B} = \frac{48}{60} = .8 = 80\%$ Decrease

18. Rate $= 100\% + 60\% = 160\%$

$P = R \times B = 1.6 \times 525 = \underline{840}$ Gigabytes

19. Rate $= 100\% - 20\% = 80\%$

$P = R \times B = .8 \times 650 = \underline{520}$ Miles per week

20. Rate $= 100\% - 40\% = 60\%$

$B = \dfrac{P}{R} = \dfrac{12}{.6} = \underline{20}$ Feet

21. Rate $= 100\% + 20\% = 120\%$

$B = \dfrac{P}{R} = \dfrac{90}{1.2} = \underline{75}$ Acres per day

22. $R = \dfrac{P}{B} = \dfrac{8}{20} = .4 = \underline{40\%}$ Increase in voters

CONCEPT REVIEW

1. A percent is a way of expressing a part of a(n)_____. (6-1)

2. In previous chapters, we expressed these parts as _____ and _____. (6-1)

3. Percent means "part per _____." The percent sign is written as _____. (6-1)

4. To convert a percent to a decimal, we remove the percent sign and _____ by 100. (6-1)

5. To convert a decimal to a percent, we multiply by 100 and write a(n) _____ sign after the number. (6-1)

6. To convert a percent to a fraction, we remove the percent sign and place the number over _____. (6-2)

7. List the steps for converting a fraction to a percent. (6-2)

8. The three basic parts of the percentage formula are the _____, _____, and _____. (6-3)

9. The percentage formula is written as _____. (6-3)

10. In the percentage formula, the _____ is the variable with the percent sign or the word *percent*. (6-4)

11. In the percentage formula, the _____ represents 100%, or the whole thing. In a sentence, it follows the word _____. (6-5)

12. Write the formula for the rate of change. (6-6)

13. When calculating amounts in percent change situations, the rate of change is added to 100% if the change is a(n) _____ and subtracted from 100% if the change is a(n) _____. (6-7)

14. Percentage _____ are a way of expressing a change from an original amount to a new amount without using a percent sign. (6-8)

ASSESSMENT TEST

Convert the following percents to decimals.

1. 88%

2. $3\dfrac{3}{4}\%$

3. 59.68%

4. 422%

5. $\dfrac{9}{16}\%$

Convert the following decimals or whole numbers to percents.

6. 12.6

7. .681

8. 53

9. $24\dfrac{4}{5}$

10. .0929

Convert the following percents to reduced fractions, mixed numbers, or whole numbers.

11. 19%   **12.** 217%   **13.** 7.44%   **14.** 126%   **15.** $25\frac{2}{5}\%$

Convert each of the following fractions or mixed numbers to percents.

16. $\frac{4}{5}$ **17.** $\frac{5}{9}$ **18.** $\frac{33}{4}$ **19.** $56\frac{3}{10}$ **20.** $\frac{745}{100}$

Solve the following for the portion, rate, or base, rounding decimals to hundredths and percents to the nearest tenth when necessary.

21. 24% of 1,700 =   **22.** 56 is _____ % of 125   **23.** 91 is 88% of _____

24. What number is 45% of 680?   **25.** $233.91 is what percent of $129.95?

26. 315 is 126% of _____   **27.** 60 increased by 15% = _____

28. If a number increases from 47 to 70.5, what is the rate of increase?

 29. What is the base if the portion is 444 and the rate is 15%?

 30. What is the portion if the base is 900 and the rate is $12\frac{3}{4}\%$?

31. What is 100% of 1,492?   **32.** 7,000 decreased by 62% = _____

Solve the following word problems for the unknown. Round decimals to hundredths and percents to the nearest tenth when necessary.

33. An ad for Target read, "This week only, all electronics 35% off!" If a television set normally sells for $349.95, what is the amount of the savings?

 34. If 453 runners out of 620 completed a marathon, what percent of the runners finished the race?

35. Last year Keystone's corporate jet required $23,040 in maintenance and repairs.

   a. If this represents 32% of the total operating costs of the airplane, what was the total cost to fly the plane for the year?

b. If the plane flew 300,000 miles last year, what is the cost per mile to operate the plane?

c. Sky King Leasing offered a deal whereby it would operate the plane for Keystone for only $0.18 per mile. What is the percent decrease in operating expense per mile being offered by Sky King?

Jets for Sale

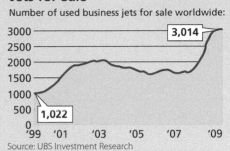

Source: UBS Investment Research

d. In the ten years from 1999 to 2009, the number of jets for sale increased significantly. Use the chart "Jets for Sale" to calculate the rate of increase of jets available in 2009 compared with 1999. Round to the nearest whole percent.

36. A letter carrier can deliver mail to 112 homes per hour by walking and 168 homes per hour by driving.

    a. By what percent is productivity increased by driving?

    b. If a new ZIP Code system improves driving productivity by 12.5%, what is the new number of homes per hour for driving?

37. Last year the Tundra Corporation had sales of $343,500. If this year's sales are forecast to be $415,700, what is the percent increase in sales?

38. After a 15% pay raise, Scott Walker now earns $27,600. What was his salary before the raise?

39. According to Autodata research, in November 2008, Toyota sold 130,307 vehicles in the United States. In November 2009, sales increased 2.6% over the previous November.

    a. How many vehicles did Toyota sell in November 2009?

    b. The research also indicated that Toyota's November U.S. market share increased from 17.4% in 2008 to 17.9% in 2009, an increase of 0.5 percentage points. What percent does this increase represent?

40. Three of every seven sales transactions at Dollar Discount are on credit cards. What percent of the transactions are *not* credit card sales?

41. A pre-election survey shows that an independent presidential candidate has increased his popularity from 26.5 percent to 31.3 percent of the electorate, an increase of 4.8 percentage points. What percent does this increase represent?

42. By what percent is a 100-watt lightbulb brighter than a 60-watt bulb?

GO ONLINE FOR MORE ACTIVITIES • www.cengagebrain.com

CHAPTER
6

43. In 1998, a 30-second television advertisement on the Super Bowl telecast cost $1.3 million. In 2010, the price of a 30-second ad had increased by 132% over the 1998 price. How much was a Super Bowl ad in 2010? Write your answer in numerical form.

44. Michael Reeves, an ice cream vendor, pays $17.50 for a five-gallon container of premium ice cream. From this quantity, he sells 80 scoops at $0.90 per scoop. If he sold smaller scoops, he could sell 98 scoops from the same container; however, he could charge only $0.80 per scoop. As his accountant, you are asked the following questions.

    a. If Michael switches to the smaller scoops, by how much will his profit per container go up or down? (Profit = Sales − Expenses)

    b. By what percent will the profit change? Round to the nearest tenth of a percent.

45. An insurance adjuster for UPS found that 12% of a shipment was damaged in transit. If the damaged goods amounted to $4,870, what was the total value of the shipment?

46. Morley Fast, a contractor, built a warehouse complex in Canmore for the following costs: land, $12,000; concrete and steel, $34,500; plumbing and electrical, $48,990; general carpentry and roof, $42,340; and other expenses, $34,220.

    a. What percent of the total cost is represented by each category of expenses?

    b. When the project was completed, Morley sold the entire complex for 185% of its cost. What was the selling price of the complex?

The Rise of E-Books in Education

Sales of digital textbooks for higher education

Use the chart "The Rise of E-Books in Education" for Exercises 47–49.

47. What was the rate of change in education e-book sales from 2008 to 2013? Round to the nearest tenth of a percent.

48. What were the sales of education e-books in 2009 if they were 10.3% higher than 2008? Round to the nearest tenth of a million.

49. If the 2013 figure represents a 19.6% increase from 2012, what are the projected education e-book sales for 2012? Round to the nearest tenth of a million.

Source: Albert N. Greco, Fordham Graduate School of Business Administration

BUSINESS DECISION: ALLOCATING OVERHEAD EXPENSES

50. You are the owner of a chain of three successful restaurants with the following number of seats in each location: airport, 340 seats; downtown, 218 seats; and suburban, 164 seats.

    a. If the liability insurance premium is $16,000 per year, how much of that premium should be allocated to each of the restaurants based on percent of total seating capacity? Round each percent to the nearest tenth.

    b. If you open a fourth location at the beach that has 150 seats and the liability insurance premium increases by 18%, what is the new allocation of insurance premium among the four locations? If necessary round percents to the nearest tenth.

    c. (Optional) What other expenses could be allocated to the four restaurants?

    d. (Optional) What other ways, besides seating capacity, could you use to allocate expenses?

COLLABORATIVE LEARNING ACTIVITY

Percents—The Language of Business

For emphasis and illustration, business percentage figures, when printed, are frequently presented in circle, bar, and line chart format. Charts add a compelling element to otherwise plain "numbers in the news."

    As a team, search business publications, annual reports, and the Internet to find 10 interesting and varied examples of business percentage figures being presented in chart form. Share your findings with the class.

Business Math JOURNAL

Green Numbers – The Power of One

According to Jim Hackler, theurbanenvironmentalist.com, "the people of the United States represent less than 5 percent of the world's population—yet that 5 percent consumes more than a quarter of our planet's resources. If the rest of the world rose to the U.S. level of consumption, four additional planets would be needed to supply the resources and absorb the waste!"

Here's a look at some of Jim's intriguing findings, "how a single act can help (or hurt) the environment—especially when it's shared by millions."

It's too Darn Hot

If the thermostat in every house in America were lowered **1 degree Fahrenheit** during the winter, the nation would save **230 million barrels of crude oil**—enough to fill an oil tanker 400 times.

Shower Power

If 40 million people were to spend **one minute less** each day in the shower over their lifetime, they would save **4 trillion gallons** of water—the total amount of snow and rain that falls over the entire lower 48 states in a day.

Straight Flush

If home builders had installed **one dual-flush toilet** instead of a standard low-flow toilet in every new house they built in 2008, they would have saved **1.65 billion gallons of water** a year.

In the Can

One soft drink can recycled by each elementary school student in America would save **24.8 million cans**. That would be enough aluminum to create 21 Boeing 737 airplanes.

Virtual Payment

If every American switched to receiving just **one bill** as an electronic statement instead of a paper statement, the one-time savings would be **217,800,000 sheets**—enough to blanket the island of Key West in a single layer of paper.

Wrapacious

One out of every 3 pounds of the waste that Americans generate is for packaging, which each year adds up to **77 million tons**—enough to fill the Louisiana Superdome 37 times.

THAT ONE IS 100% ORGANIC.

PUMPKINS

Bath Party

If every American collected **1 gallon of water** once a week while waiting for the shower or bathwater to get hot and used it to water his or her houseplants, the total saved would be **15.8 billion gallons of water** a year—enough to fill the Reflecting Pool at the National Mall in Washington, D.C. 2,338 times.

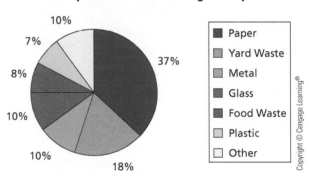

Composition Of An Average Dump

10%
7%
8%
10%
10%
18%
37%

- Paper
- Yard Waste
- Metal
- Glass
- Food Waste
- Plastic
- Other

Copyright © Cengage Learning®

Source: Green Numbers, "The Power of 1," Jim Hackler, *Sky Magazine*, March 2008, pages 48–51

Issues & Activities

1. Assume that a dump received a total of 750,000 pounds of waste last week. Use the chart above to allocate the number of pounds of waste for each category.
2. If recycling one glass bottle or jar saves enough electricity to light a 100-watt bulb for four hours, how many bottles or jars will it take to light the bulb for a year?
3. Americans use 4 million plastic bottles every hour, but only 25% of plastic bottles are recycled. At that rate, how many plastic bottles are recycled in a week?
4. In teams, research the Internet to find current trends in "greening of America" statistics. List your sources and visually report your findings to the class.

Brainteaser – "Buy the Numbers"

You recently purchased a 100-unit apartment building. As part of a fix-up project, you have decided to install new numbers on each front door. If the apartments are numbered from 1 to 100, how many nines will you need to buy?

See the end of Appendix A for the solution.

CHAPTER **7**

Invoices, Trade Discounts, and Cash Discounts

PERFORMANCE OBJECTIVES

SECTION I **7** THE INVOICE

invoice A document detailing a sales transaction that contains a list of goods shipped or services rendered with an account of all costs.

In business, merchandise is bought and sold many times as it passes from the manufacturer through wholesalers and retailers to the final consumer. A bill of sale, or an **invoice**, is a business document used to keep track of these sales and purchases. From the seller's point of view, they are sales invoices; from the buyer's point of view, they are purchase invoices or purchase orders.

Invoices are a comprehensive record of a sales transaction. They show what merchandise or services have been sold, to whom, in what quantities, at what price, and under what conditions and terms. They vary in style and format from company to company, but most contain essentially the same information. Invoices are used extensively in business, and it is important to be able to read and understand them. In this chapter, you will learn how businesses use invoices and the math applications that relate to them.

7-1 READING AND UNDERSTANDING THE PARTS OF AN INVOICE

Exhibit 7-1 shows a typical format used in business for an invoice. The important parts have been labeled and are explained in Exhibit 7-2. Some of the terms have page references, which direct you to the sections in this chapter that further explain those terms and their business math applications. Exhibit 7-2 also presents some of the most commonly used invoice abbreviations. These pertain to merchandise quantities and measurements.

With some practice, these terms and abbreviations will become familiar to you. Take some time to look them over before you continue reading.

F.O.B. shipping point The buyer pays all transportation charges from the vendor's location.

F.O.B. destination The seller pays all the shipping changes to the buyer's store or warehouse and then bills the buyer for these charges on the invoice.

F.O.B. Term used in quoting shipping charges meaning "free on board" or "freight on board."

SHIPPING TERMS

Two frequently used shipping terms that you should become familiar with are **F.O.B. shipping point** and **F.O.B. destination**. **F.O.B.** means "free on board" or "freight on board." These terms define the shipping charges and when the title (ownership) of the goods is transferred from the seller to the buyer. Ownership becomes important when insurance claims must be filed due to problems in shipment.

F.O.B. Shipping Point   When the terms are F.O.B. shipping point, the buyer pays the shipping company directly. The merchandise title is transferred to the buyer at the manufacturer's factory or at a shipping point such as a railroad freight yard or air freight terminal. From this point, the buyer is responsible for the merchandise. It is common for the seller to prepay the freight and add the amount to the invoice.

F.O.B. Destination   When the shipping terms are F.O.B. destination, the seller is responsible for prepaying the shipping charges to the destination. The destination is usually the buyer's store or warehouse. Unless prices are quoted as "delivered," the seller then bills the buyer on the invoice for the shipping charges.

Sometimes the freight terms are stated as F.O.B. with the name of a city. For example, if the seller is in Fort Worth and the buyer is in New York, F.O.B. Fort Worth means the title is transferred in Fort Worth and the buyer pays the shipping charges from Fort Worth to New York. If the terms are F.O.B. New York, the seller pays the shipping charges to New York and then bills the buyer for those charges on the invoice. Exhibit 7-3, Shipping Terms, on page 193, illustrates these transactions.

© Franck Boston/Shutterstock.com

When companies ship and receive merchandise, invoices and purchase orders are used to record the details of the transaction.

EXHIBIT 7-1 Typical Invoice Format

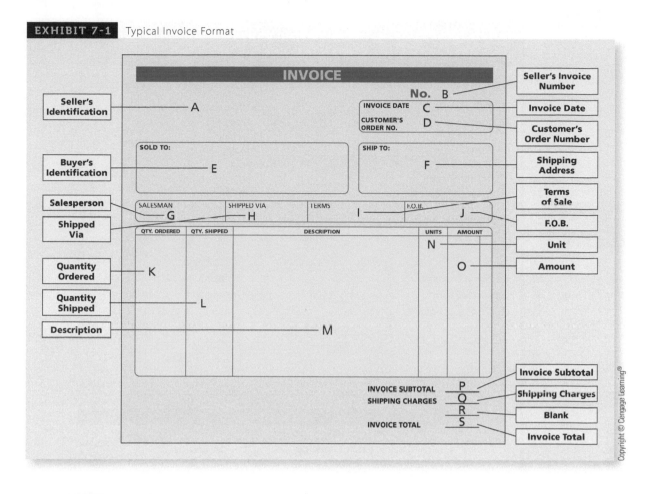

EXHIBIT 7-2 Invoice Terminology and Abbreviations

Invoice Terminology

A **Seller's Identification—**Name, address, and logo or corporate symbol of the seller

B **Seller's Invoice Number—**Seller's identification number of the transaction

C **Invoice Date—**Date the invoice was written

D **Customer's Order Number—**Buyer's identification number of the transaction

E **Buyer's Identification—**Name and mailing address of the buyer

F **Shipping Address—**Address where merchandise will be shipped

G **Salesperson—**Name of salesperson credited with the sale

H **Shipped Via—**Name of shipping company handling the shipment

I **Terms—**Terms of sale—Section detailing date of payment and cash discount

J **F.O.B.—**"Free on board"—Section detailing who pays the shipping company and when title is transferred

K **Quantity Ordered—**Number of units ordered

L **Quantity Shipped—**Number of units shipped

M **Description—**Detailed description of the merchandise, including model numbers

N **Unit—**Price per unit of merchandise

O **Amount—**Extended total—Quantity in units times the unit price for each line

P **Invoice Subtotal—**Total of the Amount column—Merchandise total

Q **Shipping Charges—**Cost to physically transport the merchandise from the seller to the buyer

R **Blank Line—**Line used for other charges such as insurance or handling

S **Invoice Total—**Total amount of the invoice—Includes merchandise plus all other charges

Invoice Abbreviations

ea	each	pr	pair	in.	inch	oz	ounce
dz or doz	dozen	dm or drm	drum	ft	foot	g or gr	gram
gr or gro	gross	bbl	barrel	yd	yard	kg	kilogram
bx	box	sk	sack	mm	millimeter	pt	pint
cs	case	@	at	cm	centimeter	qt	quart
ct or crt	crate	C	100 items	m	meter	gal	gallon
ctn or cart	carton	M	1,000 items	lb	pound	cwt	hundred weight

EXAMPLE 1   IDENTIFYING PARTS OF AN INVOICE

From the following Whole Grain Cereal Co. invoice, identify the indicated parts.

a. Seller	____	h. Salesperson	____
b. Invoice number	____	i. Shipped via	____
c. Invoice date	____	j. Insurance	____
d. Customer order #	____	k. Shipping charges	____
e. Buyer	____	l. Invoice subtotal	____
f. Terms of sale	____	m. Unit price—Fruit and Nut Flakes	____
g. Shipping address	____	n. Invoice total	____

SOLUTION STRATEGY

a. Seller	Organic Grain Cereal Co.	h. Salesperson	H. L. Mager
b. Invoice number	2112	i. Shipped via	Terminal Transport
c. Invoice date	August 19, 20XX	j. Insurance	$33.00
d. Customer order #	B-1623	k. Shipping charges	$67.45
e. Buyer	Kroger Supermarkets	l. Invoice subtotal	$2,227.05
f. Terms of sale	Net - 45 days	m. Unit price—Fruit and Nut Flakes	$19.34
g. Shipping address	1424 Peachtree Rd	n. Invoice total	$2,327.50

INVOICE

Organic Grain Cereal Co.
697 Canyon Road
Boulder, CO 80304

No. 2112

INVOICE DATE: August 19, 20XX
CUSTOMER'S ORDER NO.: B-1623

SOLD TO:
KROGER SUPERMARKETS
565 North Avenue
Atlanta, Georgia 30348

SHIP TO:
DISTRIBUTION CENTER
1424 Peachtree Road
Atlanta, Georgia 30341

SALESMAN	SHIPPED VIA	TERMS	F.O.B.
H. L. Mager	Terminal Transport	Net - 45 Days	Boulder, CO

QTY. ORDERED	QTY. SHIPPED	DESCRIPTION		UNIT	AMOUNT
55 cs.	55 cs.	Corn Crunchies	24 ounce	22.19	$1220 45
28 cs.	28 cs.	Fruit and Nut Flakes	24 ounce	19.34	541 52
41 cs.	22 cs.	Rice and Wheat Flakes	16 ounce	21.14	465 08

INVOICE SUBTOTAL	2,227.05
SHIPPING CHARGES	67.45
INSURANCE	33.00
INVOICE TOTAL	$2,327.50

TRY IT EXERCISE 1

From the following FotoFair invoice, identify the indicated parts.

a. Buyer	____	h. Salesperson	____
b. Invoice number	____	i. Shipped via	____
c. Invoice date	____	j. F.O.B.	____
d. Amount—Pocket Pro 55	____	k. Shipping charges	____
e. Seller	____	l. Invoice subtotal	____
f. Terms of sale	____	m. Unit price—Pocket Pro 75	____
g. Shipping address	____	n. Invoice total	____

CHECK YOUR ANSWERS WITH THE SOLUTIONS ON PAGE 223.

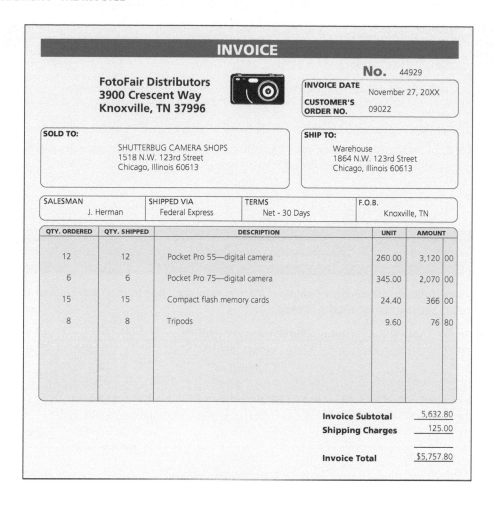

INVOICE

FotoFair Distributors
3900 Crescent Way
Knoxville, TN 37996

No. 44929

INVOICE DATE November 27, 20XX

CUSTOMER'S ORDER NO. 09022

SOLD TO:
SHUTTERBUG CAMERA SHOPS
1518 N.W. 123rd Street
Chicago, Illinois 60613

SHIP TO:
Warehouse
1864 N.W. 123rd Street
Chicago, Illinois 60613

SALESMAN	SHIPPED VIA	TERMS	F.O.B.
J. Herman	Federal Express	Net - 30 Days	Knoxville, TN

QTY. ORDERED	QTY. SHIPPED	DESCRIPTION	UNIT	AMOUNT
12	12	Pocket Pro 55—digital camera	260.00	3,120 00
6	6	Pocket Pro 75—digital camera	345.00	2,070 00
15	15	Compact flash memory cards	24.40	366 00
8	8	Tripods	9.60	76 80

Invoice Subtotal 5,632.80
Shipping Charges 125.00

Invoice Total $5,757.80

Extending and Totaling an Invoice

7-2

Extending an invoice is the process of computing the value in the Total or Amount column for each line of the invoice. This number represents the total dollar amount of each type of merchandise or service being purchased. The **invoice subtotal** is the amount of all items on the invoice before shipping and handling charges; insurance; and other adjustments such as discounts, returns, and credits. The **invoice total** is the final amount due from the buyer to the seller.

invoice subtotal The amount of all merchandise or services on the invoice before adjustments.

invoice total The final amount due from the buyer to the seller.

EXHIBIT 7-3 Shipping Terms

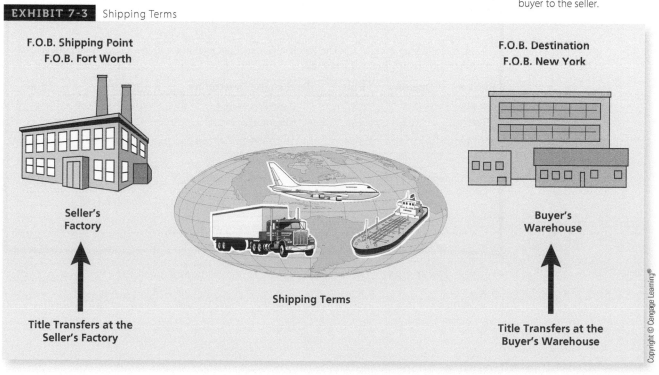

F.O.B. Shipping Point
F.O.B. Fort Worth

F.O.B. Destination
F.O.B. New York

Seller's Factory

Buyer's Warehouse

Shipping Terms

Title Transfers at the Seller's Factory

Title Transfers at the Buyer's Warehouse

STEPS TO EXTEND AND TOTAL AN INVOICE

STEP 1. For each line of the invoice, multiply the number of items by the cost per item.

Extended total = Number of items × Cost per item

STEP 2. Add all extended totals to get the invoice subtotal.

STEP 3. Calculate the invoice total by adding the freight charges, insurance, and any other charges to the subtotal.

EXAMPLE2 EXTENDING AND TOTALING AN INVOICE

From the following invoice for Computer Mart, extend each line to the Total column and calculate the invoice subtotal and total.

Stock #	Quantity	Unit	Merchandise Description	Unit Price	Total
4334	17	ea.	13" Monitors	$244.00	_____
1217	8	ea.	17" Monitors	525.80	_____
2192	2	doz.	USB Cables	24.50	_____
5606	1	bx.	Blu-ray discs	365.90	_____
				Invoice Subtotal	
				Shipping Charges	$244.75
				Invoice Total	_____

►SOLUTIONSTRATEGY

						Total
13" Monitors	17	×	$244.00	=		$4,148.00
17" Monitors	8	×	525.80	=		4,206.40
USB Cables	2	×	24.50	=		49.00
Blu-ray discs	1	×	365.90	=		365.90
			Invoice Subtotal			$8,769.30
			Shipping Charges			+ 244.75
			Invoice Total			$9,014.05

►TRYITEXERCISE 2

From the following invoice for The Kitchen Connection, extend each line to the Total column and calculate the invoice subtotal and total.

Stock #	Quantity	Unit	Merchandise Description	Unit Price	Total
R443	125	ea.	Food Processors	$89.00	_____
B776	24	ea.	Microwave Ovens	225.40	_____
Z133	6	doz.	12" Mixers	54.12	_____
Z163	1	bx.	Mixer Covers	166.30	_____
				Invoice Subtotal	
				Shipping Charges	$194.20
				Invoice Total	_____

CHECK YOUR ANSWERS WITH THE SOLUTIONS ON PAGE 223.

REVIEW EXERCISES

7 SECTION I

What word is represented by each of the following abbreviations?

1. bx.   Box
2. pt   _____
3. drm.   _____
4. kg   _____
5. gro.   Gross
6. oz   _____
7. M.   _____
8. cwt   _____

Using the Panorama Products invoice below, extend each line to the Amount column and calculate the subtotal and total. Then answer Questions 9–22. (*Note:* Although 26 boxes of 2-inch reflective tape were ordered, only 11 boxes were shipped. Charge only for the boxes shipped.)

9. Seller   Panorama Products

10. Invoice number   R-7431

11. Invoice date   _____

12. Cust. order #   _____

13. Buyer   _____

14. Terms of sale   _____

15. Shipping address   _____

16. Salesperson   _____

17. Shipped via   _____

18. Insurance   _____

19. Shipping charges   _____

20. Unit price—2" Tape   _____

21. Invoice subtotal   _____

22. Invoice total   _____

INVOICE

Panorama Products
486 5th Avenue
Eureka, CA 95501

No. R-7431

INVOICE DATE	June 16, 20XX
CUSTOMER'S ORDER NO.	12144

SOLD TO:
J. M. Hardware Supply
2051 West Adams Blvd.
Lansing, MI 48901

SHIP TO:
SAME

SALESMAN	SHIPPED VIA	TERMS	F.O.B.
H. Marshall	Gilbert Trucking	Net 30 Days	Effingham, IL

QTY. ORDERED	QTY. SHIPPED	DESCRIPTION	UNIT	AMOUNT
16 cases	16 cases	Masking Tape ½" Standard	21.90	
12 cases	12 cases	Masking Tape 1½" Standard	26.79	
26 boxes	11 boxes	2" Reflective Tape	88.56	
37 cases	37 cases	Sandpaper Assorted	74.84	

INVOICE SUBTOTAL	_____
SHIPPING CHARGES	61.45
INVOICE TOTAL	_____

IN THE
Business World

Frequently, merchandise that is ordered from vendors is "out of stock" and goes into back-order status.

As a general rule, companies charge only for the merchandise that is shipped.

BUSINESS DECISION: MANAGING MERCHANDISE

23. You are the store manager for The Bedding Warehouse. The invoice below is due for payment to one of your vendors, Hamilton Mills.

   a. Check the invoice for errors and correct any you find.

   b. Your warehouse manager reports that there were three king-size sheets and five queen-size sheets returned, along with four packages of queen pillow cases. Calculate the revised total due.

   c. The vendor has offered a 4% early payment discount that applies only to the merchandise, not the shipping or insurance. What is the amount of the discount?

   d. What is the new balance due after the discount?

Retail store managers manage stores that specialize in selling a specific line of merchandise, such as groceries, meat, liquor, apparel, furniture, automobile parts, electronic items, or household appliances.

Exactostock / SuperStock

INVOICE

Hamilton Mills
115 Rock Creek Road
Charlotte, North Carolina 28235

No. 49485

| INVOICE DATE | July 9, 20XX |
| CUSTOMER'S ORDER NO. | 49485 |

SOLD TO:
The Bedding Warehouse
406 Maple Road
Franklin, VA 23851

SHIP TO:
SAME

SALESMAN	SHIPPED VIA	TERMS	F.O.B.
	Federal Express	Net 30 Days	Charlotte, N.C.

QTY. ORDERED	QTY. SHIPPED	DESCRIPTION	UNIT	AMOUNT
42	ea.	Sheets, king	$45.10	$1,894 20
65	ea.	Sheets, queen	$37.60	$2,444 00
26	pkg.	Pillow Cases, queen	$17.85	$464 10
55	pkg.	Pillow Cases, std.	$14.35	$789 25
8	ea.	Shams	$33.25	$366 00

INVOICE SUBTOTAL	$5,957.55
SHIPPING CHARGES	$132.50
INSURANCE	$21.15
INVOICE TOTAL	$6,111.20

7 | SECTION II

TRADE DISCOUNTS—SINGLE

The path merchandise travels as it moves from the manufacturer through wholesalers and retailers to the ultimate consumer is known as a channel of distribution or trade channel. The businesses that form these channels are said to be "in the trade." In today's complex economy, a number of different trade channels are used to move goods and services efficiently.

Trade discounts are reductions from the manufacturer's suggested **list price**. They are given to businesses at various levels of the trade channel for the performance of marketing functions. These functions may include activities such as selling, advertising, storage, service, and display.

Manufacturers print catalogs showcasing their merchandise. Often these catalogs contain the manufacturer's suggested list or retail prices. Businesses in the trade receive price sheets from the manufacturer listing the trade discounts in percent form associated with each item in the catalog. By issuing updated price sheets of trade discounts, manufacturers have the flexibility of changing the prices of their merchandise without the expense of reprinting the entire catalog.

Trade discounts are sometimes quoted as a single discount and sometimes as a series or chain of discounts. The number of discounts is dependent on the extent of the marketing services performed by the channel member.

trade discounts Reductions from the manufacturer's list price given to businesses that are "in the trade" for performance of marketing functions.

list price Suggested retail selling price of an item set by the manufacturer or supplier. The original price from which discounts are taken.

CALCULATING THE AMOUNT OF A SINGLE TRADE DISCOUNT

7-3

The amount of a single trade discount is calculated by multiplying the list price by the trade discount rate.

> **Trade discount = List price × Trade discount rate**

EXAMPLE3 CALCULATING THE AMOUNT OF A SINGLE TRADE DISCOUNT

What is the amount of the trade discount on merchandise with a list price of $2,800 and a trade discount rate of 45%?

SOLUTIONSTRATEGY

Trade discount = List price × Trade discount rate
Trade discount = 2,800 × .45 = $1,260

TRYITEXERCISE 3

Gifts Galore, a retail gift shop, buys merchandise with a list price of $7,600 from a wholesaler of novelty items and toys. The wholesaler extends a 30% trade discount rate to the retailer. What is the amount of the trade discount?

CHECK YOUR ANSWER WITH THE SOLUTION ON PAGE 223.

CALCULATING NET PRICE BY USING THE NET PRICE FACTOR, COMPLEMENT METHOD

7-4

The **net price** is the amount a business actually pays for the merchandise after the discount has been deducted. It may be calculated by subtracting the amount of the trade discount from the list price.

net price The amount a business actually pays for the merchandise after the discount has been deducted.

> **Net price = List price − Trade discount**

Frequently, merchants are more interested in knowing the net price of an item than the amount of the trade discount. In that case, the net price can be calculated directly from the list price without first finding the amount of the discount.

net price factor The percent of the list price a business pays for merchandise. It is the multiplier used to calculate the net price.

The list price of an item is considered to be 100%. If, for example, the trade discount on an item is 40% of the list price, the net price will be 60% because the two must equal 100%. This 60%, the complement of the trade discount rate (100% – 40%), is the portion of the list price that *is* paid. Known as the **net price factor**, it is usually written in decimal form.

STEPS TO CALCULATE NET PRICE BY USING THE NET PRICE FACTOR

STEP 1. Calculate the net price factor, complement of the trade discount rate.

$$\textbf{Net price factor} = \textbf{100\%} - \textbf{Trade discount rate}$$

STEP 2. Calculate the net price.

$$\textbf{Net price} = \textbf{List price} \times \textbf{Net price factor}$$

Note: This procedure can be combined into one step by the formula.

$$\textbf{Net price} = \textbf{List price(100\% - Trade discount rate)}$$

Learning Tip

Complements are two numbers that add up to 100%. The trade discount rate and the net price factor are complements of each other. This means that if we know one of them, the other can be found by subtracting from 100%.

EXAMPLE 4 CALCULATING THE NET PRICE

Calculate the net price of merchandise at Astana Imports listing for $900 less a trade discount rate of 45%.

SOLUTIONSTRATEGY

$$\text{Net price} = \text{List price}(100\% - \text{Trade discount rate})$$
$$\text{Net price} = 900(100\% - 45\%)$$
$$\text{Net price} = 900(.55) = \underline{\$495}$$

TRYITEXERCISE 4

Central Hardware Store bought paint supplies listing for $2,100 with a single trade discount rate of 35%. What is the net price of the order?

CHECK YOUR ANSWER WITH THE SOLUTION ON PAGE 223.

7-5 CALCULATING TRADE DISCOUNT RATE WHEN LIST PRICE AND NET PRICE ARE KNOWN

The trade discount rate can be calculated by using the now-familiar percentage formula Rate = Portion ÷ Base. For this application, the amount of the trade discount is the portion, or numerator, and the list price is the base, or denominator.

$$\textbf{Trade discount rate} = \frac{\textbf{Trade discount}}{\textbf{List price}}$$

STEPS FOR CALCULATING TRADE DISCOUNT RATE

STEP 1. Calculate the amount of the trade discount.

$$\text{Trade discount} = \text{List price} - \text{Net price}$$

STEP 2. Calculate the trade discount rate.

$$\text{Trade discount rate} = \frac{\text{Trade discount}}{\text{List price}}$$

EXAMPLE5 CALCULATING THE SINGLE TRADE DISCOUNT AND RATE

Sterling Manufacturing sells tools to American Garden Supply. In a recent transaction, the list price of an order was $47,750 and the net price of the order was $32,100. Calculate the amount of the trade discount. What was the trade discount rate? Round your answer to the nearest tenth percent.

▶SOLUTIONSTRATEGY

$$\text{Trade discount} = \text{List price} - \text{Net price}$$
$$\text{Trade discount} = 47{,}750 - 32{,}100 = \underline{\$15{,}650}$$

$$\text{Trade discount rate} = \frac{\text{Trade discount}}{\text{List price}}$$

$$\text{Trade discount rate} = \frac{15{,}650}{47{,}750} = .3277 = \underline{\underline{32.8\%}}$$

▶TRYITEXERCISE 5

Wilson Sporting Goods recently sold tennis rackets listing for $109,500 to The Sports Authority. The net price of the order was $63,300. What was the amount of the trade discount? What was the trade discount rate? Round your answer to the nearest tenth percent.

CHECK YOUR ANSWERS WITH THE SOLUTION ON PAGE 223.

REVIEW EXERCISES

7 **SECTION II**

Calculate the following trade discounts. Round all answers to the nearest cent.

	List Price	Trade Discount Rate	Trade Discount
1.	$860.00	30%	$258.00
	Trade discount = 860.00 × .30 = $258.00		
2.	125.50	12%	_____
3.	41.75	19%	_____
4.	499.00	8%	_____
5.	88.25	50%	_____

Calculate the following trade discounts and net prices to the nearest cent.

	List Price	Trade Discount Rate	Trade Discount	Net Price
6.	$286.00	25%	$71.50	$214.50
7.	134.79	40%		
8.	21.29	18%		
9.	959.00	55%		

Calculate the following net price factors and net prices by using the complement method. Round all answers to the nearest cent.

	List Price	Trade Discount Rate	Net Price Factor	Net Price
10.	$3,499.00	37%	63%	$2,204.37
11.	565.33	24%		
12.	1,244.25	45.8%		
13.	4.60	$12\frac{3}{4}\%$		

Calculate the following trade discounts and trade discount rates. Round answers to the nearest tenth of a percent.

	List Price	Trade Discount	Trade Discount Rate	Net Price
14.	$4,500.00	$935.00	20.8%	$3,565.00
15.	345.50			225.00
16.	2.89			2.15

17. Find the amount of a trade discount of 30% on a television set that has a list price of $799.95.

18. Find the amount of a trade discount of 55% on a set of fine china that lists for $345.70.

19. What is the amount of a trade discount of 25% offered to a shoe store for merchandise purchased at a total list price of $7,800?

20. Whole Foods Market ordered 12 cases of organic vegetable soup with a list price of $18.90 per case and 8 cases of organic baked beans with a list price of $33.50 per case. The wholesaler offered Whole Foods a 39% trade discount.

    a. What is the total extended list price of the order?

    b. What is the total amount of the trade discount on this order?

    c. What is the total net amount Whole Foods owes the wholesaler for the order?

21. La Bella, a chain of clothing boutiques, purchased merchandise with a total list price of $25,450 from Sandy Sport, a manufacturer. The order has a trade discount of 34%.

    a. What is the amount of the trade discount?

    b. What is the net amount LaBella owes Sandy Sport for the merchandise?

22. An item with a trade discount of 41% has a list price of $289.50. What is the net price?

A number of supermarkets now make supporting local growers and producers a priority. Whole Foods, one such store, opened in 1980 and four years later began expanding rapidly.

Today, there are more than 310 stores in North America and the United Kingdom, and Whole Foods has acquired more than 10 natural food store chains. It is the world's leading supermarket emphasizing natural and organic foods and America's first national "Certified Organic" grocer.

© Cengage Learning

23. Nathan and David Beauty Salon places an order for beauty supplies from a wholesaler. The list price of the order is $2,800. If the vendor offers a trade discount of 46%, what is the net price of the order?

24. A watch has a list price of $889 and can be bought by Sterling Jewelers for a net price of $545.75.

    a. What is the amount of the trade discount?

    b. What is the trade discount rate?

25. Nutrition Central pays $11.90 net price for a bottle of 60 multivitamins. The price represents a 30% trade discount from the manufacturer. What is the list price of the vitamins?

26. You are the buyer for the housewares department of the Galleria Department Store. A number of vendors in your area carry similar lines of merchandise. On sets of microwavable serving bowls, Kitchen Magic offers a list price of $400 per dozen less a 38% trade discount. Pro-Chef offers a similar set for a list price of $425 less a 45% trade discount.

    a. Which vendor is offering the lower net price?

    b. If you order 500 dozen sets of the bowls, how much money will be saved by using the lower-priced vendor?

General Nutrition Centers, Inc., a wholly owned subsidiary of GNC Corporation, consists of a worldwide network of over 6,600 locations and the www.gnc.com website. GNC, Inc., is the largest global specialty retailer of health and wellness products, including vitamins, minerals and herbal supplements, sports nutrition products, and diet products.

The GNC website, www.gnc.com, provides an online library where consumers may research health-related topics.

BUSINESS DECISION: QUANTITY DISCOUNT

27. You are the purchasing manager for Tiger Electronics, a company that manufactures scanners and other computer peripherals. Your vendor for scanner motors, Enfield Industries, is now offering "quantity discounts" in the form of instant rebates and lower shipping charges as follows:

Quantity	Net Price	Rebate	Shipping
1–500 motors	$16	none	$1.30
501–1,000 motors	16	$1.20	.90
1,001–2,000 motors	16	1.80	.60

    a. Calculate the cost of the motors, including shipping charges, for each category.

    b. If you usually purchase 400 motors per month, what percent would be saved per motor by ordering 800 every two months? Round to the nearest tenth of a percent.

    c. What percent would be saved per motor by ordering 1,200 every three months? Round to the nearest tenth of a percent.

d. How much money can be saved in a year by purchasing the motors every three months instead of every month?

e. (Optional) What other factors besides price should be considered before changing your purchasing procedures?

SECTION III

7

TRADE DISCOUNTS—SERIES

chain or **series trade discounts** Term used when a vendor offers a buyer more than one trade discount.

Trade discounts are frequently offered by manufacturers to wholesalers and retailers in a series of two or more, known as **chain** or **series trade discounts**. For example, a series of 25% and 10% is verbally stated as "25 and 10." It is written 25/10. A three-discount series is written 25/10/5. Multiple discounts are given for many reasons. Some of the more common ones follow.

Position or Level in the Channel of Distribution   A manufacturer might sell to a retailer at a 30% trade discount, whereas a wholesaler in the same channel might be quoted a 30% and a 15% trade discount.

Learning Tip

Remember, when calculating the net price by using a series of trade discounts, you *cannot* simply add the trade discounts together. Each discount must be applied to a successively lower base.

Volume Buying   Many manufacturers and wholesalers grant an extra discount for buying a large volume of merchandise. For example, any purchase more than 5,000 units at one time may earn an extra 7% trade discount. Retailers with many stores or those with large storage capacity can enjoy a considerable savings (additional trade discounts) by purchasing in large quantities.

Advertising and Display   Additional discounts are often given to retailers and wholesalers who heavily advertise and aggressively promote a manufacturer's line of merchandise.

Competition   Competitive pressures often cause extra trade discounts to be offered. In certain industries such as household products and consumer electronics, price wars are not an uncommon occurrence.

7-6   CALCULATING NET PRICE AND THE AMOUNT OF A TRADE DISCOUNT BY USING A SERIES OF TRADE DISCOUNTS

Dollars AND Sense

An **industry trade group**, also known as a **trade association**, is an organization founded and funded by businesses that operate in a specific industry. An industry trade association participates in public relations activities such as advertising, education, political donations, lobbying, and publishing, but its main focus is collaboration between companies, or standardization.

Associations may offer other services, such as sponsoring conferences, providing networking, hosting charitable events, or offering classes or educational materials.

A directory of trade associations may be found at http://dir.yahoo.com/Business_and _Economy/organizations/trade_associations

Finding net price with a series of trade discounts is accomplished by taking each trade discount, one at a time, from the previous net price until all discounts have been deducted. Note that you *cannot* simply add the trade discounts together. They must be calculated individually unless the net price factor method—a handy shortcut—is used. Trade discounts can be taken in any order, although they are usually listed and calculated in descending order.

For illustrative purposes, let's begin with an example of how to calculate a series of trade discounts one at a time; then we will try the shortcut method.

EXAMPLE6   CALCULATING NET PRICE AND THE AMOUNT OF A TRADE DISCOUNT

Calculate the net price and trade discount for merchandise with a list price of $2,000 less trade discounts of 30/20/15.

▶ SOLUTIONSTRATEGY

$2,000	$2,000	$1,400	$1,400	$1,120	$1,120
× .30	− 600	× .20	− 280	× .15	− 168
$600	$1,400	$280	$1,120	$168	$952 = Net price

►TRYITEXERCISE 6

Northwest Publishers sold an order of books to The Bookworm, Inc., a chain of bookstores. The list price of the order was $25,000. The Bookworm buys in volume from Northwest. The Bookworm also prominently displays and heavily advertises Northwest's books. Northwest, in turn, gives The Bookworm a series of trade discounts amounting to 35/20/10. Calculate the net price of the order and the amount of the trade discount.

CHECK YOUR ANSWERS WITH THE SOLUTIONS ON PAGE 223.

CALCULATING THE NET PRICE OF A SERIES OF TRADE DISCOUNTS BY USING THE NET PRICE FACTOR, COMPLEMENT METHOD

7-7

As a shortcut, the net price can be calculated directly from the list price, bypassing the trade discount, by using the net price factor as before. Remember, the net price factor is the complement of the trade discount rate. With a series of discounts, we must find the complement of each trade discount to calculate the net price factor of the series.

The net price factor indicates to buyers what percent of the list price they actually *do* pay. For example, if the net price factor of a series of discounts is calculated to be .665, this means that the buyer is paying 66.5% of the list price.

STEPS FOR CALCULATING NET PRICE BY USING THE NET PRICE FACTOR

STEP 1. Find the complement of the trade discount rates in the series by subtracting each from 100% and converting them to decimal form.

STEP 2. Calculate the net price factor of the series by multiplying all the decimals together.

STEP 3. Calculate the net price by multiplying the list price by the net price factor.

Net price = List price × Net price factor

EXAMPLE7 CALCULATING NET PRICE FACTOR AND NET PRICE

The Crystal Gallery purchased merchandise from a manufacturer in Italy. The merchandise had a list price of $37,000 less trade discounts of 40/25/10. Calculate the net price factor and the net price of the order.

►SOLUTIONSTRATEGY

Step 1. Subtract each trade discount from 100% and convert to decimals.

100%	100%	100%
− 40%	− 25%	− 10%
60% = .6	75% = .75	90% = .9

Step 2. Multiply all the complements together to get the net price factor.

Net price factor = .6 × .75 × .9
Net price factor = .405

Step 3.

Net price = List price × Net price factor
Net price = 37,000 × .405
Net price = $14,985

► TRYITEXERCISE 7

Something's Fishy, a pet shop, always gets a 30/20/12 series of trade discounts from the Clearview Fish Tank Company. In June, the shop ordered merchandise with a list price of $3,500. In September, the shop placed an additional order listing for $5,800.

a. What is the net price factor for the series of trade discounts?

b. What is the net price of the merchandise purchased in June?

c. What is the net price of the merchandise purchased in September?

CHECK YOUR ANSWERS WITH THE SOLUTIONS ON PAGE 223.

7-8 CALCULATING THE AMOUNT OF A TRADE DISCOUNT BY USING A SINGLE EQUIVALENT DISCOUNT

single equivalent discount A single trade discount that equates to all the discounts in a series or chain.

Sometimes retailers and wholesalers want to know the one single discount rate that equates to a series of trade discounts. This is known as the **single equivalent discount**. We have already learned that the trade discounts *cannot* simply be added together.

Here is the logic: The list price of the merchandise is 100%. If the net price factor is the part of the list price that is paid, then 100% minus the net price factor is the part of the list price that is the trade discount. The single equivalent discount, therefore, is the complement of the net price factor (100% − Net price factor percent).

IN THE Business World

Among other indicators, economists use **wholesale prices** as an important barometer of inflation as well as other economic trends. Rising wholesale prices inevitably lead to higher consumer prices and consequently inflation.

The Producer Price Index (PPI) is a weighted index of prices measured at the wholesale, or producer, level. A monthly release from the Bureau of Labor Statistics (BLS), the PPI shows trends in the wholesale markets for manufacturing industries and commodities markets. All of the physical goods-producing industries that make up the U.S. economy are included, but imports are not. The PPI was once called the Wholesale Price Index.

Source: www.investopedia.com

STEPS TO CALCULATE THE SINGLE EQUIVALENT DISCOUNT AND THE AMOUNT OF A TRADE DISCOUNT

STEP 1. Calculate the net price factor as before by subtracting each trade discount from 100% and multiplying them all together in decimal form.

STEP 2. Calculate the single equivalent discount by subtracting the net price factor in decimal form from 1.

Single equivalent discount = 1 − Net price factor

STEP 3. Find the amount of the trade discount by multiplying the list price by the single equivalent discount.

Trade discount = List price × Single equivalent discount

EXAMPLE8 CALCULATING THE SINGLE EQUIVALENT DISCOUNT AND THE AMOUNT OF A TRADE DISCOUNT

Calculate the single equivalent discount and amount of the trade discount on merchandise listing for $10,000 less trade discounts of 30/10/5.

► SOLUTIONSTRATEGY

Step 1. Calculate the net price factor.

$$
\begin{array}{ccccc}
100\% & & 100\% & & 100\% \\
-\ 30\% & & -\ 10\% & & -\ 5\% \\
\hline
.70 & \times & .90 & \times & .95 & = .5985 = \text{Net price factor}
\end{array}
$$

Step 2. Calculate the single equivalent discount.

Single equivalent discount = 1 − Net price factor

Single equivalent discount = 1 − .5985 = .4015

Note: 40.15% is the single equivalent discount of the series 30%, 10%, and 5%.

Step 3. Calculate the amount of the trade discount.

Trade discount = List price × Single equivalent discount

Trade discount = 10,000 × .4015 = $4,015

►TRYITEXERCISE 8

The Rainbow Appliance Center purchased an order of dishwashers and ovens listing for $36,800. The manufacturer allows Rainbow a series of trade discounts of 25/15/10. What are the single equivalent discount and the amount of the trade discount?

CHECK YOUR ANSWERS WITH THE SOLUTIONS ON PAGE 223.

REVIEW EXERCISES

7 SECTION III

Calculate the following net price factors and net prices. For convenience, round net price factors to five decimal places when necessary.

	List Price	Trade Discount Rates	Net Price Factor	Net Price
1.	$360.00	12/10	.792	$285.12
2.	425.80	18/15/5		
3.	81.75	20/10/10		
4.	979.20	15/10/5		
5.	7.25	25/15/10$\frac{1}{2}$		
6.	.39	20/9/8		

Calculate the following net price factors and single equivalent discounts. Round to five places when necessary.

	Trade Discount Rates	Net Price Factor	Single Equivalent Discount
7.	15/10	.765	.235
8.	20/15/12		
9.	25/15/7		
10.	30/5/5		
11.	35/15/7.5		

Complete the following table. Round net price factors to five decimal places when necessary.

	List Price	Trade Discount Rates	Net Price Factor	Single Equivalent Discount	Trade Discount	Net Price
12.	$7,800.00	15/5/5	.76713	.23287	$1,816.39	$5,983.61
13.	1,200.00	20/15/7				
14.	560.70	25/15/5				
15.	883.50	18/12/9				
16.	4.89	12/10/10				
17.	2,874.95	30/20/5.5				

18. What is the net price factor of a 25/10 series of trade discounts?

19. What is the net price factor of a 35/15/10 series of discounts?

20. Kidzstuff.com ordered toys, games, and videos from a vendor. The order had a list price of $10,300 less trade discounts of 25/15/12.

    a. What is the net price factor?

    b. What is the net price of the order?

21. Legacy Designs places an order for furniture listing for $90,500 less trade discounts of 25/20.

    a. What is the net price factor?

    b. What is the net price of the order?

Daniel Acker/Bloomberg/Getty Images

Satellite radio, also called digital radio, receives radio signals broadcast from a network of satellites more than 22,000 miles above the earth. In contrast, traditional radio reception is usually limited to 50–100 miles.

Sirius XM Radio, Inc., offers a programming lineup of 135 channels of commercial-free music, sports, news, talk, entertainment, traffic, and weather. Subscribers can listen on more than 800 different types of devices for boats, cars, home, office, or a number of types of mobile devices. Sirius has agreements for the installation of satellite radio in vehicles with every major automaker.

22. Audio Giant received an order of Sirius XM satellite radios listing for $9,500 with trade discounts of 25/13/8.

    a. What is the net price factor?

    b. What is the single equivalent discount?

    c. What is the amount of the trade discount?

    d. What is the net price of the order?

23. The Speedy Auto Service Center can buy auto parts from Southeast Auto Supply at a series discount of 20/15/5 and from Northwest Auto Supply for 25/10/8.

    a. Which auto parts supplier offers a better discount to Speedy?

    b. If Speedy orders $15,000 in parts at list price per month, how much will it save in a year by choosing the lower-priced supplier?

24. La Fiesta Market buys merchandise from B. G. Distributors with a series discount of 35/15/7.

    a. What is the single equivalent discount?

    b. What is the amount of the trade discount on an order with a list price of $5,700?

25. Midtown Market received the following items at a discount of 25/20/10: 18 cases of canned peaches listing at $26.80 per case and 45 cases of canned pears listing at $22.50 per case.

    a. What is the total list price of this order?

    b. What is the amount of the trade discount?

    c. What is the net price of the order?

26. Shopper's Mart purchased the following items. Calculate the extended total after the trade discounts for each line, the invoice subtotal, and the invoice total.

Quantity	Unit	Merchandise	Unit List	Trade Discounts	Extended Total
150	ea.	Blenders	$59.95	20/15/15	_____
400	ea.	Toasters	$39.88	20/10/10	_____
18	doz.	Coffee Mills	$244.30	30/9/7	_____
12	doz.	Juicers	$460.00	25/10/5	_____
				Invoice subtotal	_____
		Extra $5\frac{1}{2}$% volume discount on total order			_____
				Invoice total	_____

The Pharmacy and Drug Store Industry in the United States retails a range of prescription and over-the-counter products. These include medicines; apothecaries; health and beauty items such as vitamin supplements, cosmetics, and toiletries; and photo processing services.

Top U.S. drug retailers include Rite Aid, CVS, Target, Kmart, Kroger, Safeway, Duane Reade, Supervalu, Walgreens, and Walmart.

27. Referring back to Exercise 26, you have just been hired as the buyer for the kitchen division of Shopper's Mart, a general merchandise retailer. After looking over the discounts offered to the previous buyer by the vendor, you decide to ask for better discounts.

    After negotiating with the vendor's salesperson, you now can buy blenders at trade discounts of 20/20/15 and juicers at 25/15/10. In addition, the vendor has increased the volume discount to $6\frac{1}{2}$%.

    a. How much would have been saved with your new discounts based on the quantities of the previous order (Exercise 26)?

    b. As a result of your negotiations, the vendor has offered an additional discount of 2% of the total amount due if the invoice is paid within 15 days instead of the usual 30 days. What would be the amount of this discount?

BUSINESS DECISION: THE ULTIMATE TRADE DISCOUNT

28. A General Motors incentive program designed to reduce inventory of certain low-selling models offers a $7,000 extra dealer incentive for each of these vehicles that the dealer moved into its rental or service fleets.

    As the accountant for a dealership with a number of these vehicles left in stock, your manager has asked you to calculate certain invoice figures. The normal trade discount from GM is 18%. If the average sticker price (list price) of these remaining vehicles at your dealership is $23,500, calculate the following.

    a. What is the amount of the trade discount, including the incentive?

    b. What is the trade discount rate? Round to the nearest tenth of a percent.

    c. What is the net price (invoice price) to your dealership?

    d. If the cars were then sold from the fleets at $1,000 over "invoice" (net price), what is the total percentage savings to the consumer based on the list price? Round to the nearest tenth of a percent.

    e. (Optional) Although these incentive prices reflect extraordinary discounts to the consumer, what other factors should a consumer consider before purchasing a "discontinued" brand of vehicle?

SECTION IV   **7**   CASH DISCOUNTS AND TERMS OF SALE

terms of sale The details of when an invoice must be paid and if a cash discount is being offered.

credit period The time period that the seller allows the buyer to pay an invoice.

net date, or **due date** The last day of the credit period.

cash discount An extra discount offered by the seller as an incentive for early payment of an invoice.

invoice date The date an invoice is written. The beginning of the discount and credit periods when ordinary dating is used.

cash discount period The time period in which a buyer can take advantage of the cash discount.

discount date The last day of the discount period.

As merchandise physically arrives at the buyer's back door, the invoice ordinarily arrives by mail through the front door. Today more and more arrive by e-mail. What happens next? The invoice has a section entitled **terms of sale**. The terms of sale are the details of when the invoice must be paid and whether any additional discounts will be offered.

Commonly, manufacturers allow wholesalers and retailers 30 days or even longer to pay the bill. In certain industries, the time period is as much as 60 or 90 days. This is known as the **credit period**. This gives the buyer time to unpack and check the order and, more important, begin selling the merchandise. This credit period clearly gives the wholesaler and retailer an advantage. They can generate revenue by selling merchandise that they have not paid for yet.

To encourage them to pay the bill earlier than the **net date**, or **due date**, sellers frequently offer buyers an optional extra discount over and above the trade discounts. This is known as a **cash discount**. Cash discounts are an extra few percent offered as an incentive for early payment of the invoice, usually within 10 to 15 days after the **invoice date**. This is known as the **cash discount period**. The last date for a buyer to take advantage of a cash discount is known as the **discount date**.

THE IMPORTANCE OF CASH DISCOUNTS

Both buyers and sellers benefit from cash discounts. Sellers get their money much sooner, which improves their cash flow, whereas buyers get an additional discount, which lowers their merchandise cost, thereby raising their margin or gross profit.

Cash discounts generally range from an extra 1% to 5% off the net price of the merchandise. A 1% to 5% discount may not seem significant, but it is. Let's say that an invoice is due in 30 days; however, a distributor would like payment sooner. It might offer the retailer a cash discount of 2% if the bill is paid within 10 days rather than 30 days. If the retailer chooses to take the cash discount, he or she must pay the bill by the 10th day after the date of the invoice. Note that this is *20 days* earlier than the due date. The retailer is therefore receiving a 2% discount for paying the bill 20 days early.

The logic: There are 18.25 twenty-day periods in a year (365 days divided by 20 days). By multiplying the 2% discount by the 18.25 periods, we see that on a yearly basis, 2% cash discounts can *theoretically* amount to 36.5%. Very significant!

> ## Dollars AND Sense
>
> Cash discounts are so important to wholesalers' and retailers' "profit picture" that frequently they borrow the money on a short-term basis to take advantage of the cash discount savings. This procedure is covered in Chapter 10, "Simple Interest."

CALCULATING CASH DISCOUNTS AND NET AMOUNT DUE

7-9

Cash discounts are offered in the terms of sale. A transaction with no cash discount would have terms of sale of net 30, for example. This means the **net amount** of the invoice is due in 30 days. If a cash discount is offered, the terms of sale would be written as 2/10, n/30. This means a 2% cash discount may be taken if the invoice is paid within 10 days; if not, the net amount is due in 30 days. (See Exhibit 7-4.)

Exhibit 7-5 shows a time line of the discount period and credit period on an invoice dated October 15. The 2/10, n/30 terms of sale stipulate a cash discount if the bill is paid within 10 days. If not, the balance is due in 30 days. As you can see, the cash discount period runs for 10 days from the invoice date, October 15 to October 25. The credit period, 30 days, extends from the invoice date through November 14.

Sometimes two cash discounts are offered, such as 3/15, 1/25, n/60. This means a 3% cash discount is offered if the invoice is paid within 15 days, a 1% cash discount if the invoice is paid within 25 days, with the net amount due in 60 days.

Cash discounts cannot be taken on shipping charges or returned goods, only on the net price of the merchandise. If shipping charges are included in the amount of an invoice, they must be subtracted before the cash discount is taken. After the cash discount has been deducted, the shipping charges are added back to get the invoice total.

net amount The amount of money due from the buyer to the seller.

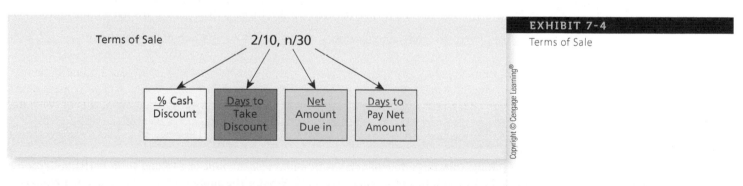

EXHIBIT 7-4

Terms of Sale

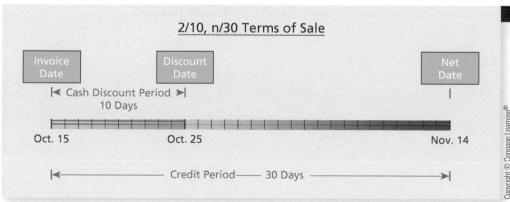

EXHIBIT 7-5

Terms of Sale Time Line

© Randy Glasbergen.
www.glasbergen.com

GLASBERGEN

**"Our terms are net 30 days. If you don't pay
after 30 days, we come after you with a net!"**

Randy Glasbergen

If arriving merchandise is damaged or is not what was ordered, those goods will be returned to the vendor. The amount of the returned goods must also be subtracted from the amount of the invoice. They are no longer a part of the transaction.

Learning Tip

Remember, shipping charges or returned items are not subject to cash discounts. These must be deducted from the invoice before the cash discount is applied. After the discount is taken, shipping charges, if any, are added back to get the invoice total.

STEPS TO CALCULATE CASH DISCOUNT AND NET AMOUNT DUE

STEP 1. Calculate the amount of the cash discount by multiplying the cash discount rate by the net price of the merchandise.

$$\text{Cash discount} = \text{Net price} \times \text{Cash discount rate}$$

STEP 2. Calculate the net amount due by subtracting the amount of the cash discount from the net price.

$$\text{Net amount due} = \text{Net price} - \text{Cash discount}$$

Note: As with trade discounts, buyers are frequently more interested in the net amount due than the amount of the discount. When that is the case, we can simplify the calculation by using the complement method to determine the net amount due.

$$\text{Net amount due} = \text{Net price}(100\% - \text{Cash discount rate})$$

EXAMPLE9   CALCULATING CASH DISCOUNT AND NET AMOUNT DUE

Rugs.com buys merchandise with an invoice amount of $16,000 from Karistan Carpet Mills. The terms of sale are 2/10, n/30. What is the amount of the cash discount? What is the net amount due on this order if the bill is paid by the 10th day?

SOLUTIONSTRATEGY

Cash discount = Net price × Cash discount rate

$$\text{Cash discount} = 16,000 \times .02 = \underline{\$320}$$

$$\text{Net amount due} = \text{Net price} - \text{Cash discount}$$

$$\text{Net amount due} = 16,000 - 320 = \underline{\$15,680}$$

▶TRYITEXERCISE 9

Valiant Plumbing ordered sinks from a supplier. The sinks had a net price of $8,300 and terms of sale of 3/15, n/45. What is the amount of the cash discount? What is the net amount due if the bill is paid by the 15th day?

CHECK YOUR ANSWERS WITH THE SOLUTIONS ON PAGE 223.

CALCULATING NET AMOUNT DUE, WITH CREDIT GIVEN FOR PARTIAL PAYMENT

7-10

Sometimes buyers do not have all the money needed to take advantage of the cash discount. Manufacturers and suppliers usually allow them to pay part of the invoice by the discount date and the balance by the end of the credit period. This **partial payment** earns partial cash discount credit. In this situation, we must calculate how much **partial payment credit** is given.

Here is how it works: Assume a cash discount of 4/15, n/45 is offered to a retailer. A 4% cash discount means that the retailer will pay 96% of the bill (100% − 4%) and receive 100% credit. Another way to look at it is that every $0.96 paid toward the invoice earns $1.00 credit. We must determine how many $0.96s are in the partial payment. This will tell us how many $1.00s of credit we receive.

partial payment When a portion of the invoice is paid within the discount period.

partial payment credit The amount of the invoice paid off by the partial payment.

STEPS TO CALCULATE PARTIAL PAYMENT CREDIT AND NET AMOUNT DUE

STEP 1. Calculate the amount of credit given for a partial payment by dividing the partial payment by the complement of the cash discount rate.

$$\text{Partial payment credit} = \frac{\text{Partial payment}}{100\% - \text{Cash discount rate}}$$

STEP 2. Calculate the net amount due by subtracting the partial payment credit from the net price.

$$\text{Net amount due} = \text{Net price} - \text{Partial payment credit}$$

IN THE Business World

The extension of partial payment credit by vendors is important to small retailers who don't always have the cash flow to take advantage of the full cash discount.

EXAMPLE10 CALCULATING NET AMOUNT DUE AFTER A PARTIAL PAYMENT

Happy Feet, a chain of children's shoe stores, receives an invoice from a tennis shoe manufacturer on September 3 with terms of 3/20, n/60. The net price of the order is $36,700. Happy Feet wants to send a partial payment of $10,000 by the discount date and the balance on the net date. How much credit does Happy Feet get for the partial payment? What is the remaining net amount due to the manufacturer?

▶SOLUTIONSTRATEGY

$$\text{Partial payment credit} = \frac{\text{Partial payment}}{100\% - \text{Case discount rate}}$$

$$\text{Partial payment credit} = \frac{10,000}{100\% - 3\%} = \frac{10,000}{.97} = \underline{\$10,309.28}$$

$$\text{Net amount due} = \text{Net price} - \text{Partial payment credit}$$

$$\text{Net amount due} = \$36,700.00 - \$10,309.28 = \underline{\$26,390.72}$$

►TRYITEXERCISE 10

All Pro Sports Center purchases $45,300 in baseball gloves from Spaulding on May 5. Spaulding allows 4/15, n/45. If All Pro sends a partial payment of $20,000 on the discount date, how much credit will be given for the partial payment? What is the net amount still due on the order?

CHECK YOUR ANSWERS WITH THE SOLUTIONS ON PAGE 223.

7-11 DETERMINING DISCOUNT DATE AND NET DATE BY USING VARIOUS TERMS OF SALE DATING METHODS

To determine the discount date and net date of an invoice, you must know how many days are in each month or use a calendar.

Following are two commonly used memory devices to help you remember how many days are in each month. Remember, in a leap year, February has 29 days. Leap years occur when the year is evenly divisible by 4 except if the year is also evenly divisible by 400. Therefore, 2016, 2020, and 2024 are examples of leap years, while 2000 was not a leap year.

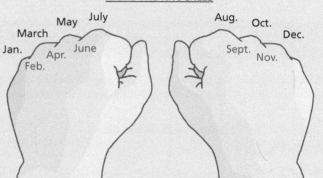

RHYME

Thirty days has September
April, June, and November
All the rest have thirty-one
Except February,
which has twenty-eight.

NAME THE KNUCKLES

Each month on a knuckle has 31 days and each month between knuckles has 30 days. February has 28.

Another way to find these dates is to use the days-in-a-year calendar shown in Exhibit 7-6. In Chapter 10, you will be able to use this calendar again to find future dates and calculate the number of days of a loan.

STEPS TO FINDING A FUTURE DATE USING A DAYS-IN-A-YEAR CALENDAR

STEP 1. Find the "day number" of the starting date.

Note: In leap years, add 1 to the day numbers beginning with March 1.

STEP 2. Add the number of days of the discount or credit period to that day number.

Note: If the new day number is over 365, subtract 365. This means the future date is in the next year.

STEP 3. Find the date by looking up the new day number from Step 2.

EXAMPLE11 FINDING THE NET DATE

If an invoice dated April 14 is due in 75 days, what is the net date?

SOLUTIONSTRATEGY

Step 1. From the calendar, April 14 is day number 104.

Step 2. $104 + 75 = 179$

Step 3. From the calendar, day number 179 is June 28.

TRYITEXERCISE 11

If an invoice dated September 12 is due in 60 days, what is the net date?

CHECK YOUR ANSWER WITH THE SOLUTION ON PAGE 223.

EXHIBIT 7-6 Days-In-A-Year Calendar

Day of month	Jan.	Feb.	Mar.	Apr.	May	June	July	Aug.	Sept.	Oct.	Nov.	Dec.
1	1	32	60	91	121	152	182	213	244	274	305	335
2	2	33	61	92	122	153	183	214	245	275	306	336
3	3	34	62	93	123	154	184	215	246	276	307	337
4	4	35	63	94	124	155	185	216	247	277	308	338
5	5	36	64	95	125	156	186	217	248	278	309	339
6	6	37	65	96	126	157	187	218	249	279	310	340
7	7	38	66	97	127	158	188	219	250	280	311	341
8	8	39	67	98	128	159	189	220	251	281	312	342
9	9	40	68	99	129	160	190	221	252	282	313	343
10	10	41	69	100	130	161	191	222	253	283	314	344
11	11	42	70	101	131	162	192	223	254	284	315	345
12	12	43	71	102	132	163	193	224	255	285	316	346
13	13	44	72	103	133	164	194	225	256	286	317	347
14	14	45	73	104	134	165	195	226	257	287	318	348
15	15	46	74	105	135	166	196	227	258	288	319	349
16	16	47	75	106	136	167	197	228	259	289	320	350
17	17	48	76	107	137	168	198	229	260	290	321	351
18	18	49	77	108	138	169	199	230	261	291	322	352
19	19	50	78	109	139	170	200	231	262	292	323	353
20	20	51	79	110	140	171	201	232	263	293	324	354
21	21	52	80	111	141	172	202	233	264	294	325	355
22	22	53	81	112	142	173	203	234	265	295	326	356
23	23	54	82	113	143	174	204	235	266	296	327	357
24	24	55	83	114	144	175	205	236	267	297	328	358
25	25	56	84	115	145	176	206	237	268	298	329	359
26	26	57	85	116	146	177	207	238	269	299	330	360
27	27	58	86	117	147	178	208	239	270	300	331	361
28	28	59	87	118	148	179	209	240	271	301	332	362
29	29		88	119	149	180	210	241	272	302	333	363
30	30		89	120	150	181	211	242	273	303	334	364
31	31		90		151		212	243		304		365

During a leap year, add 1 to the day numbers beginning with March 1.

TERMS OF SALE—DATING METHODS

ORDINARY DATING

ordinary dating When the discount period and credit period start on the invoice date.

When the discount period and the credit period start on the date of the invoice, this is known as **ordinary dating**. It is the most common method of dating the terms of sale. The last day to take advantage of the cash discount, the discount date, is found by adding the number of days in the discount period to the date of the invoice. For example, to receive a cash discount, an invoice dated November 8 with terms of 2/10, n/30 should be paid no later than November 18 (November 8 + 10 days). The last day to pay the invoice, the net date, is found by adding the number of days in the credit period to the invoice date. With terms of 2/10, n/30, the net date would be December 8 (November 8 + 30 days). If the buyer does not pay the bill by the net date, the seller may impose a penalty charge for late payment.

EXAMPLE12   USING ORDINARY DATING

AccuCare Pharmacy receives an invoice dated August 19 from Bristol Drug Wholesalers for merchandise. The terms of sale are 3/10, n/45. If AccuCare elects to take the cash discount, what is the discount date? If AccuCare does not take the cash discount, what is the net date?

▶SOLUTIONSTRATEGY

Find the discount date by adding the number of days in the discount period to the date of the invoice.

$$\text{Discount date} = \text{August 19} + \text{10 days} = \underline{\text{August 29}}$$

If the discount is not taken, find the net date by adding the number of days in the credit period to the invoice date.

$$\text{August 19} + \text{45 days} = \quad \begin{array}{l} \text{12 days left in August } (31-19) \\ + \text{ 30 days in September} \\ + \underline{\text{ 3 days in October}} \\ \quad \text{45 days} \end{array}$$

The net date, the 45th day, is October 3.

▶TRYITEXERCISE 12

Great Impressions Printing buys ink and paper from a supplier. The invoice date of the purchase is June 11. If the terms of sale are 4/10, n/60, what are the discount date and the net date of the invoice?

CHECK YOUR ANSWERS WITH THE SOLUTIONS ON PAGE 223.

EOM OR PROXIMO DATING

EOM dating End-of-month dating. Depending on invoice date, terms of sale start at the end of the month of the invoice or the end of the following month.

proximo, or **prox** Another name for EOM dating. Means "in the following month."

EOM dating, or end-of-month dating, means that the terms of sale start *after* the end of the month of the invoice. Another name for this dating method is **proximo**, or **prox**. Proximo means "in the following month." For example, 2/10 EOM, or 2/10 proximo, means that a 2% cash discount will be allowed if the bill is paid 10 days after the *end of the month* of the invoice. This is the case for any invoice dated from the 1st to the 25th of a month. If an invoice is dated after the 25th of the month, the terms of sale begin *after* the end of the *following* month. Unless otherwise specified, the net amount is due *20 days* after the discount date.

EXAMPLE13 USING EOM DATING

As the shipping manager for World Imports, answer the following questions.

a. What are the discount date and the net date of an invoice dated March 3 with terms of 3/15 EOM?

b. What are the discount date and the net date of an invoice dated March 27 with terms of 3/15 EOM?

►SOLUTIONSTRATEGY

a. Because the invoice date is between the 1st and the 25th of the month, March 3, the discount date on terms of 3/15 EOM would be 15 days *after* the end of the month of the invoice. The net date would be 20 days later.

Discount date = 15 days after the end of March = <u>April 15</u>

Net date = April 15 + 20 days = <u>May 5</u>

b. Because the invoice date is after the 25th of the month, March 27, the discount date on terms of 3/15 EOM would be 15 days *after* the end of the month *following* the invoice month. The net date would be 20 days later.

Discount date = 15 days after the end of April = <u>May 15</u>

Net date = May 15 + 20 days = <u>June 4</u>

►TRYITEXERCISE 13

As the accounts receivable manager for River Bend Industries, answer the following questions.

a. What are the discount date and the net date of an invoice dated November 18 with terms of 3/15 EOM?

b. What are the discount date and the net date of an invoice dated November 27 with terms of 3/15 EOM?

CHECK YOUR ANSWERS WITH THE SOLUTIONS ON PAGE 223.

ROG DATING

Receipt of goods dating, or **ROG dating**, is a common method used when shipping times are long, such as with special or custom orders. When ROG dating is used, the terms of sale begin the day the goods are received at the buyer's location. With this method, the buyer does not have to pay for the merchandise before it arrives. An example would be 2/10 ROG. As usual, the net date is 20 days after the discount date.

ROG dating Receipt of goods dating. Terms of sale begin on the date the goods are received by the buyer.

EXAMPLE14 USING ROG DATING

What are the discount date and the net date for an invoice dated June 23 if the shipment arrives on August 16 and the terms are 3/15 ROG?

►SOLUTIONSTRATEGY

In this case, the discount period starts on August 16, the date the shipment arrives. The net date will be 20 days after the discount date.

Discount date = August 16 + 15 days = <u>August 31</u>

Net date = August 31 + 20 days = <u>September 20</u>

►TRYITEXERCISE 14

What are the discount date and the net date of an invoice dated October 11 if the shipment arrives on December 29 and the terms are 2/20 ROG?

CHECK YOUR ANSWERS WITH THE SOLUTIONS ON PAGE 223.

EXTRA DATING

Extra, Ex, or X dating The buyer receives an extra discount period as an incentive to purchase slow-moving or out-of-season merchandise.

The last dating method commonly used in business today is called **Extra, Ex, or X dating**. With this dating method, the seller offers an extra discount period to the buyer as an incentive for purchasing slow-moving or out-of-season merchandise, such as Christmas goods in July and bathing suits in January. An example would be 3/10, 60 extra. This means the buyer gets a 3% cash discount in 10 days plus 60 *extra* days, or a total of 70 days. Once again, unless otherwise specified, the net date is 20 days after the discount date.

EXAMPLE15   USING EXTRA DATING

What are the discount date and the net date of an invoice dated February 9 with terms of 3/15, 40 Extra?

►SOLUTIONSTRATEGY

These terms, 3/15, 40 Extra, give the retailer 55 days (15 + 40) from February 9 to take the cash discount. The net date will be 20 days after the discount date.

$$\text{Discount date} = \text{February 9} + 55 \text{ days} = \underline{\text{April 5}}$$
$$\text{Net date} = \text{April 5} + 20 \text{ days} = \underline{\text{April 25}}$$

►TRYITEXERCISE 15

What are the discount date and the net date of an invoice dated February 22 with terms of 4/20, 60 Extra?

CHECK YOUR ANSWERS WITH THE SOLUTIONS ON PAGE 223.

Learning Tip

Remember, when using extra dating, unless otherwise specified, the net date is 20 days after the discount date.

SECTION IV   7   REVIEW EXERCISES

Calculate the cash discount and the net amount due for each of the following transactions.

	Amount of Invoice	Terms of Sale	Cash Discount	Net Amount Due
1.	$15,800.00	3/15, n/30	$474.00	$15,326.00
2.	12,660.00	2/10, n/45	_____	_____
3.	2,421.00	4/10, n/30	_____	_____
4.	6,940.20	2/10, n/30	_____	_____
5.	9,121.44	$3\frac{1}{2}$/15, n/60	_____	_____

For the following transactions, calculate the credit given for the partial payment and the net amount due on the invoice.

	Amount of Invoice	Terms of Sale	Partial Payment	Credit for Partial Payment	Net Amount Due
6.	$8,303.00	2/10, n/30	$2,500	$2,551.02	$5,751.98
7.	1,344.60	3/10, n/45	460	_____	_____
8.	5,998.20	4/15, n/60	3,200	_____	_____
9.	7,232.08	$4\frac{1}{2}$/20, n/45	5,500	_____	_____

Using the ordinary dating method, calculate the discount date and the net date for the following transactions.

	Date of Invoice	Terms of Sale	Discount Date(s)	Net Date
10.	November 4	2/10, n/45	Nov. 14	Dec. 19
11.	April 23	3/15, n/60	_____	_____
12.	August 11	3/20, n/45	_____	_____
13.	January 29	2/10, 1/20, n/60	_____	_____
14.	July 8	4/25, n/90	_____	_____

Using the EOM, ROG, and Extra dating methods, calculate the discount date and the net date for the following transactions. Unless otherwise specified, the net date is 20 days after the discount date.

	Date of Invoice	Terms of Sale	Discount Date	Net Date
15.	December 5	2/10, EOM	Jan. 10	Jan. 30
16.	June 27	3/15, EOM		
17.	September 1	3/20, ROG		
		Rec'd Oct. 3		
18.	February 11	2/10, 60 Extra		
19.	May 18	4/25, EOM		
20.	October 26	2/10, ROG		
		Rec'd Nov. 27		

21. The Apollo Company received an invoice from a vendor on April 12 in the amount of $1,420. The terms of sale were 2/15, n/45. The invoice included shipping charges of $108. The vendor sent $250 in merchandise that was not ordered. These goods will be returned by Apollo. (Remember, no discounts on shipping charges or returned goods.)

    a. What are the discount date and the net date?

    b. What is the amount of the cash discount?

    c. What is the net amount due?

22. An invoice is dated August 29 with terms of 4/15 EOM.

    a. What is the discount date?   b. What is the net date?

23. An invoice dated January 15 has terms of 3/20 ROG. The goods are delayed in shipment and arrive on March 2.

    a. What is the discount date?   b. What is the net date?

24. What payment should be made on an invoice in the amount of $3,400 dated August 7 if the terms of sale are 3/15, 2/30, n/45 and the bill is paid on

    a. August 19?

    b. September 3?

25. Red Tag Furniture received a SeaLand container of sofas from Thailand on April 14. The invoice, dated March 2, was for $46,230 in merchandise and $2,165 in shipping charges. The terms of sale were 3/15 ROG. Red Tag Furniture made a partial payment of $15,000 on April 27.

    a. What is the net amount due?

    b. What is the net date?

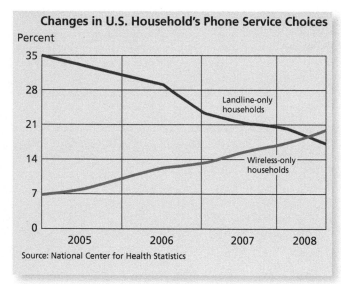

Changes in U.S. Household's Phone Service Choices

Source: National Center for Health Statistics

In 2008, for the first time, the number of U.S. households opting for only cell phones outnumbered those that had just traditional landlines, and the trend has continued since that time.

Source: National Center for Health Statistics

26. City Cellular purchased $28,900 in cell phones on April 25. The terms of sale were 4/20, 3/30, n/60. Freight terms were F.O.B. destination. Returned goods amounted to $650.

    a. What is the net amount due if City Cellular sends the manufacturer a partial payment of $5,000 on May 20?

    b. What is the net date?

    c. If the manufacturer charges a $4\frac{1}{2}\%$ late fee, how much would City Cellular owe if it did not pay the balance by the net date?

BUSINESS DECISION: THE EMPLOYMENT TEST

27. As part of the employment interview for an accounting job at Sound Design, you have been asked to answer the questions below, based on an invoice from one of Sound Design's vendors, Target Electronic Wholesalers.

**TARGET
ELECTRONIC WHOLESALERS
1979 N.E. 123 Street
Jacksonville, Florida 32204**

Sold to: Sound Design
480 McDowell Rd.
Phoenix, AZ 85008

Invoice Date: June 28, 20XX

Terms of Sale: 3/15, n/30 ROG

Stock #	Description	Unit Price	Amount
4811V	Stereo Receivers	50 × $297.50 =	_____
511CX	Blu-ray Players	25 × $132.28 =	_____
6146M	Home Theater Systems	40 × $658.12 =	_____
1031A	LCD TVs	20 × $591.00 =	_____

Merchandise Total	_____
Insurance + Shipping	$1,150.00
Invoice Total	_____

a. Extend each line and calculate the merchandise total and the total amount of the invoice, using the space provided on the invoice.

b. What are the discount date and the net date if the shipment arrived on July 16?

c. While in transit, five Blu-ray players and four LCD TVs were damaged and will be returned. What is the amount of the returned merchandise? What is the revised merchandise total?

d. What are the amount of the cash discount and the net amount due if the discount is taken?

e. If Sound Design sends in a partial payment of $20,000 within the discount period, what is the net balance still due?

CHAPTER FORMULAS

The Invoice

Extended total = Number of items × Cost per item

Trade Discounts—Single

Trade discount = List price × Trade discount rate

Net price = List price − Trade discount

Net price = List price(100% − Trade discount rate)

$$\text{Trade discount rate} = \frac{\text{Trade discount}}{\text{List price}}$$

Trade Discounts—Series

Net price = List price × Net price factor

Single equivalent discount = 1 − Net price factor

Trade discount = List price × Single equivalent discount

Cash Discounts and Terms of Sale

Net amount due = Net price(100% − Cash discount rate)

$$\text{Partial payment credit} = \frac{\text{Partial payment}}{100\% - \text{Cash discount rate}}$$

Net amount due = Net price − Partial payment credit

CHAPTER SUMMARY

Section I: The Invoice

Topic	Important Concepts	Illustrative Examples
Reading and Understanding the Parts of an Invoice **Performance Objective 7-1, Page 190**	Refer to Exhibits 7-1, 7-2, and 7-3.	

Extending and Totaling an Invoice
 	
Performance Objective 7-2, Page 193
	Extended amount =
	   Number of items × Cost per item
	Invoice subtotal =
	   Total of extended amount column
	Invoice total =
	   Invoice subtotal + Other charges
		The Great Subversion, a sandwich shop, ordered 25 lb of ham at $3.69 per pound and 22 lb of cheese at $4.25 per pound. There is a $7.50 delivery charge. Extend each item and find the invoice subtotal and invoice total.
		
		25 × 3.69 = 92.25 Ham
		22 × 4.25 = 93.50 Cheese
		                185.75 Subtotal
		              + 7.50 Delivery
		              $193.25 Invoice total

Section II: Trade Discounts—Single

Topic	Important Concepts	Illustrative Examples
Calculating the Amount of a Single Trade Discount **Performance Objective 7-3, Page 197**	Trade discounts are reductions from the manufacturer's list price given to businesses in the trade for the performance of various marketing functions. Trade discount = List price × Trade discount rate	Sunglass King ordered merchandise with a list price of $12,700 from a manufacturer. Because it is in the trade, Sunglass King gets a 35% trade discount. What is the amount of the trade discount? Trade discount = 12,700 × .35 = $4,445

Section II (continued)

Topic	Important Concepts	Illustrative Examples

Calculating Net Price by Using the Net Price Factor, Complement Method
 	
Performance Objective 7-4, Page 197
	Net price factor =
	   100% − Trade discount rate
	Net price =
	   List price(100% − Trade discount rate)
		From the previous problem, use the net price factor to find the net price of the order for Sunglass King.
		
		Net price = 12,700(100% − 35%)
		Net price = 12,700 × .65 = $8,255

Calculating Trade Discount Rate When List Price and Net Price Are Known **Performance Objective 7-5, Page 198**	Trade discount rate = $\dfrac{\text{Trade discount}}{\text{List price}}$	Cycle World Bike Shop orders merchandise listing for $5,300 from Schwinn. The net price of the order is $3,200. What is the trade discount rate? Trade discount = 5,300 − 3,200 = $2,100 Trade discount rate = $\dfrac{2{,}100}{5{,}300}$ = 39.6%

Section III: Trade Discounts—Series

Topic	Important Concepts	Illustrative Examples
Calculating Net Price and the Amount of a Trade Discount by Using a Series of Trade Discounts **Performance Objective 7-6, Page 202**	Net price is found by taking each trade discount in the series from the succeeding net price until all discounts have been deducted. Trade discount = List price − Net price	An invoice with merchandise listing for $4,700 was entitled to trade discounts of 20% and 15%. What is the net price and the amount of the trade discount? 4,700 × .20 = 940 4,700 − 940 = 3,760 3,760 × .15 = 564 3,760 − 564 = $3,196 Net price Trade discount = 4,700 − 3,196 = $1,504
Calculating Net Price of a Series of Trade Discounts by Using the Net Price Factor, Complement Method **Performance Objective 7-7, Page 203**	Net price factor is found by subtracting each trade discount rate from 100% (complement) and multiplying these complements together. Net price = List price × Net price factor	Use the net price factor method to verify your answer to the previous problem. $\begin{array}{ccc} 100\% & & 100\% \\ -\ 20\% & & -\ 15\% \\ \hline .80 & \times & .85 \end{array}$ = .68 Net price factor Net price = 4,700 × .68 = $3,196

Calculating the Amount of a Trade Discount by Using a Single Equivalent Discount
 	
Performance Objective 7-8, Page 204
	Single equivalent discount =
	   1 − Net price factor
	Trade discount =
	   List price × Single equivalent discount
		What is the single equivalent discount and the amount of the trade discount in the previous problem?
		
		Use this to verify your trade discount answer.
		
		Single equivalent discount = 1 − .68 = .32
		Trade discount = 4,700 × .32 = $1,504

Section IV: Cash Discounts and Terms of Sale

Topic	Important Concepts	Illustrative Examples

Calculating Cash Discounts and Net Amount Due
 	
Performance Objective 7-9, Page 209
	Terms of sale specify when an invoice must be paid and if a cash discount is offered. Cash discount is an extra discount offered by the seller as an incentive for early payment of an invoice.
	
	Cash discount =
	   Net price × Cash discount rate
	Net amount due =
	   Net price − Cash discount
		Action Auto Parts orders merchandise for $1,800, including $100 in freight charges. Action gets a 3% cash discount. What is the amount of the cash discount and the net amount due?
		
		1,800 − 100 = 1,700 Net price
		Cash discount = 1,700 × .03 = $51
		
		$\begin{array}{l} 1{,}700 - 51 = \ \ 1{,}649 \\ \underline{+\ \ 100}\ \ \text{Shipping} \\ \$1{,}749\ \ \text{Net amount due} \end{array}$

Section IV (continued)

Topic	Important Concepts	Illustrative Examples

Calculating Net Amount Due, with Credit Given for Partial Payment
 	
Performance Objective 7-10, Page 211
	$$\text{Partial payment credit} = \frac{\text{Partial payment}}{100\% - \text{Cash discount rate}}$$
	
	Net amount due =
	   Net price − Partial payment credit
		Elite Fashions makes a partial payment of $3,000 on an invoice of $7,900. The terms of sale are 3/15, n/30. What is the amount of the partial payment credit, and how much does Elite Fashions still owe on the invoice?
		
		$$\text{Part pmt credit} = \frac{3,000}{100\% - 3\%} = \$3,092.78$$
		Net amount due = 7,900.00
		                − 3,092.78
		                 $4,807.22

Determining Discount Date and Net Date by Using Various Terms of Sale Dating Methods Performance Objective 7-11, Page 212	Discount date: last date to take advantage of a cash discount. Net date: last date to pay an invoice without incurring a penalty charge.	
Ordinary Dating Method Performance Objective 7-11, Page 214	Ordinary dating: discount period and the credit period start on the date of the invoice.	Galaxy Jewelers receives an invoice for merchandise on March 12 with terms of 3/15, n/30. What are the discount date and the net date? Disc date = March 12 + 15 days = March 27 Net date = March 12 + 30 days = April 11

EOM or Proximo Dating Method
 	
Performance Objective 7-11, Page 214
	EOM means end of month. It is a dating method in which the terms of sale start *after* the end of the month of the invoice.
	   If the invoice is dated after the 25th of the month, the terms of sale start *after* the end of the *following* month.
	   Unless otherwise specified, the net date is *20 days* after the discount date.
	   Proximo, or prox, is another name for EOM dating. It means "in the following month."
		Majestic Cleaning Service buys supplies with terms of sale of 2/10, EOM. What are the discount date and the net date if the invoice date is
		
		a. May 5?
		b. May 27?
		
		a. May 5 invoice terms start *after* the end of May:
		     Discount date = June 10
		     Net date = June 10 + 20 days = June 30
		
		b. May 27 invoice terms start *after* the end of the *following* month, June:
		     Discount date = July 10
		     Net date = July 10 + 20 days = July 30

ROG Dating Method Performance Objective 7-11, Page 215	ROG means receipt of goods. It is a dating method in which the terms of sale begin on the date the goods are received rather than the invoice date. This is used to accommodate long shipping times. Unless otherwise specified, the net date is *20 days* after the discount date.	An invoice dated August 24 has terms of 3/10 ROG. If the merchandise arrives on October 1, what are the discount date and the net date? Disc date = October 1 + 10 days = October 11 Net date = October 11 + 20 days = October 31
Extra Dating Method Performance Objective 7-11, Page 216	Extra, Ex, or X is a dating method in which the buyer receives an extra period of time before the terms of sale begin. Vendors use extra dating as an incentive to entice buyers to purchase out-of-season or slow-moving merchandise. Unless otherwise specified, the net date is *20 days* after the discount date.	Sugar Pine Candy Company buys merchandise from a vendor with terms of 3/15, 60 Extra. The invoice is dated December 11. What are the discount date and the net date? Disc date = December 11 + 75 days = February 24 Net date = February 24 + 20 = March 16

TRY IT: EXERCISE SOLUTIONS FOR CHAPTER 7

1. **a.** Shutterbug Camera Shops

    b. 44929

    c. November 27, 20XX

    d. $3,120.00

    e. FotoFair Distributors

    f. Net - 30 days

    g. 1864 N.W. 123rd St., Chicago, IL 60613

    h. J. Herman

    i. Federal Express

    j. Knoxville, TN

    k. $125.00

    l. $5,632.80

    m. $345.00

    n. $5,757.80

2.

Stock #	Quantity	Unit	Merchandise Description	Unit Price	Total
R443	125	ea.	Food Processors	$89.00	$11,125.00
B776	24	ea.	Microwave Ovens	$225.40	$5,409.60
Z133	6	doz.	12" Mixers	$54.12	$324.72
Z163	1	bx.	Mixer Covers	$166.30	$166.30
				Invoice Subtotal	$17,025.62
				Shipping Charges	+ $194.20
				Invoice Total	$17,219.82

3. Trade discount = List price × Trade discount rate

Trade discount = 7,600 × .30 = $2,280

4. Net price = List price(100% − Trade discount rate)

Net price = 2,100(100% − 35%)

Net price = 2,100 × .65 = $1,365

5. Trade discount = List price − Net price

Trade discount = 109,500 − 63,300 = $46,200

$$\text{Trade discount rate} = \frac{\text{Trade discount}}{\text{List price}} = \frac{46,200}{109,500} = .4219 = 42.2\%$$

6.

$$\begin{array}{cccccc} 25,000 & 25,000 & 16,250 & 16,250 & 13,000 & 13,000 \\ \times\ .35 & -8,750 & \times\ .20 & -3,250 & \times\ .10 & -1,300 \\ \hline 8,750 & 16,250 & 3,250 & 13,000 & 1,300 & \$11,700 \end{array} = \text{Net price}$$

Trade discount = 25,000 − 11,700 = $13,300

7. **a.**

$$\begin{array}{ccc} 100\% & 100\% & 100\% \\ -30\% & -20\% & -12\% \\ \hline .7\ \times & .8\ \times & .88 \end{array} = .4928 = \text{Net price factor}$$

    b. Net price = List price × Net price factor

    Net price = 3,500 × .4928 = $1,724.80

    c. Net price = List price × Net price factor

    Net price = 5,800 × .4928 = $2,858.24

8.

$$\begin{array}{ccc} 100\% & 100\% & 100\% \\ -25\% & -15\% & -10\% \\ \hline .75\ \times & .85\ \times & .9 \end{array} = .57375 = \text{Net price factor}$$

Single equivalent discount = 1 − Net price factor

Single equivalent discount = 1 − .57375 = .42625

Trade discount = List price × Single equivalent discount

Trade discount = 36,800 × .42625 = $15,686

9. Cash discount = Net price × Cash discount rate

Cash discount = 8,300 × .03 = $249

Net amount due = Net price − Cash discount

Net amount due = 8,300 − 249 = $8,051

10. $\text{Partial payment credit} = \dfrac{\text{Partial payment}}{100\% - \text{Cash discount rate}}$

$\text{Partial payment credit} = \dfrac{20,000}{100\% - 4\%} = \dfrac{20,000}{.96} = \$20,833.33$

Net amount due = Net price − Partial payment credit

Net amount due = 45,300.00 − 20,833.33 = $24,466.67

11. From the calendar, September 12 is day number 255.

255 + 60 = 315

From the calendar, day number 315 is November 11.

12. Discount date = June 11 + 10 days = June 21

Net date = June 11 + 60 days

$$\begin{array}{rl} 30 & \text{Days in June} \\ -11 & \text{Discount date} \\ \hline 19 & \text{June} \\ 31 & \text{July} \\ +10 & \text{Aug} \longrightarrow \text{August 10} \\ \hline 60 & \text{Days} \end{array}$$

13. **a.** Discount date = 15 days after end of November = December 15

    Net date = December 15 + 20 days = January 4

    b. Discount date = 15 days after end of December = January 15

    Net date = January 15 + 20 days = February 4

14. Discount date = December 29 + 20 days = January 18

Net date = January 18 + 20 days = February 7

15. Discount date = February 22 + 80 days = May 13

Net date = May 13 + 20 days = June 2

CONCEPT REVIEW

1. The document detailing a sales transaction is known as a(n) _____. (7-1)

2. F.O.B. shipping point and F.O.B. destination are shipping terms that specify where the merchandise _____ is transferred. (7-1)

3. To extend an invoice, for each line, we multiply the number of items by the _____ per item. (7-2)

4. To calculate the amount of a single trade discount, we multiply the _____ price by the trade discount rate. (7-3)

5. The _____ price is the amount a business actually pays for merchandise after the discount has been deducted. (7-4)

6. To calculate the net price factor, we subtract the trade discount rate from _____ . (7-4)

7. Write the formula for the trade discount rate. (7-5)

8. In a chain or _____ of trade discounts, we calculate the final net price by taking each discount one at a time from the previous net price. (7-6)

9. As a shortcut, we can use the net price _____ method to calculate the net price. (7-7)

10. To calculate the net price factor, we subtract each trade discount rate from 100% and then _____ all the complements together. (7-7)

11. A single trade discount that equates to all the discounts in a series or chain is called a single _____ discount. (7-8)

12. The "_____ of sale" specify when an invoice must be paid and if a(n) _____ discount is being offered. (7-9)

13. To calculate the credit given for a partial payment, we divide the amount of the partial payment by 100% _____ the cash discount rate. (7-10)

14. The most common method for dating an invoice is when the discount period and the credit period start on the date of the invoice. This method is known as _____ dating. (7-11)

ASSESSMENT TEST

Answer the following questions based on the Leisure Time Industries invoice on the following page.

1. Who is the vendor?

2. What is the date of the invoice?

3. What is the stock number of rockers?

4. What does dz. mean?

5. What is the unit price of plastic lounge covers?

6. What is the destination?

7. What is the extended total for chaise lounges with no armrest?

8. Who pays the freight if the terms are F.O.B. shipping point?

9. What is the invoice subtotal?

10. What is the invoice total?

CHAPTER 7

LEISURE TIME INDUSTRIES

LTI

Patio Furniture Manufacturers
1930 Main Street
Fort Worth, Texas 76102

DATE: November 2, 20XX

SOLD TO: Patio Magic Stores
3386 Fifth Avenue
Raleigh, NC 27613

INVOICE # B-112743

TERMS OF SALE: Net 30 days

SHIPPING INFO: FedEx Freight

STOCK #	QUANTITY	UNIT	MERCHANDISE DESCRIPTION	UNIT PRICE	TOTAL
1455	40	ea.	Chaise Lounges with armrest	$169.00	_____
1475	20	ea.	Chaise Lounges—no armrest	$127.90	_____
4387	24	ea.	Rocker Chairs	$87.70	_____
8100	3	dz.	Plastic Lounge Covers	$46.55	_____

INVOICE SUBTOTAL: _____
Packing and Handling: $125.00
Shipping Charges: $477.50

INVOICE TOTAL: _____

11. Picasso Art Supplies receives an invoice for the purchase of merchandise with a list price of $5,500. Because Picasso is in the trade, it receives a 27% trade discount. What is the amount of the trade discount?

12. Natureland Garden Center buys lawn mowers that list for $679.95 less a 30% trade discount.

   a. What is the amount of the trade discount?

   b. What is the net price of each lawn mower?

13. Shorty's BBQ Restaurant places an order listing for $1,250 with a meat and poultry supplier. Shorty's receives a trade discount of $422 on the order. What is the trade discount rate on this transaction?

14. Fantasia Florist Shop purchases an order of imported roses with a list price of $2,375 less trade discounts of 15/20/20.

   a. What is the amount of the trade discount?

   b. What is the net amount of the order?

GO ONLINE FOR MORE ACTIVITIES www.cengagebrain.com

15. All-American Sports can purchase sneakers for $450 per dozen less trade discounts of 14/12 from Ideal Shoes. Fancy Footwear is offering the same sneakers for $435 less trade discounts of 18/6. Which supplier offers a lower net price?

16. **a.** What is the net price factor for trade discounts of 25/15/10?

    b. Use that net price factor to find the net price of a couch listing for $800.

17. **a.** What is the net price factor of the trade discount series 20/15/11?

    b. What is the single equivalent discount?

The U.S. Carpet Industry According to the Carpet and Rug Institute, carpet covers nearly 60% of all floors in the United States. Ninety percent of all domestic carpet is manufactured in Georgia, representing a significant economic impact to the state. Nationwide, the industry employs over 70,000 workers.

18. The Empire Carpet Company orders merchandise for $17,700, including $550 in shipping charges, from Mohawk Carpet Mills on May 4. Carpets valued at $1,390 will be returned because they are damaged. The terms of sale are 2/10, n/30 ROG. The shipment arrives on May 26, and Empire wants to take advantage of the cash discount.

    a. By what date must Empire pay the invoice?

    b. As the bookkeeper for Empire, how much will you send to Mohawk?

19. Lazy Days Laundry receives an invoice for detergent. The invoice is dated April 9 with terms of 3/15, n/30.

    a. What is the discount date?

    c. If the invoice terms are changed to 3/15 EOM, what is the new discount date?

    b. What is the net date?

    d. What is the new net date?

20. Ned's Sheds purchases building materials from Timbertown Lumber for $3,700 with terms of 4/15, n/30. The invoice is dated October 17. Ned's decides to send in a $2,000 partial payment.

    a. By what date must the partial payment be sent to take advantage of the cash discount?

    b. What is the net date?

    c. If partial payment was sent by the discount date, what is the balance still due on the order?

21. Club Z is in receipt of new electronics to control the lighting on its dance floor. The invoice, dated June 9, shows the total cost of the equipment as $14,350. Shipping charges amount to $428, and insurance is $72.80. Terms of sale are 2/10 prox. If the invoice is paid on July 9, what is the net amount due?

BUSINESS DECISION: THE BUSY EXECUTIVE

22. You are a salesperson for Victory Lane Wholesale Auto Parts. You have just taken a phone order from one of your best customers, Champion Motors. Because you were busy when the call came in, you recorded the details of the order on a notepad.

Phone Order Notes

- The invoice date is April 4, 20XX.
- The customer order no. is 443B.
- Champion Motors's warehouse is located at 7011 N.W. 4th Avenue, Columbus, Ohio 43205.
- Terms of sale—3/15, n/45.
- The order will be filled by D. Watson.
- The goods will be shipped by truck.
- Champion Motors's home office is located next to the warehouse at 7013 N.W. 4th Avenue.
- Champion ordered 44 car batteries, stock #394, listing for $69.95 each and 24 truck batteries, stock #395, listing for $89.95 each. These items get trade discounts of 20/15.
- Champion also ordered 36 cases of 10W/30 motor oil, stock #838-W, listing for $11.97 per case, and 48 cases of 10W/40 super-oil, stock #1621-S, listing for $14.97 per case. These items get trade discounts of 20/20/12.
- The shipping charges for the order amount to $67.50.
- Insurance charges amount to $27.68.

a. Transfer your notes to the invoice on the following page, extend each line, and calculate the total.

b. What is the discount date of the invoice?

c. If Champion sends a partial payment of $1,200 by the discount date, what is the balance due on the invoice?

d. What is the net date of the invoice?

e. Your company has a policy of charging a 5% late fee if invoice payments are more than five days late. What is the amount of the late fee that Champion will be charged if it fails to pay the balance due on time?

Founded in 1928, **Genuine Parts Company** is a service organization engaged in the distribution of automotive replacement parts, industrial replacement parts, office products, and electrical/electronic materials. The company serves customers from more than 1,900 locations with approximately 31,700 employees.

NAPA, representing the Automotive Parts Group at Genuine Parts, is the central hub of company activity. The group consists of 58 NAPA distribution centers serving approximately 5,800 NAPA Auto Parts Stores, of which 1,000 are company-owned.

Source: Based on www.napaonline.com

Allen Eyestone/Newscom

INVOICE

Victory Lane
Wholesale Auto Parts
422 Riverfront Road
Cincinnati, Ohio 45244

Invoice #

Invoice Date:

Sold To:

Ship To:

Customer Order No.	Salesperson	Ship via	Terms of Sale	Filled By

Quantity Ordered	Stock Number	Description	Unit List Price	Trade Discounts	Extended Amount

Invoice Subtotal   _____
Shipping Charges   _____
Insurance   _____
Invoice Total   _____

COLLABORATIVE LEARNING ACTIVITY

Comparing Invoices and Discounts

1. As a team, collect invoices from a number of businesses in different industries in your area.

   a. How are they similar?

   b. How are they different?

2. Have each member of the team speak with a wholesaler or a retailer in your area.

   a. What are the typical trade discounts in that industry?

   b. What are the typical terms of sale in that industry?

CHAPTER **8**   # Markup and Markdown

PERFORMANCE OBJECTIVES

Determining an appropriate selling price for a company's goods or services is an extremely important function in business. The price must be attractive to potential customers, yet sufficient to cover expenses and provide the company with a reasonable profit.

cost of goods sold The cost of the merchandise sold during an operating period. One of two major expense categories of a business.

In business, expenses are separated into two major categories. The first is the **cost of goods sold**. To a manufacturer, this expense would be the cost of production; to a wholesaler or retailer, the expense is the price paid to a manufacturer or distributor for the merchandise. The second category includes all the other expenses required to operate the business, such as salaries, rent, utilities, taxes, insurance, advertising, and maintenance. These expenses are known as **operating expenses**, overhead expenses, or simply **overhead**.

operating expenses, or **overhead** All business expenses, other than cost of merchandise, required to operate a business, such as payroll, rent, utilities, and insurance.

The amount added to the cost of an item to cover the operating expenses and profit is known as the **markup, markon,** or **margin**. It is the difference between the cost and the selling price of an item. Markup is applied at all levels of the marketing channels of distribution. This chapter deals with the business math applications involved in the pricing of goods and services.

markup, markon, or **margin** The amount added to the cost of an item to cover the operating expenses and profit. It is the difference between the cost and the selling price.

8-1 UNDERSTANDING AND USING THE RETAILING EQUATION TO FIND COST, AMOUNT OF MARKUP, AND SELLING PRICE OF AN ITEM

The fundamental principle on which business operates is to sell goods and services for a price high enough to cover all expenses and provide the owners with a reasonable profit. The formula that describes this principle is known as the **retailing equation**. The equation states that the selling price of an item is equal to the cost plus the markup.

retailing equation The selling price of an item is equal to the cost plus the markup.

Selling price = Cost + Markup

Using the abbreviations C for cost, M for markup, and SP for selling price, the formula is written as

$$SP = C + M$$

To illustrate, if a camera costs a retailer $60 and a $50 markup is added to cover operating expenses and profit, the selling price of the camera would be $110.

$$\$60 \text{ (cost)} + \$50 \text{ (markup)} = \$110 \text{ (selling price)}$$

In Chapter 5, we learned that equations are solved by isolating the unknowns on one side and the knowns on the other. Using this theory, when the amount of markup is the unknown, the equation can be rewritten as

Markup = Selling price − Cost $M = SP - C$

When the cost is the unknown, the equation becomes

Cost = Selling price − Markup $C = SP - M$

The following examples illustrate how these formulas are used to determine the dollar amount of cost, markup, and selling price.

EXAMPLE1 FINDING THE SELLING PRICE

Mementos Gift Shop pays $8.00 for a picture frame. If a markup of $6.50 is added, what is the selling price of the frame?

SOLUTIONSTRATEGY

Because selling price is the unknown variable, we use the formula $SP = C + M$ as follows:

$$SP = C + M$$
$$SP = 8.00 + 6.50 = 14.50$$
$$\text{Selling price} = \underline{\$14.50}$$

▶TRYITEXERCISE 1

For the following, use the basic retailing equation to solve for the unknown.

Hairbrushes cost the manufacturer $6.80 per unit to produce. If a markup of $9.40 each is added to the cost, what is the selling price per brush?

CHECK YOUR ANSWER WITH THE SOLUTION ON PAGE 256.

EXAMPLE2 FINDING THE AMOUNT OF MARKUP

Reliable Office Supply buys printing calculators from Taiwan for $22.50 each. If they are sold for $39.95, what is the amount of the markup?

▶SOLUTIONSTRATEGY

Because the markup is the unknown variable, we use the formula $M = SP - C$ as follows:

$$M = SP - C$$
$$M = 39.95 - 22.50 = 17.45$$
$$\text{Markup} = \underline{\$17.45}$$

▶TRYITEXERCISE 2

For the following, use the basic retailing equation to solve for the unknown.

The 19th Hole sells a dozen golf balls for $28.50. If the distributor was paid $16.75, what is the amount of the markup?

CHECK YOUR ANSWER WITH THE SOLUTION ON PAGE 256.

EXAMPLE3 FINDING THE COST

Safeway Supermarkets sell Corn Crunchies for $3.29 per box. If the markup on this item is $2.12, how much did the store pay for the cereal?

▶ SOLUTIONSTRATEGY

Because the cost is the unknown variable in this problem, we use the formula $C = SP - M$.

$$C = SP - M$$
$$C = 3.29 - 2.12 = 1.17$$
$$\text{Cost} = \underline{\$1.17}$$

▶ TRYITEXERCISE 3

For the following, use the basic retailing equation to solve for the unknown.

After a wholesaler adds a markup of $75 to a television set, it is sold to a retail store for $290. What is the wholesaler's cost?

CHECK YOUR ANSWER WITH THE SOLUTION ON PAGE 256.

8-2 CALCULATING PERCENT MARKUP BASED ON COST

markup based on cost When cost is 100% and the markup is expressed as a percent of that cost.

Learning Tip

A shortcut for calculating the factors of the retailing equation is to use the **markup table**. The cells represent cost, markup, and selling price in both dollars and percents.

Markup Table

	$	%
C		
+ MU		
SP		

Learning Tip

Step 1. Fill in the given information using 100% for the base and X for this unknown. **(orange)**

Step 2. Calculate the figure for the remaining cell **(red)** in the column without the X.

$89.60 − $56.00 = $33.60

	$	%
C	56.00	100
+ MU	33.60	X
SP	89.60	

Then form a box. **(yellow)**

(continue)

In addition to being expressed in dollar amounts, markup is frequently expressed as a percent. There are two ways of representing markup as a percent: based on cost and based on selling price. Manufacturers and most wholesalers use cost as the base in calculating the percent markup because cost figures are readily available to them. When markup is based on cost, the cost is 100%, and the markup is expressed as a percent of that cost. Retailers, however, use selling price figures as the base of most calculations, including percent markup. In retailing, the selling price represents 100%, and the markup is expressed as a percent of that selling price.

In Chapter 6, we used the percentage formula Portion = Rate × Base. To review these variables, portion is a *part* of a whole amount; base is the *whole amount*; and rate, as a percent, describes what part the portion is of the base. When we calculate markup as a percent, we are actually solving a rate problem using the formula Rate = Portion ÷ Base.

When the markup is based on cost, the percent markup is the rate; the dollar amount of markup is the portion; and the cost, representing 100%, is the base. The answer will describe what percent the markup is of the cost; therefore, it is called percent **markup based on cost**. We use the formula:

$$\text{Percent markup based on cost (rate)} = \frac{\text{Markup (portion)}}{\text{Cost (base)}} \quad \text{or} \quad \%M_{\text{COST}} = \frac{M}{C}$$

EXAMPLE4 CALCULATING PERCENT MARKUP BASED ON COST

Blanco Industries produces stainless steel sinks at a cost of $56.00 each. If the sinks are sold to distributors for $89.60 each, what are the amount of the markup and the percent markup based on cost?

▶ SOLUTIONSTRATEGY

$$M = SP - C$$
$$M = 89.60 - 56.00 = 33.60$$
$$\text{Markup} = \underline{\$33.60}$$

$$\%M_{\text{COST}} = \frac{M}{C}$$

$$\%M_{COST} = \frac{33.60}{56.00} = .6$$

Percent markup based on cost = <u>60%</u>

The figures in the box form a proportion.

$$\frac{56}{33.60} = \frac{100}{X}$$

Step 3. Solve the proportion for X by cross-multiplying the corner figures in the box.

$$56X = 33.60(100)$$

$$X = \frac{3,360}{56} = 60\%$$

▶TRYITEXERCISE 4

The Light Source buys lamps for $45 and sells them for $63. What are the amount of the markup and the percent markup based on cost?

CHECK YOUR ANSWERS WITH THE SOLUTIONS ON PAGE 256.

CALCULATING SELLING PRICE WHEN COST AND PERCENT MARKUP BASED ON COST ARE KNOWN

8-3

From the basic retailing equation, we know that the selling price is equal to the cost plus the markup. When the markup is based on cost, the cost equals 100%, and the selling price equals 100% plus the percent markup. If, for example, the percent markup is 30%, then

Selling price = Cost + Markup

Selling price = 100% + 30%

Selling price = 130% *of* the cost

Because *of* means multiply, we multiply the cost by (100% plus the percent markup).

Selling price = Cost(100% + Percent markup based on cost)

$$SP = C(100\% + \%M_{COST})$$

EXAMPLE5 CALCULATING THE SELLING PRICE

A wallet costs $50 to produce. If the manufacturer wants a 70% markup based on cost, what should be the selling price of the wallet?

▶SOLUTIONSTRATEGY

$$SP = C(100\% + \%M_{COST})$$
$$SP = 50(100\% + 70\%)$$
$$SP = 50(170\%) = 50(1.7) = 85$$
Selling price = <u>$85</u>

	+		= 170%
		$	%
C			
+ *MU*			
SP			170

Note: When the brown box has six cells, use the four corner figures to form the proportion.

$$100X = 50(170)$$
$$X = \underline{\$85}$$

▶TRYITEXERCISE 5

Superior Appliances buys toasters for $38. If a 65% markup based on cost is desired, what should be the selling price of the toaster?

CHECK YOUR ANSWER WITH THE SOLUTION ON PAGE 256.

8-4   CALCULATING COST WHEN SELLING PRICE AND PERCENT MARKUP BASED ON COST ARE KNOWN

To calculate cost when selling price and percent markup on cost are known, let's use our knowledge of solving equations from Chapter 5. Because we are dealing with the same three variables from the last section, simply solve the equation $SP = C(100\% + \%M_{COST})$ for the cost. Cost, the unknown, is isolated on one side of the equation by dividing both sides by (100% + Percent markup).

$$\text{Cost} = \frac{\text{Selling price}}{100\% + \text{Percent markup on cost}} \qquad C = \frac{SP}{100\% + \%M_{COST}}$$

EXAMPLE6   CALCULATING COST

American Eagle sells a blouse for $66. If a 50% markup based on cost is used, what is the cost of the blouse?

▶ SOLUTIONSTRATEGY

$$\text{Cost} = \frac{\text{Selling price}}{100\% + \text{Percent markup on cost}}$$

$$\text{Cost} = \frac{66}{100\% + 50\%} = \frac{66}{150\%} = \frac{66}{1.5} = 44$$

$$\text{Cost} = \$44$$

▶ TRYITEXERCISE 6

General Electric sells automatic coffeemakers to distributors for $39. If a 30% markup based on cost is used, how much did it cost to manufacture the coffee maker?

CHECK YOUR ANSWER WITH THE SOLUTION ON PAGE 256.

Sidebar diagram:

	$	%
C		
+ MU		
SP		150

+   = 150%

$150X = 66(100)$

$X = \$44$

SECTION I   8   REVIEW EXERCISES

For the following items, calculate the missing information. Round dollars to the nearest cent and percents to the nearest tenth of a percent.

	Item	Cost	Amount of Markup	Selling Price	Percent Markup Based on Cost
1.	television set	$161.50	$138.45	$299.95	85.7%
2.	bookcase	$32.40	$21.50	_____	_____
3.	automobile	_____	$5,400.00	$12,344.80	_____
4.	dress	$75.00	_____	_____	80%
5.	vacuum cleaner	_____	_____	$249.95	60%

Item	Cost	Amount of Markup	Selling Price	Percent Markup Based on Cost
6. hat	$46.25	$50.00	$96.25	108.1%
7. computer	$1,350.00	_____	$3,499.00	_____
8. treadmill	_____	$880.00	$2,335.00	_____
9. 1 lb potatoes	$.58	_____	_____	130%
10. wallet	_____	_____	$44.95	75%

Solve the following word problems. Round dollars to the nearest cent and percents to the nearest tenth of a percent.

11. Alarm clocks cost the manufacturer $56.10 per unit to produce. If a markup of $29.80 is added to the cost, what is the selling price per clock?

12. En Vogue Boutique sells blouses for $22.88. If the cost per blouse is $15.50, what is the amount of the markup?

13. After a wholesaler adds a markup of $125 to a stereo, it is sold for $320. What is the cost of the stereo?

14. Amazon.com purchases flat-screen computer monitors from H.P. for $275.59 and sells them for $449.99.

    a. What is the amount of the markup?

    b. What is the percent markup based on cost?

15. The Holiday Card Shop purchased stationery for $2.44 per box. A $1.75 markup is added to the stationery.

    a. What is the selling price?

    b. What is the percent markup based on cost?

16. Staples adds a $4.60 markup to calculators and sells them for $9.95.

    a. What is the cost of the calculators?

    b. What is the percent markup based on cost?

17. a. What is the amount of markup on a skateboard from Flying Wheels Skate Shop if the cost is $58.25 and the selling price is $118.88?

    b. What is the percent markup based on cost?

Amazon.com, Inc., operates as an online retailer in North America and internationally. Its product categories include books, movies, music, and games; digital downloads; electronics and computers; home and garden; toys, kids, and baby; grocery; apparel, shoes, and jewelry; health and beauty; sports and outdoors; and tools, auto, and industrial products.

The stated mission of Amazon.com is to "be Earth's most customer-centric company for four primary customer sets: consumers, sellers, enterprises, and content creators." In 1997, its first year, Amazon.com's net sales were $148 million. Ten years later net sales were $14 billion.

THE CAMERA CONNECTION

$109.99

PowerShooter **1800**

$199.99

CyberShooter **2400**

18. You are the manager of The Camera Connection. Use the advertisement for your store to answer the following questions.

   a. If the PowerShooter 1800 is marked up by $58.50, what is the cost and what is the percent markup on cost?

   b. If the CyberShooter 2400 has a cost of $88.00 what are the amount of the markup and the percent markup on cost?

   c. Which camera is more "profitable" to the store? Why?

   d. What other factors should be considered in determining profitability?

19. Crystal Auto Supply purchases water pumps from the distributor for $35.40 each. If Crystal adds a 120% markup based on cost, at what retail price should the pumps be sold?

20. Broadway Carpets sells designer rugs at retail for $875.88. If a 50% markup based on cost is added, what is the cost of the designer rugs?

21. What is the cost of a plasma TV that sells at retail for $1,750 with a 70% markup based on cost?

22. A real-wood filing cabinet from Office Solutions is marked up by $97.30 to $178.88.

   a. What is the cost?

   b. What is the percent markup based on cost?

23. The Green Thumb Garden Shop purchases automatic lawn sprinklers for $12.50 from the manufacturer. If a 75% markup based on cost is added, at what retail price should the sprinklers be marked?

24. a. What is the cost of a desk lamp at Urban Accents if the selling price is $49.95 and the markup is 70% based on the cost?

   b. What is the amount of the markup?

BUSINESS DECISION: KEYSTONE MARKUP

25. In department and specialty store retailing, a common markup strategy is to double the cost of an item to arrive at a selling price. This strategy is known as **keystoning** the markup and is widely used in apparel, cosmetics, fashion accessories, shoes, and other categories of merchandise.

    The reasoning for the high amount of markup is that these stores have particularly high operating expenses. In addition, they have a continuing need to update fixtures and remodel stores to attract customers.

    You are the buyer in the women's shoe department of the Roma Grande Department Store. You normally keystone your markups on certain shoes and handbags. This amount of markup allows you enough gross margin so that you can lower prices when "sales" occur and still have a profitable department.

    a. If you are looking for a line of handbags that will retail for $120, what is the most you can pay for the bags?

    b. At a women's wear trade show, you find a line of handbags that you like with a suggested retail price of $130. The vendor has offered you trade discounts of 30/20/5. Will this series of trade discounts allow you to keystone the handbags?

    c. (Challenge) The vendor tells you that the first two discounts, 30% and 20%, are fixed, but the 5% is negotiable. What trade discount, rounded to a whole percent, should you request in order to keystone the markup?

Top U.S. Shopping Centers
Gross Leasable Area (GLA) in sq ft

King of Prussia Mall King of Prussia, Pennsylvania	2,856,000
Mall of America Bloomington, Minnesota	2,777,918
South Coast Plaza Costa Mesa, California	2,700,000
Mill Creek Mall Erie, Pennsylvania	2,600,000
Del Amo Fashion Center Torrance, California	2,500,000
Grand Canyon Parkway Las Vegas, Nevada	2,500,000
Aventura Mall Aventura, Florida	2,400,000
Sawgrass Mills Sunrise, Florida	2,383,906
The Galleria Houston, Texas	2,298,417

Source: www.shoppingcenters.com

MARKUP BASED ON SELLING PRICE

8   SECTION II

In Section I, we calculated markup as a percentage of the cost of an item. The cost was the base and represented 100%. As noted, this method is primarily used by manufacturers and wholesalers. In this section, the markup is calculated as a percentage of the selling price; therefore, the selling price will be the base and represent 100%. This practice is used by most retailers because most retail records and statistics are kept in sales dollars.

CALCULATING PERCENT MARKUP BASED ON SELLING PRICE

8-5

The calculation of percent **markup based on selling price** is the same as that for percent markup based on cost except that the base (the denominator) changes from cost to selling price. Remember, finding percent markup is a rate problem using the now familiar percentage formula Rate = Portion ÷ Base.

markup based on selling price When selling price is 100% and the markup is expressed as a percent of that selling price.

For this application of the formula, the percent markup based on selling price is the rate, the amount of the markup is the portion, and the selling price is the base. The formula is

$$\text{Percent markup based on selling price (rate)} = \frac{\text{Markup (portion)}}{\text{Selling price (base)}} \quad \text{or} \quad \%M_{SP} = \frac{M}{SP}$$

EXAMPLE7 CALCULATING THE PERCENT MARKUP BASED ON SELLING PRICE

Quality Hardware & Garden Supply purchases electric drills for $60 each. If it sells the drills for $125, what is the amount of the markup and what is the percent markup based on selling price?

SOLUTIONSTRATEGY

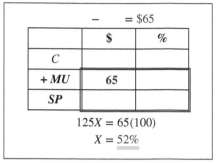

	$	%
C		
+ MU	65	
SP		

– = $65

$125X = 65(100)$

$X = 52\%$

$$M = SP - C$$
$$M = 125 - 60 = 65$$
$$\text{Markup} = \underline{\$65}$$

$$\%M_{SP} = \frac{M}{SP}$$

$$\%M_{SP} = \frac{65}{125} = .52$$

Percent markup based on selling price = 52%

TRYITEXERCISE 7

Deals on Wheels buys bicycles from the distributor for $94.50 each. If the bikes sell for $157.50, what is the amount of the markup and what is the percent markup based on selling price?

CHECK YOUR ANSWERS WITH THE SOLUTIONS ON PAGE 256.

8-6 CALCULATING SELLING PRICE WHEN COST AND PERCENT MARKUP BASED ON SELLING PRICE ARE KNOWN

When the percent markup is based on selling price, remember that the selling price is the base and represents 100%. This means the percent cost plus the percent markup must equal 100%. If, for example, the markup is 25% of the selling price, the cost must be 75% of the selling price.

$$\text{Cost} + \text{Markup} = \text{Selling price}$$
$$75\% + 25\% = 100\%$$

Because the percent markup is known, the percent cost will always be the complement, or

% Cost = 100% − Percent markup based on selling price

Because the selling price is the base, we can solve for the selling price by using the percentage formula Base = Portion ÷ Rate, where the cost is the portion and the percent cost or (100% − Percent markup on selling price) is the rate.

$$\text{Selling price} = \frac{\text{Cost}}{100\% - \text{Percent markup on selling price}} \quad \text{or} \quad SP = \frac{C}{100\% - \%M_{SP}}$$

EXAMPLE8 CALCULATING SELLING PRICE

High Point Furniture purchases wall units from the manufacturer for $550. If the store policy is to mark up all merchandise 60% based on the selling price, what is the retail selling price of the wall units?

►SOLUTIONSTRATEGY

$$SP = \frac{C}{100\% - \%M_{SP}}$$

$$SP = \frac{550}{100\% - 60\%} = \frac{550}{40\%} = 1{,}375$$

Selling price = $\underline{\underline{\$1{,}375}}$

	$	%
_		= 40%
C		40
+ MU		
SP		

$$40X = 550(100)$$
$$X = \underline{\underline{\$1{,}375}}$$

►TRYITEXERCISE 8

Grand Prix Menswear buys suits for $169 from the manufacturer. If a 35% markup based on selling price is the objective, what should be the selling price of the suit?

CHECK YOUR ANSWER WITH THE SOLUTION ON PAGE 256.

CALCULATING COST WHEN SELLING PRICE AND PERCENT MARKUP BASED ON SELLING PRICE ARE KNOWN

8-7

Often retailers know how much their customers are willing to pay for an item. The following procedure is used to determine the most a retailer can pay for an item and still get the intended markup.

To calculate the cost of an item when the selling price and percent markup based on selling price are known, we use a variation of the formula used in the last section. To solve for cost, we must isolate cost on one side of the equation by multiplying both sides of the equation by (100% – Percent markup). This yields the equation for cost:

Cost = Selling price(100% – Percent markup on selling price)

$$C = SP(100\% - \%M_{SP})$$

Learning Tip

The percent markup on cost is always *greater* than the corresponding percent markup on selling price because markup on cost uses cost as the base, which is *less* than the selling price. In the percentage formula, the lower the base, the greater the rate.

EXAMPLE9 CALCULATING COST

A buyer for a chain of boutiques is looking for a line of dresses to retail for $120. If a 40% markup based on selling price is the objective, what is the most the buyer can pay for these dresses and still get the intended markup?

►SOLUTIONSTRATEGY

$$C = SP(100\% - \%M_{SP})$$

$$C = 120(100\% - 40\%) = 120(.6) = 72$$

Cost = $\underline{\underline{\$72}}$

	$	%
_		= 60
C		60
+ MU		
SP		

$$100X = 120(60)$$
$$X = \underline{\underline{\$72}}$$

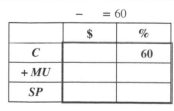

▶ TRYIT EXERCISE 9

What is the most a gift shop buyer can pay for a set of wine glasses if he wants a 55% markup based on selling price and expects to sell the glasses for $79 at retail?

CHECK YOUR ANSWER WITH THE SOLUTION ON PAGE 256.

8-8 CONVERTING PERCENT MARKUP BASED ON COST TO PERCENT MARKUP BASED ON SELLING PRICE, AND VICE VERSA

CONVERTING PERCENT MARKUP BASED ON COST TO PERCENT MARKUP BASED ON SELLING PRICE

When percent markup is based on cost, it can be converted to percent markup based on selling price by using the following formula:

$$\text{Percent markup based on selling price} = \frac{\text{Percent markup based on cost}}{100\% + \text{Percent markup based on cost}}$$

Learning Tip

This table provides a shortcut for converting between markup types. As before:

- Fill in the given information and also use 100% for the bases and X for the unknown. **(orange)**
- Calculate the figure for the remaining cell in the column without the X. **(red)**

$$100 + 60 = 160$$

- Form a proportion and solve for X.

	% C	% SP
C	100	
+ MU	60	X
SP	160	100

$$\frac{60}{160} = \frac{X}{100}$$
$$160X = 60(100)$$
$$X = \underline{37.5\%}$$

EXAMPLE10 CONVERTING BETWEEN MARKUP TYPES

If a purse is marked up 60% based on cost, what is the corresponding percent markup based on selling price?

▶ SOLUTIONSTRATEGY

$$\text{Percent markup based on selling price} = \frac{\text{Percent markup based on cost}}{100\% + \text{Percent markup based on cost}}$$

$$\text{Percent markup based on selling price} = \frac{60\%}{100\% + 60\%} = \frac{.6}{1.6} = .375$$

$$\text{Percent markup based on selling price} = \underline{37.5\%}$$

▶ TRYIT EXERCISE 10

A suitcase is marked up 50% based on cost. What is the corresponding percent markup based on selling price?

CHECK YOUR ANSWER WITH THE SOLUTION ON PAGE 256.

CONVERTING PERCENT MARKUP BASED ON SELLING PRICE TO PERCENT MARKUP BASED ON COST

When percent markup is based on selling price, it can be converted to percent markup based on cost by the formula:

$$\text{Percent markup based on cost} = \frac{\text{Percent markup based on selling price}}{100\% - \text{Percent markup based on selling price}}$$

EXAMPLE11 CONVERTING BETWEEN MARKUP TYPES

At Walmart, a Panasonic sound system is marked up 25% based on selling price. What is the corresponding percent markup based on cost? Round to the nearest tenth of a percent.

▶SOLUTIONSTRATEGY

$$\text{Percent markup based on cost} = \frac{\text{Percent markup based on selling price}}{100\% - \text{Percent markup based on selling price}}$$

$$\text{Percent markup based on cost} = \frac{25\%}{100\% - 25\%} = \frac{.25}{.75} = .3333$$

$$\text{Percent markup based on cost} = \underline{33.3\%}$$

	−	= 75
	% C	**% SP**
C		75
+ MU		
SP		

$$75X = 25(100)$$
$$X = \underline{33.3\%}$$

▶TRYITEXERCISE 11

At Video Outlet, a PlayStation 4 game is marked up 75% based on selling price. What is the corresponding percent markup based on cost? Round to the nearest tenth of a percent.

CHECK YOUR ANSWER WITH THE SOLUTION ON PAGE 256.

REVIEW EXERCISES

8 SECTION II

For the following items, calculate the missing information. Round dollars to the nearest cent and percents to the nearest tenth of a percent.

	Item	Cost	Amount of Markup	Selling Price	Percent Markup Based on Cost	Percent Markup Based on Selling Price
1.	sink	$65.00	$50.00	$115.00		43.5%
2.	textbook	$34.44	_____	$51.50		_____
3.	telephone	$75.00	_____	_____		45%
4.	bicycle	_____	_____	$133.50		60%
5.	magazine				60%	_____
6.	flashlight				_____	35%
7.	dollhouse	$71.25	$94.74	$165.99	133%	57.1%
8.	bar of soap	$1.18	$.79	_____	_____	_____
9.	truck	$15,449.00	_____	_____	_____	38%
10.	sofa	_____	_____	$1,299.00	_____	55%
11.	fan				150%	_____
12.	drill				_____	47%

Solve the following word problems. Round dollars to the nearest cent and percents to the nearest tenth of a percent.

13. You are the manager of Midtown Hardware. If the EnergyMax batteries in your advertisement have a cost of $3.25,

   a. What is the amount of the markup on these batteries?

   b. What is your percent markup based on selling price?

   c. If the vendor reduces the cost to $2.90 as a promotional trade discount this week, what is your new amount of markup and what is percent markup based on selling price?

14. A distributor purchases tractors at a cost of $6,500 and sells them for $8,995.

   a. What is the amount of the markup?

   b. What is the percent markup based on selling price?

15. Waterbed City purchases beds from the manufacturer for $212.35. If the store policy is to mark up all merchandise 42% based on selling price, what is the retail selling price of the beds?

16. Video Depot uses a 40% markup based on selling price for its video game systems. On games and accessories, they use a 30% markup based on selling price. (See advertisement.)

   a. What is the cost and the amount of the markup of the video game system?

   b. What is the cost and the amount of the markup of the Sports Package game?

   c. As a promotion this month, the manufacturer is offering its dealers a rebate of $5.50 for each additional remote sold. What is the cost and percent markup (rounded to the nearest tenth) based on selling price?

17. Galaxy Tools manufactures an 18-volt drill at a cost of $38.32. It imports rechargeable battery packs for $20.84 each. Galaxy offers its distributors a "package deal" that includes a drill and two battery packs. The markup is 36% based on selling price. What is the selling price of the package?

18. You are the buyer for The Shoe Outlet. You are looking for a line of men's shoes to retail for $79.95. If your objective is a 55% markup based on selling price, what is the most that you can pay for the shoes to still get the desired markup?

19. If the markup on a washing machine is 43% based on selling price, what is the corresponding percent markup based on cost?

20. If the markup on an oven is 200% based on cost, what is the corresponding percent markup based on selling price?

21. A purse has a cost of $21.50 and a selling price of $51.99.

    a. What is the amount of markup on the purse?

    b. What is the percent markup based on cost?

    c. What is the corresponding percent markup based on selling price?

22. As the manager of Speedy Supermarket, answer the following questions.

    a. If 2-liter Bubbly-Cola products cost Speedy $16.50 per case of 24 bottles, what are the amount of the markup and the percent markup on selling price per case?

    b. If 12-pack Bubbly-Cola products have a markup of $8.25 per case of six 12-packs at Speedy, what are the cost and the percent markup on selling price per case?

    c. Why has Speedy Supermarket chosen to use markup based on selling price?

BUSINESS DECISION: INCREASING THE MARGIN

23. If Costco pays $37.50 for the vacuum cleaner shown here,

    a. What is the percent markup based on selling price?

    b. If Costco pays $1.50 to the insurance company for each product replacement policy sold, what is the percent markup based on selling price of the vacuum cleaner and policy combination?

    c. If 6,000 vacuum cleaners are sold in a season and 40% are sold with the insurance policy, how many additional "markup dollars," the **gross margin**, was made by offering the policy?

    d. (Optional) As a housewares buyer for Costco, what is your opinion of such insurance policies, considering their effect on the "profit picture" of the department? How can you sell more policies?

SECTION III | 8 | MARKDOWNS, MULTIPLE OPERATIONS, AND PERISHABLE GOODS

markdown A price reduction from the original selling price of merchandise.

markdown cancellation Raising prices back to the original selling price after a sale is over.

The original selling price of merchandise usually represents only a temporary situation based on customer and competitor reaction to that price. A price reduction from the original selling price of merchandise is known as a **markdown**. Markdowns are frequently used in retailing because of errors in initial pricing or merchandise selection. For example, the original price may have been set too high or the buyer ordered the wrong styles, sizes, or quantities of merchandise.

Most markdowns should not be regarded as losses but as sales promotion opportunities used to increase sales and profits. When a sale has been concluded, raising prices back to the original selling price is known as a **markdown cancellation**. This section deals with the mathematics of markdowns, a series of markups and markdowns, and the pricing of perishable merchandise.

8-9 DETERMINING THE AMOUNT OF MARKDOWN AND THE MARKDOWN PERCENT

sale price The promotional price of merchandise after a markdown.

A markdown is a reduction from the original selling price of an item to a new **sale price**. To determine the amount of a markdown, we use the formula:

$$\text{Markdown} = \text{Original selling price} - \text{Sale price}$$

For example, if a sweater was originally marked at $89.95 and then was sale-priced at $59.95, the amount of the markdown would be $30.00 ($89.95 − $59.95 = $30.00).

To find the markdown percent, we use the percentage formula once again, Rate = Portion ÷ Base, where the markdown percent is the rate, the amount of the markdown is the portion, and the original selling price is the base:

$$\text{Markdown percent} = \frac{\text{Markdown}}{\text{Original selling price}}$$

Dollars AND Sense

Become a Prudent Shopper!
The price difference between two items is cash you get to put in your pocket. Even $10 saved this week will buy three dozen eggs next week. And saving $100 will give you $466.09 in 20 years at 8% interest.

Here are some of *Consumer Reports ShopSmart's* picks for the best sites to find deals:

- CouponWinner.com
- PricesandCoupons.com
- Savings.com
- Shop.com
- RetailMeNot.com
- Groupon.com
- 6pm.com
- TheOutnet.com

Sources: *The Miami Herald*, March 7, 2010, page 1E; *USA Today*, Sept. 18, 2009, page 3B.

Prudent shoppers often spend time comparing products in order to make informed buying decisions.

EXAMPLE12 — DETERMINING THE MARKDOWN AND MARKDOWN PERCENT

A blender that originally sold for $60 was marked down and sold for $48. What is the amount of the markdown and the markdown percent?

SOLUTIONSTRATEGY

$$\text{Markdown} = \text{Original selling price} - \text{Sale price}$$

$$\text{Markdown} = 60 - 48 = 12$$

$$\text{Markdown} = \underline{\$12}$$

$$\text{Markdown percent} = \frac{\text{Markdown}}{\text{Original selling price}} = \frac{12}{60} = .2$$

$$\text{Markdown percent} = \underline{20\%}$$

►TRYITEXERCISE 12

A tennis racquet that originally sold for $75 was marked down and sold for $56. What are the amount of the markdown and the markdown percent? Round your answer to the nearest tenth of a percent.

CHECK YOUR ANSWERS WITH THE SOLUTIONS ON PAGE 257.

> **Learning Tip**
>
> Note that *markdown percent* calculations are an application of *rate of decrease*, covered in Chapter 6.
>
> In the percentage formula, the markdown (portion) represents the amount of the decrease and the original selling price (base) represents the original amount.

DETERMINING THE SALE PRICE AFTER A MARKDOWN AND THE ORIGINAL PRICE BEFORE A MARKDOWN

8-10

DETERMINING SALE PRICE AFTER A MARKDOWN

In markdown calculations, the original selling price is the base, or 100%. After a markdown is subtracted from that price, the new price represents (100% − Markdown percent) *of* the original price. For example, if a chair is marked down 30%, the sale price would be 70% (100% − 30%) of the original price.

To find the new sale price after a markdown, we use the familiar percentage formula, Portion = Rate × Base, where the sale price is the portion, the original price is the base, and (100% − Markdown percent) is the rate.

> **Sale price = Original selling price(100% − Markdown percent)**

EXAMPLE13 — DETERMINING THE SALE PRICE

Fernando's Hideaway, a men's clothing store, originally sold a line of ties for $55 each. If the manager decides to mark them down 40% for a clearance sale, what is the sale price of a tie?

►SOLUTIONSTRATEGY

Remember, if the markdown is 40%, the sale price must be 60% (100% − 40%) *of* the original price.

$$\text{Sale price} = \text{Original selling price}(100\% - \text{Markdown percent})$$

$$\text{Sale price} = \$55(100\% - 40\%) = 55(.6) = 33$$

$$\text{Sale price} = \underline{\$33}$$

▶ TRYITEXERCISE 13

Craftsman's Village originally sold paneling for $27.50 per sheet. When the stock was almost depleted, the price was marked down 60% to make room for incoming merchandise. What was the sale price per sheet of paneling?

CHECK YOUR ANSWER WITH THE SOLUTION ON PAGE 257.

DETERMINING THE ORIGINAL PRICE BEFORE A MARKDOWN

To find the original selling price before a markdown, we use the sale price formula solved for the original selling price. The original selling price is isolated to one side by dividing both sides of the equation by (100% − Markdown percent). *Note*: This is actually the percentage formula Base = Portion ÷ Rate with the original selling price as the base.

$$\text{Original selling price} = \frac{\text{Sale price}}{100\% - \text{Markdown percent}}$$

Wal-Mart Stores, Inc., serves customers and members more than 200 million times per week at more than 8,000 retail units under 53 different banners in 15 countries. In 1990, Walmart's net sales were $25 billion. Twenty years later net sales had grown to $405 billion.

Source: http://walmartstores.com

EXAMPLE14 DETERMINING THE ORIGINAL SELLING PRICE

What was the original selling price of a backpack at Walmart that is currently on sale for $99 after a 25% markdown?

SOLUTIONSTRATEGY

Reasoning: $99 = 75% (100% − 25%) *of* the original price. Solve for the original price.

$$\text{Original selling price} = \frac{\text{Sale price}}{100\% - \text{Markdown percent}} = \frac{99}{100\% - 25\%} = \frac{99}{.75} = 132$$

Original selling price = $132

▶ TRYITEXERCISE 14

What was the original selling price of a necklace currently on sale for $79 after a 35% markdown? Round your answer to the nearest cent.

CHECK YOUR ANSWER WITH THE SOLUTION ON PAGE 257.

8-11 COMPUTING THE FINAL SELLING PRICE AFTER A SERIES OF MARKUPS AND MARKDOWNS

staple goods Products considered basic and routinely purchased that do not undergo seasonal fluctuations in sales, such as food, tools, and furniture.

seasonal goods Products that undergo seasonal fluctuations in sales, such as fashion apparel and holiday merchandise.

Products that do not undergo seasonal fluctuations in sales, such as food, tools, tires, and furniture, are known as **staple goods**. These products are usually marked up once and perhaps marked down occasionally, on sale. **Seasonal goods**, such as men's and women's fashion items, snow shovels, bathing suits, and holiday merchandise, may undergo many markups and markdowns during their selling season. Merchants must continually adjust prices as the season progresses. Getting caught with an excessive amount of out-of-season inventory can ruin an otherwise bright profit picture. Christmas decorations in January and snow tires in June are virtually useless profit-wise!

EXAMPLE 15 — COMPUTING A SERIES OF MARKUPS AND MARKDOWNS

In March, Swim and Sport purchased designer bathing suits for $50 each. The original markup was 60% based on the selling price. In May, the shop took a 25% markdown by having a sale. After three weeks, the sale was over and all merchandise was marked up 15%. By July, many of the bathing suits were still in stock, so the shop took a 30% markdown to stimulate sales. At the end of August, the balance of the bathing suits were put on clearance sale with a final markdown of another 25%. Compute the intermediate prices and the final selling price of the bathing suits. Round to the nearest cent.

►SOLUTIONSTRATEGY

When solving a series of markups and markdowns, remember that each should be based on the previous selling price. Use the formulas presented in this chapter and take each step one at a time.

Step 1. Find the original selling price, with markup based on the selling price.

$$\text{Selling price} = \frac{\text{Cost}}{100\% - \text{Percent markup}} = \frac{50}{100\% - 60\%} = \frac{50}{.4} = 125$$

Original selling price = $\underline{\$125}$

Step 2. Calculate the 25% markdown in May.
Sale price = Original selling price(100% − Markdown percent)
Sale price = 125(100% − 25%) = 125(.75) = 93.75
Sale price = $\underline{\$93.75}$

Step 3. Calculate the after-sale 15% markup.
Remember, the base is the previous selling price, $93.75.
Selling price = Sale price(100% + Percent markup)
Selling price = 93.75(100% + 15%) = 93.75(1.15) = 107.81
Selling price = $\underline{\$107.81}$

Step 4. Calculate the July 30% markdown.
Sale price = Previous selling price(100% − Markdown percent)
Sale price = 107.81(100% − 30%) = 107.81(.7) = 75.47
Sale price = $\underline{\$75.47}$

Step 5. Calculate the final 25% markdown.
Sale price = Previous selling price(100% − Markdown percent)
Sale price = 75.47(100% − 25%) = 75.47(.75) = 56.60
Final sale price = $\underline{\$56.60}$

►TRYITEXERCISE 15

In September, Tire Depot in Chicago purchased snow tires from a distributor for $48.50 each. The original markup was 55% based on the selling price. In November, the tires were marked down 30% and put on sale. In December, they were marked up 20%. In February, the tires were again on sale at 30% off, and in March, they cleared out with a final 25% markdown. What was the final selling price of the tires? Round to the nearest cent.

CHECK YOUR ANSWER WITH THE SOLUTION ON PAGE 257.

8-12 CALCULATING THE SELLING PRICE OF PERISHABLE GOODS

perishable goods Products that have a certain shelf life and then no value at all, such as fruits, vegetables, flowers, and dairy products.

Out-of-season merchandise still has some value, whereas **perishable goods** (such as fruits, vegetables, flowers, and dairy products) have a certain shelf life and then no value at all. For sellers of this type of merchandise to achieve their intended markups, the selling price must be based on the quantity of products sold at the original price. The quantity sold is calculated as total items less spoilage. For example, if a tomato vendor anticipates a 20% spoilage rate, the selling price of the tomatoes should be calculated based on 80% of the original stock. To calculate the selling price of perishables, use the formula:

$$\text{Selling price of perishables} = \frac{\text{Total expected selling price}}{\text{Total quantity} - \text{Anticipated spoilage}}$$

EXAMPLE16 CALCULATING THE SELLING PRICE OF PERISHABLE GOODS

The Farmer's Market buys 1,500 pounds of fresh bananas at a cost of $0.60 a pound. If a 15% spoilage rate is anticipated, at what price per pound should the bananas be sold to achieve a 50% markup based on selling price? Round to the nearest cent.

▶ SOLUTIONSTRATEGY

Step 1. Find the total expected selling price: The total expected selling price is found by applying the selling price formula, $SP = C \div (100\% - \%M_{SP})$. The cost will be the total pounds times the price per pound, $1,500 \times \$.60 = \$900$.

$$SP = \frac{\text{Cost}}{100\% - \%M_{SP}} = \frac{900}{100\% - 50\%} = \frac{900}{.5} = 1,800$$

Total expected selling price = $\underline{\$1,800}$

Step 2. Find the anticipated spoilage: To find the amount of anticipated spoilage, use the formula

Anticipated spoilage = Total quantity × Spoilage rate
Anticipated spoilage = $1,500 \times 15\% = 1,500(.15) = 225$
Anticipated spoilage = $\underline{225 \text{ pounds}}$

Step 3. Calculate the selling price of the perishables:

$$\text{Selling price of perishables} = \frac{\text{Total expected selling price}}{\text{Total quantity} - \text{Anticipated spoilage}}$$

$$\text{Selling price} = \frac{1,800}{1,500 - 225} = \frac{1,800}{1,275} = 1.411$$

Selling price of bananas = $\underline{\$1.41 \text{ per pound}}$

▶ TRYITEXERCISE 16

Enchanted Gardens, a chain of flower shops, purchases 800 dozen roses for Valentine's Day at a cost of $6.50 per dozen. If a 10% spoilage rate is anticipated, at what price per dozen should the roses be sold to achieve a 60% markup based on selling price? Round to the nearest cent.

CHECK YOUR ANSWER WITH THE SOLUTION ON PAGE 257.

REVIEW EXERCISES

8 SECTION III

For the following items, calculate the missing information. Round dollars to the nearest cent and percents to the nearest tenth of a percent.

	Item	Original Selling Price	Amount of Markdown	Sale Price	Markdown Percent
1.	fish tank	$189.95	$28.50	$161.45	15%
2.	sneakers	$53.88	_____	$37.50	_____
3.	cantaloupe	_____	$.39	$1.29	_____
4.	CD player	$264.95	_____	_____	30%
5.	1 yd carpet	_____	_____	$24.66	40%
6.	suitcase	$68.00	$16.01	$51.99	23.5%
7.	chess set	$115.77	$35.50	_____	_____
8.	necklace	_____	$155.00	$235.00	_____
9.	copier	$1,599.88	_____	_____	35%
10.	pen	_____	_____	$15.90	25%

Solve the following word problems, rounding dollars to the nearest cent and percents to the nearest tenth of a percent.

11. A motorcycle that originally sold for $9,700 was marked down and sold for $7,950.

    a. What is the amount of the markdown?

    b. What is the markdown percent?

12. A Blu-ray disc that originally sold for $34.88 at Target was marked down by $12.11.

    a. What is the sale price?

    b. What is the markdown percent?

13. a. A notebook that originally sold for $1.69 at Dollar General was marked down to $0.99. What is the amount of the markdown on these notebooks?

    b. What is the markdown percent?

    c. If the sale price is then marked up by 40%, what is the new selling price?

What would eventually become Target began in 1902 as Dayton's Dry Goods Company. The company entered the mass-market retail world in 1962, opening the very first Target. In 1995, the first SuperTarget, which includes an in-store grocery, opened. In 1999, architect Michael Graves, the first of more than 75 designers to do so, created an exclusive product line for Target. Typical Target annual revenues now exceed $60 billion.

© Cengage Learning

14. You are shopping for a headset and webcam at the Micro-Electronics Warehouse so that you can video-chat with your friends.

   a. Verify the "regular price" (original price) of each headset in the ad and calculate which headset offers the greater markdown percent, the BuddyChat 200 or BuddyChat 300.

   b. What is the markdown percent on the BuddyCam HD webcam?

   c. You have decided to purchase the headset with the greatest markdown percent and the BuddyCam HD webcam in order to take advantage of an "Extra $15 Rebate" offer when you purchase both. What is the markdown percent on your total purchase including the rebate?

15. Readers Delight, a bookstore, sells atlases for $75. If they are put on clearance sale at 60% off, what is the sale price?

16. Carousel Toys has Romper Buckaroos, wooden rocking horses for toddlers, on a 30% markdown sale for $72.09. What was the original price before they were marked down? Round to the nearest cent.

17. Lawn and Garden Galleria is having a 20% off sale on riding lawn mowers. The XL Deluxe model is on sale for $4,815. What was the original price of the mower?

18. From the Office Market coupon shown here,

   a. Calculate the markdown percent.

   b. If the offer was changed to "Buy 3, Get 2 Free," what would be the new markdown percent?

   c. Which offer is more profitable for the store? Explain.

19. In February, Golf World, a retail shop, purchased golf clubs for $453.50 per set. The original markup was 35% based on selling price. In April, the shop took a 20% markdown by having a special sale. After two weeks, the sale was over and the clubs were marked up 10%. In June, the shop offered a storewide sale of 15% off all merchandise, and in September, a final 10% markdown was taken on the clubs. What was the final selling price of the golf clubs?

20. Prestige Produce purchases 460 pounds of sweet potatoes at $0.76 per pound. If a 10% spoilage rate is anticipated, at what price per pound should the sweet potatoes be sold to achieve a 35% markup based on selling price?

21. A microwave oven cost The Appliance Warehouse $141.30 and was initially marked up by 55% based on selling price. In the next few months, the item was marked down 20%, marked up 15%, marked down 10%, and marked down a final 10%. What was the final selling price of the microwave oven?

22. The Flour Power Bakery makes 200 cherry cheesecakes at a cost of $2.45 each. If a spoilage rate of 5% is anticipated, at what price should the cakes be sold to achieve a 40% markup based on cost?

23. You have decided to purchase a set of four Good-Ride tires for your vehicle at the Tire Emporium.

    a. If the original price of these tires is $160.00 each, what are the amount of the markdown with rebate per tire and the markdown percent if you get the rebate and pay cash?

    b. What are the amount of the markdown per tire and the markdown percent if you decide to put the purchase on your Good-Ride credit card and get the double rebate?

TIRE EMPORIUM

Good-Ride Raven GT – Tire Sale

Sale Price: $115 + $20 Rebate

Double rebate when you use your Good-Ride Credit Card

c. When you purchased the set of four tires, you were offered an "Extra 5%" discount on the entire purchase if you also included wheel balancing at $5.75 per tire and a front-end alignment for $65.00. The sales tax in your state is 7.5%. What was the total amount of your purchase if you used your Good-Ride credit card? Use the unrounded markdown percent you found in part b in your calculations.

d. What are the advantages and disadvantages of using the credit card?

BUSINESS DECISION: THE PERMANENT MARKDOWN

24. You are the manager of World Wide Athlete, a chain of six sporting goods shops in your area. The shops sell 12 racing bikes per week at a retail price of $679.99. Recently, you put the bikes on sale at $599.99. At the sale price, 15 bikes were sold during the one-week sale.

a. What was your markdown percent on the bikes?

b. What is the percent increase in number of bikes sold during the sale?

c. How much more revenue would be earned in six months by permanently selling the bikes at the lower price rather than having a one-week sale each month? (6 sale weeks in 26 weeks)

d. (Optional) As manager of World Wide, would you recommend this permanent price reduction? Explain.

CHAPTER FORMULAS

Markup

Selling price = Cost + Markup

Cost = Selling price − Markup

Markup = Selling price − Cost

$$\text{Percent markup}_{\text{COST}} = \frac{\text{Markup}}{\text{Cost}}$$

$$\text{Percent markup}_{SP} = \frac{\text{Markup}}{\text{Selling price}}$$

Selling price = Cost(100% + %Markup$_{\text{COST}}$)

$$\text{Cost} = \frac{\text{Selling price}}{100\% + \%\text{Markup}_{\text{COST}}}$$

$$\text{Selling price} = \frac{\text{Cost}}{100\% - \%\text{Markup}_{SP}}$$

Cost − Selling price(100% − %Markup$_{SP}$)

$$\%\text{Markup}_{SP} = \frac{\%\text{Markup}_{\text{COST}}}{100\% + \%\text{Markup}_{\text{COST}}}$$

$$\%\text{Markup}_{\text{COST}} = \frac{\%\text{Markup}_{SP}}{100\% - \%\text{Markup}_{SP}}$$

Markdown

Markdown = Original selling price − Sale price

$$\text{Markdown\%} = \frac{\text{Markdown}}{\text{Original price}}$$

Sale price = Original price(100% − Markdown%)

$$\text{Original price} = \frac{\text{Sale price}}{100\% - \text{Markdown\%}}$$

Perishables

$$\text{Selling price}_{\text{Perishables}} = \frac{\text{Expected selling price}}{\text{Total quantity} - \text{Spoilage}}$$

CHAPTER SUMMARY

Section I: Markup Based on Cost

Topic	Important Concepts	Illustrative Examples
Using the Basic Retailing Equation **Performance Objective 8-1, Page 230**	The basic retailing equation is used to solve for selling price (*SP*), cost (*C*), and amount of markup (*M*). Selling price = Cost + Markup $SP = C + M$ Cost = Selling price − Markup $C = SP - M$ Markup = Selling price − Cost $M = SP - C$	1. What is the selling price of a blender that costs $86.00 and has a $55.99 markup? $SP = 86.00 + 55.99$ Selling price = $141.99 2. What is the cost of a radio that sells for $125.50 and has a $37.29 markup? $C = 125.50 - 37.29$ Cost = $88.21 3. What is the markup on a set of dishes costing $53.54 and selling for $89.95? $M = 89.95 - 53.54$ Markup = $36.41

Section I (continued)

Topic	Important Concepts	Illustrative Examples
Calculating Percent Markup Based on Cost **Performance Objective 8-2, Page 232**	$\%\text{Markup}_{\text{COST}} = \dfrac{\text{Markup}}{\text{Cost}}$ $\%M_{\text{COST}} = \dfrac{M}{C}$	A calculator costs \$25. If the markup is \$10, what is the percent markup based on cost? $\%M_{\text{COST}} = \dfrac{10}{25} = .4$ $\%M_{\text{COST}} = \underline{40\%}$
Calculating Selling Price **Performance Objective 8-3, Page 233**	$\text{Selling price} = \text{Cost}(100\% + \%\text{Markup}_{\text{COST}})$ $SP = C(100\% + \%M_{\text{COST}})$	A desk costs \$260 to manufacture. What should be the selling price if a 60% markup based on cost is desired? $SP = 260(100\% + 60\%)$ $SP = 260(1.6) = 416$ Selling price $= \underline{\$416}$
Calculating Cost **Performance Objective 8-4, Page 234**	$\text{Cost} = \dfrac{\text{Selling price}}{100\% + \%\text{Markup}_{\text{COST}}}$ $C = \dfrac{SP}{100\% + \%M_{\text{COST}}}$	What is the cost of a leather sofa with a selling price of \$250 and a 45% markup based on cost? $C = \dfrac{250}{100\% + 45\%} = \dfrac{250}{1.45}$ Cost $= \underline{\$172.41}$

Section II: Markup Based on Selling Price

Topic	Important Concepts	Illustrative Examples
Calculating Percent Markup Based on Selling Price **Performance Objective 8-5, Page 237**	$\%\text{Markup}_{SP} = \dfrac{\text{Markup}}{\text{Selling price}}$ $\%M_{SP} = \dfrac{M}{SP}$	What is the percent markup on the selling price of a Hewlett Packard printer with a selling price of \$400 and a markup of \$188? $\%M_{SP} = \dfrac{188}{400} = .47$ $\%M_{SP} = \underline{47\%}$
Calculating Selling Price **Performance Objective 8-6, Page 238**	$\text{Selling price} = \dfrac{\text{Cost}}{100\% - \%\text{Markup}_{SP}}$ $SP = \dfrac{C}{100\% - \%M_{SP}}$	What is the selling price of a marker pen with a cost of \$1.19 and a 43% markup based on selling price? $SP = \dfrac{1.19}{100\% - 43\%} = \dfrac{1.19}{.57}$ $SP = \underline{\$2.09}$
Calculating Cost **Performance Objective 8-7, Page 239**	$\text{Cost} = \text{Selling price}(100\% - \%\text{Markup}_{SP})$ $C = SP(100\% - \%M_{SP})$	What is the most a hardware store can pay for a drill if it will have a selling price of \$65.50 and a 45% markup based on selling price? $C = 65.50(100\% - 45\%)$ $C = 65.50(.55)$ Cost $= \underline{\$36.03}$
Converting Percent Markup Based on Cost to Percent Markup Based on Selling Price **Performance Objective 8-8, Page 240**	$\%\text{Markup}_{SP} = \dfrac{\%\text{Markup}_{\text{COST}}}{100\% + \%\text{Markup}_{\text{COST}}}$ $\%M_{SP} = \dfrac{\%M_{\text{COST}}}{100\% + \%M_{\text{COST}}}$	If a hair dryer is marked up 70% based on cost, what is the corresponding percent markup based on selling price? $\%M_{SP} = \dfrac{70\%}{100\% + 70\%} = \dfrac{.7}{1.7}$ $\%M_{SP} = .4118 = \underline{41.2\%}$

Section II (continued)

Topic	Important Concepts	Illustrative Examples
Converting Percent Markup Based on Selling Price to Percent Markup Based on Cost **Performance Objective 8-8, Page 240**	$$\%\text{Markup}_{\text{COST}} = \frac{\%\text{Markup}_{SP}}{100\% - \%\text{Markup}_{SP}}$$ $$\%M_{\text{COST}} = \frac{\%M_{SP}}{100\% - \%M_{SP}}$$	If a toaster is marked up 35% based on selling price, what is the corresponding percent markup based on cost? $$\%M_{\text{COST}} = \frac{35\%}{100\% - 35\%} = \frac{.35}{.65}$$ $$\%M_{\text{COST}} = .5384 = \underline{\underline{53.8\%}}$$

Section III: Markdowns, Multiple Operations, and Perishable Goods

Topic	Important Concepts	Illustrative Examples
Calculating Markdown and Markdown Percent **Performance Objective 8-9, Page 244**	Markdown = Original price − Sale price $MD = \text{Orig} - \text{Sale}$ $$\text{Markdown}\% = \frac{\text{Markdown}}{\text{Original price}}$$ $$MD\% = \frac{MD}{\text{Orig}}$$	Calculate the amount of markdown and the markdown percent of a television set that originally sold for \$425.00 and was then put on sale for \$299.95. Markdown = 425.00 − 299.95 Markdown = \$125.05 $$MD\% = \frac{125.05}{425.00} = .2942$$ Markdown% = $\underline{\underline{29.4\%}}$
Determining the Sale Price after a Markdown **Performance Objective 8-10, Page 245**	Sale price = Original price(100% − Markdown%) Sale = Orig(100% − $MD\%$)	What is the sale price of a computer that originally sold for \$2,500 and was then marked down by 35%? Sale = 2,500(100% − 35%) Sale = 2,500(.65) = 1,625 Sale price = $\underline{\underline{\$1,625}}$
Determining the Original Selling Price before a Markdown **Performance Objective 8-10, Page 246**	$$\text{Original price} = \frac{\text{Sale price}}{100\% - \text{Markdown}\%}$$ $$\text{Orig} = \frac{\text{Sale}}{100\% - MD\%}$$	What is the original selling price of an exercise bicycle, which is currently on sale at Scars for \$235.88, after a 30% markdown? $$\text{Original price} = \frac{235.88}{100\% - 30\%} = \frac{235.88}{.7}$$ Original price = $\underline{\underline{\$336.97}}$
Computing the Final Selling Price after a Series of Markups and Markdowns **Performance Objective 8-11, Page 246**	To solve for the final selling price after a series of markups and markdowns, calculate each step based on the previous selling price.	Compute the intermediate prices and the final selling price of an umbrella costing \$27.50 with the following seasonal activity: a. Initial markup, 40% on cost b. 20% markdown c. 15% markdown d. 10% markup e. Final clearance, 25% markdown a. Initial 40% markup: $$SP = C(100\% + \%M_{\text{COST}})$$ $$SP = 27.50(100\% + 40\%)$$ $$SP = 27.50(1.4) = 38.50$$ Original price = $\underline{\underline{\$38.50}}$ b. 20% markdown: $$\text{Sale} = \text{Orig}(100\% - MD\%)$$ $$\text{Sale} = 38.50(100\% - 20\%)$$ $$\text{Sale} = 38.50(.8)$$ Sale price = $\underline{\underline{\$30.80}}$

Section III (continued)

Topic	Important Concepts	Illustrative Examples
		c. 15% markdown: $\text{Sale} = \text{Orig}(100\% - MD\%)$ $\text{Sale} = 30.80(100\% - 15\%)$ $\text{Sale} = 30.80(.85)$ $\text{Sale price} = \underline{\$26.18}$ d. 10% markup: $SP = \text{sale price}(100\% + M\%)$ $SP = 26.18(100\% + 10\%)$ $SP = 26.18(1.10)$ $\text{Selling price} = \underline{\$28.80}$ e. Final 25% markdown: $\text{Sale} = \text{Orig}(100\% - MD\%)$ $\text{Sale} = 28.80(100\% - 25\%)$ $\text{Sale} = 28.80(.75)$ $\text{Final selling price} = \underline{\$21.60}$
Calculating the Selling Price of Perishable Goods **Performance Objective 8-12, Page 248**	$\text{Selling price}_{\text{Perishables}}$ $= \dfrac{\text{Total expected selling price}}{\text{Total quantity} - \text{Anticipated spoilage}}$ $SP_{\text{Perish.}} = \dfrac{\text{Exp. } SP}{\text{Quan.} - \text{Spoil.}}$	A grocery store purchases 250 pounds of apples from a wholesaler for \$0.67 per pound. If a 10% spoilage rate is anticipated, what selling price per pound will yield a 45% markup based on cost? $\text{Total Cost} = 250 \text{ lb @ } .67 = \$167.50$ $\text{Exp } SP = C(100\% + M_{\text{COST}})$ $\text{Exp } SP = 167.50(100\% + 45\%)$ $\text{Exp } SP = 167.50(1.45) = \$242.88$ $SP_{\text{perish}} = \dfrac{242.88}{250 - 25} = \dfrac{242.88}{225}$ $SP_{\text{perish}} = \underline{\$1.08 \text{ per lb}}$

TRY IT: EXERCISE SOLUTIONS FOR CHAPTER 8

1. $SP = C + M = 6.80 + 9.40 = \underline{\$16.20}$

2. $M = SP - C = 28.50 - 16.75 = \underline{\$11.75}$

3. $C = SP - M = 290 - 75 = \underline{\$215}$

4. $M = SP - C = 63 - 45 = \underline{\$18}$

$\%M_{\text{COST}} = \dfrac{M}{C} = \dfrac{18}{45} = .4 = \underline{40\%}$

5. $SP = C(100\% + \%M_{\text{COST}}) = 38(100\% + 65\%) = 38(1.65) = \underline{\$62.70}$

6. $C = \dfrac{SP}{100\% + \%M_{\text{COST}}} = \dfrac{39}{100\% + 30\%} = \dfrac{39}{1.3} = \underline{\$30}$

7. $M = SP - C = 157.50 - 94.50 = \underline{\$63}$

$\%M_{SP} = \dfrac{M}{SP} = \dfrac{63.00}{157.50} = .40 = \underline{40\%}$

8. $SP = \dfrac{C}{100\% - \%M_{SP}} = \dfrac{169}{100\% - 35\%} = \dfrac{169}{.65} = \underline{\$260}$

9. $C = SP(100\% - \%M_{SP}) = 79(100\% - 55\%) = 79(.45) = \underline{\$35.55}$

10. $\%M_{SP} = \dfrac{\%M_{\text{COST}}}{100\% + \%M_{\text{COST}}} = \dfrac{50\%}{100\% + 50\%} = \dfrac{.5}{1.5} = .333 = \underline{33.3\%}$

11. $\%M_{\text{COST}} = \dfrac{\%M_{SP}}{100\% - \%M_{SP}} = \dfrac{75\%}{100\% - 75\%} = \dfrac{.75}{.25} = 3 = \underline{300\%}$

12. Markdown = Original price − Sale price = 75 − 56 = $\underline{\$19}$

$$MD\% = \frac{MD}{\text{Original price}} = \frac{19}{75} = .2533 = \underline{25.3\%}$$

13. Sale price = Original price(100% − MD%) = 27.50(100% − 60%) = 27.50(.4) = $\underline{\$11}$

14. Original price = $\dfrac{\text{Sale price}}{100\% - MD\%} = \dfrac{79}{100\% - 35\%} = \dfrac{79}{.65} = \underline{\$121.54}$

15. $SD = \dfrac{C}{100\% - \%M_{SP}} = \dfrac{48.50}{100\% - 55\%} = \dfrac{48.50}{.45} = \$107.78$

Markdown #1: Original price(100% − MD%) = 107.78(.7) = $75.45
20% markup: 75.45(100% + 20%) = 75.45(1.2) = $90.54
Markdown #2: Original price(100% − MD%) = 90.54(.7) = $63.38
Final markdown: Original price(100% − MD%) = 63.38(.75) = $\underline{\$47.54}$

16. Total cost = 800 dozen @ $6.50 = $5,200

$$\text{Expected selling price} = \frac{C}{100\% - \%M_{SP}} = \frac{5{,}200}{100\% - 60\%} = \frac{5{,}200}{.4} = \$13{,}000$$

$$\text{Selling price}_{\text{Perishables}} = \frac{\text{Expected selling price}}{\text{Total quantity} - \text{Spoilage}} = \frac{13{,}000}{800 - 80} = \frac{13{,}000}{720} = \underline{\$18.06 \text{ per doz}}$$

Concept Review

1. The retailing equation states that the selling price is equal to the _____ plus the _____. (8-1)

2. In business, expenses are separated into two major categories. The cost of _____ sold and _____ expenses. (8-1)

3. There are two ways of expressing markup as a percent: based on _____ and based on _____ _____. (8-2)

4. Write the formula for calculating the selling price when markup is based on cost. (8-3)

5. To calculate cost, we divide the _____ price by 100% plus the percent markup on cost. (8-4)

6. The percent markup based on selling price is equal to the _____ divided by the selling price. (8-5)

7. When markup is based on selling price, the _____ price is the base and represents _____ percent. (8-6)

8. We use the formula for calculating _____ to find the most a retailer can pay for an item and still get the intended markup. (8-7)

9. To convert percent markup based on cost to percent markup based on selling price, we divide percent markup based on cost by 100% _____ the percent markup based on cost. (8-8)

10. To convert percent markup based on selling price to percent markup based on cost, we divide percent markup based on selling price by 100% _____ the percent markup based on selling price. (8-8)

11. A price reduction from the original selling price of merchandise is called a(n) _____. (8-9)

12. Write the formula for calculating the sale price after a markdown. (8-10)

13. In calculating a series of markups and markdowns, each calculation is based on the previous _____ price. (8-11)

14. Products that have a certain shelf life and then no value at all, such as fruit, vegetables, flowers, and dairy products, are known as _____ _____. (8-12)

Assessment Test

Solve the following word problems. Round dollars to the nearest cent and percents to the nearest tenth of a percent.

1. Electric woks cost the manufacturer $83.22 to produce. If a markup of $69.38 is added to the cost, what is the selling price per unit?

2. Castle Mountain Furniture sells desks for $346.00. If the desks cost $212.66, what is the amount of the markup?

3. After Sunset Food Wholesalers adds a markup of $15.40 to a case of tomato sauce, it sells for $33.98. What is the wholesaler's cost per case?

4. Wyatt's Western Wear purchases shirts for $47.50 each. A $34.00 markup is added to the shirts.

   a. What is the selling price?

   b. What is the percent markup based on cost?

   c. What is the percent markup based on selling price?

5. As the manager of Dollar Depot, calculate the amount of the markup and the percent markup on selling price per case if these Softies products cost your store $5.60 per case of 12 boxes.

6. Bloomingdales purchases imported perfume for $24.30 per ounce. If the store policy is to mark up all merchandise in that department 39% based on selling price, what is the retail selling price of the perfume?

7. The Carpet Gallery is looking for a new line of nylon carpeting to retail at $39.88 per square yard. If management wants a 60% markup based on selling price, what is the most that can be paid for the carpeting to still get the desired markup?

8. a. At The Luminary, the markup on a halogen light fixture is 50% based on selling price. What is the corresponding percent markup based on cost?

   b. If the markup on a fluorescent light fixture transformer is 120% based on cost, what is the corresponding percent markup based on selling price?

9. A three-day cruise on the *Island Queen* originally selling for $988 was marked down by $210 at the end of the season.

   a. What is the sale price of the cruise?

   b. What is the markdown percent?

10. You are shopping for an executive desk chair at The Furniture Gallery

    a. Calculate the original price and markdown percent of each chair to determine which has the greater markdown percent.

    b. With the purchase of either chair, The Furniture Gallery is offering a 15% discount on plastic chair mats. You have chosen a mat with an original price of $29.00. You also purchase a two-year leather protection plan on the chair for $19.95. If you choose the chair with the greater markdown percent and the sales tax in your area is 6.3%, what is the total amount of your purchase?

11. Macy's originally sold designer jackets for $277. If they are put on sale at a markdown of 22%, what is the sale price?

EXCEL 2 12. What was the original selling price of a treadmill currently on sale for $2,484 after a 20% markdown?

13. Backyard Bonanza advertised a line of inflatable pools for the summer season. The store uses a 55% markup based on selling price.

    a. If they were originally priced at $124.99, what was the cost?

    b. As the summer progressed, they were marked down 25%, marked up 15%, marked down 20%, and cleared out in October at a final 25%-off sale. What was the final selling price of the pools?

Macy's is one of the nation's premier retailers, with typical annual sales exceeding $20 billion. The company operates more than 800 Macy's department stores and furniture galleries in 45 states, the District of Columbia, Guam, and Puerto Rico, as well as 40 Bloomingdale's stores in 12 states.

Macy's diverse workforce includes approximately 167,000 employees. The company also operates macys.com and bloomingdales.com.

Source: www.macysinc.com

EXCEL 3 14. Epicure Market prepares fresh gourmet entrees each day. On Wednesday, 80 baked chicken dinners were made at a cost of $3.50 each. A 10% spoilage rate is anticipated.

    a. At what price should the dinners be sold to achieve a 60% markup based on selling price?

    b. If Epicure offers a $1-off coupon in a newspaper advertisement, what markdown percent does the coupon represent?

CHAPTER 8

15. **a.** What is the original selling price of the guitar on sale at Music Mania if the $1,999.99 sale price represents 20% off?

b. How much did the store pay for the guitar if the initial markup was 150% based on cost?

c. What is the percent markup based on selling price?

d. If next month the guitar is scheduled to be on sale for $1,599.99, what is the markdown percent from the original price?

BUSINESS DECISION: MAINTAINED MARKUP

16. The markup that a retail store actually realizes on the sale of its goods is called **maintained markup**. It is what is achieved after "retail reductions" (markdowns) have been subtracted from the initial markup. Maintained markup is one of the "keys to profitability" in retailing. It is the difference between the actual selling price and the cost and therefore has a direct effect on net profits.

$$\text{Maintained markup} = \frac{\text{Actual selling price} - \text{Cost}}{\text{Actual selling price}}$$

You are the buyer for Four Aces Menswear, a chain of men's clothing stores. For the spring season, you purchased a line of men's casual shirts with a manufacturer's suggested retail price of $29.50. Your cost was $16.00 per shirt.

a. What is the initial percent markup based on selling price?

b. The shirts did not sell as expected at the regular price, so you marked them down to $21.99 and sold them out. What is the maintained markup on the shirts?

c. When you complained to the manufacturer's sales representative about having to take excessive markdowns in order to sell the merchandise, she offered a $2 rebate per shirt. What is your new maintained markup?

COLLABORATIVE LEARNING ACTIVITY

Retailing and the Demographic Generations

Understanding the shopping and media habits of different age groups can help marketers optimize product assortment, pricing, promotion, and advertising decisions by creating targeted strategies and special offers. As an example, consider the following.

According to *USA Today*, in the book *Gen buY: How Tweens, Teens, and Twenty-Somethings Are Revolutionizing Retail*, authors Kit Yarrow and Jane O'Donnell say Generation Y—today's teens, tweens, and twenty-somethings were the least likely to cut back spending during a recession.

What's more, the authors point out that the 84 million Generation Y'ers, born from 1978 through 2000, are so influential, they've changed shopping for all consumers. They call Gen Y "the taste-makers, influencers, and most enthusiastic buyers of today" who will become "the mature, high-income purchasers of the future."

Because of Gen Y, we now have, among other things:

- More creative, technically advanced websites
- A wide availability of online customer reviews
- A faster stream of product introductions
- Bigger, more comfortable dressing rooms

Source: *USA Today*, "Generation Y forces retailers to keep up with technology, new stuff," by Richard Eisenberg, Sept. 14, 2009, page 6B.

As a team, divide up the four major demographic generations: the Silent Generation: the Baby Boomers, Generation X, and Generation Y (aka the Millennials) to research the following questions and report your findings to the class. Use visual presentations whenever possible and be sure to site your sources.

1. How did each generation get its distinctive name? List any "subgroups" that have been defined, such as Baby Boomers – Young and Baby Boomers – Old.
2. Define each generation in terms of years born, size, income and purchasing power, lifestyle preferences, and particularly consumer buying behavior.
3. How and to what extent does each generation use the Internet?
4. How do manufacturers, retailers, and shopping malls use these demographic distinctions to "target" their marketing efforts to the various generations? Give specific examples.

Payroll

Minimum Wage Rates Over the Decades

Here's how the minimum wage has increased over the years and what an hour's work at minimum wage bought.

1950:

    Minimum wage: $0.75 per hour
    Gas: $0.27 or 22 minutes
    Movie ticket: $0.48 or 38 minutes
    Rent: $42 or 56 hours

1960:

    Minimum wage: $1 per hour
    Gas: $0.31 or 19 minutes
    Movie ticket: $0.69 or 41 minutes
    Rent: $71 or 71 hours

1970:

    Minimum wage: $1.60 per hour
    Gas: $0.36 or 14 minutes
    Movie ticket: $1.55 or 58 minutes
    Rent: $108 or 67.5 hours

1980:

    Minimum wage: $3.10 per hour
    Gas: $1.25 or 24 minutes
    Movie ticket: $2.60 or 50 minutes
    Rent: $243 or 78 hours

1990:

    Minimum wage: $3.80 per hour
    Gas: $1.13 or 18 minutes
    Movie ticket: $4.23 or 1 hour, 7 minutes
    Rent: $447 or 118 hours

2000:

    Minimum wage: $5.15 per hour
    Gas: $1.49 or 17 minutes
    Movie ticket: $5.39 or 1 hour, 3 minutes
    Rent: $602 or 117 hours

2010:

    Minimum wage: $7.25 per hour
    Gas: $2.78 or 23 minutes
    Movie ticket: $7.95 or 1 hour, 6 minutes
    Rent: $789 or 109 hours

Source: MSN.COM

PERFORMANCE OBJECTIVES

SECTION I: Employee's Gross Earnings and Incentive Pay Plans

9-1: Prorating annual salary on the basis of weekly, biweekly, semimonthly, and monthly pay periods (p. 263)

9-2: Calculating gross pay by hourly wages, including regular and overtime rates (p. 264)

9-3: Calculating gross pay by straight and differential piecework schedules (p. 265)

9-4: Calculating gross pay by straight and incremental commission, salary plus commission, and drawing accounts (p. 267)

SECTION II: Employee's Payroll Deductions

9-5: Computing FICA taxes, both social security and Medicare, withheld from an employee's paycheck (p. 273)

9-6: Calculating an employee's federal income tax withholding (FIT) by the percentage method (p. 275)

9-7: Determining an employee's total withholding for federal income tax, social security, and Medicare using the combined wage bracket tables (p. 278)

SECTION III: Employer's Payroll Expenses and Self-Employed Person's Tax Responsibility

9-8: Computing FICA tax for employers and self-employment tax for self-employed persons (p. 283)

9-9: Computing the amount of state unemployment tax (SUTA) and federal unemployment tax (FUTA) (p. 285)

9-10: Calculating employer's fringe benefit expenses (p. 286)

9-11: Calculating quarterly estimated tax for self-employed persons (p. 287)

EMPLOYEE'S GROSS EARNINGS AND INCENTIVE PAY PLANS

9

SECTION I

Because payroll is frequently a company's largest operating expense, efficient payroll preparation and record keeping are extremely important functions in any business operation. Although today most businesses computerize their payroll functions, it is important for businesspeople to understand the processes and procedures involved.

Employers are responsible for paying employees for services rendered to the company over a period of time. In addition, the company is responsible for withholding certain taxes and other deductions from an employee's paycheck and depositing those taxes with the Internal Revenue Service (IRS) through authorized financial institutions. Other deductions, such as insurance premiums and charitable contributions, are also disbursed by the employer to the appropriate place.

In business, the term **gross pay**, or **gross earnings** means the *total* amount of earnings due an employee for work performed before payroll deductions are withheld. The **net pay**, **net earnings**, or **take-home pay** is the actual amount of the employee's paycheck after all payroll deductions have been withheld. This concept is easily visualized by the formula

gross pay, or **gross earnings** Total amount of earnings due an employee for work performed before payroll deductions are withheld.

net pay, **net earnings**, or **take-home pay** The actual amount of the employee's paycheck after all payroll deductions have been withheld.

> **Net pay = Gross pay − Total deductions**

This chapter deals with the business math involved in payroll management: the computation of employee gross earnings; the calculation of withholding taxes and other deductions; and the associated governmental deposits, regulations, and record keeping requirements.

PRORATING ANNUAL SALARY ON THE BASIS OF WEEKLY, BIWEEKLY, SEMIMONTHLY, AND MONTHLY PAY PERIODS

9-1

Employee compensation takes on many forms in the business world. Employees who hold managerial, administrative, or professional positions are paid a salary. A **salary** is a fixed gross amount of pay equally distributed over periodic payments without regard to the number of hours worked. Salaries are usually expressed as an annual, or yearly, amount. For example, a corporate accountant might receive an annual salary of $50,000.

salary A fixed gross amount of pay equally distributed over periodic payments without regard to the number of hours worked.

Although salaries may be stated as annual amounts, they are usually distributed to employees on a more timely basis. A once-a-year paycheck would be a real trick to manage! Employees are most commonly paid in one of the following ways:

Weekly	52 paychecks per year	Annual salary ÷ 52
Biweekly	26 paychecks per year	Annual salary ÷ 26
Semimonthly	24 paychecks per year	Annual salary ÷ 24
Monthly	12 paychecks per year	Annual salary ÷ 12

EXAMPLE1 PRORATING ANNUAL SALARY

What is the weekly, biweekly, semimonthly, and monthly amount of gross pay for a corporate accountant with an annual salary of $50,000?

▶ SOLUTIONSTRATEGY

The amount of gross pay per period is determined by dividing the annual salary by the number of pay periods per year.

$$\text{Weekly pay} = \frac{50,000}{52} = \$961.54$$

$$\text{Biweekly pay} = \frac{50,000}{26} = \$1,923.08$$

$$\text{Semimonthly pay} = \frac{50,000}{24} = \$2,083.33$$

$$\text{Monthly pay} = \frac{50,000}{12} = \$4,166.67$$

► TRY IT EXERCISE 1

An executive of a large manufacturing company earns a gross annual salary of $43,500. What is the weekly, biweekly, semimonthly, and monthly pay for this employee?

CHECK YOUR ANSWERS WITH THE SOLUTIONS ON PAGE 295.

9-2 CALCULATING GROSS PAY BY HOURLY WAGES, INCLUDING REGULAR AND OVERTIME RATES

wages Earnings for routine or manual work, usually based on the number of hours worked.

hourly wage, or **hourly rate** The amount an employee is paid for each hour worked.

overtime According to federal law, the amount an employee is paid for each hour worked over 40 hours per week.

Wages are earnings for routine or manual work, usually based on the number of hours worked. An **hourly wage**, or **hourly rate** is the amount an employee is paid for each hour worked. The hourly wage is the most frequently used pay method and is designed to compensate employees for the amount of time spent on the job. The Fair Labor Standards Act of 1938, a federal law, specifies that a standard work week is 40 hours and **overtime**, amounting to at least $1\frac{1}{2}$ times the hourly rate, must be paid for all hours worked over 40 hours per week. Paying an employee $1\frac{1}{2}$ times the hourly rate is known as time-and-a-half.

Many companies have taken overtime a step farther than required by compensating employees at time-and-a-half for all hours over 8 hours per day instead of 40 hours per week. Another common payroll benefit is when companies pay double time, twice the hourly rate, for holidays, midnight shifts, and weekend hours.

Minimum Wage Laws in the United States
U. S. Department of Labor—Wage and Hour Division (WHD)—January 1, 2013

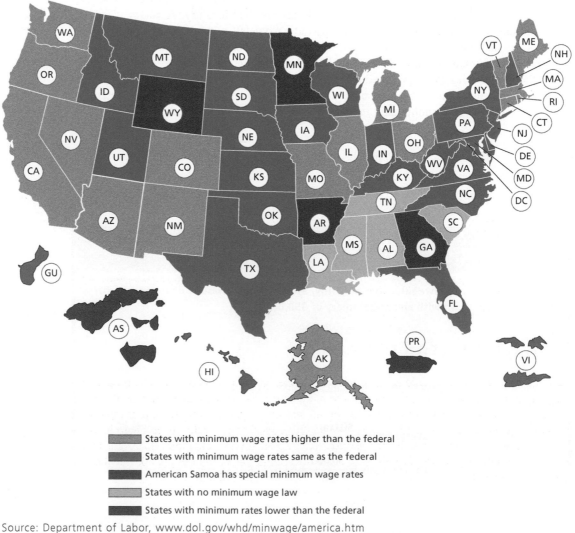

Source: Department of Labor, www.dol.gov/whd/minwage/america.htm

According to the Department of Labor, as of January 2013, 16 states and Washington, D.C., had minimum wage rates higher than the federal minimum wage. Four states and Puerto Rico had minimum wage rates lower than the federal standard.

STEPS TO CALCULATE AN EMPLOYEE'S GROSS PAY BY HOURLY WAGES

STEP 1. Calculate an employee's regular gross pay for working 40 hours or less.

$$\text{Regular pay} = \text{Hourly rate} \times \text{Regular hours worked}$$

STEP 2. Calculate an employee's overtime pay by chain multiplying the hourly rate by the overtime factor by the number of overtime hours.

$$\text{Overtime pay} = \text{Hourly rate} \times \text{Overtime factor} \times \text{Overtime hours worked}$$

STEP 3. Calculate total gross pay.

$$\text{Total gross pay} = \text{Regular pay} + \text{Overtime pay}$$

IN THE Business World

Payroll is a very important business responsibility. Employees must be paid on a regular basis, and accurate records must be kept for government reporting.

- Payroll is usually one of the largest "expense" categories of a company.

- The department responsible for the payroll function may be called Payroll, Personnel, or Human Resources.

- In recent years, companies have evolved that specialize in doing payroll. When a business hires an outside firm to perform a function such as payroll, this is known as *outsourcing*.

EXAMPLE 2 CALCULATING HOURLY PAY

Karen Sullivan earns $8 per hour as a checker on an assembly line. If her overtime rate is time-and-a-half, what is her total gross pay for working 46 hours last week?

SOLUTIONSTRATEGY

To find Karen's total gross pay, compute her regular pay plus overtime pay.

Regular pay = Hourly rate × Regular hours worked
Regular pay = 8 × 40 = $320
Overtime pay = Hourly rate × Overtime factor × Overtime hours worked
Overtime pay = 8 × 1.5 × 6 = $72
Total gross pay = Regular pay + Overtime pay
Total gross pay = 320 + 72 = $392

TRYITEXERCISE 2

Rick Morton works as a delivery truck driver for $10.50 per hour with time-and-a-half for overtime and double time on Sundays. What was his total gross pay last week if he worked 45 hours on Monday through Saturday in addition to a four-hour shift on Sunday?

CHECK YOUR ANSWER WITH THE SOLUTION ON PAGE 295.

CALCULATING GROSS PAY BY STRAIGHT AND DIFFERENTIAL PIECEWORK SCHEDULES

9-3

A **piecework** pay rate schedule is based not on time but on production output. The incentive is that the more units the worker produces, the more money he or she makes. A **straight piecework plan** is when the worker receives a certain amount of pay per unit of output regardless of output quantity. A **differential piecework plan** gives workers a greater incentive to increase output because the rate per unit increases as output goes up. For example, a straight piecework plan might pay $3.15 per unit, whereas a differential plan might pay $3.05 for the first 50 units produced, $3.45 for units 51–100, and $3.90 for any units over 100.

piecework Pay rate schedule based on an employee's production output, not hours worked.

straight piecework plan Pay per unit of output regardless of output quantity.

differential piecework plan Greater incentive method of compensation than straight piecework, where pay per unit increases as output goes up.

STEPS TO CALCULATE GROSS PAY BY PIECEWORK

Straight Piecework:

STEP 1. Multiply the number of pieces or output units by the rate per unit.

Total gross pay = Output quantity × Rate per unit

Differential Piecework:

STEP 1. Multiply the number of output units at each level by the rate per unit at that level.

STEP 2. Find the total gross pay by adding the total from each level.

EXAMPLE 3   CALCULATING PIECEWORK PAY

Barb Nelson works on a hat assembly line. Barb gets paid at a straight piecework rate of $0.35 per hat. What was Barb's total gross pay last week if she produced 1,655 hats?

▶ SOLUTION STRATEGY

Total gross pay = Output quantity × Rate per unit
Total gross pay = 1,655 × .35 = $579.25

▶ TRY IT EXERCISE 3

George Lopez works at a tire manufacturing plant. He is on a straight piecework rate of $0.41 per tire. What was George's total gross pay last week if he produced 950 tires?

CHECK YOUR ANSWER WITH THE SOLUTION ON PAGE 295.

EXAMPLE 4   CALCULATING DIFFERENTIAL PIECEWORK PAY

Paula Duke assembled 190 watches last week. Calculate her total gross pay based on the following differential piecework schedule.

Pay Level	Watches Assembled	Rate per Watch
1	1–100	$2.45
2	101–150	$2.75
3	Over 150	$3.10

▶ SOLUTION STRATEGY

To find Paula's total gross earnings, we calculate her earnings at each level of the pay schedule and add the totals. In this case, she will be paid for all of level 1, 100 watches; for all of level 2, 50 watches; and for 40 watches at level 3 (190 − 150 = 40).

Level pay = Output × Rate per piece
Level 1 = 100 × 2.45 = $245
Level 2 = 50 × 2.75 = $137.50
Level 3 = 40 × 3.10 = $124
Total gross pay = Level 1 + Level 2 + Level 3
Total gross pay = 245 + 137.50 + 124 = $506.50

►TRYITEXERCISE 4

You are the payroll manager for Trendy Toys, Inc., a manufacturer of small plastic toys. Your production workers are on a differential piecework schedule as follows.

Pay Level	Toys Produced	Rate per Toy
1	1–300	$0.68
2	301–500	$0.79
3	501–750	$0.86
4	Over 750	$0.94

Calculate last week's total gross pay for the following employees.

Name	Toys Produced	Total Gross Pay
C. Gomez	515	_____
L. Clifford	199	_____
M. Maken	448	_____
B. Nathan	804	_____

CHECK YOUR ANSWERS WITH THE SOLUTIONS ON PAGE 295.

CALCULATING GROSS PAY BY STRAIGHT AND INCREMENTAL COMMISSION, SALARY PLUS COMMISSION, AND DRAWING ACCOUNTS

9-4

STRAIGHT AND INCREMENTAL COMMISSION

Commission is a method of compensation primarily used to pay employees who sell a company's goods or services. **Straight commission** is based on a single specified percentage of the sales volume attained. For example, Delta Distributors pays its sales staff a commission of 8% on all sales. **Incremental commission** is much like the differential piecework rate whereby higher levels of sales earn increasing rates of commission. An example would be 5% commission on all sales up to $70,000, 6% on sales greater than $70,000 and up to $120,000, and 7% commission on any sales greater than $120,000.

commission Percentage method of compensation primarily used to pay employees who sell a company's goods and services.

straight commission Commission based on a specified percentage of the sales volume attained by an employee.

incremental commission Greater incentive method of compensation than straight commission whereby higher levels of sales earn increasing rates of commission.

STEPS TO CALCULATE GROSS PAY BY COMMISSION

Straight Commission:

STEP 1. Multiply the total sales by the commission rate.

Total gross pay = Total sales × Commission rate

Incremental Commission:

STEP 1. Multiply the total sales at each level by the commission rate for that level.

STEP 2. Find the total gross pay by adding the total from each level.

EXAMPLE5 CALCULATING COMMISSIONS

Diamond Industries pays its sales force a commission rate of 6% of all sales. What was the total gross pay for an employee who sold $113,500 last month?

►SOLUTIONSTRATEGY

$$\text{Total gross pay} = \text{Total sales} \times \text{Commission rate}$$
$$\text{Total gross pay} = 113{,}500 \times .06 = \underline{\$6{,}810}$$

►TRYITEXERCISE 5

Alexa Walsh sells for Supreme Designs, a manufacturer of women's clothing. Alexa is paid a straight commission of 2.4%. If her sales volume last month was $233,760, what was her total gross pay?

CHECK YOUR ANSWER WITH THE SOLUTION ON PAGE 295.

EXAMPLE6 CALCULATING INCREMENTAL COMMISSION

Vista Electronics pays its sales representatives on the following incremental commission schedule.

Level	Sales Volume	Commission Rate (%)
1	$1–$50,000	4
2	$50,001–$150,000	5
3	Over $150,000	6.5

What was the total gross pay for a sales rep who sold $162,400 last month?

►SOLUTIONSTRATEGY

Using an incremental commission schedule, we find the pay for each level and then add the totals from each level. In this problem, the sales rep will be paid for all of level 1, $50,000; for all of level 2, $100,00; and for $12,400 of level 3 ($162,400 − $150,000 = $12,400).

$$\text{Level pay} = \text{Sales per level} \times \text{Commission rate}$$
$$\text{Level 1 pay} = 50{,}000 \times .04 = \underline{\$2{,}000}$$
$$\text{Level 2 pay} = 100{,}000 \times .05 = \underline{\$5{,}000}$$
$$\text{Level 3 pay} = 12{,}400 \times .065 = \underline{\$806}$$
$$\text{Total gross pay} = \text{Level 1} + \text{Level 2} + \text{Level 3}$$
$$\text{Total gross pay} = 2{,}000 + 5{,}000 + 806 = \underline{\$7{,}806}$$

►TRYITEXERCISE 6

Mike Lamb sells copiers for Royal Business Products. He is on an incremental commission schedule of 1.7% of sales up to $100,000 and 2.5% on sales greater than $100,000. What was Mike's total gross pay last month if his sales volume was $184,600?

CHECK YOUR ANSWER WITH THE SOLUTION ON PAGE 295.

IN THE Business World

Companies often give sales managers *override* commissions. This is a small commission on the total sales of the manager's sales force.

Example: Jim and Diane sell for Apex Electronics. They each receive 15% commission on their sales. John, their sales manager, receives a 3% override on their total sales. If Jim sells $20,000 and Diane sells $30,000 in June, how much commission does each person receive?

- Jim: $20,000 × 15% = $3,000

- Diane: $30,000 × 15% = $4,500

- John: $50,000 × 3% = $1,500

SALARY PLUS COMMISSION

A variation of straight and incremental commission pay schedules is the **salary plus commission** whereby the employee is paid a guaranteed salary plus a commission on sales over a specified amount. To calculate the total gross pay, find the amount of commission and add it to the salary.

salary plus commission A guaranteed salary plus a commission on sales over a specified amount.

EXAMPLE7 CALCULATING SALARY PLUS COMMISSION

Karie Jabe works on a pay schedule of $1,500 per month salary plus a 3% commission on all sales greater than $40,000. If she sold $60,000 last month, what was her total gross pay?

►SOLUTIONSTRATEGY

To solve for Karie's total gross pay, add her monthly salary to her commission for the month.

Commission = Commission rate × Sales subject to commission
Commission = 3%(60,000 − 40,000)
Commission = .03 × 20,000 = $600
Total gross pay = Salary + Commission
Total gross pay = 1,500 + 600 = $2,100

►TRYITEXERCISE 7

Ed Diamond is a sales representative for Jersey Shore Supply, Inc. He is paid a salary of $1,400 per month plus a commission of 4% on all sales greater than $20,000. If he sold $45,000 last month, what was his total gross earnings?

CHECK YOUR ANSWER WITH THE SOLUTION ON PAGE 295.

Dollars AND Sense

Education Pays
The unemployment rate in December 2012 among people with a bachelor's degree or higher was 6.7%.
Among people whose education stopped short of a high school diploma, the rate was 12.3%.

Source: www.bls.gov

DRAW AGAINST COMMISSION

In certain industries and at certain times of the year, sales fluctuate significantly. To provide salespeople on commission with at least some income during slack periods of sales, a drawing account is used. A **drawing account**, or **draw against commission**, is a commission paid in advance of sales and later deducted from the commissions earned. If a period goes by when the salesperson does not earn enough commission to cover the draw, the unpaid balance carries over to the next period.

drawing account, or **draw against commission** Commission paid in advance of sales and later deducted from the commission earned.

EXAMPLE8 CALCULATING DRAW AGAINST COMMISSION

Bill Carpenter is a salesperson for Power Electronics. The company pays 8% commission on all sales and gives Bill a $1,500 per month draw against commission. If he receives his draw at the beginning of the month and then sells $58,000 during the month, how much commission is owed to Bill?

►SOLUTIONSTRATEGY

To find the amount of commission owed to Bill, find the total amount of commission he earned and subtract $1,500, the amount of his draw against commission.

Commission = Total sales × Commission rate
Commission = 58,000 × 8% = $4,640
Commission owed = Commission − Amount of draw
Commission owed = 4,640 − 1,500 = $3,140

▶TRYITEXERCISE 8

Howard Lockwood sells for Catalina Designs, Inc. He is on a 3.5% straight commission with a $2,000 drawing account. If he is paid the draw at the beginning of the month and then sells $120,000 during the month, how much commission is owed to Howard?

CHECK YOUR ANSWER WITH THE SOLUTION ON PAGE 295.

SECTION I | 9 | REVIEW EXERCISES

Calculate the gross earnings per pay period for the following pay schedules.

	Annual Salary	Monthly	Semimonthly	Biweekly	Weekly
1.	$15,000	$1,250.00	$625.00	$576.92	$288.46
2.	$44,200				
3.	$100,000				
4.	$21,600	$1,800.00	$900.00	$830.77	$415.38
5.			$1,450.00		
6.				$875.00	
7.					$335.00

8. Mary Jo Prenaris is an office manager with gross earnings of $1,600 semimonthly. If her company switches pay schedules from semimonthly to biweekly, what are Mary Jo's new gross earnings?

9. Deb O'Connell is an accounting professional earning a salary of $58,000 at her firm. What is her equivalent weekly gross pay?

10. Jennifer Brunner works 40 hours per week as a chef's assistant. At the rate of $7.60 per hour, what are her gross weekly earnings?

11. Alan Kimball earns $22.34 per hour as a specialty chef at Le Bistro Restaurant. If he worked 53 hours last week and was paid time-and-a-half for weekly hours over 40, what was his gross pay?

12. Paul Curcio earns $8.25 per hour for regular time up to 40 hours, time-and-a-half for overtime, and double time for the midnight shift. Last week Paul worked 58 hours, including 6 on the midnight shift. What are his gross earnings?

As the payroll manager for Stargate Industries, your task is to complete the following weekly payroll record. The company pays overtime for all hours worked over 40 at the rate of time-and-a-half. Round to the nearest cent when necessary.

Employee	M	T	W	T	F	S	S	Hourly Rate	Total Hours	Overtime Hours	Regular Pay	Overtime Pay	Total Pay
13. Peters	7	8	5	8	8	0	0	$8.70	36	0	$313.20	0	$313.20
14. Sands	6	5	9	8	10	7	0	$9.50	___	___	___	___	___
15. Warner	8	6	11	7	12	0	4	$7.25	___	___	___	___	___
16. Lee	9	7	7	7	9	0	8	$14.75	___	___	___	___	___

17. Larry Jefferson gets paid a straight piecework rate of $3.15 for each alternator he assembles for Allied Mechanical Corp. If he assembled 226 units last week, what was his gross pay?

You are the payroll manager for Euro Couture, a manufacturer of women's apparel. Your workers are paid per garment sewn on a differential piecework schedule as follows.

Pay Level	Garments Produced	Rate per Garment
1	1–50	$3.60
2	51–100	$4.25
3	101–150	$4.50
4	Over 150	$5.10

Calculate last week's total gross pay for each of the following employees.

Employee	Garments Produced	Total Gross Pay
18. Goodrich, P.	109	$433.00
19. Walker, A.	83	___
20. Fox, B.	174	___

21. Katrina Byrd assembles motor mounts for C-207 executive planes. Her company has established a differential piecework scale as an incentive to increase production due to backlogged orders. The pay scale is $11.50 for the first 40 mounts, $12.35 for the next 30 mounts, $13.00 for the next 20 mounts, and $13.40 for all remaining mounts assembled during the week. Katrina assembled 96 mounts last week. What was her total gross pay?

22. Bob Farrell works for a company that manufactures small appliances. Bob is paid $2.00 for each toaster, $4.60 for each microwave oven, and $1.55 for each food blender he assembles. If he produced 56 toasters, 31 microwave ovens, and 79 blenders, what were his total weekly gross earnings?

23. What is the total gross pay for a salesperson on a straight commission of 4.7% if his or her sales volume is $123,200?

24. Pamela Mello is paid on an incremental commission schedule. She is paid 2.6% on the first $60,000 and 3.4% on any sales over $60,000. If her weekly sales volume was $89,400, what was her total commission?

25. Dory Schrader is a buyer for Oceans of Notions. She is paid a weekly salary of $885 plus a 4% commission on sales over $45,000. If her sales were $62,000 last week, what was her total gross pay?

26. Thomas Rendell's company pays him a straight 6% commission with a $1,350 drawing account each month. If his sales last month totaled $152,480, how much commission is owed to Thomas?

27. Katie Jergens works for Dynamic Designs selling clothing. She is on a salary of $140 per week plus a commission of 7% of her sales. Last week she sold 19 dresses at $79.95 each, 26 skirts at $24.75 each, and 17 jackets at $51.50 each. What were her total gross earnings for the week?

28. Jerry King is a server in a restaurant that pays a salary of $22 per day. He also averages tips of 18% of his total gross food orders. Last week he worked 6 days and had total food orders of $2,766.50. What was his total gross pay for the week?

BUSINESS DECISION: MINIMUM WAGE TIED TO INFLATION

29. In an effort to keep low-wage workers' salaries commensurate with the cost of living, a number of states have amended their constitutions to allow the minimum wage to be adjusted with inflation.

    You are the accountant for Delicious, Inc., a company that owns a chain of 18 fast-food restaurants in Florida. Each restaurant employs 35 workers, each averaging 20 hours per week at the current federal minimum wage, $7.25 per hour.

    a. How many hours at minimum wage are paid out each week by Delicious?

    b. At the current rate of $7.25 per hour, what is the amount of the weekly "minimum wage" portion of the restaurant's payroll?

    c. If the inflation rate this year is .7%, calculate the "adjusted" minimum wage rate to be paid next year.

d. How much in "additional wages" will Delicious have to pay out next year at the adjusted rate?

e. (Optional) Go to www.dol.gov/whd/minwage/america.htm and click on your state to find the current minimum wage. Calculate the weekly "minimum wage" portion of the restaurant's payroll assuming the restaurant is located in your state.

f. (Optional) Suggest some ways that the restaurant chain or other small businesses can offset the increase in payroll and subsequent decrease in profit as a result of the minimum wage hike.

EMPLOYEE'S PAYROLL DEDUCTIONS

9 SECTION II

"Hey! What happened to my paycheck?" This is the typical reaction of employees on seeing their paychecks for the first time after a raise or a promotion. As we will see, gross pay is by no means the amount of money the employee takes home.

Employers, by federal law, are required to deduct or withhold certain funds, known as **deductions** or **withholdings**, from an employee's paycheck. Employee payroll deductions fall into two categories: mandatory and voluntary. The three major **mandatory deductions** most workers in the United States are subject to are social security, Medicare, and federal income tax. Other mandatory deductions found only in some states are state income tax and state disability insurance.

In addition to the mandatory deductions, employees may also choose to have **voluntary deductions** taken out of their paychecks. Some examples include payments for life or health insurance premiums, union or professional organization dues, credit union savings deposits or loan payments, stock or bond purchases, and charitable contributions.

After all the deductions have been subtracted from the employee's gross earnings, the remaining amount is known as net, or take-home, pay.

deductions or **withholdings** Funds withheld from an employee's paycheck.

mandatory deductions Deductions withheld from an employee's paycheck by law: social security, Medicare, and federal income tax.

voluntary deductions Deductions withheld from an employee's paycheck by request of the employee, such as insurance premiums, dues, loan payments, and charitable contributions.

Net pay = Gross pay − Total deductions

COMPUTING FICA TAXES, BOTH SOCIAL SECURITY AND MEDICARE, WITHHELD FROM AN EMPLOYEE'S PAYCHECK

9-5

In 1937 during the Great Depression, Congress enacted legislation known as the **Federal Insurance Contribution Act (FICA)** with the purpose of providing monthly benefits to retired and disabled workers and to the families of deceased workers. This social security tax, which is assessed to virtually every worker in the United States, is based on a certain percent of the worker's income up to a specified limit or **wage base** per year. When the tax began in 1937, the tax rate was 1% up to a wage base of $3,000. At that time, the maximum a worker could be taxed per year for social security was $30 (3,000 × .01).

Today the FICA tax is divided into two categories. **Social security tax** (OASDI, which stands for Old Age, Survivors, and Disability Insurance) is a retirement plan, and **Medicare tax** is for health care and hospital insurance. The social security wage base changes every year. For the most current information, consult the Internal Revenue Service, *Circular E, Employer's Tax Guide*. As this is written, the following rates and wage base were in effect for the FICA tax and should be used for all exercises in this chapter:

Federal Insurance Contribution Act (FICA) Federal legislation enacted in 1937 during the Great Depression to provide retirement funds and hospital insurance for retired and disabled workers. Today FICA is divided into two categories, social security and Medicare.

wage base The amount of earnings up to which an employee must pay social security tax.

social security tax (OASDI) Old Age, Survivors, and Disability Insurance—a federal tax based on a percentage of a worker's income up to a specified limit or wage base for the purpose of providing monthly benefits to retired and disabled workers and to the families of deceased workers.

Medicare tax A federal tax used to provide health care benefits and hospital insurance to retired and disabled workers.

	Tax Rate	Wage Base
Social Security (OASDI)	6.2%	$113,700
Medicare	1.45%	no limit

When an employee reaches the wage base for the year, he or she is no longer subject to the tax. Based on the table on the previous page, the maximum social security tax per year is limited to $7,049.40 (113,700 × .062). There is no limit on the amount of Medicare tax. The 1.45% is in effect regardless of how much an employee earns.

EXAMPLE 9 — CALCULATING SOCIAL SECURITY AND MEDICARE WITHHOLDINGS

What are the withholdings for social security and Medicare for an employee with gross earnings of $650 per week? Round to the nearest cent.

▶SOLUTIONSTRATEGY

To find the withholdings, we apply the tax rates for social security (6.2%) and Medicare (1.45%) to the gross earnings for the week:

$$\text{Social security tax} = \text{Gross earnings} \times 6.2\%$$
$$\text{Social security tax} = 650 \times .062 = \underline{\$40.30}$$
$$\text{Medicare tax} = \text{Gross earnings} \times 1.45\%$$
$$\text{Medicare tax} = 650 \times .0145 = 9.425 = \underline{\$9.43}$$

▶TRYITEXERCISE 9

What are the withholdings for social security and Medicare for an employee with gross earnings of $5,000 per month?

CHECK YOUR ANSWERS WITH THE SOLUTIONS ON PAGE 296.

REACHING THE WAGE BASE LIMIT

In the pay period when an employee's year-to-date (YTD) earnings reach and surpass the wage base for social security, the tax is applied only to the portion of the earnings below the limit.

Congress passed the Social Security Act in 1935 and passed Medicare into law in 1965.

Source: ssa.gov

Photo by Robert Brechner

EXAMPLE 10 — CALCULATING SOCIAL SECURITY WITH WAGE BASE LIMIT

Vickie Hirsh has earned $110,900 so far this year. Her next paycheck, $5,000, will put her earnings over the wage base limit for social security. What is the amount of Vickie's social security withholdings for that paycheck?

▶SOLUTIONSTRATEGY

To calculate Vickie's social security deduction, first determine how much more she must earn to reach the wage base of $113,700.

(continued)

Earnings subject to tax = Wage base − Year-to-date earnings

Earnings subject to tax = 113,700 − 110,900 = $2,800

Social security tax = Earnings subject to tax × 6.2%

Social security tax = 2,800 × .062 = $173.60

▶ TRYITEXERCISE 10

Rick Nicotera has year-to-date earnings of $109,200. If his next paycheck is $6,000, what is the amount of his social security deduction?

CHECK YOUR ANSWER WITH THE SOLUTION ON PAGE 296.

CALCULATING AN EMPLOYEE'S FEDERAL INCOME TAX WITHHOLDING (FIT) BY THE PERCENTAGE METHOD

9-6

In addition to social security and Medicare tax withholdings, an employer is also responsible, by federal law, for withholding an appropriate amount of **federal income tax (FIT)** from each employee's paycheck. This graduated tax allows the government a steady flow of tax revenues throughout the year. Self-employed persons must send quarterly tax payments based on estimated earnings to the Internal Revenue Service. By IRS rules, 90% of the income tax due for a given calendar year must be paid within that year to avoid penalties.

federal income tax (FIT) A graduated tax based on gross earnings, marital status, and number of exemptions that is paid by all workers earning over a certain amount in the United States.

The amount of income tax withheld from an employee's paycheck is determined by his or her amount of gross earnings, marital status, and the number of **withholding allowances**, or **exemptions**, claimed. Employees are allowed one exemption for themselves, one for their spouse if the spouse does not work, and one for each dependent child or elderly parent living with the taxpayer but not working.

withholding allowance, or **exemption** An amount that reduces an employee's taxable income. Employees are allowed one exemption for themselves, one for their spouse if the spouse does not work, and one for each dependent child or elderly parent living with the taxpayer but not working.

Each employee is required to complete a form called W-4, Employee's Withholding Allowance Certificate. The information provided on this form is used by the employer in calculating the amount of income tax withheld from the paycheck. Employees should keep track of their tax liability during the year and adjust the number of exemptions as their personal situations change (i.e., marriage, divorce, or birth of a child).

The **percentage method** for determining the amount of federal income tax withheld from an employee's paycheck is used by companies whose payroll processing is on a computerized system. The amount of tax withheld is based on the amount of gross earnings, the marital status of the employee, and the number of withholding allowances claimed.

percentage method An alternative method to the wage bracket tables used to calculate the amount of an employee's federal income tax withholding.

The percentage method of calculating federal income tax requires the use of two tables. The first is the Percentage Method Amount for One Withholding Allowance Table, Exhibit 9-1. This table shows the dollar amount of one withholding allowance for the various payroll periods. The second, Exhibit 9-2, is the Tables for Percentage Method of Withholding. These tables were in effect as this is written and should be used for the exercises in this chapter.

Payroll Period	One Withholding Allowance
Weekly	$ 75.00
Biweekly	150.00
Semimonthly	162.50
Monthly	325.00
Quarterly	975.00
Semiannually	1,950.00
Annually	3,900.00
Daily or miscellaneous (each day of the payroll period)	15.00

EXHIBIT 9-1

Percentage Method Amount for One Withholding Allowance

EXHIBIT 9-2 Tables for Percentage Method of Withholding

TABLE 1—WEEKLY Payroll Period

(a) SINGLE person (including head of household)—

If the amount of wages (after subtracting withholding allowances) is:

The amount of income tax to withhold is:

Not over $42 .... $0

Over—	But not over—		of excess over—
$42	—$214	......$0.00 plus 10%	—$42
$214	—$739	......$17.20 plus 15%	—$214
$739	—$1,732	......$95.95 plus 25%	—$739
$1,732	—$3,566	......$344.20 plus 28%	—$1,732
$3,566	—$7,703	......$857.72 plus 33%	—$3,566
$7,703	—$7,735	......$2,222.93 plus 35%	—$7,703
$7,735	....	$2,234.13 plus 39.6%	—$7,735

(b) MARRIED person—

If the amount of wages (after subtracting withholding allowances) is:

The amount of income tax to withhold is:

Not over $160 .... $0

Over—	But not over—		of excess over—
$160	—$503	......$0.00 plus 10%	—$160
$503	—$1,554	......$34.30 plus 15%	—$503
$1,554	—$2,975	......$191.95 plus 25%	—$1,554
$2,975	—$4,449	......$547.20 plus 28%	—$2,975
$4,449	—$7,820	......$959.92 plus 33%	—$4,449
$7,820	—$8,813	......$2,072.35 plus 35%	—$7,820
$8,813	....	$2,419.90 plus 39.6%	—$8,813

TABLE 2—BIWEEKLY Payroll Period

(a) SINGLE person (including head of household)—

If the amount of wages (after subtracting withholding allowances) is:

The amount of income tax to withhold is:

Not over $85 .... $0

Over—	But not over—		of excess over—
$85	—$428	......$0.00 plus 10%	—$85
$428	—$1,479	......$34.30 plus 15%	—$428
$1,479	—$3,463	......$191.95 plus 25%	—$1,479
$3,463	—$7,133	......$687.95 plus 28%	—$3,463
$7,133	—$15,406	......$1,715.55 plus 33%	—$7,133
$15,406	—$15,469	......$4,445.64 plus 35%	—$15,406
$15,469	....	$4,467.69 plus 39.6%	—$15,469

(b) MARRIED person—

If the amount of wages (after subtracting withholding allowances) is:

The amount of income tax to withhold is:

Not over $319 .... $0

Over—	But not over—		of excess over—
$319	—$1,006	......$0.00 plus 10%	—$319
$1,006	—$3,108	......$68.70 plus 15%	—$1,006
$3,108	—$5,950	.......$384.00 plus 25%	—$3,108
$5,950	—$8,898	......$1,094.50 plus 28%	—$5,950
$8,898	—$15,640	......$1,919.94 plus 33%	—$8,898
$15,640	—$17,627	.......$4,144.80 plus 35%	—$15,640
$17,627	....	$4,840.25 plus 39.6%	—$17,627

TABLE 3—SEMIMONTHLY Payroll Period

(a) SINGLE person (including head of household)—

If the amount of wages (after subtracting withholding allowances) is:

The amount of income tax to withhold is:

Not over $92 .... $0

Over—	But not over—		of excess over—
$92	—$464	......$0.00 plus 10%	—$92
$464	—$1,602	......$37.20 plus 15%	—$464
$1,602	—$3,752	......$207.90 plus 25%	—$1,602
$3,752	—$7,727	......$745.40 plus 28%	—$3,752
$7,727	—$16,690	......$1,858.40 plus 33%	—$7,727
$16,690	—$16,758	......$4,816.19 plus 35%	—$16,690
$16,758	....	$4,839.99 plus 39.6%	—$16,758

(b) MARRIED person—

If the amount of wages (after subtracting withholding allowances) is:

The amount of income tax to withhold is:

Not over $346 .... $0

Over—	But not over—		of excess over—
$346	—$1,090	......$0.00 plus 10%	—$346
$1,090	—$3,367	......$74.40 plus 15%	—$1,090
$3,367	—$6,446	......$415.95 plus 25%	—$3,367
$6,446	—$9,640	......$1,185.70 plus 28%	—$6,446
$9,640	—$16,944	......$2,080.02 plus 33%	—$9,640
$16,944	—$19,096	......$4,490.34 plus 35%	—$16,944
$19,096	....	$5,243.54 plus 39.6%	—$19,096

TABLE 4—MONTHLY Payroll Period

(a) SINGLE person (including head of household)—

If the amount of wages (after subtracting withholding allowances) is:

The amount of income tax to withhold is:

Not over $183 .... $0

Over—	But not over—		of excess over—
$183	—$927	......$0.00 plus 10%	—$183
$927	—$3,204	......$74.40 plus 15%	—$927
$3,204	—$7,504	......$415.95 plus 25%	—$3,204
$7,504	—$15,454	......$1,490.95 plus 28%	—$7,504
$15,454	—$33,379	......$3,716.95 plus 33%	—$15,454
$33,379	—$33,517	......$9,632.20 plus 35%	—$33,379
$33,517	....	$9,680.50 plus 39.6%	—$33,517

(b) MARRIED person—

If the amount of wages (after subtracting withholding allowances) is:

The amount of income tax to withhold is:

Not over $692 .... $0

Over—	But not over—		of excess over—
$692	—$2,179	......$0.00 plus 10%	—$692
$2,179	—$6,733	......$148.70 plus 15%	—$2,179
$6,733	—$12,892	......$831.80 plus 25%	—$6,733
$12,892	—$19,279	......$2,371.55 plus 28%	—$12,892
$19,279	—$33,888	......$4,159.91 plus 33%	—$19,279
$33,888	—$38,192	......$8,980.88 plus 35%	—$33,888
$38,192	....	$10,487.28 plus 39.6%	—$38,192

STEPS TO CALCULATE THE INCOME TAX WITHHELD BY THE PERCENTAGE METHOD

STEP 1. Using the proper payroll period, multiply one withholding allowance, Exhibit 9-1, by the number of allowances claimed by the employee.

STEP 2. Subtract that amount from the employee's gross earnings to find the wages subject to federal income tax.

STEP 3. From Exhibit 9-2, locate the proper segment (Table 1, 2, 3, or 4) corresponding to the employee's payroll period. Within that segment, use the *left* side (a) for single employees and the *right* side (b) for married employees.

STEP 4. Locate the "Over—" and "But not over—" brackets containing the employee's taxable wages from Step 2. The tax is listed to the right as a percent or a dollar amount and a percent.

EXAMPLE 11 CALCULATING INCOME TAX WITHHOLDING

Lori Fast is a manager for Wayward Wind Travel. She is single and is paid $750 weekly. She claims two withholding allowances. Using the percentage method, calculate the amount of income tax that should be withheld from her paycheck each week.

►SOLUTION STRATEGY

From Exhibit 9-1, the amount of one withholding allowance for an employee paid weekly is $75.00. Multiply this amount by the number of allowances claimed, two.

$$75.00 \times 2 = \$150.00$$

Subtract that amount from the gross earnings to get taxable income.

$$750.00 - 150.00 = \$600.00$$

From Exhibit 9-2, find the tax withheld from Lori's paycheck in Table 1(a), Weekly payroll period, Single person. Lori's taxable wages of $600.00 fall in the category "Over $214, but not over $739." The tax, therefore, is $17.20 plus 15% of the excess over $214.

$$\text{Tax} = 17.20 + .15(600.00 - 214.00)$$
$$\text{Tax} = 17.20 + .15(386.00)$$
$$\text{Tax} = 17.20 + 57.90 = \underline{\$75.10}$$

►TRYIT EXERCISE 11

Jan McMillan is married, claims five exemptions, and earns $5,670 per month. As the payroll manager of Jan's company, use the percentage method to calculate the amount of income tax that must be withheld from her paycheck.

CHECK YOUR ANSWER WITH THE SOLUTION ON PAGE 296.

9-7 DETERMINING AN EMPLOYEE'S TOTAL WITHHOLDING FOR FEDERAL INCOME TAX, SOCIAL SECURITY, AND MEDICARE USING THE COMBINED WAGE BRACKET TABLES

combined wage bracket tables IRS tables used to determine the combined amount of income tax, social security, and Medicare that must be withheld from an employee's gross earnings each pay period.

In 2001, the IRS introduced **combined wage bracket tables** that can be used to determine the combined amount of income tax, social security, and Medicare that must be withheld from an employee's gross earnings each pay period. These tables are found in *Publication 15-A, Employer's Supplemental Tax Guide*. This publication contains a complete set of tables for both single and married people, covering weekly, biweekly, semimonthly, monthly, and even daily pay periods.

Exhibit 9-3 shows a portion of the wage bracket tables for Married Persons—Weekly Payroll Period, and Exhibit 9-4 shows a portion of the wage bracket table for Single Persons—Monthly Payroll Period. These tables were in effect as this is written and should be used to solve wage bracket problems in this chapter.

IN THE Business World

All employees must have a Social Security number. Applications are available at all U.S. Post Offices or may be downloaded online at www.socialsecurity.gov.

Social Security numbers are used by the IRS as a taxpayer identification number as well as by banks, credit unions, and other financial institutions for reporting income from savings and other investments.

Information about an individual's Social Security account can be obtained by filing a Form 7004-SM—Request for Earnings and Benefit Estimate Statement. The form may be obtained by calling the Social Security Administration at 1-800-772-1213 or by transmitting your request using an online form via the Internet.

STEPS TO FIND THE TOTAL INCOME TAX, SOCIAL SECURITY, AND MEDICARE WITHHELD USING THE COMBINED WAGE BRACKET TABLE

STEP 1. Based on the employee's marital status and period of payment, find the corresponding table (Exhibit 9-3 or 9-4).

STEP 2. Note that the two left-hand columns, labeled "At least" and "But less than," are the wage brackets. Scan down these columns until you find the bracket containing the gross pay of the employee.

STEP 3. Scan across the row of that wage bracket to the intersection of the column containing the number of withholding allowances claimed by the employee.

STEP 4. The number in that column on the wage bracket row is the amount of combined tax withheld.

EXAMPLE12 USING THE COMBINED WAGE BRACKET TABLES

Use the combined wage bracket tables to determine the amount of income tax, social security, and Medicare withheld from the monthly paycheck of Erin Lane, a single employee claiming three withholding allowances and earning $2,975 per month.

▶ SOLUTIONSTRATEGY

To find Erin Lane's monthly income tax withholding, choose the table for Single Persons—Monthly Payroll Period, Exhibit 9-4. Scanning down the "At least" and "But less than" columns, we find the wage bracket containing Erin's earnings: "At least 2,960—But less than 3,000."

Next, scan across that row from left to right to the "3" withholding allowances column. The number at that intersection, $463.97, is the total combined tax to be withheld from Erin's paycheck.

▶ TRYITEXERCISE 12

Using the combined wage bracket tables, what is the total amount of income tax, social security, and Medicare that should be withheld from Brent Andrus's weekly paycheck of $835 if he is married and claims two withholding allowances?

CHECK YOUR ANSWER WITH THE SOLUTION ON PAGE 296.

EXHIBIT 9-3 Payroll Deductions—Married, Paid Weekly

MARRIED Persons—WEEKLY Payroll Period
(For Wages Paid in 20XX)

And the wages are—		And the number of withholding allowances claimed is—										
At least	But less than	0	1	2	3	4	5	6	7	8	9	10
		The amount of income, social security, and Medicare taxes to be withheld is—										
$750	$760	$129.76	$118.76	$107.76	$95.76	$87.76	$79.76	$72.76	$64.76	$57.76	$57.76	$57.76
760	770	132.52	120.52	109.52	98.52	89.52	81.52	74.52	66.52	59.52	58.52	58.52
770	780	134.29	123.29	112.29	100.29	91.29	83.29	76.29	68.29	61.29	59.29	59.29
780	790	137.05	125.05	114.05	103.05	93.05	85.05	78.05	70.05	63.05	60.05	60.05
790	800	138.82	127.82	116.82	104.82	94.82	86.82	79.82	71.82	64.82	60.82	60.82
800	810	141.58	129.58	118.58	107.58	96.58	88.58	81.58	73.58	66.58	61.58	61.58
810	820	143.35	132.35	121.35	109.35	98.35	90.35	83.35	75.35	68.35	62.35	62.35
820	830	146.11	134.11	123.11	112.11	101.11	92.11	85.11	77.11	70.11	63.11	63.11
830	840	147.88	136.88	125.88	113.88	102.88	93.88	86.88	78.88	71.88	63.88	63.88
840	850	150.64	138.64	127.64	116.64	105.64	95.64	88.64	80.64	73.64	65.64	64.64
850	860	152.41	141.41	130.41	118.41	107.41	97.41	90.41	82.41	75.41	67.41	65.41
860	870	155.17	143.17	132.17	121.17	110.17	99.17	92.17	84.17	77.17	69.17	66.17
870	880	156.94	145.94	134.94	122.94	111.94	100.94	93.94	85.94	78.94	70.94	66.94
880	890	159.70	147.70	136.70	125.70	114.70	102.70	95.70	87.70	80.70	72.70	67.70
890	900	161.47	150.47	139.47	127.47	116.47	105.47	97.47	89.47	82.47	74.47	68.47
900	910	164.23	152.23	141.23	130.23	119.23	107.23	99.23	91.23	84.23	76.23	69.23
910	920	166.00	155.00	144.00	132.00	121.00	110.00	101.00	93.00	86.00	78.00	71.00
920	930	168.76	156.76	145.76	134.76	123.76	111.76	102.76	94.76	87.76	79.76	72.76
930	940	170.53	159.53	148.53	136.53	125.53	114.53	104.53	96.53	89.53	81.53	74.53
940	950	173.29	161.29	150.29	139.29	128.29	116.29	106.29	98.29	91.29	83.29	76.29
950	960	175.06	164.06	153.06	141.06	130.06	119.06	108.06	100.06	93.06	85.06	78.06
960	970	177.82	165.82	154.82	143.82	132.82	120.82	109.82	101.82	94.82	86.82	79.82
970	980	179.59	168.59	157.59	145.59	134.59	123.59	112.59	103.59	96.59	88.59	81.59
980	990	182.35	170.35	159.35	148.35	137.35	125.35	114.35	105.35	98.35	90.35	83.35
990	1,000	184.12	173.12	162.12	150.12	139.12	128.12	117.12	107.12	100.12	92.12	85.12
1,000	1,010	186.88	174.88	163.88	152.88	141.88	129.88	118.88	108.88	101.88	93.88	86.88
1,010	1,020	188.65	177.65	166.65	154.65	143.65	132.65	121.65	110.65	103.65	95.65	88.65
1,020	1,030	191.41	179.41	168.41	157.41	146.41	134.41	123.41	112.41	105.41	97.41	90.41
1,030	1,040	193.18	182.18	171.18	159.18	148.18	137.18	126.18	114.18	107.18	99.18	92.18
1,040	1,050	195.94	183.94	172.94	161.94	150.94	138.94	127.94	116.94	108.94	100.94	93.94
1,050	1,060	197.71	186.71	175.71	163.71	152.71	141.71	130.71	118.71	110.71	102.71	95.71
1,060	1,070	200.47	188.47	177.47	166.47	155.47	143.47	132.47	121.47	112.47	104.47	97.47
1,070	1,080	202.24	191.24	180.24	168.24	157.24	146.24	135.24	123.24	114.24	106.24	99.24
1,080	1,090	205.00	193.00	182.00	171.00	160.00	148.00	137.00	126.00	116.00	108.00	101.00
1,090	1,100	206.77	195.77	184.77	172.77	161.77	150.77	139.77	127.77	117.77	109.77	102.77
1,100	1,110	209.53	197.53	186.53	175.53	164.53	152.53	141.53	130.53	119.53	111.53	104.53
1,110	1,120	211.30	200.30	189.30	177.30	166.30	155.30	144.30	132.30	121.30	113.30	106.30
1,120	1,130	214.06	202.06	191.06	180.06	169.06	157.06	146.06	135.06	124.06	115.06	108.06
1,130	1,140	215.83	204.83	193.83	181.83	170.83	159.83	148.83	136.83	125.83	116.83	109.83
1,140	1,150	218.59	206.59	195.59	184.59	173.59	161.59	150.59	139.59	128.59	118.59	111.59
1,150	1,160	220.36	209.36	198.36	186.36	175.36	164.36	153.36	141.36	130.36	120.36	113.36
1,160	1,170	223.12	211.12	200.12	189.12	178.12	166.12	155.12	144.12	133.12	122.12	115.12
1,170	1,180	224.89	213.89	202.89	190.89	179.89	168.89	157.89	145.89	134.89	123.89	116.89
1,180	1,190	227.65	215.65	204.65	193.65	182.65	170.65	159.65	148.65	137.65	125.65	118.65
1,190	1,200	229.42	218.42	207.42	195.42	184.42	173.42	162.42	150.42	139.42	128.42	120.42
1,200	1,210	232.18	220.18	209.18	198.18	187.18	175.18	164.18	153.18	142.18	130.18	122.18
1,210	1,220	233.95	222.95	211.95	199.95	188.95	177.95	166.95	154.95	143.95	132.95	123.95
1,220	1,230	236.71	224.71	213.71	202.71	191.71	179.71	168.71	157.71	146.71	134.71	125.71
1,230	1,240	238.48	227.48	216.48	204.48	193.48	182.48	171.48	159.48	148.48	137.48	127.48
1,240	1,250	241.24	229.24	218.24	207.24	196.24	184.24	173.24	162.24	151.24	139.24	129.24
1,250	1,260	243.01	232.01	221.01	209.01	198.01	187.01	176.01	164.01	153.01	142.01	131.01
1,260	1,270	245.77	233.77	222.77	211.77	200.77	188.77	177.77	166.77	155.77	143.77	132.77
1,270	1,280	247.54	236.54	225.54	213.54	202.54	191.54	180.54	168.54	157.54	146.54	135.54
1,280	1,290	250.30	238.30	227.30	216.30	205.30	193.30	182.30	171.30	160.30	148.30	137.30
1,290	1,300	252.07	241.07	230.07	218.07	207.07	196.07	185.07	173.07	162.07	151.07	140.07
1,300	1,310	254.83	242.83	231.83	220.83	209.83	197.83	186.83	175.83	164.83	152.83	141.83
1,310	1,320	256.60	245.60	234.60	222.60	211.60	200.60	189.60	177.60	166.60	155.60	144.60
1,320	1,330	259.36	247.36	236.36	225.36	214.36	202.36	191.36	180.36	169.36	157.36	146.36
1,330	1,340	261.13	250.13	239.13	227.13	216.13	205.13	194.13	182.13	171.13	160.13	149.13
1,340	1,350	263.89	251.89	240.89	229.89	218.89	206.89	195.89	184.89	173.89	161.89	150.89
1,350	1,360	265.66	254.66	243.66	231.66	220.66	209.66	198.66	186.66	175.66	164.66	153.66
1,360	1,370	268.42	256.42	245.42	234.42	223.42	211.42	200.42	189.42	178.42	166.42	155.42
1,370	1,380	270.19	259.19	248.19	236.19	225.19	214.19	203.19	191.19	180.19	169.19	158.19
1,380	1,390	272.95	260.95	249.95	238.95	227.95	215.95	204.95	193.95	182.95	170.95	159.95

$1,390 and over Do not use this table. See page 46 for instructions.

EXHIBIT 9-4 Payroll Deductions—Single, Paid Weekly

SINGLE Persons—MONTHLY Payroll Period
(For Wages Paid in 20XX)

And the wage are—		And the number of withholding allowances claimed is—										
At least	But less than	0	1	2	3	4	5	6	7	8	9	10
		The amount of income, social security, and Medicare taxes to be withheld is—										
$2,400	$2,440	$483.13	$435.13	$386.13	$337.13	$288.13	$246.13	$214.13	$185.13	$185.13	$185.13	$185.13
2,440	2,480	492.19	444.19	395.19	346.19	297.19	253.19	221.19	188.19	188.19	188.19	188.19
2,480	2,520	501.25	453.25	404.25	355.25	306.25	260.25	228.25	195.25	191.25	191.25	191.25
2,520	2,560	510.31	462.31	413.31	364.31	315.31	267.31	235.31	202.31	194.31	194.31	194.31
2,560	2,600	519.37	471.37	422.37	373.37	324.37	276.37	242.37	209.37	197.37	197.37	197.37
2,600	2,640	528.43	480.43	431.43	382.43	333.43	285.43	249.43	216.43	200.43	200.43	200.43
2,640	2,680	537.49	489.49	440.49	391.49	342.49	294.49	256.49	223.49	203.49	203.49	203.49
2,680	2,720	546.55	498.55	449.55	400.55	351.55	303.55	263.55	230.55	206.55	206.55	206.55
2,720	2,760	555.61	507.61	458.61	409.61	360.61	312.61	270.61	237.61	209.61	209.61	209.61
2,760	2,800	564.67	516.67	467.67	418.67	369.67	321.67	277.67	244.67	212.67	212.67	212.67
2,800	2,840	573.73	525.73	476.73	427.73	378.73	330.73	284.73	251.73	219.73	215.73	215.73
2,840	2,880	582.79	534.79	485.79	436.79	387.79	339.79	291.79	258.79	226.79	218.79	218.79
2,880	2,920	591.85	543.85	494.85	445.85	396.85	348.85	299.85	265.85	233.85	221.85	221.85
2,920	2,960	600.91	552.91	503.91	454.91	405.91	357.91	308.91	272.91	240.91	224.91	224.91
2,960	3,000	609.97	561.97	512.97	463.97	414.97	366.97	317.97	279.97	247.97	227.97	227.97
3,000	3,040	619.03	571.03	522.03	473.03	424.03	376.03	327.03	287.03	255.03	231.03	231.03
3,040	3,080	628.09	580.09	531.09	482.09	433.09	385.09	336.09	294.09	262.09	234.09	234.09
3,080	3,120	637.15	589.15	540.15	491.15	442.15	394.15	345.15	301.15	269.15	237.15	237.15
3,120	3,160	646.21	598.21	549.21	500.21	451.21	403.21	354.21	308.21	276.21	243.21	240.21
3,160	3,200	655.27	607.27	558.27	509.27	460.27	412.27	363.27	315.27	283.27	250.27	243.27
3,200	3,240	666.33	616.33	567.33	518.33	469.33	421.33	372.33	323.33	290.33	257.33	246.33
3,240	3,280	679.39	625.39	576.39	527.39	478.39	430.39	381.39	332.39	297.39	264.39	249.39
3,280	3,320	692.45	634.45	585.45	536.45	487.45	439.45	390.45	341.45	304.45	271.45	252.45
3,320	3,360	705.51	643.51	594.51	545.51	469.51	448.51	399.51	350.51	311.51	278.51	255.51
3,360	3,400	718.57	652.57	603.57	554.57	505.57	457.57	408.57	359.57	318.57	285.57	258.57
3,400	3,440	731.63	661.63	612.63	563.63	514.63	466.63	417.63	368.63	325.63	292.63	261.63
3,440	3,480	744.69	670.69	621.69	572.69	523.69	475.69	429.69	377.69	332.69	299.69	267.69
3,480	3,520	757.75	679.75	630.75	581.75	532.75	484.75	435.75	386.75	339.75	306.75	274.75
3,520	3,560	770.81	689.81	639.81	590.81	541.81	493.81	444.81	395.81	346.81	313.81	281.81
3,560	3,600	783.87	702.87	648.87	599.87	550.87	453.87	453.87	404.87	355.87	320.87	288.87
3,600	3,640	769.93	715.93	657.93	608.93	559.93	511.93	462.93	413.93	364.93	327.93	295.93
3,640	3,680	809.99	728.99	666.99	617.99	568.99	520.99	471.99	422.99	373.99	334.99	302.99
3,680	3,720	823.05	742.05	676.05	627.05	578.05	530.05	481.05	432.05	383.05	342.05	310.05
3,720	3,760	836.11	755.11	685.11	636.11	587.11	539.11	490.11	441.11	392.11	349.11	317.11
3,760	3,800	849.17	768.17	694.17	645.17	596.17	548.17	499.17	450.17	401.17	356.17	324.17
3,800	3,840	862.23	781.23	703.23	654.23	605.23	557.23	508.23	459.23	410.23	363.23	331.23
3,840	3,880	875.29	794.29	712.29	663.29	614.29	566.29	517.29	468.29	419.29	371.29	338.29
3,880	3,920	888.35	807.35	725.35	672.35	623.35	575.35	526.35	477.35	428.35	380.35	345.35
3,920	3,960	901.41	820.41	738.41	681.41	632.41	584.41	535.41	486.41	437.41	389.41	352.41
3,960	4,000	914.47	833.47	751.47	690.47	641.47	593.47	544.47	495.47	446.47	398.47	359.47
4,000	4,040	927.53	846.53	764.53	699.53	650.53	602.53	553.53	504.53	455.53	407.53	366.53
4,040	4,080	940.59	859.59	777.59	708.59	659.59	611.59	562.59	513.59	464.59	416.59	373.59
4,080	4,120	953.65	872.65	790.65	717.65	668.65	620.65	571.65	522.65	473.65	425.65	380.65
4,120	4,160	966.71	885.71	803.71	726.71	677.71	629.71	580.71	531.71	482.71	434.71	387.71
4,160	4,200	979.77	898.77	816.77	735.77	686.77	638.77	589.77	540.77	491.77	443.77	394.77
4,200	4,240	992.83	911.83	829.83	748.83	695.83	647.83	598.83	549.83	500.83	452.83	403.83
4,240	4,280	1,005.89	924.89	842.89	761.89	704.89	656.89	607.89	558.89	509.89	461.89	412.89
4,280	4,320	1,018.95	937.95	855.95	774.95	713.95	665.95	616.95	567.95	518.95	470.95	421.95
4,320	4,360	1,032.01	951.01	869.01	788.01	723.01	675.01	626.01	577.01	528.01	480.01	431.01
4,360	4,400	1,045.07	964.07	882.07	801.07	732.07	684.07	635.07	586.07	537.07	489.07	440.07
4,400	4,440	1,058.13	977.13	895.13	814.13	741.13	693.13	644.13	595.13	546.13	498.13	449.13
4,440	4,480	1,071.19	990.19	908.19	827.19	750.19	702.19	653.19	604.19	555.19	507.19	458.19
4,480	4,520	1,084.25	1,003.25	921.25	840.25	759.25	711.25	662.25	613.25	564.25	516.25	467.25
4,520	4,560	1,097.31	1,016.31	934.31	853.31	772.31	720.31	671.31	622.31	573.31	525.31	476.31
4,560	4,600	1,110.37	1,029.37	947.37	866.37	785.37	729.37	680.37	631.37	582.37	534.37	485.37
4,600	4,640	1,123.43	1,042.43	960.43	879.43	798.43	738.43	689.43	640.43	591.43	543.43	494.43
4,640	4,680	1,136.49	1,055.49	973.49	892.49	811.49	747.49	698.49	649.49	600.49	552.49	503.49
4,680	4,720	1,149.55	1,068.55	986.55	905.55	824.55	756.55	707.55	658.55	609.55	561.55	512.55
4,720	4,760	1,162.61	1,081.61	999.61	918.61	837.61	765.61	716.61	667.61	618.61	570.61	521.61
4,760	4,800	1,175.67	1,094.67	1,012.67	931.67	850.67	774.67	725.67	676.67	627.67	579.67	530.67
4,800	4,840	1,188.73	1,107.73	1,025.73	944.73	863.73	783.73	734.73	685.73	636.73	588.73	539.73
4,840	4,880	1,201.79	1,120.79	1,038.79	957.79	876.79	795.79	743.79	694.79	645.79	597.79	548.79
4,880	4,920	1,214.85	1,133.85	1,051.85	970.85	889.85	808.85	752.85	703.85	654.85	606.85	557.85
4,920	4,960	1,227.91	1,146.91	1,064.91	983.91	902.91	821.91	761.91	712.91	663.91	615.91	566.91
4,960	5,000	1,240.97	1,159.97	1,077.97	996.97	915.97	834.97	770.97	721.97	672.97	624.97	575.97
5,000	5,040	1,254.03	1,173.03	1,091.03	1,010.03	929.03	848.03	780.03	731.03	682.03	634.03	585.03

$5,040 and over Do not use this table. See page 47 for instructions.

REVIEW EXERCISES

9 SECTION II

Solve the following problems using 6.2%, up to $113,700, for social security tax and 1.45%, no wage limit, for Medicare tax.

1. What are the withholdings for social security and Medicare for an employee with gross earnings of $825 per week?

   $825 \times .062 = \underline{\underline{\$51.15}}$ Social security
   $825 \times .0145 = \underline{\underline{\$11.96}}$ Medicare

2. What are the social security and Medicare withholdings for an executive whose annual gross earnings are $118,430?

3. Brian Hickman is an executive with Westco Distributors. His gross earnings are $9,800 per month.

   a. What are the withholdings for social security and Medicare for Brian in his January paycheck?

   b. In what month will Brian's salary reach the social security wage base limit?

   c. What are the social security and Medicare tax withholdings for Brian in the month named in part b?

4. Kristy Dunaway has biweekly gross earnings of $1,750. What are her total social security and Medicare tax withholdings for a whole year?

As payroll manager for Freeport Enterprises, it is your task to calculate the monthly social security and Medicare withholdings for the following employees.

Employee	Year-to-Date Earnings	Current Month	Social Security	Medicare
5. Perez, J.	$23,446	$3,422	$212.16	$49.62
6. Graham, C.	$14,800	$1,540	_____	_____
7. Jagger, R.	$105,200	$4,700	_____	_____
8. Andretti, K.	$145,000	$12,450	_____	_____

Use the percentage method of income tax calculation to complete the following payroll roster.

Employee	Marital Status	Withholding Allowances	Pay Period	Gross Earnings	Income Tax Withholding
9. Randolph, B.	M	2	Weekly	$594	$28.40
10. White, W.	S	0	Semimonthly	$1,227	_____
11. Milian, B.	S	1	Monthly	$4,150	_____
12. Farley, D.	M	4	Biweekly	$1,849	_____

Use the combined wage bracket tables, Exhibits 9-3 and 9-4, to solve Exercises 13–19.

13. How much combined tax should be withheld from the paycheck of a married employee earning $1,075 per week and claiming four withholding allowances?

14. How much combined tax should be withheld from the paycheck of a single employee earning $3,185 per month and claiming zero withholding allowances?

15. Jeremy Dunn is single, claims two withholding allowances, and earns $4,025 per month. Calculate the amount of Jeremy's paycheck after his employer withholds social security, Medicare, and federal income tax.

Employee	Marital Status	Withholding Allowances	Pay Period	Gross Earnings	Combined Withholding
16. Alton, A.	S	3	Monthly	$4,633	$879.43
17. Emerson, P.	M	5	Weekly	$937	_____
18. Reese, S.	M	4	Weekly	$1,172	_____
19. Benson, K.	S	1	Monthly	$3,128	_____

BUSINESS DECISION: TAKE HOME PAY

20. You are the payroll manager for the Canyon Ridge Resort. Mark Kelsch, the marketing director, earns a salary of $43,200 per year, payable monthly. He is married and claims four withholding allowances. His social security number is 444-44-4444.

    In addition to federal income tax, social security, and Medicare, Mark pays 2.3% state income tax, $\frac{1}{2}$% for state disability insurance (both based on gross earnings), $23.74 for term life insurance, $122.14 to the credit union, and $40 to the United Way.

    Fill out the following payroll voucher for Mark for the month of April.

Canyon Ridge Resort
Payroll Voucher

Employee: _____   Tax Filing Status: _____

SSN: _____   Withholding Allowances: ___

Full-time Pay Period From _____ To _____

Primary Withholdings: Additional Withholdings:

Federal income tax	_____
Social security	_____
Medicare	_____
State income tax	_____
State disability	_____

Additional Withholdings:
_____
_____
_____

Gross Earnings: _____

– Total withholdings: _____

NET PAY _____

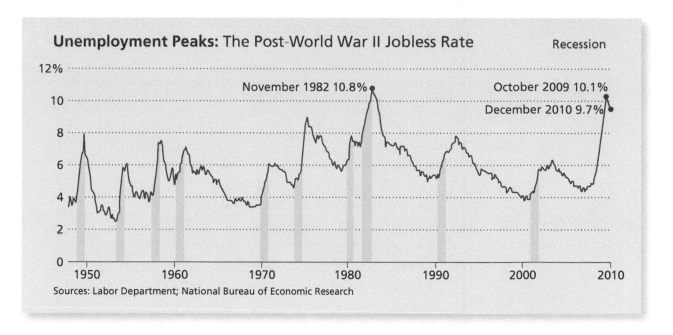

EMPLOYER'S PAYROLL EXPENSES AND SELF-EMPLOYED PERSON'S TAX RESPONSIBILITY

9

SECTION III

To this point, we have discussed payroll deductions from the employee's point of view. Now let's take a look at the payroll expenses of the employer. According to the Fair Labor Standards Act, employers are required to maintain complete and up-to-date earnings records for each employee.

Employers are responsible for the payment of four payroll taxes: social security, Medicare, state unemployment tax (SUTA), and federal unemployment tax (FUTA). In addition, most employers are responsible for a variety of **fringe benefits** that are offered to their employees. These are benefits over and above an employee's normal earnings and can be a significant expense to the employer. Some typical examples are retirement plans, stock option plans, holiday leave, sick days, health and dental insurance, and tuition reimbursement. This section deals with the calculation of these employer taxes as well as the tax responsibility of self-employed persons.

fringe benefits Employer-provided benefits and service packages over and above an employee's paycheck, such as pension funds, paid vacations, sick leave, and health insurance.

COMPUTING FICA TAX FOR EMPLOYERS AND SELF-EMPLOYMENT TAX FOR SELF-EMPLOYED PERSONS

9-8

FICA TAX FOR EMPLOYERS

Employers are required to *match* all FICA tax payments, both social security and Medicare, made by each employee. For example, if a company withheld a total of $23,000 in FICA taxes from its employee paychecks this month, the company would be responsible for a matching share of $23,000.

EXAMPLE13   COMPUTING FICA TAX FOR EMPLOYEES AND THE EMPLOYER

Spectrum Engineering has 25 employees, each with gross earnings of $250 per week.

a. What are the total FICA (social security and Medicare) taxes that should be withheld from each employee's weekly paycheck?

b. At the end of the first quarter (13 weeks), what were the accumulated totals of the employee's share and the matching taxes for FICA that Spectrum had sent to the IRS?

► SOLUTIONSTRATEGY

To solve for the total FICA tax due quarterly from the employees and the employer, calculate the tax due per employee per week, multiply by 25 to find the total weekly FICA for all employees, and multiply by 13 weeks to find the total quarterly amount withheld from all employees. The employer's share will be an equal amount.

a. Social security tax = Gross earnings × 6.2% = 250 × .062 = $15.50
    Medicare tax = Gross earnings × 1.45% = 250 × .0145 = $3.63
    Total FICA tax per employee per week = 15.50 + 3.63 = $19.13

b. Total FICA tax per week = FICA tax per employee × 25 employees
    Total FICA tax per week = 19.13 × 25 = $478.25

    Total FICA tax first quarter = Total FICA tax per week × 13 weeks
    Total FICA tax first quarter = 478.25 × 13 = 6,217.25

    Total FICA tax first quarter—Employee's share = $6,217.25
    Total FICA tax first quarter—Employer's share = $6,217.25

► TRYITEXERCISE 13

Big Pine Tree Service has 18 employees, 12 with gross earnings of $350 per week and 6 with gross earnings of $425 per week. What are the employee's share and the employer's share of the social security and Medicare tax for the first quarter of the year?

CHECK YOUR ANSWERS WITH THE SOLUTIONS ON PAGE 296.

SELF-EMPLOYMENT TAX

The self-employment tax, officially known as the Self-Employment Contributions Act (SECA) tax, is the self-employed person's version of the FICA tax. It is due on the net earnings from self-employment.

Self-employed persons are responsible for social security and Medicare taxes at twice the rate deducted for employees. Technically, they are the employee and the employer and therefore must pay both shares. For a self-employed person, the social security and Medicare tax rates are twice the normal rates, as follows:

	Tax Rate	Wage Base
Social Security	12.4% (6.2% × 2)	$113,700
Medicare	2.9% (1.45% × 2)	No limit

EXAMPLE 14 — CALCULATING SELF-EMPLOYMENT TAX

What are the social security and Medicare taxes of a self-employed landscaper with net earnings of $43,800 per year?

► SOLUTIONSTRATEGY

To find the amount of self-employment tax due, we apply the self-employed tax rates, 12.4% for social security and 2.9% for Medicare, to the net earnings.

Social security tax = Net earnings × Tax rate
Social security tax = 43,800 × .124 = $5,431.20
Medicare tax = Net earnings × Tax rate
Medicare tax = 43,800 × .029 = $1,270.20

▶TRYITEXERCISE 14

Les Roberts, a self-employed commercial artist, had total net earnings of $60,000 last year. What was the amount of the social security and Medicare taxes Les was required to send the IRS last year?

CHECK YOUR ANSWERS WITH THE SOLUTIONS ON PAGE 296.

COMPUTING THE AMOUNT OF STATE UNEMPLOYMENT TAX (SUTA) AND FEDERAL UNEMPLOYMENT TAX (FUTA)

9-9

The **Federal Unemployment Tax Act (FUTA)**, together with state unemployment systems, provides for payments of unemployment compensation to workers who have lost their jobs. Most employers are responsible for both a federal and a state unemployment tax.

Generally, an employer can take a credit against the FUTA tax for amounts paid into state unemployment funds. These state taxes are commonly known as the **State Unemployment Tax Act (SUTA)**. This credit cannot be more than 5.4% of the first $7,000 of employees' taxable wages.

SUTA tax rates vary from state to state according to the employment record of the company. These merit-rating systems found in many states provide significant SUTA tax savings to companies with good employment records.

The FUTA may change from year to year. In this chapter we'll use a FUTA tax rate of .6%. (This assumes an unreduced FUTA tax of 6% for the first $7,000 of wages paid to each employee during the year reduced by a 5.4% SUTA credit. That is, 6% − 5.4% = .6% FUTA tax rate.)

Federal Unemployment Tax Act (FUTA) A federal tax that is paid by employers for each employee to provide unemployment compensation to workers who have lost their jobs.

State Unemployment Tax Act (SUTA) A state tax that is paid by employers for each employee to provide unemployment compensation to workers who have lost their jobs.

EXAMPLE15 CALCULATING SUTA AND FUTA TAXES

Uniphase Industries, Inc., had a total payroll of $50,000 last month. Uniphase pays a SUTA tax rate of 5.4% and a FUTA rate of 6.0% less the SUTA credit. If none of the employees had reached the $7,000 wage base, what is the amount of SUTA and FUTA tax the company must pay?

▶SOLUTIONSTRATEGY

To calculate the SUTA and FUTA taxes, apply the appropriate tax rates to the gross earnings subject to the tax, in this case, all the gross earnings.

$$\text{SUTA tax} = \text{Gross earnings} \times 5.4\%$$
$$\text{SUTA tax} = 50,000 \times .054 = \underline{\$2,700}$$

The FUTA tax rate will be .6%. Remember, it is actually 6.0% less the 5.4% credit.

$$\text{FUTA tax} = \text{Gross earnings} \times .6\%$$
$$\text{FUTA tax} = 50,000 \times .006 = \underline{\$300}$$

▶TRYITEXERCISE 15

Sunshine Catering had a total payroll of $10,000 last month. Sunshine pays a SUTA tax rate of 5.4% and a FUTA rate of 6.0% less the SUTA credit. If none of the employees had reached the $7,000 wage base, what is the amount of SUTA and FUTA tax the company must pay?

CHECK YOUR ANSWERS WITH THE SOLUTIONS ON PAGE 296.

9-10 CALCULATING EMPLOYER'S FRINGE BENEFIT EXPENSES

In addition to compensating employees with a paycheck, most companies today offer employee fringe benefit and services packages. These packages include a wide variety of benefits such as pension plans, paid vacations and sick leave, day-care centers, tuition assistance, and health insurance. Corporate executives may receive benefits such as company cars, first-class airline travel, and country club memberships. At the executive level of business, these benefits are known as **perquisites**, or **perks**.

Over the past decade, employee benefits have become increasingly important to workers. They have grown in size to the point where today total benefits may cost a company as much as 40% to 50% of payroll. Frequently, employees are given a *menu* of fringe benefits from which to choose up to a specified dollar amount. These plans are known as **cafeteria style**, or **flexible benefit programs**.

perquisites, or **perks** Executive-level fringe benefits such as first-class airline travel, company cars, and country club membership.

cafeteria style, or **flexible benefit programs** A plan whereby employees are given a menu of fringe benefits from which to choose up to a specified dollar amount.

IN THE Business World

Although paid vacations and health insurance are still the most popular among company-sponsored benefits, there is a trend today toward more "work-life initiatives." These are benefits that help employees balance their professional and personal lives, such as child-care assistance and flexible work hours.

STEPS TO CALCULATE EMPLOYER'S FRINGE BENEFITS EXPENSE

STEP 1. If the fringe benefit is a percent of gross payroll, multiply that percent by the amount of the gross payroll. If the fringe benefit is a dollar amount per employee, multiply that amount by the number of employees.

STEP 2. Find the total fringe benefits by adding all the individual fringe benefit amounts.

STEP 3. Calculate the fringe benefit percent by using the percentage formula Rate = Portion ÷ Base with total fringe benefits as the portion and gross payroll as the base (remember to convert your answer to a percent).

$$\text{Fringe benefit percent} = \frac{\text{Total fringe benefits}}{\text{Gross payroll}}$$

EXAMPLE16 CALCULATING FRINGE BENEFITS

In addition to its gross payroll of $150,000 per month, Premier Distributors, Inc., with 75 employees, pays 7% of payroll to a retirement fund, 9% for health insurance, and $25 per employee for a stock purchase plan.

a. What are the company's monthly fringe benefit expenses?

b. What percent of payroll does this represent?

▶SOLUTIONSTRATEGY

a. To solve for monthly fringe benefits, compute the amount of each benefit and add them to find the total.

Retirement fund expense = Gross payroll × 7%
Retirement fund expense = 150,000 × .07 = $10,500

Health insurance expense = Gross payroll × 9%
Health insurance expense = 150,000 × .09 = $13,500

Stock plan expense = Number of employees × $25
Stock plan expense = 75 × 25 = $1,875

Total fringe benefits = Retirement + Health + Stock
Total fringe benefits = 10,500 + 13,500 + 1,875 = $25,875

b. $\text{Fringe benefit percent} = \dfrac{\text{Total fringe benefits}}{\text{Gross payroll}} = \dfrac{25,875}{150,000} = .1725 = 17.25\%$

Paid vacation time is one of the many fringe benefits offered by employers today.

Photo by Robert Brechner

► TRYITEXERCISE 16

Dynamo Productions employs 250 workers with a gross payroll of $123,400 per week. Fringe benefits are 5% of gross payroll for sick days and holiday leave, 8% for health insurance, and $12.40 per employee for dental insurance.

a. What is the total weekly cost of fringe benefits for Dynamo?

b. What percent of payroll does this represent?

c. What is the cost of these fringe benefits to the company for a year?

CHECK YOUR ANSWERS WITH THE SOLUTIONS ON PAGE 296.

CALCULATING QUARTERLY ESTIMATED TAX FOR SELF-EMPLOYED PERSONS

9-11

By IRS rules, you must pay self-employment tax if you had net earnings of $400 or more as a self-employed person. This is income that is not subject to withholding tax. Quarterly estimated tax is the method used to pay tax on these earnings. You may pay all of your estimated tax by April or in four equal amounts: in April, June, September, and January of the following year.

To calculate the quarterly estimated tax of a self-employed person, we divide the total of social security, Medicare, and income tax by 4. (There are 4 quarters in a year.) Internal Revenue Service form 1040 ES, Quarterly Estimated Tax Payment Voucher, Exhibit 9-5, is used to file this tax with the IRS each quarter.

$$\text{Quarterly estimated tax} = \frac{\text{Social security} + \text{Medicare} + \text{Income tax}}{4}$$

EXHIBIT 9-5 Quarterly Estimated Tax Payment Voucher

Form **1040-ES**
Department of the Treasury
Internal Revenue Service

20XX Payment Voucher **4**

OMB No. 1545-0087

File only if you are making a payment of estimated tax by check or money order. Mail this voucher with your check or money order payable to the **"United States Treasury."** Write your social security number and "20XX Form 1040-ES" on your check or money order. Do not send cash. Enclose, but do not staple or attach, your payment with this voucher.

Calendar year—Due Jan. 15,

Amount of estimated tax you are paying by check or money order. $

Type or print

Your first name and initial	Your last name	Your social security number

If joint payment, complete for spouse

Spouse's first name and initial	Spouse's last name	Spouse's social security number

Address (number, street, and apt. no.)

City, state, and ZIP code (If a foreign address, enter city, province or state, postal code, and country.)

For Privacy Act and Paperwork Reduction Act Notice, see instructions on page 5.
Page 6

Dollars AND Sense

EXAMPLE17 — CALCULATING QUARTERLY ESTIMATED TAX FOR SELF-EMPLOYED PERSONS

Ben Qualls is a self-employed marketing consultant. His estimated annual earnings this year are $118,000. His social security tax rate is 12.4% up to the wage base, Medicare is 2.9%, and his estimated federal income tax rate is 18%. How much estimated tax must he send to the IRS each quarter?

▶ SOLUTIONSTRATEGY

Note that Ben's salary is above the social security wage base limit.

$$\text{Social security} = 113{,}700 \times .124 = \$14{,}098.80$$
$$\text{Medicare} = 118{,}000 \times .029 = \$3{,}422$$
$$\text{Income tax} = 118{,}000 \times .18 = \$21{,}240$$

$$\text{Quarterly estimated tax} = \frac{\text{Social security} + \text{Medicare} + \text{Income tax}}{4}$$

$$\text{Quarterly estimated tax} = \frac{14{,}098.80 + 3{,}422.00 + 21{,}240.00}{4} = \frac{38{,}760.80}{4} = \$9{,}690.20$$

▶ TRYITEXERCISE 17

Howard Lockwood is a self-employed freelance editor and project director for a large publishing company. His annual salary this year is estimated to be $120,000 with a federal income tax rate of 20%. What is the amount of estimated tax Howard must send to the IRS each quarter?

CHECK YOUR ANSWER WITH THE SOLUTION ON PAGE 296.

SECTION III   9   REVIEW EXERCISES

1. Westside Auto Supply has 8 delivery truck drivers, each with gross earnings of $570 per week.

   a. What are the total social security and Medicare taxes that should be withheld from these employees' paychecks each week?

   $570 \times 8 = \$4{,}560$ Gross earnings per week
   $4{,}560 \times .062 = \$282.72$ Total social security
   $4{,}560 \times .0145 = \$66.12$ Total Medicare

   b. What is the employer's share of these taxes for these employees for the first quarter of the year?

   $282.72 \times 13 = \$3{,}675.36$ Social security for the first quarter
   $66.12 \times 13 = \$859.56$ Medicare for the first quarter

2. Fandango Furniture Manufacturing, Inc., has 40 employees on the assembly line, each with gross earnings of $325 per week.

   a. What are the total social security and Medicare taxes that should be withheld from the employees' paychecks each week?

   b. What is the employer's share of these taxes for the first quarter of the year for these employees?

3. Arrow Asphalt & Paving Company has 24 employees, 15 with gross earnings of $345 per week and nine with gross earnings of $385 per week. What is the total social security and Medicare tax the company must send to the Internal Revenue Service for the first quarter of the year?

4. What are the social security and Medicare taxes due on gross earnings of $53,200 per year for Tricia Marvel, a self-employed commercial artist?

   53,200 × .124 = $6,596.80 Social security
   53,200 × .029 = $1,542.80 Medicare

5. What are the social security and Medicare taxes due on gross earnings of $42,600 per year for a self-employed person?

6. Lee Sutherlin is a self-employed electrical consultant. He estimates his annual net earnings at $38,700. How much social security and Medicare must he pay this year?

7. Barry Michaels earns $36,500 per year as the housewares manager at the Home Design Center.

   a. If the SUTA tax rate is 5.4% of the first $7,000 earned each year, how much SUTA tax must the company pay each year for Barry?

      7,000 × .054 = $378 SUTA annually

   b. If the FUTA tax rate is 6.0% of the first $7,000 earned in a year minus the SUTA tax paid, how much FUTA tax must the company pay each year for Barry?

      7,000 × .006 = $42 FUTA annually

8. Dave O'Bannon earns $41,450 annually as a line supervisor for Redwood Manufacturers.

   a. If the SUTA tax rate is 5.4% of the first $7,000 earned in a year, how much SUTA tax must Redwood pay each year for Dave?

   b. If the FUTA tax rate is 6.0% of the first $7,000 earned in a year minus the SUTA tax paid, how much FUTA tax must the company pay each year for Dave?

9. Tanya Willis worked part time last year as a cashier in a Safeway Supermarket. Her total gross earnings were $6,440.

   a. How much SUTA tax must the supermarket pay to the state for Tanya?

   b. How much FUTA tax must be paid for her?

10. Amazon Appliance Company has three installers. Larry earns $355 per week, Curly earns $460 per week, and Moe earns $585 per week. The company's SUTA rate is 5.4%, and the FUTA rate is 6.0% minus the SUTA. As usual, these taxes are paid on the first $7,000 of each employee's earnings.

   a. How much SUTA and FUTA tax does Amazon owe for the first quarter of the year?

   b. How much SUTA and FUTA tax does Amazon owe for the second quarter of the year?

11. Jiffy Janitorial Service employs 48 workers and has a gross payroll of $25,200 per week. Fringe benefits are 6.4% for sick days and holiday leave, 5.8% for health and hospital insurance, and $14.50 per employee per week for uniform allowance.

   a. What is the total weekly cost of fringe benefits for Jiffy?

$$25,200 \times .064 = \$1,612.80$$
$$25,200 \times .058 = 1,461.60$$
$$48 \times 14.50 = 696.00$$
$$\underline{\$3,770.40}$$

   b. What percent of payroll does this represent?

$$R = \frac{P}{B} = \frac{3,770.40}{25,200.00} = .1496 = \underline{\underline{15\%}}$$

   c. What is Jiffy's annual cost of fringe benefits?

$$3,770.40 \times 52 = \underline{\$196,060.80} \text{ Annual cost of fringe benefits}$$

12. North Beach Limousine Service employs 166 workers and has a gross payroll of $154,330 per week. Fringe benefits are $4\frac{1}{2}\%$ of gross payroll for sick days and maternity leave, 7.4% for health insurance, 3.1% for the retirement fund, and $26.70 per employee per week for a stock purchase plan.

   a. What is the total weekly cost of fringe benefits for the company?

   b. What percent of payroll does this represent? Round to the nearest tenth of a percent.

   c. What is the company's annual cost of fringe benefits?

13. Marc Batchelor, a self-employed sales consultant, has estimated annual earnings of $300,000 this year. His social security tax rate is 12.4% up to the wage base, Medicare is 2.9%, and his federal income tax rate is 24%.

   a. How much estimated tax must Marc send to the IRS each quarter?

   b. What form should he use?

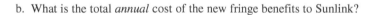

BUSINESS DECISION: NEW FRINGE BENEFITS

14. You are the Human Resource Manager for Sunlink International, a cellular phone company with 800 employees. Top management has asked you to implement three additional fringe benefits that were negotiated with employee representatives and agreed upon by a majority of the employees. These include group term life insurance, a group legal services plan, and a wellness center.

   The life insurance is estimated to cost $260 per employee per quarter. The legal plan will cost $156 semiannually per employee. The company will contribute 40% to the life insurance premium and 75% to the cost of the legal services plan. The employees will pay the balance through payroll deductions from their biweekly paychecks. In addition, they will be charged $\frac{1}{4}$% of their gross earnings per paycheck for maintaining the wellness center. The company will pay the initial cost of $500,000 to build the center. This expense will be spread over 5 years.

   a. What total amount should be deducted *per paycheck* for these new fringe benefits for an employee earning $41,600 per year?

   b. What is the total *annual* cost of the new fringe benefits to Sunlink?

mocdboard/Alamy

Human Resource managers handle or oversee all aspects of human resources work. Typical areas of responsibility include unemployment compensation, fringe benefits, training, and employee relations. They held about 904,900 jobs in 2008, with median annual earnings of $96,130. The middle 50% earned between $73,480 and $126,050.

CHAPTER FORMULAS

Hourly Wages

Regular pay = Hourly rate × Regular hours worked

Overtime pay = Hourly rate × Overtime factor × Overtime hours worked

Total gross pay = Regular pay + Overtime pay

Piecework

Total gross pay = Output quantity × Rate per unit

Commission

Total gross pay = Total sales × Commission rate

Payroll Deductions

Total deductions = Social security + Medicare + Income tax + Voluntary deductions

Net pay = Gross pay − Total deductions

Fringe Benefits

$$\text{Fringe benefit percent} = \frac{\text{Total fringe benefits}}{\text{Gross payroll}}$$

Quarterly Estimated Tax

$$\text{Quarterly estimated tax} = \frac{\text{Social security} + \text{Medicare} + \text{Income tax}}{4}$$

CHAPTER SUMMARY

Section I: Employee's Gross Earnings and Incentive Pay Plans

Topic	Important Concepts	Illustrative Examples
Prorating Annual Salary to Various Pay Periods **Performance Objective 9-1, Page 263**	Salaried employees are most commonly paid based on one of the following pay schedules: *Weekly:* 52 paychecks per year Annual salary ÷ 52 *Biweekly:* 26 paychecks per year Annual salary ÷ 26 *Semimonthly:* 24 paychecks per year Annual salary ÷ 24 *Monthly:* 12 paychecks per year Annual salary ÷ 12	What are the gross earnings of an employee with an annual salary of $40,000 based on weekly, biweekly, semimonthly, and monthly pay schedules? $\text{Weekly} = \dfrac{40,000}{52} = \underline{\$769.233}$ $\text{Biweekly} = \dfrac{40,000}{26} = \underline{\$1,538.46}$ $\text{Semimonthly} = \dfrac{40,000}{24} = \underline{\$1,666.67}$ $\text{Monthly} = \dfrac{40,000}{12} = \underline{\$3,333.33}$
Calculating Gross Pay by Regular Hourly Wages and Overtime **Performance Objective 9-2, Page 264**	An hourly wage is the amount an employee is paid for each hour worked. 　　Regular time specifies that a standard work week is 40 hours. 　　Overtime amounting to at least time-and-a-half must be paid for all hours over 40. Some employers pay double time for weekend, holiday, and midnight shifts. Regular pay = Hourly rate × Hours worked Overtime pay = Hourly rate × Overtime factor × Hours worked Total gross pay = Regular pay + Overtime pay	Sami Brady earns $9.50 per hour as a supervisor in a plant. If her overtime rate is time-and-a-half and holidays are double time, what is Sami's total gross pay for working 49 hours last week, including 4 holiday hours? Regular pay = 9.50 × 40 = $\underline{\$380.00}$ Time-and-a-half pay = 9.50 × 1.5 × 5 = $\underline{\$71.25}$ Double-time pay = 9.50 × 2 × 4 = $\underline{\$76.00}$ Total gross pay = 380.00 + 71.25 + 76.00 = $\underline{\$527.25}$

Section I (continued)

Topic	Important Concepts	Illustrative Examples
Calculating Gross Pay by Straight and Differential Piecework Schedules **Performance Objective 9-3, Page 265**	A piecework pay rate schedule is based on production output, not time. Straight piecework pays the worker a certain amount of pay per unit regardless of quantity. In differential piecework, the rate per unit increases as output quantity goes up. Total gross pay = Output quantity × Rate per unit	Chemical Labs pays its workers $2.50 per unit of production. What is the gross pay of a worker producing 233 units? Gross pay = 233 × 2.50 = <u>$582.50</u> Fortune Manufacturing pays its production workers $0.54 per unit up to 5,000 units and $0.67 per unit above 5,000 units. What is the gross pay of an employee who produces 6,500 units? $5{,}000 \times .54 = 2{,}700$ $1{,}500 \times .67 = 1{,}005$ Total gross pay <u>$3,705</u>
Calculating Gross Pay by Straight and Incremental Commission **Performance Objective 9-4, Page 267**	Commission is a method of compensation primarily used to pay employees who sell goods and services. Straight commission is based on a single specified percentage of the sales volume attained. Incremental commission, like differential piecework, is when various levels of sales earn increasing rates of commission. Total gross pay = Total sales × Commission rate	Horizon Products pays 4% straight commission on all sales. What is the gross pay of an employee who sells $135,000? Gross pay = 135,000 × .04 = <u>$5,400</u> Discovery Imports pays incremental commissions of 3.5% on sales up to $100,000 and 4.5% on all sales greater than $100,000. What is the gross pay of an employee selling $164,000? $100{,}000 \times .035 = 3{,}500$ $64{,}000 \times .045 = 2{,}880$ Gross pay <u>$6,380</u>
Calculating Gross Pay by Salary Plus Commission **Performance Objective 9-4, Page 269**	Salary plus commission is a pay schedule whereby the employee receives a guaranteed salary in addition to a commission on sales over a specified amount.	An employee is paid a salary of $350 per week plus a 2% commission on sales greater than $8,000. If he sold $13,400 last week, how much did he earn? $350 + 2\%(13{,}400 - 8{,}000)$ $350 + .02 \times 5{,}400$ $350 + 108 = $ <u>$458</u>
Calculating Gross Pay with Drawing Accounts **Performance Objective 9-4, Page 269**	A drawing account, or draw against commission, is a commission paid in advance of sales and later deducted from the commission earned.	Steve Korb sells for a company that pays $6\frac{1}{2}\%$ commission with a $600 per month drawing account. If Steve takes the draw and then sells $16,400 in goods, how much commission is he owed? $(16{,}400 \times .065) - 600$ $1{,}066 - 600 = $ <u>$466</u>

Section II: Employee's Payroll Deductions

Topic	Important Concepts	Illustrative Examples
Computing FICA Taxes, Both Social Security and Medicare **Performance Objective 9-5, Page 273**	FICA taxes are divided into two categories: social security and Medicare. When employees reach the wage base for the year, they are no longer subject to the tax. <table><tr><td></td><td>Tax Rate</td><td>Wage Base</td></tr><tr><td>Social Security</td><td>6.2%</td><td>$113,700</td></tr><tr><td>Medicare</td><td>1.45%</td><td>no limit</td></tr></table>	What are the FICA tax withholdings for social security and Medicare for an employee with gross earnings of $760 per week? Social security = $760 × 6.2% = <u>$47.12</u> Medicare = $760 × 1.45% = <u>$11.02</u>
Calculating Federal Income Tax Using Percentage Method (continued)	1. Multiply one withholding allowance, in Exhibit 9-1, by the number of allowances the employee claims.	Michelle Wolf is single, earns $1,800 per week as a loan officer for Bank of America, and claims three withholding allowances.

Section II (continued)

Topic	Important Concepts	Illustrative Examples
Performance Objective 9-6, Page 275	2. Subtract that amount from the employee's gross earnings to find the income subject to income tax. 3. Determine the amount of tax withheld from the appropriate section of Exhibit 9-2.	Calculate the amount of federal income tax withheld from Michelle's weekly paycheck. From Exhibit 9-1: $\quad 75.00 \times 3 = \$225.00$ Taxable income = $\quad 1,800 - 225.00 = \$1,575.00$ From Exhibit 9-2: Withholding tax = $\quad\quad 95.95 + .25(1,575.00 - 739.00)$ $\quad\quad 95.95 + .25(836.00)$ $\quad\quad 95.95 + 209.00 = \underline{\$304.95}$
Determining an Employee's Total Withholding for Federal Income Tax, Social Security, and Medicare Using the Combined Wage Bracket Tables **Performance Objective 9-7, Page 278**	1. Based on marital status and payroll period, choose either Exhibit 9-3 or 9-4. 2. Scan down the left-hand columns until you find the bracket containing the gross pay of the employee. 3. Scan across the row of that wage bracket to the intersection of that employee's "withholding allowances claimed" column. 4. The number in that column on the wage bracket row is the amount of combined withholding tax.	What amount of combined tax should be withheld from the monthly paycheck of a single employee claiming two withholding allowances and earning $3,495 per month? Use Exhibit 9-4. Scan down the wage brackets to $3,480 − $3,520. Scan across to "2" withholding allowances to find the tax, $630.75.

Section III: Employer's Payroll Expenses and Self-Employed Person's Tax Responsibility

Topic	Important Concepts	Illustrative Examples
Computing FICA Tax for Employers **Performance Objective 9-8, Page 283**	Employers are required to match all FICA tax payments made by each employee.	Last month Midland Services withheld a total of $3,400 in FICA taxes from employee paychecks. What is the company's FICA liability? The company is responsible for a matching amount withheld from the employees, $3,400.
Computing Self-Employment Tax **Performance Objective 9-8, Page 284**	Self-employed persons are responsible for social security and Medicare taxes at twice the rate deducted for employees. Technically, they are the employee and the employer; therefore, they must pay both shares, as follows: *Social Security* $\quad$ 12.4% (6.2% × 2), wage base $113,700 *Medicare* $\quad$ 2.9% (1.45% × 2), no limit	What are the social security and Medicare taxes due on gross earnings of $4,260 per month for a self-employed person? *Social security* Gross earnings × 12.4% = $\quad\quad 4,260 \times .124 \quad = \underline{\$528.24}$ *Medicare* Gross earnings × 2.9% = $\quad\quad 4,260 \times .029 \quad = \underline{123.54}$
Computing the Amount of State Unemployment Tax (SUTA) and Federal Unemployment Tax (FUTA) **Performance Objective 9-9, Page 285**	SUTA and FUTA taxes provide for unemployment compensation to workers who have lost their jobs. These taxes are paid by the employer. The SUTA tax rate is 5.4% of the first $7,000 of earnings per year by each employee. The FUTA tax rate used in this chapter is 6.0% of the first $7,000 minus the SUTA tax paid (6.0% − 5.4% = 0.6%).	Trans Lux, Inc., had a total payroll of $40,000 last month. If none of the employees has reached the $7,000 wage base, what is the amount of SUTA and FUTA tax due? SUTA = 40,000 × 5.4% = $\underline{\$2,160}$ FUTA = 40,000 × .6% = $\underline{\$240}$

Section III (continued)

Topic	Important Concepts	Illustrative Examples
Calculating Employer's Fringe Benefit Expenses **Performance Objective 9-10, Page 286**	In addition to compensating employees with a paycheck, most companies offer benefit packages that may include pensions, paid sick days, tuition assistance, and health insurance. Fringe benefits represent a significant expense to employers. $$\text{Fringe benefit percent} = \frac{\text{Total fringe benefits}}{\text{Gross payroll}}$$	Linear Industries employs 48 workers and has a monthly gross payroll of $120,000. In addition, the company pays 6.8% to a pension fund, 8.7% for health insurance, and $30 per employee for a stock purchase plan. What are Linear's monthly fringe benefit expenses? What percent of payroll does this represent? $120,000 \times 6.8\% = 8,160$ $120,000 \times 8.7\% = 10,440$ $48 \times \$30 = \underline{+\ 1,440}$ Total fringe benefits $\underline{\$20,040}$ $$\text{Fringe benefit \%} = \frac{20,040}{120,000} = \underline{16.7\%}$$
Calculating Quarterly Estimated Tax for Self-Employed Persons **Performance Objective 9-11, Page 287**	Each quarter self-employed persons must send to the IRS Form 1040-ES along with a tax payment for social security, Medicare, and income tax. Quarterly estimated tax $$= \frac{\text{Social security} + \text{Medicare} + \text{Income tax}}{4}$$	Amanda Turner is a self-employed decorator. She estimates her annual net earnings at $44,000 for the year. Her income tax rate is 10%. What is the amount of her quarterly estimated tax? $44,000 \times .124 = \$5,456$ Social security $44,000 \times .029 = \$1,276$ Medicare $44,000 \times .10 = \$4,400$ Income tax $$\text{Quarterly estimated tax} = \frac{5,456 + 1,276 + 4,400}{4}$$ $$= \frac{11,132}{4} = \underline{2,783}$$

TRY IT: EXERCISE SOLUTIONS FOR CHAPTER 9

1. Weekly pay $= \dfrac{\text{Annual salary}}{50} = \dfrac{43,500}{52} = \underline{\$836.54}$

Biweekly pay $= \dfrac{\text{Annual salary}}{26} = \dfrac{43,500}{26} = \underline{\$1,673.08}$

Semimonthly pay $= \dfrac{\text{Annual salary}}{24} = \dfrac{43,500}{24} = \underline{1,812.50}$

Monthly pay $= \dfrac{\text{Annual salary}}{12} = \dfrac{43,500}{12} = \underline{\$3,625.00}$

2. Regular pay = Hourly rate × Regular hours worked
Regular pay = 10.50 × 40 = $\underline{\$420}$

Time-and-a-half pay
   = Hourly rate × Overtime factor × Hours worked
Time-and-a-half pay = 10.50 × 1.5 × 5 = $\underline{\$78.75}$

Double time pay
   = Hourly rate × Overtime factor × Hours worked
Double time pay = 10.50 × 2 × 4 = $\underline{\$84}$

Total gross pay = Regular pay + Overtime pay
Total gross pay = 420.00 + 78.75 + 84.00 = $\underline{\$582.75}$

3. Total gross pay = Output quantity × Rate per unit
Total gross pay = 950 × .41 = $\underline{\$389.50}$

4. Level pay = Output rate per piece
Gomez: 300 × .68 = $204.00
          200 × .79 =   158.00
            15 × .86 = + 12.90
                    $\underline{\$374.90}$ Total gross pay

Clifford: 199 × .68 = $\underline{\$135.32}$ Total gross pay

Maken: 300 × .68 = $204.00
          148 × .79 = + 116.92
                    $\underline{\$320.92}$ Total gross pay

Nathan: 300 × .68 = $204.00
          200 × .79 =   158.00
          250 × .86 =   215.00
            54 × .94 = + 50.76
                    $\underline{\$627.76}$ Total gross pay

5. Total gross pay = Total sales × Commission rate
Total gross pay = 233,760 × .024 = $\underline{\$5,610.24}$

6. Level pay = Sales per level × Commission rate
Level pay = 100,000 × .017 = $1,700
          84,600 × .025 = + 2,115
                            $\underline{\$3,815}$

7. Commission = Commission rate × Sales subject to commission
Commission = 4%(45,000 − 20,000)
Commission = .04 × 25,000 = $1,000

Total gross pay = Salary + Commission
Total gross pay = 1,400 + 1,000 = $\underline{\$2,400}$

8. Commission = Total sales × Commission rate
Commission = 120,000 × 3.5% = $4,200

Commission owed = Commission − Amount of draw
Commission owed = 4,200 − 2,000 = $\underline{\$2,200}$

GO ONLINE FOR MORE ACTIVITIES www.cengagebrain.com

9. Social security tax = Gross earnings × 6.2%
   Social security tax = 5,000 × .062 = $310

   Medicare tax = Gross earnings × 1.45%
   Medicare tax = 5,000 × .0145 = $72.50

10. Earnings subject to tax = Wage base − Year-to-date earnings
    Earnings subject to tax = 113,700 − 109,200 = $4,500

    Social security tax = Earnings subject to tax × 6.2%
    Social security tax = 4,500 × .062 = $279.00

11. From Exhibit 9-1
    Withholding allowance = 1 allowance × Exemptions
    Withholding allowance = $325.00 × 5 = $1,625

    Taxable income = Gross pay − Withholding allowance
    Taxable income = 5,670 − 1,625 = $4,045.00

    From Exhibit 9-2, Table 4(b):
    Category $2,179 to $6,733

    Withholding Tax = 148.70 + 15% of amount greater than $2,179
    Withholding Tax = 148.70 + .15(4,045 − 2,179)
    Withholding Tax = 148.70 + .15(1,866)
    Withholding Tax = 148.70 + 279.90 = $428.60

12. From Exhibit 9-3
    $835 Weekly, married, 2 allowances = $125.88

13. *12 employees @ $350*

    Social security = 350 × .062 = 21.70
    Medicare = 350 × .0145 = 5.08

    Total FICA per employee = 21.70 + 5.08 = $26.78
    Total FICA per week = 26.78 × 12 employees = $321.36
    Total FICA per quarter = 321.36 × 13 weeks = $4,177.68

    6 employees @ $425

    Social security = 425 × .062 = 26.35
    Medicare = 425 × .0145 = 6.16

    Total FICA per employee = 26.35 + 6.16 = $32.51
    Total FICA per week = 32.51 × 6 employees = $195.06
    Total FICA per quarter = 195.06 × 13 weeks = $2,535.78

Total FICA per quarter:
    Employees' share = 4,177.68 + 2,535.78 = $6,713.46
    Employer's share = 4,177.68 + 2,535.78 = $6,713.46

14. Social security = 60,000 × .124 = $7,440
    Medicare = 60,000 × .029 = $1,740

15. SUTA tax = Gross earnings × 5.4%
    SUTA tax = 10,000 × .054 = $540

    FUTA tax = Gross earnings × .6%
    FUTA tax = 10,000 × .006 = $60

16. a. Fringe benefits
        Sick days = Gross payroll × 5%
        Sick days = 123,400 × .05 = $6,170

        Health insurance = Gross payroll × 8%
        Health insurance = 123,400 × .08 = $9,872

        Dental insurance = Number of employees × 12.40
        Dental insurance = 250 × 12.40 = $3,100

        Total fringe benefits = 6,170 + 9,872 + 3,100 = $19,142

    b. Fringe benefit percent = $\dfrac{\text{Total fringe benefit}}{\text{Gross payroll}}$

        Fringe benefit percent = $\dfrac{19,142}{123,400}$ = .155 = 15.5%

    c. Yearly fringe benefits = Weekly total × 52
        Yearly fringe benefits = 19,142 × 52 = $995,384

17. Social security = 113,700 × .124 = $14,098.80
    Medicare = 120,000 × .029 = $3,480.00
    Income tax = 120,000 × .2 = $24,000.00

    Quarterly estimated tax = $\dfrac{\text{Social security} + \text{Medicare} + \text{Income tax}}{4}$

    Quarterly estimated tax = $\dfrac{14,098.80 + 3,480.00 + 24,000.00}{4}$

    $= \dfrac{41,578.80}{4} = \$10,394.70$

CONCEPT REVIEW

1. Gross pay is the amount of earnings before payroll _____ are withheld; net pay is the actual amount of the _____. (9.1)

2. Annual salaries are commonly prorated to be paid weekly, biweekly, _____ and _____. (9-1)

3. Total gross pay includes regular pay and _____ pay, which according to federal law is for hours worked over _____ hours per week. (9-2)

4. When employees are paid on their production output, not hours worked, this is called _____. (9-3)

5. To calculate total gross pay for an employee paid on commission, we multiply the total _____ by the commission rate. (9-4)

6. A draw against commission is commission paid in _____ of sales and later _____ from the commission earned. (9-4)

7. The current employee tax rate for social security is _____ percent of gross earnings; the current tax rate for Medicare is _____ percent of gross earnings. (9-5)

8. The wage base limit for social security used in this chapter is _____. (9-5)

9. In addition to social security and Medicare tax withholdings, an employer is also responsible, by federal law, for withholding an appropriate amount of federal _____ tax from each employee's paycheck. (9-6)

10. The combined wage bracket table is based on the _____ status of the employee and the _____ period used. The columns list the combined taxes to be withheld based on the number of withholding _____ claimed. (9-7)

11. Self-employed persons are responsible for social security and Medicare taxes at _____ the rate deducted for employees. This amounts to _____ percent for social security and _____ percent for Medicare. (9-8)

12. For companies with full and timely payments to the state unemployment system, the SUTA tax rate is _____ percent of gross earnings and the FUTA tax rate is _____ percent of gross earnings. (9-9)

13. A plan whereby employees are given a menu of fringe benefits from which to choose is known as the _____ style or _____ benefit program. (9-10)

14. Write the formula for quarterly estimated tax for self-employed persons. (9-11)

ASSESSMENT TEST

1. Bill Pearson earns $2,800 semimonthly as a congressional aide for a senator in the state legislature.

   a. How much are his annual gross earnings?

   b. If the senator switches pay schedules from semimonthly to biweekly, what will Bill's new gross earnings be per payroll period?

2. Barbara Sultan works 40 hours per week as a registered nurse. At the rate of $31.50 per hour, what are her gross weekly earnings?

3. Eric Shotwell's company pays him $18.92 per hour for regular time up to 40 hours and time-and-a-half for overtime. His time card for Monday through Friday last week had 8.3, 8.8, 7.9, 9.4, and 10.6 hours. What was Eric's total gross pay?

4. Mitch Anderson is a security guard. He earns $7.45 per hour for regular time up to 40 hours, time-and-a-half for overtime, and double time for the midnight shift. If Mitch worked 56 hours last week, including 4 on the midnight shift, how much were his gross earnings?

© StockLite/Shutterstock.com

Registered nurses (RNs) treat patients, educate patients and the public about various medical conditions, and provide advice and emotional support to patients' family members. RNs record patients' medical histories and symptoms, help perform diagnostic tests and analyze results, operate medical machinery, administer treatment and medications, and help with patient follow-up and rehabilitation.

Overall job opportunities for registered nurses are excellent. Employment of registered nurses is expected to grow by 22 percent from 2008 to 2018, much faster than the average for all other occupations.

5. Fergie Nelson assembles toasters for the Gold Coast Corporation. She is paid on a differential piecework rate of $2.70 per toaster for the first 160 toasters and $3.25 for each toaster over 160. If she assembled 229 units last week, how much were her gross earnings?

6. You work in the payroll department of Universal Manufacturing. The following piece rate schedule is used for computing earnings for assembly line workers. As an overtime bonus, on Saturdays, each unit produced counts as $1\frac{1}{2}$ units.

1–100	$2.30
101–150	2.60
151–200	2.80
over 200	3.20

Calculate the gross earnings for the following Universal Manufacturing employees.

	Employee	Mon.	Tues.	Wed.	Thurs.	Fri.	Sat.	Total Units	Gross Earnings
a.	Shane	0	32	16	36	27	12	_____	_____
b.	Gonzales	18	26	24	10	13	0	_____	_____
c.	Bethards	26	42	49	51	34	20	_____	_____

7. Kate Fitzgerald's company pays differential piecework for electronic product manufacturing. Production pay rates for a particular circuit board assembly and soldering are $18.20 per board for the first 14 boards, $19.55 each for boards 15–30, $20.05 each for boards 31–45, and $20.48 each for boards 46 and up. If Kate assembled and soldered 52 boards last week, what was her total gross pay?

8. Foremost Fish Market pays a straight commission of 18% on gross sales, divided equally among the three employees working the counter. If Foremost sold $22,350 in seafood last week, how much was each counter employee's total gross pay?

9. Bryan Vincent booked $431,000 in new sales last month. Commission rates are 1% for the first $150,000, 1.8% for the next $200,000, and 2.3% for amounts over $350,000. What was Bryan's total gross pay?

10. Spencer Morris works in the telemarketing division for a company that pays a salary of $735 per month plus a commission of $3\frac{1}{2}$% of all sales greater than $15,500. If he sold $45,900 last month, what was his total gross pay?

11. Bonnie Woodruff is on a 2.1% straight commission with a $700 drawing account. If she is paid the draw at the beginning of the month and then sells $142,100 during the month, how much commission is owed to Bonnie?

12. Arturo Muina is the captain on a charter fishing boat. He is paid a salary of $140 per day. He also averages tips amounting to 12% of the $475 daily charter rate. Last month during a fishing tournament, Arturo worked 22 days. What were his total gross earnings for the month?

Regardless of what they sell, **telemarketers** are responsible for initiating telephone sales calls to potential clients, using a prepared selling script. They are usually paid on a commission based on the amount of their sales volume or number of new "leads" they generate.

Solve the following problems using 6.2% up to $113,700 for social security withholding and 1.45% for Medicare.

13. What are the withholdings for social security and Medicare for an employee with gross earnings of $725 per week?

14. Dan Dietrich is an executive with Coronado Distributors. His gross earnings are $16,700 per month.

    a. What are the withholdings for social security and Medicare for Dan's January paycheck?

    b. In what month will his salary reach the social security wage base limit?

    c. What are the social security and Medicare tax withholdings for Dan in the month named in part b?

Use the *percentage method* to solve the following.

15. Larry Alison is single, claims one withholding allowance, and earns $2,450 per month.

    a. What is the amount of Larry's paycheck after his employer withholds social security, Medicare, and income tax?

    b. If Larry gets married and changes to two withholding allowances, what will be the new amount of his paycheck?

    c. If he then gets a 15% raise, what is the new amount of his paycheck?

**IN THE
Business world**

Consider the tax implications of a pay raise. In part c, Larry got a 15% raise, but his total deductions increased by 21.7%! His net pay raise, after taxes, was 14.1%

Use the *combined wage bracket tables*, Exhibits 9-3 and 9-4, for Exercises 16 and 17.

16. How much combined tax should be withheld from the paycheck of a married employee earning $910 per week and claiming three withholding allowances?

17. How much combined tax should be withheld from the paycheck of a single employee earning $4,458 per month and claiming zero withholding allowances?

CHAPTER 9

18. Fran Mallory is married, claims five withholding allowances, and earns $3,500 per month. In addition to social security, Medicare, and FIT, Fran pays 2.1% state income tax, $\frac{1}{2}$% for state disability insurance (both based on gross income), $43.11 for life insurance, and $72.30 to the credit union. As payroll manager for Fran's company, calculate her net take-home pay per month.

19. Vanguard Fabricators has 83 employees on the assembly line, each with gross earnings of $329 per week.

    a. What are the total social security and Medicare taxes that should be withheld from the employee paychecks each week?

    b. At the end of the first quarter (13 weeks), what are the accumulated totals of the employee's share and the *matching* taxes for FICA that Vanguard had sent to the IRS?

20. Paul Warren is a self-employed mechanic. Last year he had total gross earnings of $44,260. What are Paul's quarterly social security and Medicare payments due to the IRS?

21. Tim Ries earns $48,320 annually as a supervisor for the Lakeside Bank.

    a. If the SUTA tax rate is 5.4% of the first $7,000 earned in a year, how much SUTA tax must the bank pay each year for Tim?

    b. If the FUTA tax rate is 6.0% of the first $7,000 earned in a year minus the SUTA tax paid, how much FUTA tax must the bank pay each year for Tim?

22. Universal Exporting has three warehouse employees: John Abner earns $422 per week, Anne Clark earns $510 per week, and Todd Corbin earns $695 per week. The company's SUTA tax rate is 5.4%, and the FUTA rate is 6.0% minus the SUTA. As usual, these taxes are paid on the first $7,000 of each employee's earnings.

    a. How much SUTA and FUTA tax did the company pay on these employees in the first quarter of the year?

    b. How much SUTA and FUTA tax did Universal pay in the second quarter of the year?

23. Sky High Crane Company employs 150 workers and has a gross payroll of $282,100 per week. Fringe benefits are $6\frac{1}{2}\%$ of gross payroll for sick days and holiday leave, 9.1% for health and hospital insurance, 4.6% for the retirement fund, and $10.70 per employee per week for a stock purchase plan.

   a. What is the total weekly cost of fringe benefits for the company?

   b. What percent of payroll does this represent?

   c. What is the company's annual cost of fringe benefits?

24. Ransford Alda is a self-employed security consultant with estimated annual earnings of $90,000. His social security tax rate is 12.4%, Medicare is 2.9%, and his federal income tax rate is 14%.

   a. How much estimated tax must Ransford send to the IRS each quarter?

   b. What form should he use?

BUSINESS DECISION: THE BRIDE, THE GROOM, AND THE TAX MAN

25. Two of your friends, Chuck and Joan, have been dating for a year. Chuck earns $3,000 per month as the manager of an Aeropostale store. Joan is a sophomore in college and is not currently working. They plan to marry but cannot decide whether to get married now or wait a year or two.

   After studying the payroll chapter in your business math class, you inform Chuck that married couples generally pay less income taxes and that if they got married now instead of waiting, he would have less income tax withheld from his paychecks. Chuck's current tax filing status is single, one exemption. If he and Joan got married, he could file as married, two exemptions. Use the percentage method and Exhibits 9-1 and 9-2 to calculate the following:

   a. How much income tax is withheld from Chuck's paycheck each month now?

   b. How much income tax would be withheld from Chuck's check if he and Joan got married?

c. Assuming Joan has three more years of full-time college before going to work and Chuck expects a 10% raise in one year and a 15% raise the year after, what is the total three-year tax advantage of their getting married now?

COLLABORATIVE LEARNING ACTIVITY

Researching the Job Market

1. As a team, collect "Help Wanted" ads from the classified section of your local newspaper. (Note: Weekend editions are usually the most comprehensive.) Find examples of various jobs that are paid by salary, hourly rate, piece rate, and commission. Answer the following for similar jobs.

   a. How much do they pay?
   b. What pay periods are used?
   c. What fringe benefits are being offered?

2. As a team, research the Internet or library for the following payroll information. Present your findings to the class. List your sources for the answers.

   a. Starting salaries of employees in various industries and in government occupations.
   b. Personal and household income by area of the country or by state. How does your area or state compare?
   c. Starting salaries by amount of education for various professions.

Business Math JOURNAL

The Alphabet of Internet Commerce

E-Commerce

Electronic commerce, commonly known as e-commerce or e-business, consists of the buying and selling of products and services over the Internet. Electronic commerce that is conducted between businesses is referred to as business-to-business, or B2B. Electronic commerce that is conducted between businesses and consumers, on the other hand, is referred to as business-to-consumer, or B2C.

Online retailers are sometimes known as e-tailers, and online retail is referred to as e-tail. Today most big retailers have an electronic commerce presence on the Internet.

According to Forrester Research,

Estimates of the number of people in the United States making purchases online:

- 167 million—more than half the population—in 2011
- 192 million in 2016
- Estimates of average yearly online spending:
- $1,207 in 2011
- $1,738 in 2016

U.S. Online Retail Sales Estimates ($ billions)

	2009	2010	2011	2012	2013	2014
	$155.2	$172.9	$191.7	$210.0	$229.8	$248.7
% of total US retail sales	6%	7%	7%	7%	8%	8%

Source: Forrester Research

You'll see, Chet; sales will pick up as soon as this whole Internet fad blows over.

"QUOTE...UNQUOTE"

"Make 'someday' today." –Dove Chocolate

"You can't do today's job with yesterday's methods and be in business tomorrow." –MIT Sloan

M-Commerce

Mobile commerce, also known as m-commerce, is the ability to conduct commerce using a mobile device, such as a mobile phone, a personal digital assistant (PDA), or a smartphone.

Mobile commerce began in 1997 when the first two mobile-phone-enabled Coca Cola vending machines were installed in the Helsinki area in Finland. The machines accepted payment via SMS text messages. The first banking service based on mobile phones was launched in 1997 by Merita Bank of Finland, also using SMS.

Sources: www.wikipedia.org; www.internetretailer.com, Paul Demery, "Big Retailers See Big Impact of Mobile on Web and Store Sales," Oct. 10, 2010.

Estimated Annual Mobile Visits to the Top 500 Mobile Commerce Sites

Year	Visits (billions)
2010	1.3
2011	5.0
2012	10.1
2013	17.6
2014	26.4
2015	33.0

Source: Internet Retailer, www.internetretailer.com, Bill Siwicki, April 21, 2012

Issues & Activities

1. Use the chart at the left to respond to the following:
   a. Calculate the percent increase in sales from year to year to determine which year is estimated to have the greatest increase.
   b. In 2014, online retail sales of $248.7 billion have been estimated to represent 8% of total retail sales. Using these figures, calculate the estimated total retail sales in 2014.
2. Use the table above to find the estimated percent age increase from 2010 to 2015.
3. In teams, research the Internet to find current trends in "Internet Commerce" statistics. List your sources and visually report your findings to the class.

Brainteaser—"Work, Don't Work"

You have agreed to work under the conditions that you are to be paid $55 for every day you work and you must pay back $66 for every day you don't work. If after 30 days you have earned $924, how many days did you work?

See the end of Appendix A for the solution.

Simple Interest and Promissory Notes

PERFORMANCE OBJECTIVES

UNDERSTANDING AND COMPUTING SIMPLE INTEREST

10 SECTION I

The practice of borrowing and lending money dates back in history for thousands of years. Today institutions such as banks, savings and loans, and credit unions are specifically in business to borrow and lend money. They constitute a significant portion of the service sector of the American economy.

Interest is the rental fee charged by a lender to a business or an individual for the use of money. The amount of interest charged is determined by three factors: the amount of money being borrowed or invested, known as the **principal**; the percent of interest charged on the money per year, known as the **rate**; and the length of time of the loan, known as **time**. The manner in which the interest is computed is an additional factor that influences the amount of interest. The two most commonly used methods in business today for computing interest are simple and compound.

Simple interest means that the interest is calculated *only once* for the entire time period of the loan. At the end of the time period, the borrower repays the principal plus the interest. Simple interest loans are usually made for short periods of time, such as a few days, weeks, or months. **Compound interest** means that the interest is calculated *more than once* during the time period of the loan. When compound interest is applied to a loan, each succeeding time period accumulates interest on the previous interest in addition to interest on the principal. Compound interest loans are generally for time periods of a year or longer.

This chapter discusses the concepts of simple interest; simple discount, which is a variation of a simple interest loan; and promissory notes. Chapter 11 covers the concepts and calculations related to compound interest and present value.

interest The price or rental fee charged by a lender to a borrower for the use of money.

principal A sum of money, either invested or borrowed, on which interest is calculated.

rate The percent that is charged or earned for the use of money per year.

time Length of time, expressed in days, months, or years, of an investment or loan.

simple interest Interest calculated solely on the principal amount borrowed or invested. It is calculated only once for the entire time period of the loan.

compound interest Interest calculated at regular intervals on the principal and previously earned interest. Covered in Chapter 11.

COMPUTING SIMPLE INTEREST FOR LOANS WITH TERMS OF YEARS OR MONTHS

10-1

Simple interest is calculated by using a formula known as the simple interest formula. It is stated as

> **Interest = Principal × Rate × Time**
> $I = PRT$

When using the simple interest formula, the time factor, T, must be expressed in years or a fraction of a year.

SIMPLE INTEREST FORMULA—YEARS OR MONTHS

Years

When the time period of a loan is a year or longer, use the number of years as the time factor, converting fractional parts to decimals. For example, the time factor for a 2-year loan is 2, 3 years is 3, $1\frac{1}{2}$ years is 1.5, $4\frac{3}{4}$ years is 4.75, and so on.

Months

When the time period of a loan is for a specified number of months, express the time factor as a fraction of a year. The number of months is the numerator, and 12 months (1 year) is the denominator. A loan for 1 month would have a time factor of $\frac{1}{12}$; a loan for 2 months would have a factor of $\frac{2}{12}$, or $\frac{1}{6}$; a 5-month loan would use $\frac{5}{12}$ as the factor; a loan for 18 months would use $\frac{18}{12}$, or $1\frac{1}{2}$, written as 1.5.

Banking institutions all over the world are in business specifically to borrow and lend money at a profitable rate of interest.

EXAMPLE1 CALCULATING SIMPLE INTEREST

a. What is the amount of interest for a loan of $8,000 at 9% interest for 1 year?

▶SOLUTIONSTRATEGY

To solve this problem, we apply the simple interest formula:

$$\text{Interest} = \text{Principal} \times \text{Rate} \times \text{Time}$$
$$\text{Interest} = 8,000 \times 9\% \times 1$$
$$\text{Interest} = 8,000 \times .09 \times 1$$
$$\text{Interest} = \underline{\$720}$$

b. What is the amount of interest for a loan of $16,500 at $12\frac{1}{2}$% interest for 7 months?

▶SOLUTIONSTRATEGY

In this example, the rate is converted to .125 and the time factor is expressed as a fraction of a year, $\frac{7}{12}$.

$$\text{Interest} = \text{Principal} \times \text{Rate} \times \text{Time}$$
$$\text{Interest} = 16,500 \times .125 \times \frac{7}{12}$$
$$\text{Interest} = \underline{\$1,203.13}$$

Calculator Sequence: 16500 $\boxed{\times}$ .125 $\boxed{\times}$ 7 $\boxed{\div}$ 12 $\boxed{=}$ $\underline{\$1,203.13}$

▶TRYITEXERCISE 1

Find the amount of interest on each of the following loans.

	Principal	Rate (%)	Time
a.	$4,000	7	$2\frac{1}{4}$ years
b.	$45,000	$9\frac{3}{4}$	3 months
c.	$130,000	10.4	42 months

CHECK YOUR ANSWERS WITH THE SOLUTIONS ON PAGE 334.

10-2 CALCULATING SIMPLE INTEREST FOR LOANS WITH TERMS OF DAYS BY USING THE EXACT INTEREST AND ORDINARY INTEREST METHODS

There are two methods for calculating the time factor, T, when applying the simple interest formula using days. Because time must be expressed in years, loans whose terms are given in days must be made into a fractional part of a year. This is done by dividing the days of a loan by the number of days in a year.

SIMPLE INTEREST FORMULA—DAYS

Exact Interest

exact interest Interest calculation method using 365 days (366 in leap year) as the time factor denominator.

The first method for calculating the time factor is known as **exact interest**. Exact interest uses *365 days* as the time factor denominator. This method is used by government agencies, the Federal Reserve Bank, and most credit unions.

$$\text{Time} = \frac{\textbf{Number of days of a loan}}{\textbf{365}}$$

Ordinary Interest

The second method for calculating the time factor is known as **ordinary interest**. Ordinary interest uses *360 days* as the denominator of the time factor. This method dates back to the time before electronic calculators and computers. In the past, when calculating the time factor manually, a denominator of 360 was easier to use than 365.

Regardless of today's electronic sophistication, banks and most other lending institutions still use ordinary interest because it yields a somewhat higher amount of interest than does the exact interest method. Over the years, ordinary interest has become known as the **banker's rule**.

ordinary interest or **banker's rule**
Interest calculation method using 360 days as the time factor denominator.

$$\text{Time} = \frac{\text{Number of days of a loan}}{360}$$

EXAMPLE2 CALCULATING EXACT INTEREST

Using the exact interest method, what is the amount of interest on a loan of $4,000 at 7% interest for 88 days?

►SOLUTIONSTRATEGY

Because we are looking for exact interest, we will use 365 days as the denominator of the time factor in the simple interest formula:

$$\text{Interest} = \text{Principal} \times \text{Rate} \times \text{Time}$$

$$\text{Interest} = 4,000 \times .07 \times \frac{88}{365}$$

$$\text{Interest} = 67.506849$$

$$\text{Interest} = \underline{\$67.51}$$

Calculator Sequence: 4000 ☒ .07 ☒ 88 ÷ 365 ═ $67.51

►TRYITEXERCISE 2

Joe Hale goes to a credit union and borrows $23,000 at 8% for 119 days. If the credit union calculates interest by the exact interest method, what is the amount of interest on the loan?

CHECK YOUR ANSWER WITH THE SOLUTION ON PAGE 334.

EXAMPLE3 CALCULATING ORDINARY INTEREST

Using the ordinary interest method, what is the amount of interest on a loan of $19,500 at 6% interest for 160 days?

►SOLUTIONSTRATEGY

Because we are looking for ordinary interest, we will use 360 days as the denominator of the time factor in the simple interest formula:

$$\text{Interest} = \text{Principal} \times \text{Rate} \times \text{Time}$$

$$\text{Interest} = 19,500 \times .06 \times \frac{160}{360}$$

$$\text{Interest} = \underline{\$520}$$

Calculator Sequence: 19500 ☒ .06 ☒ 160 ÷ 360 ═ $520

►TRYITEXERCISE 3

Karen Mitroff goes to the bank and borrows $15,000 at $9\frac{1}{2}\%$ for 250 days. If the bank uses the ordinary interest method, how much interest will Karen have to pay?

CHECK YOUR ANSWER WITH THE SOLUTION ON PAGE 334.

10-3 CALCULATING THE MATURITY VALUE OF A LOAN

maturity value The total payback of principal and interest of an investment or a loan.

When the time period of a loan is over, the loan is said to mature. At that time, the borrower repays the original principal plus the interest. The total payback of principal and interest is known as the **maturity value** of a loan. Once the interest has been calculated, the maturity value can be found by using the formula:

> **Maturity value = Principal + Interest**
> $$MV = P + I$$

For example, if a loan for $50,000 had interest of $8,600, the maturity value would be found by adding the principal and the interest: $50,000 + 8,600 = $58,600$.

Maturity value can also be calculated directly without first calculating the interest by using the following formula:

> **Maturity value = Principal(1 + Rate × Time)**
> $$MV = P(1 + RT)$$

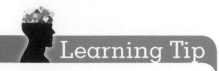
Learning Tip

When using the maturity value formula, $MV = P(1 + RT)$, the order of operation is
- Multiply Rate by Time
- Add the 1
- Multiply by the Principal

EXAMPLE4   CALCULATING MATURITY VALUE

What is the maturity value of a loan for $25,000 at 11% for $2\frac{1}{2}$ years?

▶SOLUTIONSTRATEGY

Because this example asks for the maturity value, not the amount of interest, we will use the formula for finding maturity value directly, $MV = P(1 + RT)$. Remember to multiply the rate and time first, then add the 1. Note that the time, $2\frac{1}{2}$ years, should be converted to the decimal equivalent 2.5 for ease in calculation.

$$\text{Maturity value} = \text{Principal}(1 + \text{Rate} \times \text{Time})$$
$$\text{Maturity value} = 25,000(1 + .11 \times 2.5)$$
$$\text{Maturity value} = 25,000(1 + .275)$$
$$\text{Maturity value} = 25,000(1.275)$$
$$\text{Maturity value} = \underline{\$31,875}$$

▶TRYITEXERCISE 4

a. What is the amount of interest and the maturity value of a loan for $15,400 at $6\frac{1}{2}$% simple interest for 24 months? (Use the formula $MV = P + I$.)

b. Apollo Air Taxi Service borrowed $450,000 at 8% simple interest for 9 months to purchase a new airplane. Use the formula $MV = P(1 + RT)$ to find the maturity value of the loan.

CHECK YOUR ANSWERS WITH THE SOLUTIONS ON PAGE 334.

CALCULATING THE NUMBER OF DAYS OF A LOAN

10-4

The first day of a loan is known as the **loan date**, and the last day is known as the **due date** or **maturity date**. When these dates are known, the number of days of the loan can be calculated by using the "Days in Each Month" chart and the steps that follow.

loan date The first day of a loan.

due date or **maturity date** The last day of a loan.

Days in Each Month

28 Days	30 Days	31 Days
February	April	January
(29 leap year)	June	March
	September	May
	November	July
		August
		October
		December

STEPS FOR DETERMINING THE NUMBER OF DAYS OF A LOAN

STEP 1. Determine the number of days remaining in the first month by subtracting the loan date from the number of days in that month.

STEP 2. List the number of days for each succeeding whole month.

STEP 3. List the number of loan days in the last month.

STEP 4. Add the days from Steps 1, 2, and 3.

EXAMPLE5 CALCULATING DAYS OF A LOAN

Kevin Krease borrowed money from the Charter Bank on August 18 and repaid the loan on November 27. What was the number of days of the loan?

SOLUTIONSTRATEGY

The number of days from August 18 to November 27 would be calculated as follows:

Step 1.	Days remaining in first month	Aug. 31 Aug. −18		
		13 → August		13 days
Step 2.	Days in succeeding whole months → September			30 days
	→ October			31 days
Step 3.	Days of loan in last month → November			+ 27 days
Step 4.	Add the days			Total 101 days

Learning Tip

An alternative method for calculating the number of days of a loan is to use the Days-in-a-Year Calendar, Exhibit 7-6, page 213.

• Subtract the "day number" of the loan date from the "day number" of the maturity date.

• If the maturity date is in the next year, add 365 to that day number, then subtract. *Note:* In leap years, add 1 to the day numbers beginning with March 1.

TRYITEXERCISE 5

a. A loan was made on April 4 and had a due date of July 18. What was the number of days of the loan?

b. Ryan McPherson borrowed $3,500 on June 15 at 11% interest. If the loan was due on October 9, what was the amount of interest on Ryan's loan using the exact interest method?

CHECK YOUR ANSWERS WITH THE SOLUTIONS ON PAGE 334.

10-5 DETERMINING THE MATURITY DATE OF A LOAN

When the loan date and number of days of the loan are known, the maturity date can be found as follows:

STEPS FOR DETERMINING THE MATURITY DATE OF A LOAN

STEP 1. Find the number of days remaining in the first month by subtracting the loan date from the number of days in that month.

STEP 2. Subtract the days remaining in the first month (Step 1) from the number of days of the loan.

STEP 3. Continue subtracting days in each succeeding whole month until you reach a month with a difference less than the total days in that month. At that point, the maturity date will be the day that corresponds to the difference.

Learning Tip

An alternative method for calculating the maturity date of a loan is to use the Days-in-a-Year Calendar, Exhibit 7-6, page 213. Follow the steps for finding a future date, page 212.

EXAMPLE6 DETERMINING MATURITY DATE OF A LOAN

What is the maturity date of a loan taken out on April 14 for 85 days?

SOLUTIONSTRATEGY

Step 1.	Days remaining in first month	30 Days in April
		−14 Loan date April 14
	Days remaining in April	16

Step 2.	Subtract remaining days in first month from days of the loan	85 Days of the loan
		−16 Days remaining in April
	Difference	69

Step 3.	Subtract succeeding whole months	69 Difference
		−31 Days in May
	Difference	38

		38 Difference
		−30 Days in June
	Difference	8

At this point, the difference, 8, is less than the number of days in the next month, July; therefore, the maturity date is <u>July 8</u>.

TRYITEXERCISE 6

a. What is the maturity date of a loan taken out on September 9 for 125 days?

b. On October 21, Jill Voorhis went to the Regal National Bank and took out a loan for $9,000 at 10% ordinary interest for 80 days. What is the maturity value and maturity date of this loan?

CHECK YOUR ANSWERS WITH THE SOLUTIONS ON PAGE 334.

SECTION I 10 REVIEW EXERCISES

Find the amount of interest on each of the following loans.

	Principal	Rate (%)	Time	Interest
1.	$5,000	8	2 years	$800.00
2.	$75,000	$10\frac{3}{4}$	6 months	_____
3.	$100,000	5.5	18 months	_____

	Principal	Rate (%)	Time	Interest
4.	$80,000	6	$3\frac{1}{2}$ years	_____
5.	$6,440	$5\frac{1}{2}$	7 months	_____
6.	$13,200	9.2	$4\frac{3}{4}$ years	_____

Use the exact interest method (365 days) and the ordinary interest method (360 days) to compare the amount of interest for the following loans.

	Principal	Rate (%)	Time (days)	Exact Interest	Ordinary Interest
7.	$45,000	13	100	$1,602.74	$1,625.00
8.	$184,500	7.75	58	_____	_____
9.	$32,400	8.6	241	_____	_____
10.	$7,230	9	18	_____	_____
11.	$900	$10\frac{1}{4}$	60	_____	_____
12.	$100,000	10	1	_____	_____
13.	$2,500	12	74	_____	_____
14.	$350	14.1	230	_____	_____
15.	$50,490	$9\frac{1}{4}$	69	_____	_____
16.	$486,000	$13\frac{1}{2}$	127	_____	_____

Find the amount of interest and the maturity value of the following loans. Use the formula $MV = P + I$ to find the maturity values.

	Principal	Rate (%)	Time	Interest	Maturity Value
17.	$54,000	11.9	2 years	$12,852.00	$66,852.00
18.	$125,000	$12\frac{1}{2}$	5 months	_____	_____
19.	$33,750	8.4	10 months	_____	_____
20.	$91,000	$9\frac{1}{4}$	$2\frac{1}{2}$ years	_____	_____
21.	$56,200	10.2	4 years	_____	_____
22.	$135,000	7.7	18 months	_____	_____

Find the maturity value of the following loans. Use $MV = P(1 + RT)$ to find the maturity values.

	Principal	Rate (%)	Time	Maturity Value
23.	$1,500	9	2 years	$1,770.00
24.	$18,620	$10\frac{1}{2}$	30 months	_____
25.	$1,000,000	11	3 years	_____
26.	$750,000	13.35	11 months	_____
27.	$128,400	8.3	2.5 years	_____
28.	$5,200	14.8	16 months	_____

From the following information, determine the number of days of each loan.

	Loan Date	Due Date	Number of Days
29.	September 5	December 12	98
30.	June 27	October 15	_____
31.	January 23	November 8	_____
32.	March 9	July 30	_____
33.	August 3	September 27	_____
34.	November 18	March 2	_____

From the following information, determine the maturity date of each loan.

	Loan Date	Time of Loan (days)	Maturity Date
35.	October 19	45	December 3
36.	February 5	110	_____
37.	May 26	29	_____
38.	July 21	200	_____
39.	December 6	79	_____
40.	January 13	87	_____
41.	April 27	158	_____

Solve the following word problems. Round to the nearest cent when necessary.

42. On April 12, Michelle Lizaro borrowed $5,000 from her credit union at 9% for 80 days. The credit union uses the ordinary interest method.

   a. What is the amount of interest on the loan?

   b. What is the maturity value of the loan?

   c. What is the maturity date of the loan?

43. What is the maturity value of a $60,000 loan for 100 days at 12.2% interest using the exact interest method?

44. Central Auto Parts borrowed $350,000 at 9% interest on July 19 for 120 days.

   a. If the bank uses the ordinary interest method, what is the amount of interest on the loan?

   b. What is the maturity date?

Credit unions differ from banks and other financial institutions in that the members who are account holders are the owners of the credit union. Credit unions serve groups that share something in common, such as where they work or where they live. The largest credit union in the United States is Navy Federal Credit Union in Vienna, Virginia, with $36.4 billion in assets and 3.2 million members.

45. Emil Benson missed an income tax payment of $9,000. The Internal Revenue Service charges a 13% simple interest penalty calculated by the exact interest method. If the tax was due on April 15 but was paid on August 19, what was the amount of the penalty charge?

46. At the City National Credit Union, a 7%, $8,000 loan for 180 days had interest charges of $276.16. What type of interest did City National use, ordinary or exact?

47. Kyle Rohrs borrowed $1,080 on June 16 at 9.2% exact interest from the Wells Fargo Bank. On August 10, Kyle repaid the loan. How much interest did he pay?

BUSINESS DECISION: COMPETING BANKS

48. You are the accounting manager for Kool Ragz, Inc., a manufacturer of men's and women's clothing. The company needs to borrow $1,800,000 for 90 days in order to purchase a large quantity of material at "closeout" prices. The interest rate for such loans at your bank, Rimrock Bank, is 11% using ordinary interest.

    a. What is the amount of interest on this loan?

    b. After making a few "shopping" calls, you find that Southside National Bank will lend at 11% using exact interest. What is the amount of interest on this offer?

    c. So that you can keep your business, Rimrock Bank has offered a loan at 10.5% using ordinary interest. What is the amount of interest on this offer?

    d. (Challenge) If Southside National wants to beat Rimrock's last offer (part c) by charging $1,250 less interest, what rate, rounded to the nearest hundredths of a percent, must it quote using exact interest?

There are approximately 7,000 commercial banks in the United States. Roughly 25% of these banks have assets in excess of $300 million.

© Pavel L Photo and Video/Shutterstock.com

USING THE SIMPLE INTEREST FORMULA

10

SECTION II

In Section I, we used the simple interest formula, $I = PRT$, to solve for the interest. Frequently in business, however, the principal, rate, or time might be the unknown factor. Remember from Chapter 5 that an equation can be solved for any of the variables by isolating that variable to one side of the equation. In this section, we convert the simple interest formula to equations that solve for each of the other variable factors.

If you find this procedure difficult to remember, use the magic triangle, as we did in Chapter 6, to calculate the portion, rate, and base. Remember, to use the Magic Triangle, cover the variable you are solving for and the new formula will "magically" appear!

**Magic Triangle
Simple Interest Formula**

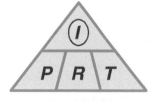

$$I = PRT$$

SOLVING FOR THE PRINCIPAL

10-6

When using the simple interest formula to solve for principal, P, we isolate the P on one side of the equation by dividing both sides of the equation by RT. This yields the new equation:

$$\text{Principal} = \frac{\text{Interest}}{\text{Rate} \times \text{Time}} \qquad P = \frac{I}{RT}$$

We can also find the formula in the Magic Triangle by covering the unknown variable, P, as follows:

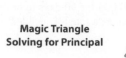
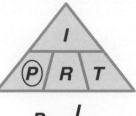

Magic Triangle
Solving for Principal

$$P = \frac{I}{RT}$$

Learning Tip

This formula provides a good opportunity to use your calculator's memory keys. Use M+ to store a number in memory and MR to retrieve it.

Some financial and scientific calculators use STO (store) and RCL (recall) keys for the memory function.

EXAMPLE7   FINDING THE PRINCIPAL OF A LOAN

Allied Bank loaned Checkpoint Industries money at 8% interest for 90 days. If the amount of interest was $4,000, use the ordinary interest method to find the amount of principal borrowed.

▶ SOLUTIONSTRATEGY

To solve for the principal, we use the formula $P = \frac{I}{RT}$.

$P = \frac{I}{RT}$ Substitute the known variables into the equation.

$P = \dfrac{4,000}{.08 \times \dfrac{90}{360}}$ Calculate the denominator first.
                                   Calculator sequence: .08 × 90 ÷ 360 = M+

$P = \dfrac{4,000}{.02}$ Next, divide the numerator by the denominator.
                                   Calculator sequence: 4000 ÷ MR = 200,000

Principal = $200,000   The company borrowed $200,000 from the bank.

▶ TRYITEXERCISE 7

Telex Electronics borrowed money at 9% interest for 125 days. If the interest charge was $560, use the ordinary interest method to calculate the amount of principal of the loan.

CHECK YOUR ANSWER WITH THE SOLUTION ON PAGE 334.

10-7   SOLVING FOR THE RATE

When we solve the simple formula for rate, the answer will be a decimal that must be converted to a percent. In business, interest rates are always expressed as a percent.

When the rate is the unknown variable, we isolate the R on one side of the equation by dividing both sides of the equation by PT. This yields the new equation:

$$\text{Rate} = \frac{\text{Interest}}{\text{Principal} \times \text{Time}} \qquad R = \frac{I}{PT}$$

We can also find the formula in the Magic Triangle by covering the unknown variable, R, as follows:

Magic Triangle
Solving for Rate

$$R = \frac{I}{PT}$$

EXAMPLE8 FINDING THE RATE OF A LOAN

Using the ordinary interest method, what is the rate of interest on a loan of $5,000 for 125 days if the amount of interest is $166? Round your answer to the nearest hundredth of a percent.

►SOLUTIONSTRATEGY

To solve for the rate, we use the formula $R = \dfrac{I}{PT}$.

$R = \dfrac{I}{PT}$ Substitute the known variables into the equation.

$R = \dfrac{166}{5,000 \times \dfrac{125}{360}}$ Calculate the denominator first.

Calculator sequence: 5000 ☒ 125 ☒ 360 ☒ M+
Next, divide the numerator by the denominator.

$R = \dfrac{166}{1,736.111111}$ *Note:* Don't round the denominator.
Calculator sequence: 166 ☒ MR ☒ .095616

$R = .095616$ Round the answer to the nearest hundredth percent.

Rate = 9.56%   The bank charged 9.56% interest.

►TRYITEXERCISE 8

Using the ordinary interest method, what is the rate of interest on a loan of $25,000 for 245 days if the amount of interest is $1,960? Round your answer to the nearest hundredth of a percent.

CHECK YOUR ANSWER WITH THE SOLUTION ON PAGE 334.

SOLVING FOR THE TIME

10-8

When solving the simple interest formula for time, a whole number in the answer represents years and a decimal represents a portion of a year. The decimal should be converted to days by multiplying it by 360 for ordinary interest or by 365 for exact interest. Lending institutions consider any part of a day to be a full day. Therefore, any fraction of a day is rounded up to the next higher day even if it is less than .5.

For example, an answer of 3 means 3 years. An answer of 3.22 means 3 years and .22 of the next year. Assuming ordinary interest, multiply the decimal portion of the answer, .22, by 360. This gives 79.2, which represents the number of days. The total time of the loan would be 3 years and 80 days. Remember to always round up any fraction of a day.

When using the simple interest formula to solve for time, T, we isolate the T on one side of the equation by dividing both sides of the equation by PR. This yields the new equation:

> ### Learning Tip
>
> Remember, when time, T, is calculated, any fraction of a day is rounded up to the next higher day even if it is less than .5.
> For example, 25.1 days would round up to 26 days.

$$\text{Time} = \frac{\text{Interest}}{\text{Principal} \times \text{Rate}} \qquad T = \frac{I}{PR}$$

We can also find the formula in the Magic Triangle by covering the unknown variable, T, as follows:

Magic Triangle Solving for Time

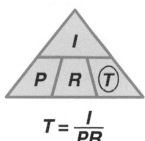

$$T = \frac{I}{PR}$$

EXAMPLE9   FINDING THE TIME PERIOD OF A LOAN

What would be the time period of a loan for $7,600 at 11% ordinary interest if the amount of interest is $290?

SOLUTIONSTRATEGY

To solve for the time, we use the formula $T = \dfrac{I}{PR}$.

$T = \dfrac{I}{PR}$ Substitute the known variables into the equation.

$T = \dfrac{290}{7,600 \times .11}$ Calculate the denominator first.
Calculator sequence: 7600 ☒ .11 ☐ M+

$T = \dfrac{290}{836}$ Next, divide the numerator by the denominator.
Calculator sequence: 290 ÷ MR ☐ .3468899

$T = .3468899$ years   Because the answer is a decimal, the time is less than 1 year. Using ordinary interest, we multiply the entire decimal by 360 to find the number of days of the loan.

$T = .3468899 \times 360$ Calculator Sequence: .3468899 ☒ 360 ☐ 124.8 or 125 days

Time = 124.8 days, or 125 days

TRYITEXERCISE 9

What is the time period of a loan for $15,000 at 9.5% ordinary interest if the amount of interest is $650?

CHECK YOUR ANSWER WITH THE SOLUTION ON PAGE 334.

10-9   CALCULATING LOANS INVOLVING PARTIAL PAYMENTS BEFORE MATURITY

U.S. rule Method for distributing early partial payments of a loan whereby the payment is first used to pay off the accumulated interest to date, with the balance used to reduce the principal.

Frequently, businesses and individuals who have borrowed money for a specified length of time find that they want to save some interest by making one or more partial payments on the loan before the maturity date. The most commonly used method for this calculation is known as the **U.S. rule.** The rule states that when a partial payment is made on a loan, the payment is first used to pay off the accumulated interest to date and the balance is used to reduce the principal. In this application, the ordinary interest method (360 days) will be used for all calculations.

STEPS FOR CALCULATING MATURITY VALUE OF A LOAN AFTER ONE OR MORE PARTIAL PAYMENTS

STEP 1. Using the simple interest formula with *ordinary* interest, compute the amount of interest due from the date of the loan to the date of the partial payment.

STEP 2. Subtract the interest from Step 1 from the partial payment. This pays the interest to date.

STEP 3. Subtract the balance of the partial payment after Step 2 from the original principal of the loan. This gives the adjusted principal.

STEP 4. If another partial payment is made, repeat Steps 1, 2, and 3 using the adjusted principal and the number of days since the last partial payment.

STEP 5. The maturity value is computed by adding the interest since the last partial payment to the adjusted principal.

Learning Tip

Remember to use *ordinary interest*, 360 days, for all calculations involving partial payments.

To help you visualize the details of a loan with partial payments, construct a timeline such as the one illustrated in Exhibit 10-1.

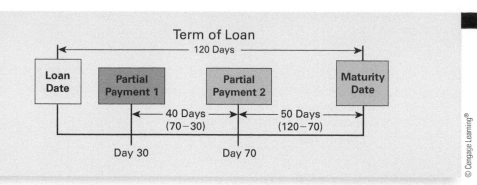

EXHIBIT 10-1
Partial Payment Timeline

© Cengage Learning®

EXAMPLE10 — CALCULATING LOANS INVOLVING PARTIAL PAYMENTS

Ray Windsor borrowed $10,000 at 9% interest for 120 days. On day 30, Ray made a partial payment of $2,000. On day 70, he made a second partial payment of $3,000. What is the maturity value of the loan after the partial payments?

▶SOLUTIONSTRATEGY

Step 1. Compute the interest from the date of the loan to the partial payment. In this problem, the first partial payment was made on day 30.

$$I = PRT$$

$$I = 10,000 \times .09 \times \frac{30}{360} = 75$$

$$I = \$75$$

Step 2. Subtract the interest from the partial payment.

$2,000 Partial payment
− 75 Accumulated interest
$1,925 Amount of partial payment left to reduce the principal

Step 3. Reduce the principal.

$10,000 Original principal
− 1,925 Amount of partial payment used to reduce principal
$8,075 Adjusted principal

Step 4. A second partial payment of $3,000 was made on day 70. We now repeat Steps 1, 2, and 3 to credit the second partial payment properly. Remember, use the adjusted principal and 40 days (70 − 30 = 40) for this calculation.

Step 1.

$$I = PRT$$

$$I = \$8,075 \times .09 \times \frac{40}{360}$$

$$I = \$80.75 \quad \text{Accumulated interest since last partial payment}$$

Step 2.

$3,000.00 Partial payment
− 80.75 Accumulated interest
$2,919.25 Amount of partial payment left to reduce principal

Step 3.

$8,075.00 Principal
− 2,919.25 Amount of partial payment used to reduce principal
$5,155.75 Adjusted principal

Step 5.   Once all partial payments have been credited, we find the maturity value of the loan by calculating the interest due from the last partial payment to the maturity date and adding it to the last adjusted principal.

Note: The last partial payment was made on day 70 of the loan; therefore, 50 days remain on the loan (120 − 70 = 50 days).

$$I = PRT$$

$$I = \$5{,}155.75 \times .09 \times \frac{50}{360}$$

$I = \$64.45$ Interest from last partial payment to maturity date

Maturity Value = Principal + Interest

Maturity Value = \$5,155.75 + \$64.45

Maturity Value = $\underline{\$5{,}220.20}$

►TRYITEXERCISE 10

Rita Peterson borrowed $15,000 at 12% ordinary interest for 100 days. On day 20 of the loan, she made a partial payment of $4,000. On day 60, she made another partial payment of $5,000. What is the maturity value of the loan after the partial payments?

CHECK YOUR ANSWER WITH THE SOLUTION ON PAGE 334.

SECTION II   10   REVIEW EXERCISES

Compute the principal for the following loans. Use ordinary interest when time is stated in days.

	Principal	Rate (%)	Time	Interest
1.	$1,250	12	2 years	$300
2.	_____	9	$1\frac{1}{2}$ years	$675
3.	_____	8	9 months	$3,000
4.	_____	10.7	90 days	$5,350
5.	_____	5	210 days	$917
6.	_____	6	6 months	$2,250
7.	_____	10.5	3 years	$8,190

Compute the rate for the following loans. Round answers to the nearest tenth of a percent; use ordinary interest when time is stated in days.

	Principal	Rate (%)	Time	Interest
8.	$5,000	8	3 years	$1,200
9.	$1,800	____	5 months	$105
10.	$48,000	____	60 days	$728
11.	$4,600	____	168 days	$275
12.	$125,000	____	2 years	$18,750
13.	$36,700	____	190 days	$2,000
14.	$295,500	____	14 months	$39,800

Use the ordinary interest method to compute the time for the following loans. Round answers to the next higher day when necessary.

	Principal	Rate (%)	Time	Interest
15.	$18,000	12	158 days	$948
16.	$7,900	10.4	_____	$228
17.	$4,500	$9\frac{3}{4}$	_____	$375
18.	$25,000	8.9	_____	$4,450
19.	$680	15	_____	$51
20.	$41,000	6.4	_____	$3,936
21.	$3,600	14.3	_____	$125

Calculate the missing information for the following loans. Round percents to the nearest tenth and days to the next higher day when necessary.

	Principal	Rate (%)	Time (days)	Interest Method	Interest	Maturity Value
22.	$16,000	13	___	Ordinary	$760	_____
23.	_____	9.5	100	Exact	$340	_____
24.	$3,600	___	160	Exact	$225	_____
25.	$25,500	$11\frac{1}{4}$	300	Ordinary	_____	_____
26.	_____	10.4	___	Exact	$4,000	$59,000

Solve the following word problems. Round answers to the nearest cent when necessary.

27. Kendall Motors, a Buick dealership, borrowed $225,000 on April 16 to purchase a shipment of new cars. The interest rate was 9.3% using the ordinary interest method. The amount of interest was $9,600.

    a. For how many days was the loan?

    b. What was the maturity date of the loan?

28. Mike Drago took out a loan for $3,500 at the Gold Coast Bank for 270 days. If the bank uses the ordinary interest method, what rate of interest was charged if the amount of interest was $269? Round your answer to the nearest tenth of a percent.

29. Tiffany Francis borrowed money from her credit union to buy a car at 13.5% simple interest. If the loan was repaid in 2 years and the amount of interest was $2,700, how much did Tiffany borrow?

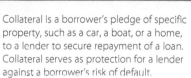

Dollars AND Sense

30. What is the maturity date of a loan for $5,000 at 15% exact interest taken out on June 3? The amount of interest on the loan was $150.

31. You are the owner of a Supercuts Hair Salon. What rate of interest were you charged on an ordinary interest loan for $135,000 in equipment if the interest was $4,400 and the time period was from January 16 to April 27? Round your answer to the nearest tenth of a percent.

Supercuts, with over 2,300 locations, has been ranked the number one hair care franchise in the United States and the fifth best franchise opportunity overall in *Entrepreneur* magazine's annual "Franchise 500" issue.

Initial investment to franchise a Supercuts salon is $111,000–$239,700. Financial requirements are $100,000 liquid assets and $300,000 net worth. The franchise fee is $22,500 for the first salon and $12,500 for each additional salon.

Supercuts is owned by **Regis Corporation,** global leader in salon and hair care services.

Since its inception in 1922, Regis has grown to over 60 distinct brands of salons, education centers, and specialized hair service centers, serving 160 million customers annually through 12,800 worldwide locations. With approximately 55,000 full-time employees, typical annual revenues for Regis Corporation total over $2 billion dollars.

32. Michelle Payne deposited $8,000 in a savings account paying 6.25% simple interest. How long will it take for her investment to amount to $10,000?

33. The Actor's Playhouse theater borrowed $100,000 at 8% ordinary interest for 90 days to purchase new stage lighting equipment. On day 40 of the loan, the theater made a partial payment of $35,000. What is the new maturity value of the loan?

$$I = PRT = 100,000 \times .08 \times \frac{40}{360} = \$888.89$$

$35,000.00 Paid	$100,000.00
− 888.89 Interest	− 34,111.11
$34,111.11	$65,888.89
	Adjusted Principal

$$MV = P(1 + RT) = 65,888.89\left(1 + .08 \times \frac{50}{360}\right) = \$66,620.99$$

34. Steve Perry borrowed $10,000 at 12% ordinary interest for 60 days. On day 20 of the loan, Steve made a partial payment of $4,000. What is the new maturity value of the loan?

35. Pamela Boyd borrowed $20,000 at 6.5% ordinary interest for 150 days. On day 30 of the loan, she made a partial payment of $8,000. What is the new maturity value of the loan?

36. The Mutt Hut Pet Shop borrowed $60,000 on March 15 for 90 days. The rate was 13% using the ordinary interest method. On day 25 of the loan, The Mutt Hut made a partial payment of $16,000, and on day 55 of the loan, The Mutt Hut made a second partial payment of $12,000.

a. What is the new maturity value of the loan?

b. What is the maturity date of the loan?

37. a. How many years will it take $5,000 invested at 8% simple interest to double to $10,000?

b. How long will it take if the interest rate is increased to 10%?

BUSINESS DECISION: THE OPPORTUNITY COST

38. You are the owner of four Taco Bell restaurant locations. You have a business loan with Citizens Bank taken out 60 days ago that is due in 90 days. The amount of the loan is $40,000, and the rate is 9.5% using ordinary interest.

   You currently have some excess cash. You have the choice of sending Citizens $25,000 now as a partial payment on your loan or purchasing an additional $25,000 of serving supplies such as food containers, cups, and plastic dinnerware for your inventory at a special discount price that is "10% off" your normal cost of these items.

a. How much interest will you save on this loan if you make the partial payment and don't purchase the additional serving supplies?

b. How much will you save by purchasing the discounted serving supplies and not making the partial payment?

c. (Optional) What other factors should you consider before making this decision?

Gerrit de Heus/A amy

Taco Bell serves more than 2 billion consumers each year in more than 5,800 restaurants in the United States. The initial investment to franchise a Taco Bell is $1.3 million–$2.3 million. Franchise fees are $45,000 initial fee, then 5.5% monthly royalty fees and 4.5% monthly advertising fees.

Yum! Brands, Inc., based in Louisville, Kentucky, is the world's largest restaurant company in terms of system restaurants, with more than 37,000 restaurants in over 110 countries and territories and more than 1 million associates. Yum! is ranked in the top 250 companies on the Fortune 500 list. Four of the restaurant brands—KFC, Pizza Hut, Taco Bell, and Long John Silver's— are the global leaders of the chicken, pizza, Mexican-style food, and quick-service seafood categories, respectively.

promissory note A debt instrument in which one party agrees to repay money to another within a specified period of time. Promissory notes may be noninterest-bearing at no interest or interest-bearing at a specified rate of interest.

Technically, the document that states the details of a loan and is signed by the borrower is known as a **promissory note**. *Promissory* means it is a promise to pay the principal back to the lender on a certain date. *Note* means that the document is a negotiable instrument and can be transferred or sold to others not involved in the original loan. Much like a check, with proper endorsement by the payee, the note can be transferred to another person, company, or lending institution.

Promissory notes are either noninterest-bearing or interest-bearing. When a note is noninterest-bearing, the maturity value equals the principal because there is no interest being charged. With interest-bearing notes, the maturity value equals the principal plus the interest.

Exhibit 10-2 is an example of a typical promissory note with its parts labeled. Notice the similarity between a note and a check. A list explaining the labels follows.

Maker: The person or company borrowing the money and issuing the note.

Payee: The person or institution lending the money and receiving the payment.

Term: The time period of the note, usually stated in days. (Use ordinary interest.)

Date: The date that the note is issued.

Face Value or Principal: The amount of money borrowed.

Interest Rate: The annual rate of interest being charged.

Maturity Date or Due Date: The date when maturity value is due the payee.

EXHIBIT 10-2   Interest-Bearing Promissory Note

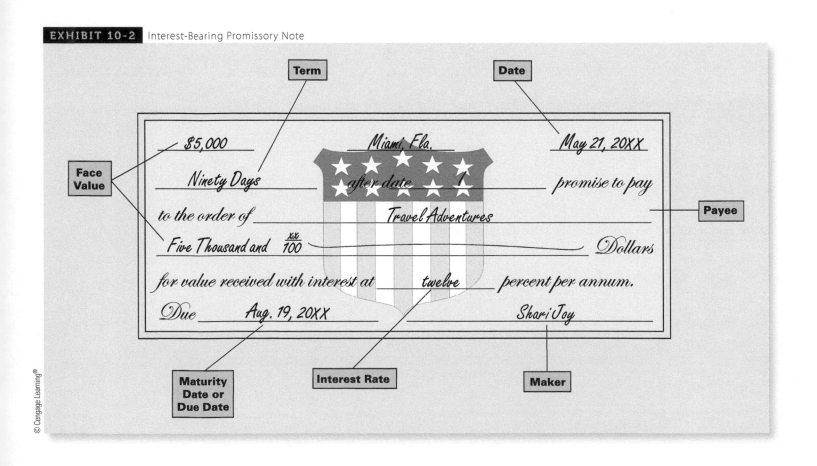

© Cengage Learning®

CALCULATING BANK DISCOUNT AND PROCEEDS FOR A SIMPLE DISCOUNT NOTE

10-10

To this point, we have been dealing with *simple interest notes* in which the interest was added to the principal to determine the maturity value. Another way of lending money is to deduct the interest from the principal at the beginning of the loan and give the borrower the difference. These are known as **simple discount notes**. When this method is used, the amount of interest charged is known as the **bank discount** and the amount that the borrower receives is known as the **proceeds**. When the term of the note is over, the borrower will repay the entire principal, or face value, of the note as the maturity value.

For example, Julie goes to a bank and signs a simple interest note for $5,000. If the interest charge amounts to $500, she will receive $5,000 at the beginning of the note and repay $5,500 on maturity of the note. If the bank used a simple discount note for Julie's loan, the bank discount (interest) would be deducted from the face value (principal). Julie's proceeds on the loan would be $4,500, and on maturity she would pay $5,000.

simple discount notes Promissory notes in which the interest is deducted from the principal at the beginning of the loan.

bank discount The amount of interest charged (deducted from principal) on a discounted promissory note.

proceeds The amount of money that the borrower receives at the time a discounted note is made.

BANK DISCOUNT

Because bank discount is the same as interest, we use the formula $I = PRT$ as before, substituting bank discount for interest, face value for principal, and discount rate for interest rate. *Note:* Use ordinary interest, 360 days, for simple discount notes whose terms are stated in days.

> **Bank discount = Face value × Discount rate × Time**

PROCEEDS

The proceeds of a note are calculated using the following formula:

> **Proceeds = Face value − Bank discount**

EXAMPLE11 — CALCULATING BANK DISCOUNT AND PROCEEDS

What are the bank discount and proceeds of a $7,000 note at a 7% discount rate for 270 days?

SOLUTIONSTRATEGY

$$\text{Bank discount} = \text{Face value} \times \text{Discount rate} \times \text{Time}$$

$$\text{Bank discount} = \$7,000 \times .07 \times \frac{270}{360}$$

$$\text{Bank discount} = \$367.50$$

$$\text{Proceeds} = \text{Face value} - \text{Bank discount}$$

$$\text{Proceeds} = \$7,000 - \$367.50$$

$$\text{Proceeds} = \$6,632.50$$

TRYITEXERCISE 11

Erin Lang signed a $20,000 simple discount promissory note at the Sovereign Bank for a student loan. The discount rate is 13%, and the term of the note is 330 days. What is the amount of the bank discount, and what are Erin's proceeds on the loan?

CHECK YOUR ANSWERS WITH THE SOLUTIONS ON PAGE 334.

Dollars AND Sense

Student Aid

The U.S. Department of Education student aid programs are the largest source of student aid in America. The Free Application for Federal Student Aid (FAFSA) is the form used by virtually all two- and four-year colleges, universities, and career schools for federal, state, and college aid.

A number of student loans allow for a grace period before the loan must be repaid. However, interest may accrue during this time. For more information, visit www.fafsa.ed.gov and http://ibrinfo.org.

10-11　CALCULATING TRUE, OR EFFECTIVE, RATE OF INTEREST FOR A SIMPLE DISCOUNT NOTE

In a simple interest note, the borrower receives the full face value, whereas with a simple discount note, the borrower receives only the proceeds. Because the proceeds are less than the face value, the stated discount rate is not the true or actual interest rate of the note.

To protect the consumer, the U.S. Congress has passed legislation requiring all lending institutions to quote the **true, or effective, interest rate** for all loans. Effective interest rate is calculated by substituting the bank discount for interest and the proceeds for principal in the rate formula,

true, or effective, interest rate The actual interest rate charged on a discounted note. Takes into account the fact that the borrower does not receive the full amount of the principal.

$$\text{Effective interest rate} = \frac{\text{Bank discount}}{\text{Proceeds} \times \text{Time}}$$

EXAMPLE12　CALCULATING EFFECTIVE INTEREST RATE

What is the effective interest rate of a simple discount note for $10,000 at a bank discount rate of 14% for a period of 90 days? Round to the nearest tenth of a percent.

SOLUTIONSTRATEGY

To find the effective interest rate, we must first calculate the amount of the bank discount and the proceeds of the note, then substitute these numbers in the effective interest rate formula.

Step 1.　Bank Discount

$$\text{Bank discount} = \text{Face value} \times \text{Discount rate} \times \text{Time}$$

$$\text{Bank discount} = \$10,000 \times .14 \times \frac{90}{360}$$

$$\text{Bank discount} = \$350$$

Step 2.　Proceeds

$$\text{Proceeds} = \text{Face value} - \text{Bank discount}$$
$$\text{Proceeds} = 10,000 - 350$$
$$\text{Proceeds} = \$9,650$$

Step 3.　Effective Interest Rate

$$\text{Effective interest rate} = \frac{\text{Bank discount}}{\text{Proceeds} \times \text{Time}}$$

$$\text{Effective interest rate} = \frac{350}{9,650 \times \frac{90}{360}}$$

$$\text{Effective interest rate} = \frac{350}{2,412.50}$$

$$\text{Effective interest rate} = .14507, \text{ or } \underline{14.5\%}$$

TRYITEXERCISE 12

What is the effective interest rate of a simple discount note for $40,000 at a bank discount rate of 11% for a period of 270 days? Round your answer to the nearest hundredth of a percent.

CHECK YOUR ANSWER WITH THE SOLUTION ON PAGE 334.

10-12　DISCOUNTING NOTES BEFORE MATURITY

Frequently in business, companies extend credit to their customers by accepting short-term promissory notes as payment for goods or services. These notes are simple interest and are usually for less than one year. Prior to the maturity date of these notes, the payee (lender) may take the note to a bank and sell it. This is a convenient way for a company or individual to *cash in* a note at any time before maturity. This process is known as **discounting a note**.

When a note is discounted at a bank, the original payee receives the proceeds of the discounted note and the bank (the new payee) receives the maturity value of the note when it matures. The time period used to calculate the proceeds is from the date the note is discounted to the maturity date. This is known as the **discount period**.

Exhibit 10-3 illustrates the timeline for a 90-day simple interest note discounted on the 60th day.

discounting a note A process whereby a company or an individual can cash in or sell a promissory note at a discount at any time before maturity.

discount period The time period between the date a note is discounted and the maturity date. Used to calculate the proceeds of a discounted note.

EXHIBIT 10-3
Timeline for Discounted Note

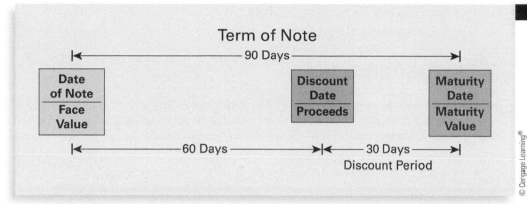

© Cengage Learning®

STEPS FOR DISCOUNTING A NOTE BEFORE MATURITY

STEP 1. Calculate the maturity value of the note. If the original note was noninterest-bearing, the maturity value will be the same as the face value. If the original note was interest-bearing, the maturity value should be calculated as usual:

$$\text{Maturity value} = \text{Principal}(1 + \text{Rate} \times \text{Time})$$

STEP 2. Determine the number of days or months of the discount period. The discount period is used as the numerator of the time in Step 3.

STEP 3. Calculate the amount of the bank discount by using the following formula. *Note*: Use ordinary interest, 360 days, for discounting a note before maturity, when the terms are stated in days.

$$\text{Bank discount} = \text{Maturity value} \times \text{Discount rate} \times \text{Time}$$

STEP 4. Calculate the proceeds of the note by using the formula:

$$\text{Proceeds} = \text{Maturity value} - \text{Bank discount}$$

EXAMPLE 13 CALCULATING PROCEEDS OF A DISCOUNTED NOTE

Continental Industries received a $15,000 promissory note for 150 days at 12% simple interest from one of its customers. After 90 days, Continental needed cash, so it discounted the note at the InterAmerican Bank at a discount rate of 14%. What are the proceeds Continental will receive from the discounted note?

SOLUTIONSTRATEGY

Step 1. Calculate the maturity value of the original note:

$$\text{Maturity value} = \text{Principal}(1 + \text{Rate} \times \text{Time})$$

$$\text{Maturity value} = 15{,}000\left(1 + .12 \times \frac{150}{360}\right)$$

$$\text{Maturity value} = 15{,}000(1 + .05) = 15{,}000(1.05)$$

$$\text{Maturity value} = \$15{,}750$$

Step 2. Find the number of days of the discount period: In this example, the note was discounted after 90 days of a 150-day note; therefore, the discount period is 60 days $(150 - 90 = 60)$.

Step 3. Calculate the amount of the bank discount:

$$\text{Bank discount} = \text{Maturity value} \times \text{Discount rate} \times \text{Time}$$

$$\text{Bank discount} = \$15,750 \times .14 \times \frac{60}{360}$$

$$\text{Bank discount} = \$367.50$$

Step 4. Calculate the proceeds of the discounted note:

$$\text{Proceeds} = \text{Maturity value} - \text{Bank discount}$$

$$\text{Proceeds} = \$15,750.00 - \$367.50$$

$$\text{Proceeds} = \underline{\$15,382.50}$$

▶TRYITEXERCISE 13

Legacy Lumber received a $35,000 promissory note at 10% simple interest for 6 months from one of its customers. After 4 months, the note was discounted at the Keystone Bank at a discount rate of 14%. What are the proceeds Legacy will receive from the discounted note?

CHECK YOUR ANSWER WITH THE SOLUTION ON PAGE 335.

10-13   PURCHASING U.S. TREASURY BILLS

U.S. Treasury bills, or **T-bills** Short-term government securities that represent loans to the U.S. government.

U.S. Treasury bills, or **T-bills**, are short-term government securities with maturities of 4 weeks, 13 weeks, and 26 weeks. Sold by banks, brokers, and dealers in increments of $1,000, these securities represent loans to the U.S. government and are considered to be among the safest of investments. Just like discounted bank notes, T-bills are sold at a discount from their face value.

For example, you might pay $970 for a T-bill with a face value of $1,000. When the bill matures, you would be paid its face value, $1,000. Your interest is the difference between the face value and the purchase price—in this example, $30. The interest is determined by the discount rate, which is set when the bills are initially auctioned by the U.S. Treasury.

When comparing T-bills to discounted bank notes, the interest of a T-bill is the equivalent of the bank discount of a note; the face value of a T-bill is the equivalent of the proceeds of a note. Use the following formulas for T-bill calculations:

$$\text{Interest} = \text{Face value} \times \text{Discount rate} \times \text{Time}$$

$$\text{Purchase price} = \text{Face value} - \text{Interest}$$

$$\text{Effective interest rate} = \frac{\text{Interest}}{\text{Purchase price} \times \text{Time}}$$

EXAMPLE14   PURCHASING U.S. TREASURY BILLS

Peggy Estes purchased $5,000 in U.S. Treasury bills with a discount rate of 4% for a period of 13 weeks.

a. How much interest did Peggy earn on the T-bill investment?

b. How much was the purchase price of Peggy's T-bills?

c. What was the effective interest rate of Peggy's T-bill investment? Round to the nearest hundredth of a percent.

▶SOLUTIONSTRATEGY

a. Interest = Face value × Discount rate × Time

$$\text{Interest} = \$5,000 \times .04 \times \frac{13}{52} = \underline{\$50}$$

Dollars AND Sense

For more information about Treasury bills, go to www.ustreas.gov.

b. Purchase price = Face value − Interest
   Purchase price = 5,000 − 50 = $4,950

c. Effective interest rate = $\dfrac{\text{Interest}}{\text{Purchase price} \times \text{Time}}$

   Effective interest rate = $\dfrac{50}{4,950 \times \dfrac{13}{52}}$ = .040404 = 4.04%

▶TRYITEXERCISE 14

Bob Schaller purchased $10,000 in U.S. Treasury bills with a discount rate of 4.6% for a period of 26 weeks.

a. How much interest did Bob earn on the T-bill investment?

b. How much was the purchase price of Bob's T-bills?

c. What was the effective interest rate of Bob's T-bill investment? Round to the nearest hundredth of a percent.

CHECK YOUR ANSWERS WITH THE SOLUTIONS ON PAGE 335.

REVIEW EXERCISES

10 SECTION III

Calculate the bank discount and proceeds for the following simple discount notes. Use the ordinary interest method, 360 days, when applicable.

	Face Value	Discount Rate (%)	Term	Bank Discount	Proceeds
1.	$4,500	13	6 months	$292.50	$4,207.50
2.	$235	11.3	50 days	_____	_____
3.	$1,850	$12\frac{1}{2}$	1 year	_____	_____
4.	$35,000	9.65	11 months	_____	_____
5.	$7,800	$8\frac{1}{4}$	130 days	_____	_____

Using ordinary interest, 360 days, calculate the missing information for the following simple discount notes.

	Face Value	Discount Rate (%)	Date of Note	Term (days)	Maturity Date	Bank Discount	Proceeds
6.	$16,800	10	June 3	80	Aug. 22	$373.33	$16,426.67
7.	$5,000	14.7	April 16	_____	July 9	_____	_____
8.	$800	12.1	Sept. 3	109	_____	_____	_____
9.	$1,300	$9\frac{1}{2}$	Aug. 19	_____	Nov. 27	_____	_____
10.	$75,000	5	May 7	53	_____	_____	_____

Using ordinary interest, 360 days, calculate the bank discount, proceeds, and effective rate for the following simple discount notes. Round effective rate to the nearest hundredth of a percent.

	Face Value	Discount Rate (%)	Term (days)	Bank Discount	Proceeds	Effective Rate (%)
11.	$2,700	14	126	$132.30	$2,567.70	14.72
12.	$6,505	10.39	73	_____	_____	_____

	Face Value	Discount Rate (%)	Term (days)	Bank Discount	Proceeds	Effective Rate (%)
13.	$3,800	7.25	140	_____	_____	_____
14.	$95,000	9.7	45	_____	_____	_____
15.	$57,500	$12\frac{3}{4}$	230	_____	_____	_____

The following interest-bearing promissory notes were discounted at a bank by the payee before maturity. Use the ordinary interest method, 360 days, to calculate the missing information.

	Face Value	Interest Rate (%)	Date of Note	Term of Note (days)	Maturity Date	Maturity Value	Date of Discount	Discount Period (days)	Discount Rate (%)	Proceeds
16.	$2,500	12	Mar. 4	70	May 13	$2,558.33	Apr. 15	28	13	$2,532.46
17.	$4,000	10.4	Dec. 12	50	_____	_____	Jan. 19	_____	15	_____
18.	$850	$13\frac{1}{2}$	June 7	125	_____	_____	Sept. 3	_____	16.5	_____
19.	$8,000	9	May 10	90	_____	_____	July 5	_____	10.2	_____
20.	$1,240	7.6	Sept. 12	140	_____	_____	Dec. 5	_____	11.8	_____

Calculate the interest, purchase price, and effective interest rate of the following Treasury bill (T-bill) purchases. Round effective interest rate to the nearest hundredth of a percent.

	Face Value	Discount Rate (%)	Term (weeks)	Interest	Purchase Price	Effective Rate (%)
21.	$15,000	5.20	13	$195	$14,805	5.27
22.	$50,000	4.40	26	_____	_____	____
23.	$80,000	4.82	13	_____	_____	____
24.	$35,000	3.80	4	_____	_____	____
25.	$100,000	4.15	26	_____	_____	____

Use the ordinary interest method, 360 days, to solve the following word problems. Round to the nearest cent when necessary.

26. Roni Lockard signed a $24,000 simple discount promissory note at the Pacific National Bank. The discount rate was 14%, and the note was made on February 19 for 50 days.

   a. What proceeds will Roni receive on the note?

   b. What is the maturity date of the note?

27. Chris Gill signed a $10,000 simple discount promissory note at a bank discount rate of 13%. If the term of the note was 125 days, what was the effective interest rate of the note? Round your answer to the nearest hundredth of a percent.

28. Pinnacle Manufacturing received a $40,000 promissory note at 12% simple interest for 95 days from one of its customers. On day 70, Pinnacle discounted the note at the Berryville Bank at a discount rate of 15%. The note was made on September 12.

   a. What was the maturity date of the note?

   b. What was the maturity value of the note?

   c. What was the discount date of the note?

   d. What proceeds did Pinnacle receive after discounting the note?

29. Christy Thomas purchased $150,000 in U.S. Treasury bills with a discount rate of 4.2% for a period of 4 weeks.

   a. How much interest did Christy earn on the T-bill investment?

   b. How much was the purchase price of Christy's T-bills?

   c. What was the effective interest rate of Christy's T-bill investment? Round to the nearest hundredth of a percent.

BUSINESS DECISION: FINANCING THE DEALERS

30. Richie Powers is the owner of American Eagle Boats, a manufacturer of custom pleasure boats. Because of the economic recession and slow boat sales recently, American Eagle has begun accepting promissory notes from its dealers to help finance large orders. This morning American Eagle accepted a 90-day, 9.5% promissory note for $600,000 from Champion Marine, one of its sales dealers.

   You are a manager for Atlantic Bank, and Richie is one of your clients. Atlantic's discount rate is currently 16%. Richie's goal is to discount the note as soon as possible, but not until the proceeds are at least equal to the face value of the note, $600,000.

   a. As his banker, Richie has asked you to "run the numbers" at ten-day intervals starting with day 20 and advise him as to when he can discount the note and still receive his $600,000.

According to the National Marine Manufacturers Association, the top five boating states are Florida, Texas, California, North Carolina, and New York. Typical sales and service expenditures for recreational boating exceed $30 billion annually.

b. (Challenge) Calculate the exact day the note should be discounted to meet Richie's goal.

CHAPTER FORMULAS

Simple Interest

Interest = Principal × Rate × Time

$$\text{Time (exact interest)} = \frac{\text{Number of days of a loan}}{365}$$

$$\text{Time (ordinary interest)} = \frac{\text{Number of days of a loan}}{360}$$

Maturity value = Principal + Interest

Maturity value = Principal(1 + Rate × Time)

The Simple Interest Formula

$$\text{Principal} = \frac{\text{Interest}}{\text{Rate} \times \text{Time}}$$

$$\text{Rate} = \frac{\text{Interest}}{\text{Principal} \times \text{Time}}$$

$$\text{Time} = \frac{\text{Interest}}{\text{Principal} \times \text{Rate}}$$

Simple Discount Notes

Bank discount = Face value × Discount rate × Time

Proceeds = Face value − Bank discount

$$\text{Effective interest rate} = \frac{\text{Bank discount}}{\text{Proceeds} \times \text{Time}}$$

Discounting a Note before Maturity

Bank discount = Maturity value × Discount rate × Time

Proceeds = Maturity value − Bank discount

Purchasing U.S. Treasury Bills

Interest = Face value × Discount rate × Time

Purchase price = Face value − Interest

$$\text{Effective interest rate} = \frac{\text{Interest}}{\text{Purchase price} \times \text{Time}}$$

CHAPTER SUMMARY

Section I: Understanding and Computing Simple Interest

Topic	Important Concepts	Illustrative Examples
Computing Simple Interest for Loans with Terms of Years or Months **Performance Objective 10-1, Page 305**	Simple interest is calculated by using the formula $I = PRT$. $$\text{Interest} = \text{Principal} \times \text{Rate} \times \text{Time}$$ *Note*: Time is always expressed in years or fractions of a year.	What is the amount of interest for a loan of $20,000 at 12% simple interest for 9 months? $$I = 20{,}000 \times .12 \times \frac{9}{12}$$ Interest = $1,800
Calculating Simple Interest for Loans with Terms of Days by Using the Exact Interest Method **Performance Objective 10-2, Page 306**	Exact interest uses *365 days* as the time factor denominator. $$\text{Time (exact)} = \frac{\text{Number of days of a loan}}{365}$$	Using the exact interest method, what is the amount of interest on a loan of $5,000 at 8% for 95 days? $$I = PRT$$ $$I = 5{,}000 \times .08 \times \frac{95}{365}$$ Interest = $104.11
Calculating Simple Interest for Loans with Terms of Days by Using the Ordinary Interest Method **Performance Objective 10-2, Page 307**	Ordinary interest uses *360 days* as the time factor denominator. $$\text{Time (ordinary)} = \frac{\text{Number of days of a loan}}{360}$$	Using the ordinary interest method, what is the amount of interest on a loan of $8,000 at 9% for 120 days? $$I = PRT$$ $$I = 8{,}000 \times .09 \times \frac{120}{360}$$ Interest = $240
Calculating the Maturity Value of a Loan **Performance Objective 10-3, Page 308**	When the time period of a loan is over, the loan is said to mature. The total payback of principal and interest is known as the maturity value of a loan. $$\text{Maturity value} = \text{Principal} + \text{Interest}$$ $$\text{Maturity value} = \text{Principal}(1 + \text{Rate} \times \text{Time})$$	What is the maturity value of a loan for $50,000 at 12% interest for 3 years? $$MV = 50{,}000(1 + .12 \times 3)$$ $$MV = 50{,}000(1.36)$$ Maturity value = $68,000
Calculating the Number of Days of a Loan **Performance Objective 10-4, Page 309**	1. Determine the number of days remaining in the first month by subtracting the loan date from the number of days in that month. 2. List the number of days for each succeeding whole month. 3. List the number of loan days in the last month. 4. Add the days from Steps 1, 2, and 3.	Steve Adams borrowed money from the Republic Bank on May 5 and repaid the loan on August 19. For how many days was this loan? $$\begin{array}{r} \text{May } 31 \\ - \text{ May } \ 5 \\ \hline 26 \text{ Days in May} \\ 61 \text{ June–July} \\ +19 \text{ August} \\ \hline 106 \text{ Days} \end{array}$$

Determining the Maturity Date of a Loan
 	
Performance Objective 10-5, Page 310
	1. Determine the number of days remaining in the first month.
	2. Subtract days from Step 1 from number of days in the loan.
	3. Subtract days in each succeeding whole month until you reach a month in which the difference is less than the days in that month. The maturity date will be the day of that month that corresponds to the difference.
		What is the maturity date of a loan taken out on June 9 for 100 days?
		
		June 30 100 Days of the loan
		June −9 − 21 Days in June
		 21 Days in June 79
		      − 31 Days in July
		      48
		      − 31 Days in August
		      17
		At this point, the difference, 17, is less than the days in September; therefore, the maturity date is September 17.

GO ONLINE FOR MORE ACTIVITIES www.cengagebrain.com

Section II: Using the Simple Interest Formula

Topic	Important Concepts	Illustrative Examples
Solving for the Principal **Performance Objective 10-6, Page 313**	$$\text{Principal} = \frac{\text{Interest}}{\text{Rate} \times \text{Time}}$$ *(I over P R T triangle)*	Kye Morrow borrowed money at 10% interest for 2 years. If the interest charge was $800, how much principal did Kye borrow? $$\text{Principal} = \frac{800}{.10 \times 2} = \frac{800}{.2}$$ $$\text{Principal} = \underline{\$4,000}$$
Solving for the Rate **Performance Objective 10-7, Page 314**	$$\text{Rate} = \frac{\text{Interest}}{\text{Principal} \times \text{Time}}$$ *(I over P R T triangle)*	Arnold Parker borrowed $3,000 for 75 days. If the interest was $90 using ordinary interest, what was the rate on Arnold's loan? $$\text{Rate} = \frac{90}{3,000 \times \dfrac{75}{360}} = \frac{90}{625}$$ $$\text{Rate} = .144 = \underline{14.4\%}$$
Solving for the Time **Performance Objective 10-8, Page 315**	When solving for time, whole numbers are years and decimals are multiplied by 360 or 365 to get days. Any fraction of a day should be rounded up to the next higher day because lending institutions consider any portion of a day to be another day. $$\text{Time} = \frac{\text{Interest}}{\text{Principal} \times \text{Rate}}$$ *(I over P R T triangle)*	What is the time period of a loan for $20,000 at 9% ordinary interest if the amount of interest is $1,000? $$\text{Time} = \frac{1,000}{20,000 \times .09} = \frac{1,000}{1,800} = .555555$$ $$\text{Time} = .555555 \times 360 = 199.99 = \underline{200 \text{ Days}}$$
Calculating Loans Involving Partial Payments before Maturity **Performance Objective 10-9, Page 316**	1. Using the simple interest formula with *ordinary* interest, compute the amount of interest due from the date of the loan to the date of the partial payment. 2. Subtract the interest from Step 1 from the partial payment. This pays the interest to date. 3. Subtract the balance of the partial payment after Step 2 from the original principal of the loan. This gives the adjusted principal. 4. If another partial payment is made, repeat Steps 1, 2, and 3 using the adjusted principal and the number of days since the last partial payment. 5. The maturity value is computed by adding the interest since the last partial payment to the adjusted principal.	Sue Williams borrowed $7,000 at 10% ordinary interest for 120 days. On day 90, Sue made a partial payment of $3,000. What was the new maturity value of the loan? $$I = PRT$$ $$I = 7,000 \times .10 \times \frac{90}{360} = \$175$$ $\begin{array}{ll} \$3,000 & \text{Partial payment} \\ -\ 175 & \text{Accumulated interest} \\ \hline \$2,825 & \text{Reduces principal} \\ \$7,000 & \text{Original principal} \\ -2,825 & \\ \hline \$4,175 & \text{Adjusted principal} \end{array}$ Days remaining = 120 − 90 = 30 $$I = PRT$$ $$I = 4,175 \times .10 \times \frac{30}{360} = \$34.79$$ Maturity value = $P + I$ $$MV = 4,175 + 34.79$$ Maturity value = $\underline{\$4,209.79}$

Section III: Understanding Promissory Notes and Discounting

Topic	Important Concepts	Illustrative Examples
Calculating Bank Discount and Proceeds for a Simple Discount Note **Performance Objective 10-10, Page 323**	With discounting, the interest, known as the bank discount, is deducted from the face value of the loan. The borrower gets the difference, known as the proceeds. Bank discount = $\qquad$ Face value × Discount rate × Time Proceeds = Face value − Bank discount	What are the bank discount and proceeds of a $10,000 note discounted at 12% for 6 months? Bank discount = $10,000 \times .12 \times \dfrac{6}{12}$ Bank discount = $600 $\qquad$ Proceeds = 10,000 − 600 = $\underline{\$9,400}$
Calculating True, or Effective, Rate of Interest for a Simple Discount Note **Performance Objective 10-11, Page 324**	Because the proceeds are less than the face value of a loan, the true, or effective, interest rate is higher than the stated bank discount rate. Effective interest rate = $\dfrac{\text{Bank discount}}{\text{Proceeds} \times \text{Time}}$	What is the effective rate of a simple discount note for $20,000 at a bank discount of 15% for a period of 9 months? Bank discount = $FV \times R \times T$ Bank discount = $20,000 \times .15 \times \dfrac{9}{12}$ Bank discount = $2,250 Proceeds = Face value − Bank discount Proceeds = 20,000 − 2,250 Proceeds = $17,750 Effective interest rate = $\dfrac{2,250}{17,750 \times \dfrac{9}{12}}$ Effective interest rate = $\underline{16.9\%}$
Discounting Notes before Maturity **Performance Objective 10-12, Page 324**	Frequently, companies extend credit to their customers by accepting short-term promissory notes as payment for goods or services. These notes can be cashed in early by discounting them at a bank and receiving the proceeds. 1. Calculate the maturity value. $\qquad MV = P(1 + RT)$ 2. Determine the discount period. 3. Calculate the bank discount. $\qquad$ Bank discount = $MV \times R \times T$ 4. Calculate the proceeds. $\qquad$ Proceeds = MV − Bank discount	Reliable Food Wholesalers received a $100,000 promissory note for 6 months at 11% interest from SuperSaver Supermarkets. If Reliable discounts the note after 4 months at a discount rate of 15%, what proceeds will it receive? $MV = 100,000\left(1 + .11 \times \dfrac{6}{12}\right)$ $MV = \$105,500$ Discount period − 2 months (6 − 4) Bank discount = $105,500 \times .15 \times \dfrac{2}{12}$ Bank discount = $2,637.50 Proceeds = 105,500.00 − 2,637.50 Proceeds = $\underline{\$102,862.50}$
Purchasing U.S. Treasury Bills **Performance Objective 10-13, Page 326**	U.S. Treasury bills, or T-bills, are short-term government securities with maturities of 4 weeks, 13 weeks, and 26 weeks. Sold by banks, brokers, and dealers in increments of $1,000, these securities represent loans to the U.S. government. Just like discounted bank notes, T-bills are sold at a discount from their face value. Interest = Face value × Discount rate × Time Purchase price = Face value − Interest Effective interest rate = $\dfrac{\text{Interest}}{\text{Purchase price} \times \text{Time}}$	Cindy Lane purchased $3,000 in U.S. Treasury bills with a discount rate of 5% for a period of 26 weeks. a. How much interest did Cindy earn on the T-bill investment? Interest = $3,000 \times .05 \times \dfrac{26}{52} = \underline{\$75}$ b. How much was the purchase price of Cindy's T-bills? Purchase price = 3,000 − 75 = $\underline{\$2,925}$ c. What was the effective interest rate of Cindy's T-bill investment? Round to the nearest hundredth of a percent. Effective interest rate = $\dfrac{75}{2,925 \times \dfrac{26}{52}}$ $= .05128 = \underline{5.13\%}$

TRY IT: EXERCISE SOLUTIONS FOR CHAPTER 10

1a. $I = PRT = 4,000 \times .07 \times 2.25 = \underline{\$630}$

1b. $I = PRT = 45,000 \times .0975 \times \dfrac{3}{12} = \underline{\$1,096.88}$

1c. $I = PRT = 130,000 \times .104 \times \dfrac{42}{12} = \underline{\$47,320}$

2. $I = PRT = 23,000 \times .08 \times \dfrac{119}{365} = \underline{\$599.89}$

3. $I = PRT = 15,000 \times .095 \times \dfrac{250}{360} = \underline{\$989.58}$

4a. $I = PRT = 15,400 \times .065 \times \dfrac{24}{12} = \underline{\$2,002}$

$MV = P + I = 15,400 + 2,002 = \underline{\$17,402}$

4b. $MV = P(1 + RT) = 450,000\left(1 + .08 \times \dfrac{9}{12}\right) = \underline{\$477,000}$

5a.
$$\begin{array}{r} 30 \\ -\ 4 \\ \hline 26 \text{ Days} \end{array} \quad \begin{array}{l} \text{26 April} \\ \text{61 May–June} \\ +18 \text{ July} \\ \hline 105 \text{ Days} \end{array}$$

5b.
$$\begin{array}{r} 30 \\ -15 \\ \hline 15 \text{ Days} \end{array} \quad \begin{array}{l} \text{15 June} \\ \text{92 July–Sept.} \\ +9 \text{ Oct.} \\ \hline 116 \text{ Days} \end{array}$$

$I = PRT = 3,500 \times .11 \times \dfrac{116}{365} = \underline{\$122.36}$

6a.
$$\begin{array}{l} \text{Days in Sept. } 30 \\ \text{Loan date } -9 \\ \hline \text{Days of Sept. } 21 \end{array} \quad \begin{array}{l} 125 \text{ Days of loan} \\ -21 \text{ Days of Sept.} \\ \hline 104 \\ -31 \text{ October} \\ \hline 73 \\ -30 \text{ November} \\ \hline 43 \\ -31 \text{ December} \\ \hline 12 \longrightarrow \text{January 12} \end{array}$$

6b. $MV = P(1 + RT) = 9,000\left(1 + .10 \times \dfrac{80}{360}\right) = \underline{\$9,200}$

$$\begin{array}{r} 31 \\ -21 \\ \hline 10 \text{ Days} \end{array} \quad \begin{array}{l} \text{10 Oct.} \\ \text{61 Nov.–Dec.} \\ +9 \text{ Jan.} \longrightarrow \text{January 9} \\ \hline 80 \text{ Days} \end{array}$$

7. $P = \dfrac{I}{RT} = \dfrac{560}{.09 \times \dfrac{125}{360}} = \underline{\$17,920}$

8. $R = \dfrac{I}{PT} = \dfrac{1,960}{25,000 \times \dfrac{245}{360}} = .1152 = \underline{11.52\%}$

9. $I = \dfrac{I}{PR} = \dfrac{650}{15,000 \times .095} = \begin{array}{r} .4561404 \\ \times\ \ 360 \\ \hline 164.2 = \underline{165 \text{ Days}} \end{array}$

10. $I = PRT = 15,000 \times .12 \times \dfrac{20}{360} = \$100$ 1st partial payment = 20 days

$$\begin{array}{l} 4,000 \text{ Payment} \\ -100 \text{ Interest} \\ \hline 3,900 \end{array} \quad \begin{array}{l} 15,000 \\ -3,900 \\ \hline 11,100 \text{ Adjustment Principal} \end{array}$$

$I = PRT = 11,100 \times .12 \times \dfrac{40}{360} = \$148$ 2nd partial payment = 40 days (60 − 20)

$$\begin{array}{l} 5,000 \text{ Payment} \\ -\ 148 \text{ Interest} \\ \hline 4,852 \end{array} \quad \begin{array}{l} 11,100 \\ -4,852 \\ \hline 6,248 \text{ Adjustment Principal} \end{array}$$ Days remaining = 40 (100 − 60)

$I = PRT = 6,248 \times .12 \times \dfrac{40}{360} = \$83.31$

Final due $= P + I = 6,248.00 + 83.31 = \underline{\$6,331.31}$

11. Bank discount $= FV \times R \times T = 20,000 \times .13 \times \dfrac{330}{360} = \underline{\$2,383.33}$

Proceeds = Face value − Bank discount = 20,000.00 − 2,383.33 = $\underline{\$17,616.67}$

12. Bank discount $= FV \times R \times T = 40,000 \times .11 \times \dfrac{270}{360} = \underline{\$3,300}$

Proceeds = Face value − Bank discount = 40,000 − 3,300 = $\underline{\$36,700}$

Effective interest rate $= \dfrac{\text{Bank discount}}{\text{Proceeds} \times \text{Time}} = \dfrac{3,300}{36,700 \times \dfrac{270}{360}} = \underline{11.99\%}$

13. $MV = P(1 + RT) = 35,000\left(1 + .10 \times \dfrac{6}{12}\right) = \underline{\$36,750}$

$$\begin{array}{r} 6 \text{ months} \\ -4 \text{ months} \\ \hline \end{array}$$
Discount period = 2 months

Bank discount = $MV \times R \times T = 36,750 \times .14 \times \dfrac{2}{12} = \$857.50$

Proceeds = Maturity value − Bank discount = $36,750.00 − 857.50 = \underline{\$35,892.50}$

14. **a.** Interest = Face value × Discount rate × Time = $10,000 \times .046 \times \dfrac{26}{52} = \underline{\$230}$

   b. Purchase price = Face value − Interest = $10,000 − 230 = \underline{\$9,770}$

   c. Effective interest rate = $\dfrac{\text{Interest}}{\text{Purchase price} \times \text{Time}} = \dfrac{230}{9,770 \times \dfrac{26}{52}} = .04708 = \underline{4.71\%}$

CONCEPT REVIEW

1. The price or rental fee charged by a lender to a borrower for the use of money is known as _____. (10-1)

2. List the three factors that determine the amount of interest charged on a loan. (10-1)

3. Interest calculated solely on the principal amount borrowed is known as _____ interest, while interest calculated at regular intervals on the principal and previously earned interest is known as _____ interest. (10-1)

4. The interest calculation method that uses 365 days (366 in leap year) as the time factor denominator is known as _____ interest. (10-2)

5. The interest calculation method that uses 360 days as the time factor denominator is known as _____ interest. (10-2)

6. Maturity value is the total payback of principal and interest of a loan. List the two formulas for calculating maturity value. (10-3)

7. The first day of a loan is known as the _____ date; the last day of a loan is known as the _____ date. (10-4, 10-5)

8. Write the formula for calculating simple interest. (10-6)

9. When solving the simple interest formula for principal, rate, or time, the _____ is always the numerator. (10-6, 10-7, 10-8)

10. The U.S. rule states that when a partial payment is made on a loan, the payment is first used to pay off the accumulated _____ to date and the balance is used to reduce the _____. (10-9)

11. The amount of money that the borrower receives at the time a discounted note is made is known as the _____. (10-10)

12. The actual interest rate charged on a discounted note is known as the _____, or _____, interest rate. (10-11)

13. When a note is discounted before maturity, the proceeds are calculated by subtracting the amount of the bank discount from the _____ value of the loan. (10-12)

14. Discounted short term loans made to the U.S. government are known as U.S. Treasury _____. (10-13)

CHAPTER 10

ASSESSMENT TEST

Using the exact interest method (365 days), find the amount of interest on the following loans.

	Principal	Rate (%)	Time (days)	Exact Interest
1.	$15,000	13	120	_____
2.	$1,700	$12\frac{1}{2}$	33	_____

Using the ordinary interest method (360 days), find the amount of interest on the following loans.

	Principal	Rate (%)	Time (days)	Ordinary Interest
3.	$20,600	12	98	_____
4.	$286,000	$13\frac{1}{2}$	224	_____

What is the maturity value of the following loans? Use $MV = P(1 + RT)$ to find the maturity values.

	Principal	Rate (%)	Time	Maturity Value
5.	$15,800	7	4 years	_____
6.	$120,740	$11\frac{3}{4}$	7 months	_____

From the following information, determine the number of days of each loan.

	Loan Date	Due Date	Number of Days
7.	April 16	August 1	_____
8.	October 20	December 18	_____

From the following information, determine the maturity date of each loan.

	Loan Date	Time Loan (days)	Maturity Date
9.	November 30	55	_____
10.	May 15	111	_____

Compute the principal for the following loans. Round answers to the nearest cent.

	Principal	Rate (%)	Time	Interest
11.	_____	12	2 years	$2,800
12.	_____	$10\frac{1}{2}$	10 months	$5,900

Compute the rate for the following loans. Round answers to the nearest tenth of a percent.

	Principal	Rate (%)	Time	Interest
13.	$2,200	_____	4 years	$800
14.	$50,000	_____	9 months	$4,500

Use the ordinary interest method to compute the time for the following loans. Round answers to the next higher day when necessary.

	Principal	Rate (%)	Time (days)	Interest
15.	$13,500	13	_____	$350
16.	$7,900	10.4	_____	$625

Calculate the missing information for the following loans. Round percents to the nearest tenth and days to the next higher day when necessary.

	Principal	Rate (%)	Time (days)	Interest Method	Interest	Maturity Value
17.	$13,000	14	_____	Ordinary	$960	_____
18.	_____	12.2	133	Exact	$1,790	_____
19.	$2,500	_____	280	Ordinary	$295	_____

CHAPTER 10

Using ordinary interest, calculate the missing information for the following simple discount notes.

	Face Value	Discount Rate (%)	Date of Note	Term (days)	Maturity Date	Bank Discount	Proceeds
20.	$50,000	13	Apr. 5	_____	Aug. 14	_____	_____
21.	$875,000	$9\frac{1}{2}$	Oct. 25	87		_____	_____

Using ordinary interest (360 days), calculate the bank discount, proceeds, and effective rate for the following simple discount notes. Round effective rate to the nearest hundredth of a percent.

	Face Value	Discount Rate (%)	Term (days)	Bank Discount	Proceeds	Effective Rate (%)
22.	$22,500	$10\frac{1}{2}$	60	_____	_____	_____
23.	$290,000	11.9	110	_____	_____	_____

The following interest-bearing promissory notes were discounted at a bank by the payee before maturity. Use the ordinary interest method (360 days) to solve for the missing information.

	Face Value	Interest Rate (%)	Date of Note	Term of Note (days)	Maturity Date	Maturity Value	Date Note Discounted	Discount Period (days)	Discount Rate (%)	Proceeds
24.	$8,000	11	Jan. 12	83	_____	_____	Mar. 1	_____	15	_____
25.	$5,500	$13\frac{1}{2}$	June 17	69	_____	_____	July 22		13.7	_____

Calculate the interest, purchase price, and effective interest rate of the following Treasury bill (T-bill) purchases. Round effective interest rate to the nearest hundredth of a percent.

	Face Value	Discount Rate (%)	Term (weeks)	Interest	Purchase Price	Effective Rate (%)
26.	$75,000	5.15	4	_____	_____	_____
27.	$28,000	4.90	26	_____	_____	_____

Solve the following word problems. Round to the nearest cent when necessary.

EXCEL 1

28. On May 23, Samantha Best borrowed $4,000 from the Tri City Credit Union at 13% for 160 days. The credit union uses the exact interest method.

    a. What was the amount of interest on the loan?

    b. What was the maturity value of the loan?

    c. What is the maturity date of the loan?

29. Ronald Brown missed an income tax payment of $2,600. The Internal Revenue Service charges a 15% simple interest penalty calculated by the exact interest method. If the tax was due on April 15 but was paid on July 17, what was the amount of the penalty charge?

EXCEL 2

30. Katie Chalmers borrowed money from her credit union at 13.2% simple interest to buy furniture. If the loan was repaid in $2\frac{1}{2}$ years and the amount of interest was $1,320, how much did Katie borrow?

31. Mickey Sporn took out a loan for $5,880 at the Linville Ridge Bank for 110 days. The bank uses the ordinary method for calculating interest. What rate of interest was charged if the amount of interest was $275? Round to the nearest tenth of a percent.

32. Alicia Eastman deposited $2,000 in a savings account at the Biltmone Bank paying 6% ordinary interest. How long will it take for her investment to amount to $2,600?

33. Laurie Carron borrowed $16,000 at 14% ordinary interest for 88 days. On day 30 of the loan, she made a partial payment of $7,000. What was the new maturity value of the loan?

34. Euromart Tile Company borrowed $40,000 on April 6 for 66 days. The rate was 14% using the ordinary interest method. On day 25 of the loan, Euromart made a partial payment of $15,000, and on day 45 of the loan, Euromart made a second partial payment of $10,000.

   a. What was the new maturity value of the loan?

   b. What was the maturity date of the loan?

35. Brandi Lee signed a $30,000 simple discount promissory note at the Signature Bank. The discount rate was 13% ordinary interest, and the note was made on August 9 for 95 days.

   a. What proceeds did Brandi receive on the note?

   b. What was the maturity date of the note?

   c. What was the effective interest rate of the note? Round the answer to the nearest hundredth of a percent.

36. Varsity Press, a publisher of college textbooks, received a $70,000 promissory note at 12% ordinary interest for 60 days from one of its customers, Reader's Choice Bookstores. After 20 days, Varsity Press discounted the note at the Grove Isle Bank at a discount rate of 14.5%. The note was made on March 21.

   a. What was the maturity date of the note?

   b. What was the maturity value of the note?

   c. What was the discount date of the note?

   d. What proceeds did Varsity Press receive after discounting the note?

On-campus and online **bookstores** are the main sources of textbooks for college students. Electronic textbooks represent an ever increasing portion of total textbook sales. Some digital textbooks can be made to expire anywhere from 6 to 18 months after the date of purchase.

37. Fernando Rodriguez purchased $64,000 in U.S. Treasury bills with a discount rate of 4.7% for a period of 13 weeks.

   a. How much interest did Fernando earn on the T-bill investment?

   b. How much was the purchase price of Fernando's T-bills?

   c. What was the effective interest rate of Fernando's T-bill investment? Round to the nearest hundredth of a percent.

BUSINESS DECISION: BORROWING TO TAKE ADVANTAGE OF A CASH DISCOUNT

EXCEL 3

38. You are the accountant for Suite Dreams, a retail furniture store. Recently, an order of sofas and chairs was received from a manufacturer with terms of 3/15, n/45. The order amounted to $230,000, and Suite Dreams can borrow money at 13% ordinary interest.

   a. How much can be saved by borrowing the funds for 30 days to take advantage of the cash discount? (Remember, Suite Dreams must borrow only the net amount due after the cash discount is taken.)

   b. What would you recommend?

Dollars AND Sense

This Business Decision illustrates an important business concept—borrowing money to take advantage of a cash discount.

Note how much can be saved by taking the cash discount even if the money is borrowed.

For a review of cash discounts, see Section IV in Chapter 7.

© Cengage Learning 2015

CHAPTER 10

COLLABORATIVE LEARNING ACTIVITY

The Automobile Loan

As a team, choose a particular type of automobile category that you want to research (such as sport utility vehicle, sports car, hybrid, or luxury sedan). Then have each member of the team choose a different manufacturer's model within that category.

For example, if the team picked sport utility vehicle, individual choices might include Chevy Equinox, Mazda CX-7, Ford Escape, or Honda CRV.

a. From your local newspaper and the Internet, collect advertisements and offers for the purchase of the model you have chosen.

b. Visit or call a dealership for the vehicle you picked. Speak with a salesperson about the types of "deals" currently being offered on that model.

- What loan rates and terms are available from the dealer?
- Who is the actual lender?

c. Contact various lending institutions (banks, finance companies, credit unions) and inquire about vehicle loans.

- What loan rates and terms are being offered?
- Which lending institution is offering the best deal? Why?
- How do these rates and terms compare with those from the dealership?

CHAPTER 1

Compound Interest and Present Value

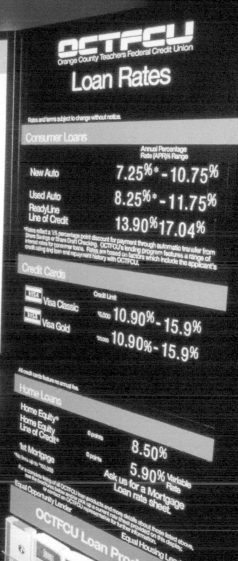

PERFORMANCE OBJECTIVES

compound interest Interest that is applied a number of times during the term of a loan or an investment. Interest paid on principal and previously earned interest.

In Chapter 10, we studied simple interest in which the formula $I = PRT$ was applied once during the term of a loan or an investment to find the amount of interest. In business, another common way of calculating interest is by using a method known as *compounding*, or **compound interest**, in which the interest calculation is applied a number of times during the term of the loan or investment.

Compound interest yields considerably higher interest than simple interest does because the investor is earning interest on the interest. With compound interest, the interest earned for each period is reinvested or added to the previous principal before the next calculation or compounding. The previous principal plus interest then becomes the new principal for the next period. For example, $100 invested at 8% interest is worth $108 after the first year ($100 principal + $8 interest). If the interest is not withdrawn, the interest for the next period will be calculated based on $108 principal.

As this compounding process repeats itself each period, the principal keeps growing by the amount of the previous interest. As the number of compounding periods increases, the amount of interest earned grows dramatically, especially when compared with simple interest, as illustrated in Exhibit 11-1.

EXHIBIT 11-1   The Time Value of Money

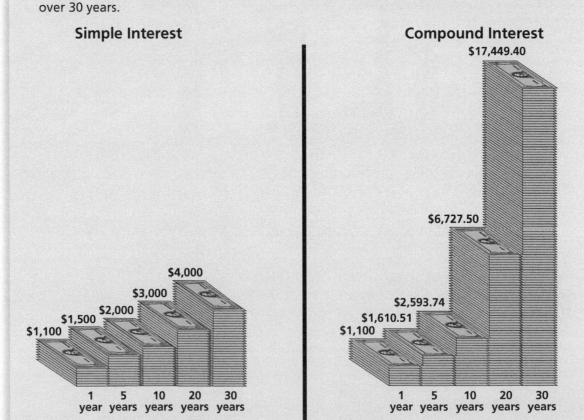

THE VALUE OF COMPOUND INTEREST

The growth of an investment may vary greatly depending on whether simple or compound interest is involved. For example, the chart below shows the growth of $1,000 invested in an account paying 10% annual simple interest versus the same amount invested in an account paying 10% annual compound interest. As this chart shows, compound interest yields more than four times the value generated by simple interest over 30 years.

time value of money The idea that money "now," or in the present, is more desirable than the same amount of money in the future because it can be invested and earn interest as time goes by.

This chapter introduces you to an all-important business concept, the **time value of money**. Consider this: If you were owed $1,000, would you rather have it now or 1 year from now? If you answered "now," you already have a feeling for the concept. Money "now," or in the *present*, is more desirable than the same amount of money in the *future* because it can be invested and earn interest as time goes by.

In this chapter, you learn to calculate the **compound amount (future value)** of an investment at compound interest when the **present amount (present value)** is known. You also learn to calculate the present value that must be deposited now at compound interest to yield a known future amount. (See Exhibit 11-2.)

compound amount, or **future value (FV)**
The total amount of principal and accumulated interest at the end of a loan or an investment.

present amount, or **present value (PV)**
An amount of money that must be deposited today at compound interest to provide a specified lump sum of money in the future.

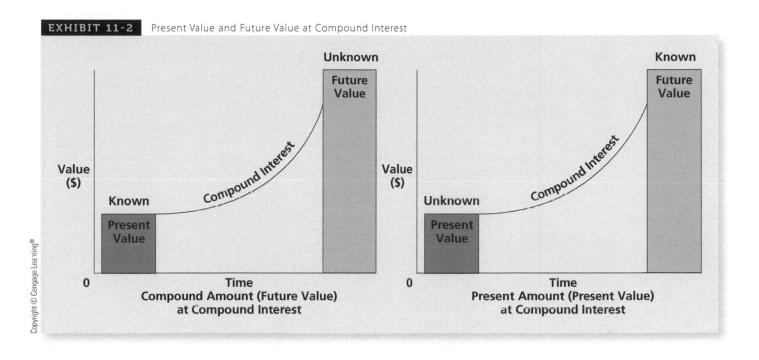

EXHIBIT 11-2   Present Value and Future Value at Compound Interest

Copyright © Cengage Learning®

MANUALLY CALCULATING COMPOUND AMOUNT (FUTURE VALUE) AND COMPOUND INTEREST

11-1

Compounding divides the time of a loan or an investment into compounding periods or simply periods. To manually calculate the compound amount or future value of an investment, we must compound or calculate the interest as many times as there are compounding periods at the interest rate per period.

For example, an investment made for 5 years at 6% compounded annually (once per year) would have five compounding periods (5 years × 1 period per year), each at 6%. If the same investment was compounded semiannually (two times per year), there would be 10 compounding periods (5 years × 2 periods per year), each at 3% (6% annual rate ÷ 2 periods per year).

The amount of compound interest is calculated by subtracting the principal from the compound amount.

> **Compound interest = Compound amount − Principal**

The Time Value of Money

Copyright © Cengage Learning®

EXAMPLE1   MANUALLY CALCULATING COMPOUND INTEREST

a. Katie Trotta invested $20,000 in a passbook savings account at 5% interest compounded annually for 2 years. Manually calculate the compound amount of the investment and the total amount of compound interest Katie earned.

►SOLUTIONSTRATEGY

To solve this compound interest problem manually, we must apply the simple interest formula twice because there are two compounding periods (2 years × 1 period per year). Note how the interest from the first period is reinvested or added to the original principal to earn interest in the second period.

Original principal	$20,000.00
Interest—period 1	+ 1,000.00 $(I = PRT = 20,000.00 \times .05 \times 1)$
Principal—period 2	21,000.00
Interest—period 2	+ 1,050.00 $(I = PRT = 21,000.00 \times .05 \times 1)$
Compound Amount	$22,050.00
Compound Amount	$22,050.00
Principal	− 20,000.00
Compound Interest Earned	$2,050.00

b. Manually recalculate the compound amount and compound interest from the previous example by using semiannual compounding (two times per year). How much more interest would Katie earn if the bank offered semiannual compounding?

▶SOLUTIONSTRATEGY

To solve this compound interest problem, we must apply the simple interest formula four times because there are four compounding periods (2 years × 2 periods per year). Note that the time factor is now $\frac{6}{12}$, or $\frac{1}{2}$, because semiannual compounding means every 6 months.

Original principal	$20,000.00
Interest—period 1	+ 500.00 $(I = PRT = 20,000.00 \times .05 \times \frac{1}{2})$
Principal—period 2	20,500.00
Interest—period 2	+ 512.50 $(I = PRT = 20,500.00 \times .05 \times \frac{1}{2})$
Principal—period 3	21,012.50
Interest—period 3	+ 525.31 $(I = PRT = 21,012.50 \times .05 \times \frac{1}{2})$
Principal—period 4	21,537.81
Interest—period 4	+ 538.45 $(I = PRT = 21,537.81 \times .05 \times \frac{1}{2})$
Compound Amount	$22,076.26
Compound Amount	$22,076.26
Principal	− 20,000.00
Compound Interest	$2,076.26

For the same investment values, semiannual compounding yields $26.26 more than annual compounding:

Interest with semiannual compounding	2,076.26
Interest with annual compounding	− 2,050.00
	$26.26

▶TRYITEXERCISE 1

Gail Parker invested $10,000 at 6% interest compounded semiannually for 3 years. Manually calculate the compound amount and the compound interest of Gail's investment.

CHECK YOUR ANSWERS WITH THE SOLUTIONS ON PAGE 363.

11-2 COMPUTING COMPOUND AMOUNT (FUTURE VALUE) AND COMPOUND INTEREST BY USING COMPOUND INTEREST TABLES

You do not have to work many compound interest problems manually, particularly those with numerous compounding periods, before you start wishing for an easier way! In actuality, there are two other methods for solving compound interest problems. The first uses a compound interest formula, and the second uses compound interest tables.

The compound interest formula, $A = P(1 + i)^n$, contains an exponent and therefore requires the use of a calculator with an exponential function key. The use of the compound interest formula is covered in Performance Objective 11-5.

A compound interest table, such as Table 11-1 on page 345, is a useful set of factors that represent the future values of $1 at various interest rates for a number of compounding periods. Because these factors are based on $1, the future values of other principal amounts are found by multiplying the appropriate table factor by the number of dollars of principal.

TABLE 11-1 Compound Interest Table (Future Value of $1 at Compound Interest)

Periods	$\frac{1}{2}\%$	1%	$1\frac{1}{2}\%$	2%	3%	4%	5%	6%	7%	8%	Periods
1	1.00500	1.01000	1.01500	1.02000	1.03000	1.04000	1.05000	1.06000	1.07000	1.08000	1
2	1.01003	1.02010	1.03023	1.04040	1.06090	1.08160	1.10250	1.12360	1.14490	1.16640	2
3	1.01508	1.03030	1.04568	1.06121	1.09273	1.12486	1.15763	1.19102	1.22504	1.25971	3
4	1.02015	1.04060	1.06136	1.08243	1.12551	1.16986	1.21551	1.26248	1.31080	1.36049	4
5	1.02525	1.05101	1.07728	1.10408	1.15927	1.21665	1.27628	1.33823	1.40255	1.46933	5
6	1.03038	1.06152	1.09344	1.12616	1.19405	1.26532	1.34010	1.41852	1.50073	1.58687	6
7	1.03553	1.07214	1.10984	1.14869	1.22987	1.31593	1.40710	1.50363	1.60578	1.71382	7
8	1.04071	1.08286	1.12649	1.17166	1.26677	1.36857	1.47746	1.59385	1.71819	1.85093	8
9	1.04591	1.09369	1.14339	1.19509	1.30477	1.42331	1.55133	1.68948	1.83846	1.99900	9
10	1.05114	1.10462	1.16054	1.21899	1.34392	1.48024	1.62889	1.79085	1.96715	2.15892	10
11	1.05640	1.11567	1.17795	1.24337	1.38423	1.53945	1.71034	1.89830	2.10485	2.33164	11
12	1.06168	1.12683	1.19562	1.26824	1.42576	1.60103	1.79586	2.01220	2.25219	2.51817	12
13	1.06699	1.13809	1.21355	1.29361	1.46853	1.66507	1.88565	2.13293	2.40985	2.71962	13
14	1.07232	1.14947	1.23176	1.31948	1.51259	1.73168	1.97993	2.26090	2.57853	2.93719	14
15	1.07768	1.16097	1.25023	1.34587	1.55797	1.80094	2.07893	2.39656	2.75903	3.17217	15
16	1.08307	1.17258	1.26899	1.37279	1.60471	1.87298	2.18287	2.54035	2.95216	3.42594	16
17	1.08849	1.18430	1.28802	1.40024	1.65285	1.94790	2.29202	2.69277	3.15882	3.70002	17
18	1.09393	1.19615	1.30734	1.42825	1.70243	2.02582	2.40662	2.85434	3.37993	3.99602	18
19	1.09940	1.20811	1.32695	1.45681	1.75351	2.10685	2.52695	3.02560	3.61653	4.31570	19
20	1.10490	1.22019	1.34686	1.48595	1.80611	2.19112	2.65330	3.20714	3.86968	4.66096	20
21	1.11042	1.23239	1.36706	1.51567	1.86029	2.27877	2.78596	3.39956	4.14056	5.03383	21
22	1.11597	1.24472	1.38756	1.54598	1.91610	2.36992	2.92526	3.60354	4.43040	5.43654	22
23	1.12155	1.25716	1.40838	1.57690	1.97359	2.46472	3.07152	3.81975	4.74053	5.87146	23
24	1.12716	1.26973	1.42950	1.60844	2.03279	2.56330	3.22510	4.04893	5.07237	6.34118	24
25	1.13280	1.28243	1.45095	1.64061	2.09378	2.66584	3.38635	4.29187	5.42743	6.84848	25

Periods	9%	10%	11%	12%	13%	14%	15%	16%	17%	18%	Periods
1	1.09000	1.10000	1.11000	1.12000	1.13000	1.14000	1.15000	1.16000	1.17000	1.18000	1
2	1.18810	1.21000	1.23210	1.25440	1.27690	1.29960	1.32250	1.34560	1.36890	1.39240	2
3	1.29503	1.33100	1.36763	1.40493	1.44290	1.48154	1.52088	1.56090	1.60161	1.64303	3
4	1.41158	1.46410	1.51807	1.57352	1.63047	1.68896	1.74901	1.81064	1.87389	1.93878	4
5	1.53862	1.61051	1.68506	1.76234	1.84244	1.92541	2.01136	2.10034	2.19245	2.28776	5
6	1.67710	1.77156	1.87041	1.97382	2.08195	2.19497	2.31306	2.43640	2.56516	2.69955	6
7	1.82804	1.94872	2.07616	2.21068	2.35261	2.50227	2.66002	2.82622	3.00124	3.18547	7
8	1.99256	2.14359	2.30454	2.47596	2.65844	2.85259	3.05902	3.27841	3.51145	3.75886	8
9	2.17189	2.35795	2.55804	2.77308	3.00404	3.25195	3.51788	3.80296	4.10840	4.43545	9
10	2.36736	2.59374	2.83942	3.10585	3.39457	3.70722	4.04556	4.41144	4.80683	5.23384	10
11	2.58043	2.85312	3.15176	3.47855	3.83586	4.22623	4.65239	5.11726	5.62399	6.17593	11
12	2.81266	3.13843	3.49845	3.89598	4.33452	4.81790	5.35025	5.93603	6.58007	7.28759	12
13	3.06580	3.45227	3.88328	4.36349	4.89801	5.49241	6.15279	6.88579	7.69868	8.59936	13
14	3.34173	3.79750	4.31044	4.88711	5.53475	6.26135	7.07571	7.98752	9.00745	10.14724	14
15	3.64248	4.17725	4.78459	5.47357	6.25427	7.13794	8.13706	9.26552	10.53872	11.97375	15
16	3.97031	4.59497	5.31089	6.13039	7.06733	8.13725	9.35762	10.74800	12.33030	14.12902	16
17	4.32763	5.05447	5.89509	6.86604	7.98608	9.27646	10.76126	12.46768	14.42646	16.67225	17
18	4.71712	5.55992	6.54355	7.68997	9.02427	10.57517	12.37545	14.46251	16.87895	19.67325	18
19	5.14166	6.11591	7.26334	8.61276	10.19742	12.05569	14.23177	16.77652	19.74838	23.21444	19
20	5.60441	6.72750	8.06231	9.64629	11.52309	13.74349	16.36654	19.46076	23.10560	27.39303	20
21	6.10881	7.40025	8.94917	10.80385	13.02109	15.66758	18.82152	22.57448	27.03355	32.32378	21
22	6.65860	8.14027	9.93357	12.10031	14.71383	17.86104	21.64475	26.18640	31.62925	38.14206	22
23	7.25787	8.95430	11.02627	13.55235	16.62663	20.36158	24.89146	30.37622	37.00623	45.00763	23
24	7.91108	9.84973	12.23916	15.17863	18.78809	23.21221	28.62518	35.23642	43.29729	53.10901	24
25	8.62308	10.83471	13.58546	17.00006	21.23054	26.46192	32.91895	40.87424	50.65783	62.66863	25

The values in Table 11-1 were generated by the formula $FV = (1 + i)^n$ rounded to five decimal places, where i is the interest rate per period and n is the total number of periods.

Copyright © Cengage Learning®

EXHIBIT 11-3
Compounding Periods per Year

Interest Compounded		Compounding Periods per Year
Annually	Every year	1
Semiannually	Every 6 months	2
Quarterly	Every 3 months	4
Monthly	Every month	12
Daily	Every day	365
Continuously		Infinite

> **Compound amount (future value) = Table factor × Principal**

To use the compound interest tables, we must know the number of compounding periods and the interest rate per period. Exhibit 11-3 above shows the various compounding options and the corresponding number of periods per year. *Note*: The greater the number of compounding periods per year, the higher the interest earned on the investment. Today interest can actually be calculated on a continuous basis—that is, up to the minute. In competitive markets, many banks offer continuous compounding as an incentive to attract new deposits.

To find the number of compounding periods of an investment, multiply the number of years by the number of periods per year.

> **Compounding periods = Years × Periods per year**

To find the interest rate per period, divide the annual, or nominal, rate by the number of periods per year.

$$\text{Interest rate per period} = \frac{\text{Nominal rate}}{\text{Period per year}}$$

STEPS FOR USING COMPOUND INTEREST TABLES

STEP 1. Scan across the top row to find the interest rate per period.

STEP 2. Look down that column to the row corresponding to the number of periods.

STEP 3. The table factor at the intersection of the rate-per-period column and the number-of-periods row is the future value of $1 at compound interest. Multiply the table factor by the principal to determine the compound amount.

> **Compound amount = Table factor × Principal**

EXAMPLE2   USING COMPOUND INTEREST TABLES

John Anderson invested $1,200 in an account at 8% interest compounded quarterly for 5 years. Use Table 11-1 to find the compound amount of John's investment. What is the amount of the compound interest?

SOLUTIONSTRATEGY

To solve this compound interest problem, we must first find the interest rate per period and the number of compounding periods.

$$\text{Interest rate per period} = \frac{\text{Nominal rate}}{\text{Periods per year}}$$

$$\text{Interest rate per period} = \frac{8\%}{4} = 2\%$$

$$\text{Compounding periods} = \text{Years} \times \text{Periods per year}$$

$$\text{Compounding periods} = 5 \times 4 = 20$$

IN THE
Business World

Today most banks, savings and loan institutions, and credit unions pay compound interest on depositors' money. The U.S. government also uses compounding for savings bonds.

Dollars
AND **Sense**

The Federal Deposit Insurance Corporation (FDIC) is an independent agency of the U.S. government that protects the funds depositors place in banks and savings associations. FDIC insurance is backed by the full faith and credit of the U.S. government. FDIC insurance covers all deposit accounts, including checking and savings accounts, money market deposit accounts, and certificates of deposit.

The standard insurance amount currently is $250,000 per depositor, per insured bank.

Now find the table factor by scanning across the top row of the compound interest table to 2% and down the 2% column to 20 periods. The table factor at that intersection is 1.48595. The compound amount is found by multiplying the table factor by the principal:

Compound amount = Table factor × Principal
Compound amount = 1.48595 × 1,200 = $1,783.14

The amount of interest is found by subtracting the principal from the compound amount.

Compound interest = Compound amount − Principal
Compound interest = 1,783.14 − 1,200.00 = $583.14

▶ TRYITEXERCISE 2

Jenny Chao invested $20,000 at 6% interest compounded semiannually for 8 years. Use Table 11-1 to find the compound amount of her investment. What is the amount of compound interest Jenny earned?

CHECK YOUR ANSWERS WITH THE SOLUTIONS ON PAGE 363.

CREATING COMPOUND INTEREST TABLE FACTORS FOR PERIODS BEYOND THE TABLE

11-3

When the number of periods of an investment is greater than the number of periods provided by the compound interest table, you can compute a new table factor by multiplying the factors for any two periods that add up to the number of periods required. For answer consistency in this chapter, use the two table factors that represent *half*, or values as close as possible to half, of the periods required. For example,

20 periods
          ⟶ 40 periods
20 periods

20 periods
          ⟶ 41 periods
21 periods

STEPS FOR CREATING NEW COMPOUND INTEREST TABLE FACTORS

STEP 1. For the stated interest rate per period, find the two table factors that represent *half*, or values as close as possible to half, of the periods required.

STEP 2. Multiply the two table factors from Step 1 to form the new factor.

STEP 3. Round the new factor to five decimal places.

EXAMPLE3 CALCULATING COMPOUND AMOUNT FOR PERIODS BEYOND THE TABLE

Calculate a new table factor and find the compound amount of $10,000 invested at 12% compounded monthly for 3 years.

▶ SOLUTIONSTRATEGY

This investment requires a table factor for 36 periods (12 periods per year for 3 years). Because Table 11-1 provides factors only up to 25 periods, we must create one using the steps above.

Step 1. At 12% interest compounded monthly, the rate per period is 1%. Because we are looking for 36 periods, we will use the factors for 18 and 18 periods at 1%.

Table factor for 18 periods, 1% = 1.19615
Table factor for 18 periods, 1% = 1.19615

Step 2. Multiply the factors for 18 and 18 periods.

1.19615 × 1.19615 = 1.4307748

Step 3. Round to five decimal places.

The new table factor for 36 periods is <u>1.43077</u>.

The compound amount of the $10,000 investment is

Compound amount = Table factor × Principal
Compound amount = 1.43077 × 10,000 = <u>$14,307.70</u>

▶TRYITEXERCISE 3

Stan Gray invests $3,500 at 8% interest compounded quarterly for 7 years. Calculate a new table factor and find the compound amount of Stan's investment.

CHECK YOUR ANSWERS WITH THE SOLUTIONS ON PAGE 363.

Source: www.hetemeel.com

INTERFOTO/Personalities/Alamy

IN THE Business World

The Rule of 72
There is an easy method for calculating approximately how long it takes an amount of money to double in value at compound interest. Simply divide the number 72 by the interest rate. The result is the number of years it takes to double in value.

$$\text{Years to double} = \frac{72}{\text{Compound interest rate}}$$

- For example, if you invested money at 6% compound interest, it would take 12 years ($\frac{72}{6} = 12$) to double your money.

- If you were able to find an investment that paid 9% interest, you could double your money in 8 years ($\frac{72}{9} = 8$).

11-4 CALCULATING ANNUAL PERCENTAGE YIELD (APY) OR EFFECTIVE INTEREST RATE

annual, or **nominal**, **rate** The advertised or stated interest rate of an investment or loan. The rate used to calculate the compound interest.

In describing investments and loans, the advertised or stated interest rate is known as the **annual**, or **nominal**, **rate**. It is also the rate used to calculate the compound interest. Consider, however, what happens to an investment of $100 at 12% nominal interest.

As we learned in Performance Objective 11-2, the greater the number of compounding periods per year, the higher the amount of interest earned. (See Exhibit 11-4.) Although the nominal interest rate is 12%, with monthly compounding, the $100 earns more than 12%. This is why many investment offers today advertise daily or continuous compounding. How much are these investments really earning?

EXHIBIT 11-4
Compound Interest Earned on $100 at 12%

Compounding	Interest Earned
Annually	$12.00
Semiannually	$12.36
Quarterly	$12.55
Monthly	$12.68

The **annual percentage yield (APY)**, or **effective rate**, reflects the real rate of return on an investment. APY is calculated by finding the total compound interest earned in 1 year and dividing by the principal. *Note*: This is actually the simple interest formula (from Chapter 10) solved for rate $R = I \div PT$, where T is equal to 1.

$$\text{Annual percentage (APY)} = \frac{\text{Total compound interest earned in 1 year}}{\text{Principal}}$$

From Exhibit 11-4, we can see that the annual percentage yield is the same as the nominal rate when interest is compounded annually; however, it jumps to 12.36% ($12.36) when the compounding is changed to semiannually and to 12.68 % ($12.68) when compounded monthly.

annual percentage yield (APY), or **effective rate** The real or true rate of return on an investment. It is the total compound interest earned in 1 year divided by the principal. The more compounding periods per year, the higher the APY.

EXAMPLE 4   CALCULATING APY

What is the compound amount, compound interest, and annual percentage yield of $4,000 invested for 1 year at 8% compounded semiannually?

▶SOLUTIONSTRATEGY

First, we must find the total compound interest earned in 1 year. We can find the compound amount using the factor for 4%, two periods, from Table 11-1.

Compound amount = Table factor × Principal
Compound amount = 1.08160 × 4,000 = $4,326.40

Compound interest = Compound amount − Principal
Compound interest = 4,326.40 − 4,000 = $326.40

$$\text{Annual percentage yield} = \frac{\text{Total compound interest earned in 1 year}}{\text{Principal}}$$

$$\text{Annual percentage yield} = \frac{326.40}{4,000.00} = 8.16\%$$

▶TRYITEXERCISE 4

Jill Quinn invested $7,000 in a certificate of deposit for 1 year at 6% interest compounded quarterly. What is the compound amount, compound interest, and annual percentage yield of Jill's investment? Round the APY to the nearest hundredth of a percent.

CHECK YOUR ANSWERS WITH THE SOLUTIONS ON PAGE 363.

Dollars AND Sense

Regulation DD of the Truth in Savings Law, enacted by Congress in 1993, requires banks and other depository institutions to fully disclose the terms of deposit accounts to consumers. The major provisions of the regulation require institutions to:

- Provide consumer account holders with written information about important terms of an account, including the **annual percentage yield**.

- Provide fee and other information on any periodic statement sent to consumers.

- Use prescribed methods to determine the balance on which interest is calculated.

- Comply with special requirements when advertising deposit accounts.

CALCULATING COMPOUND AMOUNT (FUTURE VALUE) BY USING THE COMPOUND INTEREST FORMULA

11-5

If your calculator has an exponential function key, y^x, you can calculate the compound amount of an investment by using the compound interest formula.

The compound interest formula states:

$$A = P(1 + i)^n$$

where:

A = **Compound amount**

P = **Principal**

i = **Interest rate per period (expressed as a decimal)**

n = **Total compounding periods (years × periods per year)**

STEPS FOR SOLVING THE COMPOUND INTEREST FORMULA

STEP 1. Add the 1 and the interest rate per period, i.

STEP 2. Raise the sum from Step 1 to the nth (number of compounding periods) power by using the y^x key on your calculator.

STEP 3. Multiply the principal, P, by the answer from Step 2.

Calculator Sequence: 1 $+$ i $=$ y^x n $\times$ P $=$ A

EXAMPLE5   USING THE COMPOUND INTEREST FORMULA

Use the compound interest formula to calculate the compound amount of $5,000 invested at 10% interest compounded semiannually for 3 years.

▶SOLUTIONSTRATEGY

This problem is solved by substituting the investment information into the compound interest formula. It is important to solve the formula using the sequence of steps outlined above. Note that the rate per period, i, is 5% (10% ÷ 2 periods per year). The total number of periods, the exponent n, is 6 (3 years × 2 periods per year).

$$A = P(1 + i)^n$$
$$A = 5,000(1 + .05)^6$$
$$A = 5,000(1.05)^6$$
$$A = 5,000(1.3400956) = 6,700.4782 = \$6,700.48$$

Calculator Sequence: 1 $+$ .05 $=$ y^x 6 $\times$ 5000 $=$ $6,700.4782 = \underline{\$6,700.48}$

▶TRYITEXERCISE 5

Use the compound interest formula to calculate the compound amount of $3,000 invested at 8% interest compounded quarterly for 5 years.

CHECK YOUR ANSWER WITH THE SOLUTION ON PAGE 363.

SECTION I 11 REVIEW EXERCISES

For the following investments, find the total number of compounding periods and the interest rate per period.

	Term of Investment	Nominal (Annual) Rate (%)	Interest Compounded	Compounding Periods	Rate per Period (%)
1.	3 years	13	annually	3	13
2.	5 years	4	quarterly		
3.	12 years	8	semiannually		
4.	6 years	6	monthly		
5.	4 years	6	quarterly		
6.	9 years	10.5	semiannually		
7.	9 months	4	quarterly		

Manually calculate the compound amount and compound interest for the following investments.

	Principal	Time Period (years)	Nominal Rate (%)	Interest Compounded	Compound Amount	Compound Interest
8.	$4,000	2	10	annually	$4,840.00	$840.00
9.	$10,000	1	4	quarterly	_____	_____
10.	$8,000	3	8	semiannually	_____	_____
11.	$2,000	4	6	annually	_____	_____

Using Table 11-1, calculate the compound amount and compound interest for the following investments.

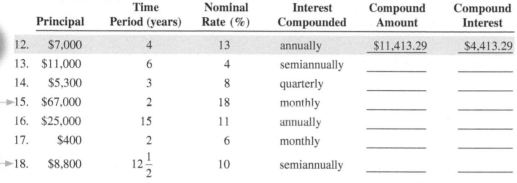

	Principal	Time Period (years)	Nominal Rate (%)	Interest Compounded	Compound Amount	Compound Interest
12.	$7,000	4	13	annually	$11,413.29	$4,413.29
13.	$11,000	6	4	semiannually	_____	_____
14.	$5,300	3	8	quarterly	_____	_____
15.	$67,000	2	18	monthly	_____	_____
16.	$25,000	15	11	annually	_____	_____
17.	$400	2	6	monthly	_____	_____
18.	$8,800	$12\frac{1}{2}$	10	semiannually	_____	_____

The following investments require table factors for periods beyond the table. Create the new table factor, rounded to five places, and calculate the compound amount for each.

	Principal	Time Period (years)	Nominal Rate (%)	Interest Compounded	New Table Factor	Compound Amount
19.	$13,000	3	12	monthly	1.43077	$18,600.01
20.	$19,000	29	9	annually	_____	_____
21.	$34,700	11	16	quarterly	_____	_____
22.	$10,000	40	13	annually	_____	_____
23.	$1,000	16	14	semiannually	_____	_____

For the following investments, compute the amount of compound interest earned in 1 year and the annual percentage yield (APY).

	Principal	Nominal Rate (%)	Interest Compounded	Compound Interest Earned in 1 Year	Annual Percentage Yield (APY)
24.	$5,000	10	semiannually	$512.50	10.25%
25.	$2,000	13	annually	_____	_____
26.	$36,000	12	monthly	_____	_____
27.	$1,000	8	quarterly	_____	_____
28.	$8,000	6	semiannually	_____	_____

Solve the following word problems by using Table 11-1.

29. Sherry Smith invested $3,000 at the Horizon Bank at 6% interest compounded quarterly.

   a. What is the annual percentage yield of this investment?

b. What will Sherry's investment be worth after 6 years?

30. As a savings plan for college, when their son Bob was born, the Wilburs deposited $10,000 in an account paying 8% compounded annually. How much will the account be worth when Bob is 18 years old?

31. You are owner of a UPS Store franchise. You have just deposited $12,000 in an investment account earning 12% compounded monthly. This account is intended to pay for store improvements in $2\frac{1}{2}$ years. At that rate, how much will be available in the account for the project?

32. The First National Bank is offering a 6-year certificate of deposit (CD) at 4% interest compounded quarterly; Second National Bank is offering a 6-year CD at 5% interest compounded annually.

a. If you were interested in investing $8,000 in one of these CDs, calculate the compound amount of each offer.

b. What is the annual percentage yield of each CD?

c. (Optional) If Third National Bank has a 6-year CD at 4.5% interest compounded monthly, use the compound interest formula to calculate the compound amount of this offer.

33. A certain animal husbandry program has a flock of sheep that increases in size by 15% every year. If there are currently 48 sheep, how many sheep are expected to be in the flock in 5 years? Round to the nearest whole sheep.

34. The rate of bacteria growth in a laboratory experiment was measured at 16% per hour. If this experiment is repeated and begins with 5 grams of bacteria, how much bacteria should be expected after 12 hours? Round to the nearest tenth of a gram.

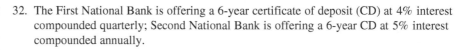

UPS Store franchises have consistently been recognized as leading opportunities in this sector. With 4,300 locations, the minimum requirements are $60,000–$100,000 in cash or liquid assets.

Some of the products and services UPS Stores provide include packing and shipping services, mailbox and postal services, copying, faxing, notary services, finishing and printing services, and packaging and moving supplies.

SG cityscapes/Alamy

Learning Tip

Compounding Sheep!
The concept of compounding may also be used to compound "other variables" besides money. Use the compound interest table or formula for Exercises 33 and 34.

Solve the following exercises and word problems by using the compound interest formula.

	Principal	Time Period (years)	Nominal Rate (%)	Interest Compounded	Compound Amount	Compound Interest
35.	$5,000	4	4.2	semiannually	$5,904.40	$904.40
36.	$700	8	1.5	monthly	_____	_____
37.	$2,800	$2\frac{1}{2}$	3.1	quarterly	_____	_____
38.	$12,450	10	2.6	annually	_____	_____

39. Gabriel Hopen, a 32-year-old commercial artist, has just signed a contract with an advertising agency. Gabriel's starting salary is $47,800. The agency has agreed to increase his salary by 8.5% annually. How much will Gabriel's salary be after 5 years? Round to the nearest whole dollar.

40. The FernRod Motorcycle Company invested $250,000 at 4.5% compounded monthly to be used for the expansion of their manufacturing facilities. How much money will be available for the project in $3\frac{1}{2}$ years?

- -

BUSINESS DECISION: DAILY COMPOUNDING

41. As an incentive to attract savings deposits, most financial institutions today offer **daily** and even **continuous compounding**. This means that savings, or passbook, accounts, as well as CDs, earn interest compounded each day or even more frequently, such as every hour or even every minute. (Continuous compounding, in which compounding occurs every instant, involves a different formula that is derived from the formula we've been using.) Let's take a look at daily compounding.

To calculate the compound amount, A, of an investment with daily compounding, use the compound interest formula modified as follows:

- Rate per period (daily) $= \dfrac{i}{365}$ (nominal interest rate, i, divided by 365)
- Number of periods (days), n, = number of days of the investment.

$$A = P\left(1 + \frac{i}{365}\right)^n$$

Calculator Sequence: 1 $+$ $($ i $\div$ 365 $)$ y^x n $\times$ P $=$ A

a. On April 19, Thomas Ash deposited $2,700 in a passbook savings account at 3.5% interest compounded daily. What is the compound amount of his account on August 5?

b. Using daily compounding, recalculate the compound amount for each of the three certificates of deposit in Exercise 32.

SECTION II   11   PRESENT VALUE

In Section I, we learned how to find a future value when the present value was known. Let's take a look at the reverse situation, also commonly found in business. When a future value (an amount needed in the future) is known, the present value is the amount that must be invested today to accumulate with compound interest to that future value. For example, if a corporation wants $100,000 in 5 years (future value—known) to replace its fleet of trucks, what amount must be invested today (present value—unknown) at 8% compounded quarterly to achieve this goal? (See Exhibit 11-5.)

EXHIBIT 11-5
Present Value to Future Value

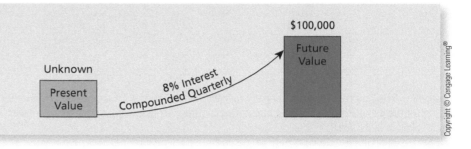

11-6   CALCULATING THE PRESENT VALUE OF A FUTURE AMOUNT BY USING PRESENT VALUE TABLES

Just as there are compound interest tables to aid in the calculation of compound amounts, present value tables help calculate the present value of a known future amount. Table 11-2 is such a table. Note that this table is similar to the compound interest table in that the table factors are based on the interest rate per period and the number of compounding periods.

STEPS FOR USING PRESENT VALUE TABLES

STEP 1. Scan across the top row to find the interest rate per period.

STEP 2. Look down that column to the row corresponding to the number of periods.

STEP 3. The table factor found at the intersection of the rate-per-period column and the number-of-periods row is the present value of $1 at compound interest. Multiply the table factor by the compound amount to determine the present value.

Present value = Table factor × Compound amount (future value)

EXAMPLE6   CALCULATING PRESENT VALUE

Charlie Watson will need $5,000 in 8 years. Use Table 11-2 to find how much he must invest now at 6% interest compounded semiannually to have $5,000, 8 years from now.

▶SOLUTIONSTRATEGY

To solve this present value problem, we will use 3% per period (6% nominal rate ÷ 2 periods per year) and 16 periods (8 years × 2 periods per year).

Step 1. Scan the top row of the present value table to 3%.

Step 2. Look down that column to the row corresponding to 16 periods.

TABLE 11-2 Present Value Table (Present Value of $1 at Compound Interest)

Periods	$\frac{1}{2}\%$	1%	$1\frac{1}{2}\%$	2%	3%	4%	5%	6%	7%	8%	Periods
1	0.99502	0.99010	0.98522	0.98039	0.97087	0.96154	0.95238	0.94340	0.93458	0.92593	1
2	0.99007	0.98030	0.97066	0.96117	0.94260	0.92456	0.90703	0.89000	0.87344	0.85734	2
3	0.98515	0.97059	0.95632	0.94232	0.91514	0.88900	0.86384	0.83962	0.81630	0.79383	3
4	0.98025	0.96098	0.94218	0.92385	0.88849	0.85480	0.82270	0.79209	0.76290	0.73503	4
5	0.97537	0.95147	0.92826	0.90573	0.86261	0.82193	0.78353	0.74726	0.71299	0.68058	5
6	0.97052	0.94205	0.91454	0.88797	0.83748	0.79031	0.74622	0.70496	0.66634	0.63017	6
7	0.96569	0.93272	0.90103	0.87056	0.81309	0.75992	0.71068	0.66506	0.62275	0.58349	7
8	0.96089	0.92348	0.88771	0.85349	0.78941	0.73069	0.67684	0.62741	0.58201	0.54027	8
9	0.95610	0.91434	0.87459	0.83676	0.76642	0.70259	0.64461	0.59190	0.54393	0.50025	9
10	0.95135	0.90529	0.86167	0.82035	0.74409	0.67556	0.61391	0.55839	0.50835	0.46319	10
11	0.94661	0.89632	0.84893	0.80426	0.72242	0.64958	0.58468	0.52679	0.47509	0.42888	11
12	0.94191	0.88745	0.83639	0.78849	0.70138	0.62460	0.55684	0.49697	0.44401	0.39711	12
13	0.93722	0.87866	0.82403	0.77303	0.68095	0.60057	0.53032	0.46884	0.41496	0.36770	13
14	0.93256	0.86996	0.81185	0.75788	0.66112	0.57748	0.50507	0.44230	0.38782	0.34046	14
15	0.92792	0.86135	0.79985	0.74301	0.64186	0.55526	0.48102	0.41727	0.36245	0.31524	15
16	0.92330	0.85282	0.78803	0.72845	0.62317	0.53391	0.45811	0.39365	0.33873	0.29189	16
17	0.91871	0.84438	0.77639	0.71416	0.60502	0.51337	0.43630	0.37136	0.31657	0.27027	17
18	0.91414	0.83602	0.76491	0.70016	0.58739	0.49363	0.41552	0.35034	0.29586	0.25025	18
19	0.90959	0.82774	0.75361	0.68643	0.57029	0.47464	0.39573	0.33051	0.27651	0.23171	19
20	0.90506	0.81954	0.74247	0.67297	0.55368	0.45639	0.37689	0.31180	0.25842	0.21455	20
21	0.90056	0.81143	0.73150	0.65978	0.53755	0.43883	0.35894	0.29416	0.24151	0.19866	21
22	0.89608	0.80340	0.72069	0.64684	0.52189	0.42196	0.34185	0.27751	0.22571	0.18394	22
23	0.89162	0.79544	0.71004	0.63416	0.50669	0.40573	0.32557	0.26180	0.21095	0.17032	23
24	0.88719	0.78757	0.69954	0.62172	0.49193	0.39012	0.31007	0.24698	0.19715	0.15770	24
25	0.88277	0.77977	0.68921	0.60953	0.47761	0.37512	0.29530	0.23300	0.18425	0.14602	25

Periods	9%	10%	11%	12%	13%	14%	15%	16%	17%	18%	Periods
1	0.91743	0.90909	0.90090	0.89286	0.88496	0.87719	0.86957	0.86207	0.85470	0.84746	1
2	0.84168	0.82645	0.81162	0.79719	0.78315	0.76947	0.75614	0.74316	0.73051	0.71818	2
3	0.77218	0.75131	0.73119	0.71178	0.69305	0.67497	0.65752	0.64066	0.62437	0.60863	3
4	0.70843	0.68301	0.65873	0.63552	0.61332	0.59208	0.57175	0.55229	0.53365	0.51579	4
5	0.64993	0.62092	0.59345	0.56743	0.54276	0.51937	0.49718	0.47611	0.45611	0.43711	5
6	0.59627	0.56447	0.53464	0.50663	0.48032	0.45559	0.43233	0.41044	0.38984	0.37043	6
7	0.54703	0.51316	0.48166	0.45235	0.42506	0.39964	0.37594	0.35383	0.33320	0.31393	7
8	0.50187	0.46651	0.43393	0.40388	0.37616	0.35056	0.32690	0.30503	0.28478	0.26604	8
9	0.46043	0.42410	0.39092	0.36061	0.33288	0.30751	0.28426	0.26295	0.24340	0.22546	9
10	0.42241	0.38554	0.35218	0.32197	0.29459	0.26974	0.24718	0.22668	0.20804	0.19106	10
11	0.38753	0.35049	0.31728	0.28748	0.26070	0.23662	0.21494	0.19542	0.17781	0.16192	11
12	0.35553	0.31863	0.28584	0.25668	0.23071	0.20756	0.18691	0.16846	0.15197	0.13722	12
13	0.32618	0.28966	0.25751	0.22917	0.20416	0.18207	0.16253	0.14523	0.12989	0.11629	13
14	0.29925	0.26333	0.23199	0.20462	0.18068	0.15971	0.14133	0.12520	0.11102	0.09855	14
15	0.27454	0.23939	0.20900	0.18270	0.15989	0.14010	0.12289	0.10793	0.09489	0.08352	15
16	0.25187	0.21763	0.18829	0.16312	0.14150	0.12289	0.10686	0.09304	0.08110	0.07078	16
17	0.23107	0.19784	0.16963	0.14564	0.12522	0.10780	0.09293	0.08021	0.06932	0.05998	17
18	0.21199	0.17986	0.15282	0.13004	0.11081	0.09456	0.08081	0.06914	0.05925	0.05083	18
19	0.19449	0.16351	0.13768	0.11611	0.09806	0.08295	0.07027	0.05961	0.05064	0.04308	19
20	0.17843	0.14864	0.12403	0.10367	0.08678	0.07276	0.06110	0.05139	0.04328	0.03651	20
21	0.16370	0.13513	0.11174	0.09256	0.07680	0.06383	0.05313	0.04430	0.03699	0.03094	21
22	0.15018	0.12285	0.10067	0.08264	0.06796	0.05599	0.04620	0.03819	0.03162	0.02622	22
23	0.13778	0.11168	0.09069	0.07379	0.06014	0.04911	0.04017	0.03292	0.02702	0.02222	23
24	0.12640	0.10153	0.08170	0.06588	0.05323	0.04308	0.03493	0.02838	0.02310	0.01883	24
25	0.11597	0.09230	0.07361	0.05882	0.04710	0.03779	0.03038	0.02447	0.01974	0.01596	25

The values in Table 11-2 were generated by the formula $PV = \dfrac{1}{(1 + i)^n}$ rounded to five decimal places, where i is the interest rate per period and n is the total number of periods.

Step 3. Find the table factor at the intersection of Steps 1 and 2 and multiply it by the compound amount to find the present value. Table factor = .62317.

$$\text{Present value} = \text{Table factor} \times \text{Compound amount}$$
$$\text{Present value} = .62317 \times 5{,}000 = \underline{\$3{,}115.85}$$

▶TRYITEXERCISE 6

Count Gustav wants to renovate his castle in Boulogne in 3 years. He estimates the cost to be $3,000,000. Use Table 11-2 to find how much the count must invest now at 8% interest compounded quarterly to have $3,000,000, 3 years from now.

CHECK YOUR ANSWER WITH THE SOLUTION ON PAGE 363.

11-7 CREATING PRESENT VALUE TABLE FACTORS FOR PERIODS BEYOND THE TABLE

Just as with the compound interest tables, there may be times when the number of periods of an investment or a loan is greater than the number of periods provided by the present value tables. When this occurs, you can create a new table factor by multiplying the table factors for any two periods that add up to the number of periods required.

For answer consistency in this chapter, use the two table factors that represent *half*, or values as close as possible to half, of the periods required. For example,

STEPS FOR CREATING NEW TABLE FACTORS

STEP 1. For the stated interest rate per period, find the two table factors that represent *half*, or values as close as possible to half, of the periods required.

STEP 2. Multiply the two table factors from Step 1 to form the new factor.

STEP 3. Round the new factor to five decimal places.

EXAMPLE7 CREATING PRESENT VALUE TABLE FACTORS

Calculate a new table factor and find the present value of $2,000 if the interest rate is 12% compounded quarterly for 8 years.

▶SOLUTIONSTRATEGY

This investment requires a table factor for 32 periods, four periods per year for 8 years. Because Table 11-2 provides factors only up to 25 periods, we must create one by using the steps above.

Step 1. At 12% interest compounded quarterly, the rate per period is 3%. Because we are looking for 32 periods, we will use the factors for 16 and 16 periods at 3%.

Table factor for 16 periods, 3% = .62317
Table factor for 16 periods, 3% = .62317

Step 2. Multiply the factors for 16 and 16 periods:

.62317 × .62317 = .3883408

Step 3. Rounding to five decimal places, the new table factor for 32 periods is .38834. The present value of the $2,000 investment is

Present value = Table factor × Compound amount

Present value = .38834 × 2,000 = $776.68

▶TRYITEXERCISE 7

Calculate a new table factor and find the present value of $8,500 if the interest rate is 6% compounded quarterly for 10 years.

CHECK YOUR ANSWERS WITH THE SOLUTIONS ON PAGE 363.

CALCULATING PRESENT VALUE OF A FUTURE AMOUNT BY USING THE PRESENT VALUE FORMULA

11-8

If your calculator has an exponential function key, y^x, you can calculate the present value of an investment by using the present value formula.

The present value formula states:

$$PV = \frac{A}{(1+i)^n}$$

where:

PV = **Present value**

A = **Compound amount**

i = **Interest rate per period (expressed as a decimal)**

n = **Total compounding periods (years × periods per year)**

STEPS FOR SOLVING THE PRESENT VALUE FORMULA

STEP 1. Add the 1 and the interest rate per period, i.

STEP 2. Raise the sum from Step 1 to the nth power by using the y^x key on your calculator.

STEP 3. Divide the compound amount, A, by the answer from Step 2.

Calculator sequence 1 $+$ i $=$ y^x n $=$ M+ A $\div$ MR $=$ PV

EXAMPLE8   USING THE PRESENT VALUE FORMULA

Use the present value formula to calculate the present value of $3,000 if the interest rate is 8% compounded quarterly for 6 years.

▶SOLUTIONSTRATEGY

This problem is solved by substituting the investment information into the present value formula. It is important to solve the formula using the sequence of steps outlined. Note the rate per period, i, is 2% (8% ÷ 4 periods per year). The total number of periods, the exponent n, is 24 (6 years × 4 periods per year).

$$\text{Present value} = \frac{A}{(1+i)^n}$$

$$\text{Present value} = \frac{3,000}{(1+.02)^{24}}$$

$$\text{Present value} = \frac{3,000}{(1.02)^{24}}$$

$$\text{Present value} = \frac{3,000}{1.608437249} = \$1,865.16$$

Calculator Sequence: 1 $+$ .02 $=$ y^x 24 $=$ M+ 3000 $\div$ MR $=$ $1,865.16

▶TRYITEXERCISE 8

Sam and Rosa Alonso want to accumulate $30,000, 17 years from now as a college fund for their baby son, Michael. Use the present value formula to calculate how much they must invest now at an interest rate of 8% compounded semiannually to have $30,000 in 17 years.

CHECK YOUR ANSWER WITH THE SOLUTION ON PAGE 363.

SECTION II 11 REVIEW EXERCISES

For the following investments, calculate the present value (principal) and the compound interest. Use Table 11-2. Round your answers to the nearest cent.

	Compound Amount	Term of Investment	Nominal Rate (%)	Interest Compounded	Present Value	Compound Interest
1.	$6,000	3 years	9	annually	$4,633.08	$1,366.92
2.	$24,000	6 years	14	semiannually		
3.	$650	5 years	8	quarterly		
4.	$2,000	12 years	6	semiannually		
5.	$50,000	25 years	11	annually		
6.	$14,500	18 months	10	semiannually		
7.	$9,800	4 years	12	quarterly		
8.	$100,000	10 years	9	annually		
9.	$250	1 year	6	monthly		
10.	$4,000	27 months	8	quarterly		

The following investments require table factors for periods beyond the table. Create the new table factor rounded to five places and calculate the present value for each.

	Compound Amount	Term of Investment (years)	Nominal Rate (%)	Interest Compounded	New Table Factor	Present Value
11.	$12,000	10	16	quarterly	.20829	$2,499.48
12.	$33,000	38	7	annually		
13.	$1,400	12	12	quarterly		
14.	$1,000	45	13	annually		
15.	$110,000	17	8	semiannually		

Solve the following word problems by using Table 11-2.

16. How much must be invested today at 6% compounded quarterly to have $8,000 in 3 years?

17. Samantha Wimberly is planning a vacation in Europe in 4 years, after graduation. She estimates that she will need $3,500 for the trip.

   a. If her bank is offering 4-year certificates of deposit with 8% interest compounded quarterly, how much must Samantha invest now to have the money for the trip?

   b. How much compound interest will be earned on the investment?

18. Pinnacle Homes, a real estate development company, is planning to build five homes, each costing $125,000, in $2\frac{1}{2}$ years. The Galaxy Bank pays 6% interest compounded semiannually. How much should the company invest now to have sufficient funds to build the homes in the future?

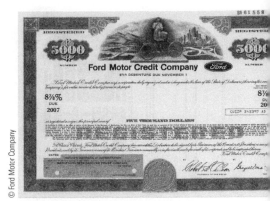
© Ford Motor Company

Corporate bonds are debt obligations, or IOUs, issued by private and public corporations. They are typically issued in multiples of $1,000. Bonds are commonly used to finance company modernization and expansion programs.

When you buy a bond, you are lending money to the corporation that issued it. The corporation promises to return your money (or principal) on a specified maturity date. Until that time, it also pays you a stated rate of interest.

19. Tri Star Airlines intends to pay off a $20,000,000 corporate bond issue that comes due in 4 years. How much must the company set aside now at 6% interest compounded monthly to accumulate the required amount of money?

20. Stuart Daniels estimates that he will need $25,000 to set up a small business in 7 years.

   a. How much must Stuart invest now at 8% interest compounded quarterly to achieve his goal?

   b. How much compound interest will he earn on the investment?

21. Summertime songbird population within the Mid-America flyway is predicted to increase over the next 8 years at the rate of 2% per year. If the songbird population is predicted to reach 55 million in 8 years, how many songbirds are there today? Round to the nearest million.

Learning Tip

Present Value of a Songbird!
Just as with compounding, the concept of present value of a future amount may also be applied to "other variables" besides money. Use the present value table or formula for Exercises 21 and 22.

22. The requirement for computer server capacity at Acme Industries is expected to increase at a rate of 15% per year for the next 5 years. If the server capacity is expected to be 1,400 gigabytes in 5 years, how many gigabytes of capacity are there today? Round to the nearest whole gigabyte.

Solve the following exercises and word problems by using the present value formula

	Principal	Term of Investment	Nominal Rate (%)	Interest Compounded	Present Value	Compound Interest
23.	$4,500	7 years	3.8	annually	$3,466.02	$1,033.98
24.	$15,000	8 years	4.5	monthly	_____	_____
25.	$18,900	10 years	1.9	semiannually	_____	_____
26.	$675	15 months	2.7	quarterly	_____	_____

27. Alana and Eva Rodriguez are planning a cross-country road trip in 3 years. They estimate $6,000 will be needed to cover expenses. The National Bank of Pinecrest is offering a 3-year CD paying 3.62% interest compounded quarterly.

  a. How much should they set aside now to achieve their goal? Round to the nearest whole dollar.

  b. How much interest will Alana and Eva earn on the CD?

28. Mike Gioulis would like to have $25,000 in 4 years to pay off a balloon payment on his business mortgage. His money market account is paying 1.825% compounded daily. Disregarding leap years, how much money must Mike put in his account now to achieve his goal? Round to the nearest whole dollar.

BUSINESS DECISION: THE INFLATION FACTOR

29. You are the finance manager for Olympia Industries. The company plans to purchase $1,000,000 in new assembly line machinery in 5 years.

  a. How much must be set aside now at 6% interest compounded semiannually to accumulate the $1,000,000 in 5 years?

  b. If the inflation rate on this type of equipment is 4% per year, what will be the cost of the equipment in 5 years, adjusted for inflation?

  c. Use the inflation-adjusted cost of the equipment to calculate how much must be set aside now.

  d. Use the present value formula to calculate how much would be required now if you found a bank that offered 6% interest compounded daily.

Dollars AND Sense

Inflation should be taken into account when making financial plans that cover time periods longer than a year.

CHAPTER FORMULAS

Compound Interest

Compound interest = Compound amount − Principal

Compounding periods = Years × Periods per year

$$\text{Interest rate per period} = \frac{\text{Nominal rate}}{\text{Periods per year}}$$

Compound amount = Table factor × Principal

$$\text{Annual percentage yield (APY)} = \frac{\text{Total compound interest earned in 1 year}}{\text{Principal}}$$

Compound amount = Principal(1 + Interest rate per period)^{periods}

Present Value

Present value = Table factor × Compound amount

$$\text{Present value} = \frac{\text{Compound amount}}{(1 + \text{Interest rate per period})^{\text{periods}}}$$

CHAPTER SUMMARY

Section I: Compound Interest—The Time Value of Money

Topic	Important Concepts	Illustrative Examples
Manually Calculating Compound Amount (Future Value) **Performance Objective 11-1, Page 343**	In compound interest, the interest is applied a number of times during the term of an investment. Compound interest yields considerably higher interest than simple interest does because the investor is earning interest on the interest. 　　Interest can be compounded annually, semiannually, quarterly, monthly, daily, and continuously. 1. Determine the number of compounding periods (years × periods per year). 2. Apply the simple interest formula, $I = PRT$, as many times as there are compounding periods, adding interest to principal before each succeeding calculation.	Manually calculate the compound amount of a $1,000 investment at 8% interest compounded annually for 2 years. Original principal　　　　1,000.00 Interest — period 1　　　+　80.00 Principal — period 2　　　1,080.00 Interest — period 2　　　+　86.40 Compound amount　　　$1,166.40
Calculating Amount of Compound Interest **Performance Objective 11-1, Page 343**	Amount of compound interest is calculated by subtracting the original principal from the compound amount. **Compound interest** 　　　= Compound amount − Principal	What is the amount of compound interest earned in the problem above? 1,166.40 − 1,000.00 = $166.40
Computing Compound Amount (Future Value) by Using Compound Interest Tables **Performance Objective 11-2, Page 344**	1. Scan across the top row of Table 11-1 to find the interest rate per period. 2. Look down that column to the row corresponding to the number of compounding periods. 3. The table factor found at the intersection of the rate-per-period column and the periods row is the future value of $1.00 at compound interest. **Compound amount = Table factor × Principal**	Use Table 11-1 to find the compound amount of an investment of $2,000 at 12% interest compounded quarterly for 6 years. Rate = 3% per period (12% ÷ 4) Periods = 24 (6 years × 4) Table factor = 2.03279 Compound amount = 2.03279 × 2,000 　　　　　　　　 = $4,065.58
Creating Compound Interest Table Factors for Periods beyond the Table **Performance Objective 11-3, Page 347**	1. For the stated interest rate per period, find the two table factors that represent *half*, or values as close as possible to half, of the periods required. 2. Multiply the two table factors from Step 1 to form the new factor. 3. Round the new factor to five decimal places.	Create a new table factor for 5% interest for 30 periods. 　　Multiply the 5% factors for 15 and 15 periods from Table 11-1. 5%, 15 periods =　　2.07893 5%, 15 periods = × 2.07893 　　30　　　　　4.3219499 New factor rounded = 4.32195

Section I (continued)

Topic	Important Concepts	Illustrative Examples
Calculating Annual Percentage Yield (APY) or Effective Interest Rate **Performance Objective 11-4, Page 348**	To calculate annual percentage yield, divide total compound interest earned in 1 year by the principal. $\text{Annual percentage yield(APY)} = \dfrac{\text{1 year compound interest}}{\text{Principal}}$	What is the annual percentage yield of $5,000 invested for 1 year at 12% compounded monthly? From Table 11-1, we use the table factor for 12 periods, 1%, to find the compound amount: $1.12683 \times 5,000 = 5,634.15$ Interest = Cmp. amt. − Principal Interest = $5,634.15 - 5,000.00 = 634.15$ $\text{APY} = \dfrac{634.15}{5,000} = \underline{\underline{12.68\%}}$

Calculating Compound Amount (Future Value) by Using the Compound Interest Formula
 	
Performance Objective 11-5, Page 349
	In addition to the compound interest tables, another method for calculating compound amount is by using the compound interest formula.
	
	$A = P(1 + i)^n$
	where:
	  $A = $ Compound amount
	  $P = $ Principal
	  $i = $ Interest rate per period (decimal form)
	  $n = $ Number of compounding periods
		What is the compound amount of $3,000 invested at 8% interest compounded quarterly for 10 years?
		
		$A = P(1 + i)^n$
		$A = 3,000(1 + .02)^{40}$
		$A = 3,000(1.02)^{40}$
		$A = 3,000(2.2080396)$
		$A = \underline{\underline{\$6,624.12}}$

Section II: Present Value

Topic	Important Concepts	Illustrative Examples

Calculating the Present Value of a Future Amount by Using Present Value Tables
 	
Performance Objective 11-6, Page 354
	When the future value, an amount needed in the future, is known, the present value is the amount that must be invested today to accumulate, with compound interest, to that future value.
	
	1. Scan across the top row of Table 11-2 to find the rate per period.
	2. Look down that column to the row corresponding to the number of periods.
	3. The table factor found at the intersection of the rate-per-period column and the periods row is the present value of $1 at compound interest.
	
	  Present value
	    = Table factor × Compound amount
		How much must be invested now at 10% interest compounded semiannually to have $8,000, 9 years from now?
		
		Rate = 5% (10% ÷ 2)
		Periods = 18 (9 years × 2)
		Table factor = .41552
		Present value = .41552 × 8,000
		Present value = $\underline{\underline{\$3,324.16}}$

Creating Present Value Table Factors for Periods beyond the Table
 	
Performance Objective 11-7, Page 356
	1. For the stated interest rate per period, find the two table factors that represent *half*, or values as close as possible to half, of the periods required.
	2. Multiply the two table factors from Step 1 for the new factor.
	3. Round the new factor to five decimal places.
		Create a new table factor for 6% interest for 41 periods.
		Multiply the 6% factors for 21 and 20 periods from Table 11-2.
		  6%, 21 periods = .29416
		  6%, <u>20</u> periods = <u>× .31180</u>
		  41 .0917191
		New factor rounded = $\underline{.09172}$

Calculating Present Value of a Future Amount by Using the Present Value Formula
 	
Performance Objective 11-8, Page 357
	If your calculator has an exponential function key, y^x, you can calculate the present value of an investment by using the present value formula.
	
	$PV = \dfrac{A}{(1 + i)^n}$
	where:
	  $PV = $ Present value
	  $A = $ Compound amount
	  $i = $ Interest rate per period (decimal form)
	  $n = $ Total compounding periods
		How much must be invested now to have $12,000 in 10 years if the interest rate is 12% compounded quarterly?
		
		$\text{Present value} = \dfrac{12,000}{(1 + .03)^{40}}$
		$PV = \dfrac{12,000}{(1.03)^{40}} = \dfrac{12,000}{3.2620378}$
		Present value = $\underline{\underline{\$3,678.68}}$

Try It: Exercise Solutions for Chapter 11

1.

10,000.00	Original principal
+ 300.00	($I = PRT = 10{,}000 \times .06 \times \frac{1}{2} = 300$)
10,300.00	Principal period 2
+ 309.00	($I = PRT = 10{,}300.00 \times .06 \times \frac{1}{2} = 309$)
10,609.00	Principal period 3
+ 318.27	($I = PRT = 10{,}609.00 \times .06 \times \frac{1}{2} = 318.27$)
10,927.27	Principal period 4
+ 327.82	($I = PRT = 10{,}927.27 \times .06 \times \frac{1}{2} = 327.82$)
11,255.09	Principal period 5
+ 337.65	($I = PRT = 11{,}255.09 \times .06 \times \frac{1}{2} = 337.65$)
11,592.74	Principal period 6
+ 347.78	($I = PRT = 11{,}592.74 \times .06 \times \frac{1}{2} = 347.78$)
$11,940.52	Compound amount

Compound Interest = 11,940.52 − 10,000.00 = **$1,940.52**

2. 3%, 16 periods
Compound amount = Table factor × Principal
Compound amount = 1.60471 × 20,000 = **$32,094.20**
Compound interest = Compound amount − Principal
Compound interest = 32,094.20 − 20,000.00 = **$12,094.20**

3. Table factor required = 2%, 28 periods
2%, 14 periods: 1.31948
2%, 14 periods: × 1.31948

28 periods 1.74102747 = 1.74103 New table factor
                                            2%, 28 periods
Compound amount = 1.74103 × 3,500 = **$6,093.61**

4. $1\frac{1}{2}$%, 4 periods

Compound amount = 1.06136 × 7,000 = **$7,429.52**
Compound interest = 7,429.52 − 7,000.00 = **$429.52**

$$\frac{\text{Annual}}{\text{percentage yield}} = \frac{1 \text{ year interest}}{\text{Principal}} = \frac{429.52}{7{,}000.00} = 6.14\%$$

5. $A = P(1 + i)^n$ $P = \$3{,}000$

$i = \dfrac{8\%}{4} = .02$

$n = 5 \times 4 = 20$

$A = 3{,}000(1 + .02)^{20}$
$A = 3{,}000(1.02)^{20}$
$A = 3{,}000(1.4859474)$
$A = \underline{\$4{,}457.84}$

6. 2%, 12 periods
Present value = Table factor × Compound amount
Present value = .78849 × 3,000,000 = **$2,365,470**

7. Table factor required = $1\frac{1}{2}$%, 40 Periods

$1\frac{1}{2}$%, 20 periods: .74247

$1\frac{1}{2}$%, 20 periods: × .74247
40 periods = .5512617 = .55126 New table factor
                                            $1\frac{1}{2}$%, 40 periods

Present value = .55126 × 8,500 = **$4,685.71**

8. $PV = \dfrac{A}{(1 + i)^n}$ $A = 30{,}000$

$i = \dfrac{8\%}{2} = .04$

$n = 17 \times 2 = 34$

$PV = \dfrac{30{,}000}{(1 + .04)^{34}}$

$PV = \dfrac{30{,}000}{(1.04)^{34}}$

$PV = \dfrac{30{,}000}{3.7943163} = \$7{,}906.56$

Concept Review

1. Interest calculated solely on the principal is known as _____ interest, whereas interest calculated on the principal and previously earned interest is known as _____ interest. (11-1)

2. The concept that money "now," or in the present, is more desirable than the same amount of money in the future because it can be invested and earn interest as time goes by is known as the _____ of money. (11-1)

3. The total amount of principal and accumulated interest at the end of a loan or an investment is known as the _____ amount or _____ value. (11-1)

4. An amount of money that must be deposited today at compound interest to provide a specified lump sum of money in the future is known as the _____ amount or _____ value. (11-1, 11-6)

5. The amount of compound interest is calculated by subtracting the _____ from the compound amount. (11-1)

6. Compound interest is actually the _____ interest formula applied a number of times. (11-1)

7. A compound interest table is a useful set of factors that represent the future value of _____ at various interest rates for a number of compounding periods. (11-2)

8. A shortcut method for calculating approximately how long it takes money to double in value at compound interest is called the Rule of _____. (11-3)

9. Write the formula for calculating the number of compounding periods of a loan or an investment. (11-2)

10. Write the formula for calculating the interest rate per period of a loan or an investment. (11-2)

11. Newly created table factors for compound interest and present value should be rounded to _____ decimal places. (11-3, 11-7)

12. The annual percentage yield (APY) is equal to the total compound interest earned in _____ year divided by the _____. (11-4)

13. When using the compound interest table or the present value table, the factor is found at the intersection of the rate-per-_____ column and the number-of-_____ row. (11-2, 11-6)

14. To use the compound interest formula and the present value formula, you need a calculator with a(n) _____ function (y^x) key. (11-5, 11-8)

ASSESSMENT TEST

Note: Round to the nearest cent when necessary.

Using Table 11-1, calculate the compound amount and compound interest for the following investments.

	Principal	Time Period (years)	Nominal Rate (%)	Interest Compounded	Compound Amount	Compound Interest
1.	$14,000	6	14	semiannually		
2.	$7,700	5	6	quarterly		
3.	$3,000	1	6	monthly		
4.	$42,000	19	11	annually		

The following investments require table factors for periods beyond the table. Create the new table factor and calculate the compound amount for each.

	Principal	Time Period (years)	Nominal Rate (%)	Interest Compounded	New Table Factor	Compound Amount
5.	$20,000	11	16	quarterly		
6.	$10,000	4	6	monthly		

For the following investments, compute the amount of compound interest earned in 1 year and the annual percentage yield. Round APY to the nearest hundredth of a percent.

	Principal	Nominal Rate (%)	Interest Compounded	Compound Interest Earned in 1 Year	Annual Percentage Yield (APY)
7.	$8,500	12	monthly		
8.	$1,000,000	8	quarterly		

Calculate the present value (principal) and the compound interest for the following investments. Use Table 11-2. Round answers to the nearest cent.

	Compound Amount	Term of Investment	Nominal Rate (%)	Interest Compounded	Present Value	Compound Interest
9.	$150,000	22 years	15	annually		
10.	$20,000	30 months	14	semiannually		
11.	$900	$1\frac{3}{4}$ years	18	monthly		
12.	$5,500	15 months	8	quarterly		

The following investments require table factors for periods beyond the table. Create the new table factor and the present value for each.

	Compound Amount	Time Period (years)	Nominal Rate (%)	Interest Compounded	New Table Factor	Present Value
13.	$1,300	4	12	monthly		
14.	$100,000	50	5	annually		

Solve the following word problems by using Table 11-1 or 11-2. When necessary, create new table factors. Round dollars to the nearest cent and percents to the nearest hundredth of a percent.

CHAPTER
11

15. What is the compound amount and compound interest of $36,000 invested at 12% compounded semiannually for 7 years?

16. What is the present value of $73,000 in 11 years if the interest rate is 8% compounded semiannually?

17. What is the compound amount and compound interest of $15,000 invested at 6% compounded quarterly for 27 months?

18. What is the annual percentage yield of a $10,000 investment for 1 year at 12% interest compounded monthly?

19. City Wide Delivery Service uses vans costing $24,800 each. How much will the company have to invest today to accumulate enough money to buy six new vans at the end of 4 years? City Wide's bank is currently paying 12% interest compounded quarterly.

20. You are the owner of a Jani-King cleaning service franchise. Your accountant has determined that the business will need $27,500 in new equipment in 3 years. If your bank is paying 6% interest compounded monthly, how much must you invest today to meet this financial goal? Round to the nearest whole dollar.

Jani-King is the world's largest commercial cleaning franchise company with over 12,000 owners worldwide. Jani-King contracts commercial cleaning services for many different facilities including healthcare, office, hotel/resort, manufacturing, restaurant, and sporting venues.

Jani-King has been rated the #1 Commercial Cleaning Franchise Company for 23 years in a row by *Entrepreneur Magazine*. In most regions, one may start a Jani-King franchise for as little as $3,000. Cleaning services is a $100 billion industry and is projected to grow to more than $155 billion. The U.S. Bureau of Labor Statistics reports that professional cleaning specialists will be the fastest-growing occupation in this decade.

21. Valerie Walton invested $8,800 at the Northern Trust Credit Union at 12% interest compounded quarterly.

   a. What is the annual percentage yield of this investment?

   b. What will Valerie's investment be worth after 6 years?

22. Bob and Joy Salkind want to save $50,000 in $5\frac{1}{2}$ years for home improvement projects. If the Bank of Aventura is paying 8% interest compounded quarterly, how much must they deposit now to have the money for the project?

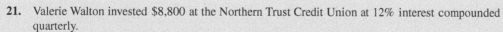

23. While rummaging through the attic, you discover a savings account left to you by a relative. When you were 5 years old, he invested $20,000 in your name at 6% interest compounded semiannually. If you are now 20 years old, how much is the account worth?

24. Applegate Industries is planning to expand its production facility in a few years. New plant construction costs are estimated to be $4.50 per square foot. The company invests $850,000 today at 8% interest compounded quarterly.

   a. How many square feet of new facility could be built after $3\frac{1}{2}$ years? Round to the nearest whole square foot.

   b. If the company waits 5 years and construction costs increase to $5.25 per square foot, how many square feet could be built? Round to the nearest whole square foot. What do you recommend?

25. Over the past 10 years, you've made the following investments:

   1. Deposited $10,000 at 8% compounded semiannually in a 3-year certificate of deposit.
   2. After the 3 years, you took the maturity value (principal and interest) of that CD and added another $5,000 to buy a 4-year, 6% certificate compounded quarterly.
   3. When that certificate matured, you added another $8,000 and bought a 3-year, 7% certificate compounded annually.
     a. What was the total worth of your investment when the last certificate matured?

     b. What is the total amount of compound interest earned over the 10-year period?

26. Fred North owns Redlands Farms, a successful strawberry farm. The strawberry plants increase at a compound rate of 12% per year. Each year Fred brings new land under cultivation for the new strawberry plants. If the farm has 50 acres of strawberry plants today, how many acres of strawberry plants will the farm have in 8 years? Round to the nearest whole acre.

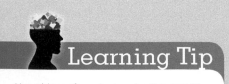

Use tables or formulas to solve Exercises 26 and 27.

27. At Reliable Trucking, Inc., annual sales are predicted to increase over the next 3 years at a rate of 6% per year. Sales equate to "fleet miles." If Reliable's fleet miles are predicted to reach 4.4 million in 3 years, what is the number of fleet miles today? Round to the nearest tenth of a million.

Solve the following exercises and word problems using formulas.

	Principal	Time Period (years)	Nominal Rate (%)	Interest Compounded	Compound Amount	Compound Interest
28.	$3,425	11	6.6	monthly		
29.	$21,800	6	2.9	semiannually		
30.	$400	$2\frac{1}{2}$	4.2	quarterly		
31.	$9,630	5	3.1	annually		

	Principal	Term of Investment	Nominal Rate (%)	Interest Compounded	Present Value	Compound Interest
32.	$6,300	14 years	6.3	annually		
33.	$80,200	9 months	4.8	quarterly		
34.	$27,500	10 years	3.6	semiannually		
35.	$2,440	5 years	1.5	monthly		

36. What is the compound amount and compound interest of a $73,000 investment earning 2.9% interest compounded semiannually for 4 years? Round to the nearest whole dollar.

37. Jorge Rodriguez would like to pay off his condo when he retires. How much must he invest now at 2.3% interest compounded quarterly to have $125,000 in 11 years? Round to the nearest whole dollar.

38. Quinn and Julius inherited $50,000 each from their great-grandmother's estate. Quinn invested her money in a 5-year CD paying 1.6% interest compounded semiannually. Julius deposited his money in a money market account paying 1.05% compounded monthly.

   a. How much money will each have in 5 years? Round to the nearest whole dollar.

   b. How much compound interest will they each have earned at the end of the 5 years?

39. Greg and Verena Sava need $20,000 in 3 years to expand their goat cheese business. The Bank of Sutton is offering a 3-year CD paying 3.9% compounded monthly. How much should they invest now to achieve their goal? Round to the nearest whole dollar.

CHAPTER 11

Dollars AND Sense

Pay Me Now, Pay Me Later is a good example of how the "time value of money" concept can be applied in business.
Remember: *When interest can be earned, money today is more desirable than the same amount of money in the future.*

BUSINESS DECISION: PAY ME NOW, PAY ME LATER

40. You are the owner of an apartment building that is being offered for sale for $1,500,000. You receive an offer from a prospective buyer who wants to pay you $500,000 now, $500,000 in 6 months, and $500,000 in 1 year.

   a. What is the actual present value of this offer considering you can earn 12% interest compounded monthly on your money?

   b. If another buyer offers to pay you $1,425,000 cash now, which is a better deal?

   c. Because you understand the "time value of money" concept, you have negotiated a deal with the original buyer from part a whereby you will accept the three-payment offer but will charge 12% interest compounded monthly on the two delayed payments. Calculate the total purchase price under this new arrangement.

   d. Now calculate the present value of the new deal to verify that you will receive the original asking price of $1,500,000 for your apartment building.

COLLABORATIVE LEARNING ACTIVITY

Putting Your Money To Work

As a team, research financial institutions in your area (brick-and-mortar banks), as well as Internet-only institutions (virtual banks and e-banks), to find and list various certificates of deposit currently being offered. Assume that you want to invest $10,000 for 12 months.

a. What interest rates do these CDs pay? How often is interest compounded?
b. What is the early withdrawal penalty?
c. Are these CDs insured? If so, by whom? What is the limit per account?
d. Overall, which institution offers the CD that would earn the most interest after 12 months?

Consumer and Business Credit

PERFORMANCE OBJECTIVES

OPEN-END CREDIT—CHARGE ACCOUNTS, CREDIT CARDS, AND LINES OF CREDIT

13

SECTION I

"Buy now, pay later" is a concept that has become an everyday part of the way individuals and businesses purchase goods and services. Merchants in all categories, as well as lending institutions, encourage us to just say "charge it!" Consumers are offered a wide variety of charge accounts with many extra services and incentives attached. Many businesses have charge accounts in the company name. These accounts may be used to facilitate employee travel and entertainment expenses or to fill up the company delivery truck with gasoline without having to deal with cash. Exhibit 13-1 shows a sample credit card and its parts.

Lending and borrowing money comprise a huge portion of the U.S. economic system. Over the years, as the practice became more prevalent, the federal government enacted various legislation to protect the consumer from being misled about credit and finance charges. One of the most important and comprehensive pieces of legislation, known as Regulation Z, covers both installment credit and **open-end credit**.

Regulation Z of the Consumer Credit Protection Act, also known as the Truth in Lending Act, as well as the Fair Credit and Charge Card Disclosure Act, require that lenders fully disclose to the customer, in writing, the cost of the credit and detailed information about their terms. Features such as finance charge, annual percentage rate (APR), cash advances, and annual fees must be disclosed in writing at the time you apply. The **finance charge** is the dollar amount that is paid for the credit. The **annual percentage rate (APR)** is the effective or true annual interest rate being charged. If a card company offers you a written "preapproved" credit solicitation, the offer must include these terms. Also, card issuers must inform customers if they make certain changes in rates or coverage for credit insurance.

open-end credit A loan arrangement in which there is no set number of payments. As the balance of the loan is reduced, the borrower can renew the amount of the loan up to a pre-approved credit limit. A form of revolving credit.

finance charge Dollar amount that is paid for credit. Total of installment payments for an item less the cost of that item.

annual percentage rate (APR) Effective or true annual interest rate being charged for credit. Must be revealed to borrowers under the Truth in Lending Act.

EXHIBIT 13-1 Parts of a Credit Card

© Cengage Learning®

unsecured loans Loans that are backed simply by the borrower's "promise" to repay, without any tangible asset pledged as collateral. These loans carry more risk for the lender and therefore have higher interest rates than secured loans.

secured loans Loans that are backed by a tangible asset, such as a car, boat, or home, which can be repossessed and sold if the borrower fails to pay back the loan. These loans carry less risk for the lender and therefore have lower interest rates than do unsecured loans.

revolving credit Loans made on a continuous basis and billed periodically. Borrower makes minimum monthly payments or more and pays interest on the outstanding balance. This is a form of open-end credit extended by many retail stores and credit card companies.

In 2010, the Federal Reserve implemented a series of amendments to Regulation Z, known as the Credit Card Accountability, Responsibility, and Disclosure Act (the Credit Card Act). These amendments were designed to further protect consumers who use credit cards from a number of costly and undisclosed bank practices. Exhibit 13-2 outlines the major provisions of these new credit card reforms. Exhibits 13-3 and 13-5 illustrate how these reforms now appear on your monthly credit card statement and bank credit card offer disclosures.

When loans are backed by a simple promise to repay, they are known as **unsecured loans**. Most open-end credit accounts are unsecured. Loans that are backed by tangible assets, such as car and boat loans and home mortgage loans, are known as **secured loans**. These loans are backed, or secured, by an asset that can be repossessed and sold by the lender if the borrower fails to comply with the rules of the loan. Secured loans are covered in Section II of this chapter and in Chapter 14.

Revolving credit is the most popular type of open-end credit. Under this agreement, the consumer has a prearranged credit limit and two payment options. The first option is to use the account as a regular charge account, whereby the balance is paid off at the end of the month with no finance charge. The second option is to make a minimum payment or portion of the payment but less than the full balance. This option leaves a carryover balance, which accrues finance charges by using the simple interest formula

$$\text{Interest} = \text{Principal} \times \text{Rate} \times \text{Time}$$

The name *revolving credit* comes from the fact that there is no set number of payments as with installment credit. The account revolves month to month, year to year—technically never being paid off as long as minimum monthly payments are made. Exhibit 13-3 illustrates a typical revolving credit monthly statement.

Using Smartphones for Payment In a survey conducted by the Pew Research Center, 65% of the experts surveyed predicted that by 2020 using smartphones as a payment method will almost entirely replace the use of credit cards.

Source: www.technewsdaily.com

EXHIBIT 13-2 How Credit Card Reforms Affect You

How Credit Card Reforms Affect You

What your credit card company has to tell you
- When they plan to increase your rate or other fees
- How long it will take to pay off your balance

New rules regarding rates, fees, and limits
- No interest rate increases for the first year unless the cardholder goes 60 days past due on the account.
- Promotional rates must remain in effect for at least six months.
- Increased rates apply only to new charges
- Restrictions on over-the-limit transactions
- Caps on high-fee cards
- Protection for underage consumers

Changes to billing and payments
- Standard payment dates and times
- Payments directed to highest interest balances first
- No two-cycle (double-cycle) billing

Reasonable penalty fees and protections
- No fees of more than $25 ($35 in special cases)
- No inactivity fees
- One fee limit for a single transaction
- Explanation of rate increases
- Re-evaluation of increases every six months

© Cengage Learning®

13-1 CALCULATING THE FINANCE CHARGE AND NEW BALANCE BY USING THE UNPAID OR PREVIOUS MONTH'S BALANCE METHOD

billing cycles Time periods, usually 28 to 31 days, used in billing revolving credit accounts. Account statements are sent to the borrower after each billing cycle.

Open-end credit transactions are divided into time periods known as **billing cycles**. These cycles are commonly between 28 and 31 days. At the end of a billing cycle, a statement is sent to the account holder much like the one in Exhibit 13-3.

EXHIBIT 13-3 Reformed Bank Credit Card Account Statement

XXX Bank Credit Card Account Statement
Account Number XXXX XXXX XXXX XXXX
February 21, 2014 to March 22, 2014

Summary of Account Activity

Previous Balance	$535.07
Payments	−$450.00
Other Credits	−$13.45
Purchases	+$529.57
Balance Transfers	+$785.00
Cash Advances	+$318.
Past Due Amount	+$0.
Fees Charged	+$69.4
Interest Charged	+$10.89
New Balance	$1,784.53
Credit limit	$2,000.00
Available credit	$215.47
Statement closing date	3/22/2012
Days in billing cycle	30

①

Questions?

Call Customer Service	1-XXX-XXX-XXXX
Lost or Stolen Credit Card	1-XXX-XXX-XXXX

Payment Information

New Balance	$1,784.53
Minimum Payment Due	$53.00
Payment Due Date	4/20/14

②

Late Payment Warning: If we do not receive your minimum payment by the date listed above, you may have to pay a $35 e fee and your APRs may be increased up to the Penalty R of 28.99%

③

Minimum Payment Warning: If you make only the minim payment each period, you will pay more in interest and take you longer to pay off your balance. For example:

④

If you make no additional charges using this card and each month you pay...	You will pay off the balance shown on this statement in about...	And you will end up paying an estimated total of...
Only the minimum payment	10 years	$3,284
$62	3 years	$2,232 (Savings=$1,052)

If you would like information about credit counseling services, call 1-800-XXX-XXXX.

Please send billing inquiries and correspondence to:
PO Box XXXX, Anytown, Anystate XXXXX

Notice of Changes to Your Interest Rates ⑤

You have triggered the Penalty APR of 28.99%.

Current rates will continue to apply to these transactions. However, if you are more than 60 days late on your account, the Penalty APR will apply to those transactions as well.

1) Summary of account activity

A summary of the transactions on your account—your payments, credits, purchases, balance transfers, cash advances, fees, interest charges, and amounts past due. It will also show your new balance, your available credit, and the last day of the billing period.

2) Payment information

Your total new balance, the minimum payment amount, and the date your payment is due.

3) Late payment warning

This section states any additional fees and the higher interest rate that may be charged if your payment is late.

4) Minimum payment warning

This is an estimate of how long it can take to pay off your credit card balance if you make only the minimum payment each month and an estimate of how much you likely will pay, including interest, in order to pay off your bill in three years.

5) Notice of changes to your interest rates

If you trigger the penalty rate, your credit card company may notify you that your rates will be increasing. The credit card company must tell you at least 45 days before your rates change.

Source: Federal Reserve

continued

EXHIBIT 13-3   Reformed Bank Credit Card Account Statement   *(continued)*

Important Changes to Your Account Terms ⑥

The following is a summary of changes that are being made to your account terms. For more detailed information, please refer to the booklet enclosed with this statement.

As of 5/10/14, any changes to APRs described below will apply to these transactions.

If you are already being charged a higher Penalty APR for purchases: In this case, any changes to APRs described below will not go into effect at this time. These changes will go into effect when the Penalty APR no longer applies to your account.

Revised Terms, as of 5/10/14	
APR for Purchases	16.99%

Transactions ⑦

Reference Number	Trans Date	Post Date	Description of Transaction or Credit	Amount
5884186PS0388W6YM	2/22	2/23	Store #1	$133.74
854338203FS8OO0Z5	2/25	2/25	Pymt Thank You	$450.00
564891561545KOSHD	2/25	2/26	Store #2	$247.36
1542202074TWWZV48	2/26	2/26	Cash Advance	$318.00
4545754784KOHUIOS	2/27	3/1	Balance Transfer	$785.00
2564561023184102315	2/28	3/1	Store #3	$34.32
045148714518979874	3/4	3/5	Store #4	$29.45
0547810544898718AF	3/15	3/17	Store #5	$72.25
Fees				
9525156489SFD4545Q	2/23	2/23	Late Fee	$35.00
84151564SADS8745H	2/27	2/27	Balance Transfer Fee	$23.55
256489156189451516L	2/28	2/28	Cash Advance Fee	$10.90
			TOTAL FEES FOR THIS PERIOD	**$69.45**
Interest Charged				
			Interest Charge on Purchases	$6.31
			Interest Charge on Cash Advances	$4.58
			TOTAL INTEREST FOR THIS PERIOD	**$10.89**

⑧

2014 Totals Year-to-Date	
Total fees charged in 2014	$90.14
Total interest charged in 2014	$18.27

⑨

Interest Charge Calculation ⑩

Your **Annual Percentage Rate (APR)** is the   interest rate on your account.

Type of Balance	Annual Percentage Rate (APR)	Balance Subject to Interest Rate	Interest Charge
Purchases	14.99% (v)	$512.14	$6.31
Cash Advances	21.99% (v)	$253.50	$4.58
Balance Transfers	0.00%	$637.50	$0.00

(v) = Variable Rate

6) Other changes to your account terms

If your credit card company is going to raise interest rates or fees or make other significant changes to your account, it must notify you at least 45 days before the changes take effect.

7) Transactions

A list of all the transactions that have occurred since your last statement (purchases, payments, credits, cash advances, and balance transfers).

8) Fees and interest charges

Credit card companies must list the fees and interest charges separately on your monthly bill. Interest charges must be listed by type of transaction.

9) Year-to-date totals

This is the total that you have paid in fees and interest charges for the current year. You can avoid some fees, such as over-the-limit fees, by managing how much you charge and by paying on time to avoid late payment fees.

10) Interest charge calculation

A summary of the interest rates on the different types of transactions, account balances, the amount of each, and the interest charged for each type of transaction.

STEPS TO CALCULATE THE FINANCE CHARGE AND NEW BALANCE BY USING THE UNPAID BALANCE METHOD

STEP 1. Divide the annual percentage rate by 12 to find the monthly or periodic interest rate. (Round to the nearest hundredth percent when necessary.)

$$\text{Periodic rate} = \frac{\text{Annual percentage rate}}{12}$$

STEP 2. Calculate the finance charge by multiplying the previous month's balance by the periodic interest rate from Step 1.

$$\textbf{Finance charge} = \textbf{Previous month's balance} \times \textbf{Periodic rate}$$

STEP 3. Total all the purchases and cash advances for the month.

STEP 4. Total all the payments and credits for the month.

STEP 5. Use the following formula to determine the new balance:

$$\begin{array}{c}\textbf{New} \\ \textbf{balance}\end{array} = \begin{array}{c}\textbf{Previous} \\ \textbf{balance}\end{array} + \begin{array}{c}\textbf{Finance} \\ \textbf{charge}\end{array} + \begin{array}{c}\textbf{Purchases and} \\ \textbf{cash advances}\end{array} - \begin{array}{c}\textbf{Payments and} \\ \textbf{credits}\end{array}$$

EXAMPLE1 CALCULATING THE FINANCE CHARGE AND NEW BALANCE BY USING THE UNPAID BALANCE METHOD

Jake Morrison has a revolving department store credit account with an annual percentage rate of 18%. His balance from last month is $322.40. During the month, he purchased shirts for $65.60 and a baseball bat for $43.25. He returned a tie for a credit of $22.95 and made a $50 payment. If the department store uses the unpaid balance method, what is the finance charge on the account and what is Jake's new balance?

▶ SOLUTIONSTRATEGY

Step 1. Periodic rate $= \dfrac{\text{Annual percentage rate}}{12}$

Periodic rate $= \dfrac{18\%}{12} = 1.5\%$

Step 2. Finance charge = Previous month's balance × Periodic rate
Finance charge $= 322.40 \times .015$
Finance charge $= 4.836 = \underline{\$4.84}$

Step 3. Total the purchases for the month:
$$\$65.60 + \$43.25 = \$108.85$$

Step 4. Total the payments and credits for the month:
$$\$50.00 + \$22.95 = \$72.95$$

Step 5. Find the new balance for Jake's account by using the formula

$$\begin{array}{c}\text{New} \\ \text{balance}\end{array} = \begin{array}{c}\text{Previous} \\ \text{balance}\end{array} + \begin{array}{c}\text{Finance} \\ \text{charge}\end{array} + \begin{array}{c}\text{Purchases and} \\ \text{cash advances}\end{array} - \begin{array}{c}\text{Payments and} \\ \text{credits}\end{array}$$

$$\begin{array}{c}\text{New} \\ \text{balance}\end{array} = \$322.40 + \$4.84 + \$108.85 - \$72.95$$

New balance $= \underline{\$363.14}$

Dollars AND Sense

The Fair Credit Billing Act gives consumers the right to dispute a credit card purchase or billing error.

- Your maximum liability for unauthorized credit card charges: $50.
- Number of days you have to report unauthorized credit card use: no limit.
- Number of days you have to file a billing dispute: 60.
- Number of days the card issuer has to respond 90.
- Maximum number of days a dispute may drag on: 270.

►TRYITEXERCISE 1

Mike Dennis has a Bank of America account with an annual percentage rate of 15%. His previous month's balance is $214.90. During July, Mike's account showed the following activity.

Statement of Account   Bank of America.

NAME	DATE	DESCRIPTION OF TRANSACTIONS	CHARGES
MIKE DENNIS	07/06	Royal Cleaners	$35.50
	07/09	Payment	40.00
ACCOUNT NUMBER	07/15	Macy's	133.25
097440	07/16	Antonio's Restaurant	41.10
BILLING CYCLE	07/21	CVS Pharmacy	29.00
JULY 1–31	07/27	CVS Pharmacy (credit)	9.12

What is the finance charge for July, and what is Mike's new balance?

CHECK YOUR ANSWERS WITH THE SOLUTIONS ON PAGE 442.

13-2 CALCULATING THE FINANCE CHARGE AND NEW BALANCE BY USING THE AVERAGE DAILY BALANCE METHOD

average daily balance In revolving credit, the most commonly used method for determining the finance charge for a billing cycle. It is the total of the daily balances divided by the number of days in the cycle.

In business today, the method most widely used to calculate the finance charge on a revolving credit account is known as the **average daily balance**. This method precisely tracks the activity in an account on a daily basis. Each day's balance of a billing cycle is totaled and then divided by the number of days in that cycle. This gives an average of all the daily balances.

For accounts in which many charges are made each month, the average daily balance method results in much higher interest than the unpaid balance method because interest starts accruing on the day purchases are made or cash advances are taken.

STEPS TO CALCULATE THE FINANCE CHARGE AND NEW BALANCE BY USING THE AVERAGE DAILY BALANCE

STEP 1. Starting with the previous month's balance as the first unpaid balance, multiply each by the number of days that balance existed until the next account transaction.

STEP 2. At the end of the billing cycle, find the sum of all the daily balance figures.

STEP 3. Find the average daily balance.

$$\text{Average daily balance} = \frac{\text{Sum of the daily balances}}{\text{Days in billing cycle}}$$

STEP 4. Calculate the finance charge.

$$\text{Finance charge} = \text{Average daily balance} \times \text{Periodic rate}$$

STEP 5. Compute the new balance as before.

$$\frac{\text{New}}{\text{balance}} = \frac{\text{Previous}}{\text{balance}} + \frac{\text{Finance}}{\text{charge}} + \frac{\text{Purchases and}}{\text{cash advances}} - \frac{\text{Payments and}}{\text{credits}}$$

EXAMPLE2 USING THE AVERAGE DAILY BALANCE METHOD

Morgan Patrick has a Bank of America revolving credit account with a 15% annual percentage rate. The finance charge is calculated by using the average daily balance method. The billing date is the first day of each month, and the billing cycle is the number of days in that month. During the month of March, Morgan's account showed the following activity.

Statement of Account — Bank of America

NAME	DATE	DESCRIPTION OF TRANSACTIONS	CHARGES
MORGAN PATRICK	03/01	Previous month's balance	$215.60
	03/07	Sports Authority	125.11
ACCOUNT NUMBER	03/10	Texaco	23.25
1229-3390-0038	03/12	Payment	75.00
	03/17	Amazon.com (credit)	54.10
BILLING CYCLE	03/23	H.L. Mager, DDS	79.00
MARCH 1–31	03/23	Texaco	19.43
	03/24	Dollar General	94.19

What is the finance charge for March, and what is Morgan's new balance?

▶SOLUTIONSTRATEGY

Steps 1 and 2. To calculate the daily balances and their sum, set up a chart like the one below that lists the activity in the account by dates and number of days.

Dates	Number of Days	Activity/Amount		Unpaid Balance	Daily Balances (unpaid bal. × days)
March 1–6	6	Previous balance		$215.60	$1,293.60
March 7–9	3	Charge	+$125.11	340.71	1,022.13
March 10–11	2	Charge	+23.25	363.96	727.92
March 12–16	5	Payment	−75.00	288.96	1,444.80
March 17–22	6	Credit	−54.10	234.86	1,409.16
March 23	1	Charges	+79.00		
			+19.43	333.29	333.29
March 24–31	8	Charge	+94.19	427.48	3,419.84
	31 days in cycle				Total $9,650.74

Step 3. Average daily balance $= \dfrac{\text{Sum of the daily balances}}{\text{Days in billing cycle}} = \dfrac{9,650.74}{31} = \$311.31$

Step 4. The periodic rate is 1.25% (15% ÷ 12).

Finance charge = Average daily balance × Periodic rate

Finance charge = 311.31 × .0125 = $3.89

Step 5.

$$\text{New balance} = \text{Previous balance} + \text{Finance charge} + \text{Purchases and cash advances} - \text{Payments and credits}$$

New balance = $215.60 + $3.89 + $340.98 − $129.10

New balance = $431.37

Learning Tip

Shortcut
"New Balance" can be calculated by adding the finance charge to the last "Unpaid Balance" of the month.
$427.48 + $3.89 = $431.37

▶TRYITEXERCISE 2

Kendra Wolf has a Bank of America revolving credit account with an 18% annual percentage rate. The finance charge is calculated by using the average daily balance method. The billing date is the first day of each month, and the billing cycle is the number of days in that month. During the month of August, Kendra's account showed the following activity.

Statement of Account   Bank of America.

NAME				
KENDRA WOLF				

DATE	DESCRIPTION OF TRANSACTIONS	CHARGES
08/01	Previous month's balance	$158.69
08/05	Nathan's Beauty Salon	55.00
08/11	Payment	100.00
08/15	Walmart	43.22
08/17	Saks Fifth Avenue	54.10
08/20	eBay.com	224.50
08/26	Cash Advance	75.00

ACCOUNT NUMBER
2967-39460-0098

BILLING CYCLE
AUGUST 1–31

What is the finance charge for August, and what is Kendra's new balance?

CHECK YOUR ANSWERS WITH THE SOLUTIONS ON PAGE 442.

13-3 CALCULATING THE FINANCE CHARGE AND NEW BALANCE OF BUSINESS AND PERSONAL LINES OF CREDIT

line of credit Pre-approved amount of open-end credit based on borrower's ability to pay.

One of the most useful types of open-end credit is the business or personal **line of credit**. In this section, we investigate the unsecured credit line, which is based on your own merit. In Chapter 14, we discuss the home equity line of credit, which is secured by a home or another piece of real estate property.

A line of credit is an important tool for ongoing businesses and responsible individuals. For those who qualify, unsecured lines of credit generally range from $2,500 to $250,000. The amount is based on your ability to pay as well as your financial and credit history. This pre-approved borrowing power essentially gives you the ability to become your own private banker. Once the line has been established, you can borrow money by simply writing a check. Lines of credit usually have an annual usage fee of between $50 and $100, and most lenders require that you update your financial information each year.

With credit lines, you pay interest only on the outstanding average daily balance of your loan. For most lines and some credit cards, the interest rate is variable and is based on, or indexed to, the prime rate. The **U.S. prime rate** is the lending rate at which the largest and most creditworthy corporations in the country borrow money from banks. The current prime rate is published daily in the *Wall Street Journal* in a chart entitled "Consumer Rates and Returns to Investors." Exhibit 13-4 shows an example of this chart.

U.S. prime rate Lending rate at which the largest and most creditworthy corporations borrow money from banks. The interest rate of most lines of credit is tied to the movement of the prime rate.

A typical line of credit quotes interest as the prime rate plus a fixed percent, such as "prime + 3%" or "prime + 6.8%." Some lenders have a minimum rate regardless of the prime rate, such as "prime + 3%, minimum 10%." In this case, when the prime is greater than 7%, the rate varies up and down. When the prime falls to less than 7%, the minimum 10% rate applies. This guarantees the lender at least a 10% return on funds loaned. Exhibit 13-5 is an example of a credit card rate disclosure indexed to the prime rate.

Like the calculation of finance charges and new balances on credit cards (see the steps on page 412), the finance charge on a line of credit is based on average daily balance and is calculated by

Finance charge = Average daily balance × Periodic rate

This means that interest begins as soon as you write a check for a loan. Typically, the loan is paid back on a flexible schedule. In most cases, balances of $100 or less must be paid in full. Larger balances require minimum monthly payments of $100 or 2% of the outstanding balance, whichever is greater. As you repay, the line of credit renews itself. The new balance of the line of credit is calculated by

New balance = Previous balance + Finance charge + Loans − Payments

EXHIBIT 13-4
Consumer Money Rates

Consumer Money Rates							Monday, October 15, 2012

Interest Rate	YIELD/RATE (%)		52-WEEK		CHANGE IN PCT. PTS	
	Last	Wk Ago	High	Low	52-Wk	3-Yr
Federal-funds rate target	0–0.25	0–0.25	0–0.25	0–0.25	...	...
Prime rate*	3.25	3.25	3.25	3.25	...	...
Libor, 3-month	0.33	0.35	0.58	0.33	–0.08	0.05
Money market, annual yield	0.52	0.51	0.54	0.44	–0.02	–0.56
Five-year CD, annual yield	1.37	1.38	1.62	1.30	–0.24	–1.33
30-year mortgage, fixed	3.59	3.61	4.41	3.54	–0.80	–1.55
15-year mortgage, fixed	3.03	3.05	3.69	3.01	–0.66	–1.55
Jumbo mortgages, $417,000-plus	4.06	4.08	5.04	4.04	–0.98	–2.16
Five-year adj mortgage (ARM)	3.19	3.15	3.22	2.83	–0.01	–1.10
New-car loan, 48 month	3.72	3.19	4.36	2.97	–0.43	–3.59
HELOC, $30,000	4.64	4.65	4.92	4.57	–0.08	–1.10

*Base rate posted by 70% of the nation's largest banks.

Source: SIX Financial Information, WSJ Market Data Group, Bankrate.com

EXAMPLE3 CALCULATING FINANCE CHARGES ON A LINE OF CREDIT

Shari's Chocolate Shop has a $20,000 line of credit with the Shangri-La National Bank. The annual percentage rate charged on the account is the current prime rate plus 4%. There is a minimum APR on the account of 10%. The starting balance on April 1 was $2,350. On April 9, Shari borrowed $1,500 to pay for a shipment of assorted gift items. On April 20, she made a $3,000 payment on the account. On April 26, she borrowed another $2,500 to pay for air conditioning repairs. The billing cycle for April has 30 days. If the current prime rate is 8%, what is the finance charge on the account and what is Shari's new balance?

►SOLUTIONSTRATEGY

To solve this problem, we must find the annual percentage rate, the periodic rate, the average daily balance, the finance charge, and the new balance.

Annual percentage rate: The annual percentage rate is prime plus 4%, with a minimum of 10%. Because the current prime is 8%, the APR on this line of credit is 12% (8% + 4%).

Periodic rate:

$$\text{Periodic rate} = \frac{\text{Annual percentage rate}}{12 \text{ months}} = \frac{12\%}{12} = 1\%$$

Average daily balance: From the information given, we construct the following chart showing the account activity.

Dates	Number of Days	Activity/Amount	Unpaid Balance	Daily Balances (unpaid balance × days)
April 1–8	8	Previous balance	$2,350	$18,800
April 9–19	11	Borrowed $1,500	3,850	42,350
April 20–25	6	Payment $3,000	850	5,100
April 26–30	5	Borrowed $2,500	3,350	16,750
	30 days in cycle			Total $83,000

$$\text{Average daily balance} = \frac{\text{Sum of the daily balances}}{\text{Days in billing cycle}} = \frac{83,000}{30} = \$2,766.67$$

Finance charge:

$$\text{Finance charge} = \text{Average daily balance} \times \text{Periodic rate}$$
$$\text{Finance charge} = 2,766.67 \times .01 = \$27.67$$

New balance:

$$\text{New balance} = \frac{\text{Previous}}{\text{balance}} + \frac{\text{Finance}}{\text{charge}} + \frac{\text{Loan}}{\text{amounts}} - \text{Payments}$$
$$\text{New balance} = \$2,350 + \$27.67 + \$4,000 - \$3,000$$
$$\text{New balance} = \$3,377.67$$

▶ TRYITEXERCISE 3

Angler Marine has a $75,000 line of credit with Harborside Bank. The annual percentage rate is the current prime rate plus 4.5%. The balance on November 1 was $12,300. On November 7, Angler borrowed $16,700 to pay for a shipment of fishing equipment, and on November 21, it borrowed another $8,800. On November 26, a $20,000 payment was made on the account. The billing cycle for November has 30 days. If the current prime rate is 8.5%, what is the finance charge on the account and what is Angler's new balance?

CHECK YOUR ANSWERS WITH THE SOLUTIONS ON PAGES 442–443.

EXHIBIT 13-5   Reformed Credit Card Rate Disclosure

Interest Rates and Interest Charges	
Annual Percentage Rate (APR) for Purchases ①	**8.99%, 10.99%, or 12.99%** introductory APR for one year, based on your creditworthiness After that, your APR will be **14.99%**. This APR will vary with the market based on the Prime Rate.
APR for Balance Transfers ②	**15.99%** This APR will vary with the market based on the Prime Rate.
APR for Cash Advances ③	**21.99%** This APR will vary with the market based on the Prime Rate.
Penalty APR and When it Applies ④	**28.99%** This APR may be applied to your account if you: 1) Make a late payment. 2) Go over your credit limit. 3) Make a payment that is returned. 4) Do any of the above on another account that you have with us. **How Long Will the Penalty APR Apply?** If your APRs are increased for any of these reasons, the Penalty APR will apply until you make six consecutive minimum payments when due.
How to Avoid Paying Interest on Purchases ⑤	Your due date is at least 25 days after the close of each billing cycle. We will not charge you any interest on purchases if you pay your entire balance by the due date each month.
Minimum Interest Charge ⑥	If you are charged interest, the charge will be no less than $1.50.
For Credit Card Tips from the Federal Reserve Board	To learn more about factors to consider when applying for or using a credit card, visit the website of the Federal Reserve Board at http://www.federalreserve.gov/creditcard.

1) APR for purchases
The interest rate you pay on an annual basis if you carry over balances on purchases from one billing cycle to the next.

2) APR for balance transfers
The interest rate you pay if you transfer a balance from another card. Balance transfer fees may also apply.

3) APR for cash advances
The interest rate you pay if you withdraw a cash advance from your credit card account. Cash advance fees may also apply.

4) Penalty APR and when it applies
Your credit card company may increase your interest rate (with 45 days' advance notice) if you pay your bill late, go over your credit limit, or make a payment that is returned.

How long will the penalty APR apply?
Credit card companies must tell you how long the penalty rates will be in effect. You may be able to go back to regular rates if you pay your bills on time for a period of time.

5) How to avoid paying interest on purchases
You can avoid interest charges on purchases by paying your bill in full by the due date.

6) Minimum interest charge
Credit card companies often have a minimum interest amount. These charges typically range from $0.50 to $2.00 per month.

EXHIBIT 13-5   Reformed Credit Card Rate Disclosure

Fees	
Set-up and Maintenance Fees (7)	NOTICE: Some of these set-up and maintenance fees will be assessed before you begin using your card and will reduce the amount of credit you initially have available. For example, if you are assigned the minimum credit limit of $250, your initial available credit will be only about $209 (or about $204 if you choose to have an additional card).
• Annual Fee	$20
• Account Set-up Fee	$20 (one-time fee)
• Participation Fee	$12 annually ($1 per month)
• Additional Card Fee	$5 annually (if applicable)
Transaction Fees (8)	
• Balance Transfer	Either **$5** or **3%** of the amount of each transfer, whichever is greater (maximum fee: $100).
• Cash Advance	Either **$5** or **3%** of the amount of each cash advance, whichever is greater.
• Foreign Transaction	**2%** of each transaction in U.S. dollars.
Penalty Fees (9)	
• Late Payment	**$29** if balance is less than or equal to $1,000; **$35** if balance is more than $1,000
• Over-the Credit Limit	**$29**
• Returned Payment	**$35** (10)

(11)

How We Will Calculate Your Balance: We use a method called "average daily balance (including new purchases)."

(12)

Loss of Introductory APR: We may end your introductory APR and apply the Penalty APR if you become more than 60 days late in paying your bill.

7) Set-up and maintenance fees
Some credit cards offered to people with lower, or subprime, credit scores may charge a variety of fees.

8) Transaction Fees
Credit card companies may charge you a fee (either a fixed dollar amount or a percentage of the transaction) for transferring a balance, getting a cash advance, or making a transaction in a foreign country.

9) Penalty fees
Fee if you pay your bill late, your balance goes over your credit limit, or you make a payment but you don't have enough money in your account to cover the payment.

10) Other fees
Some cards require other fees (known as "account protection") for credit insurance, debt cancellation, or debt suspension coverage.

11) How we will calculate your balance
Credit card companies can use one of several methods to calculate your outstanding balance.
- Adjusted balance method
- Average daily balance method, including new purchases
- Average daily balance method, excluding new purchases
- Previous balance method

12) Loss of introductory APR
If your card has a special lower rate that is called an "introductory rate," this area will list the ways you can lose this lower rate.

SECTION I 13 REVIEW EXERCISES

Calculate the missing information on the following revolving credit accounts. Interest is calculated on the unpaid or previous month's balance.

	Previous Balance	Annual Percentage Rate (APR)	Monthly Periodic Rate	Finance Charge	Purchases and Cash Advances	Payments and Credits	New Balance
1.	$167.88	18%	1.5%	$2.52	$215.50	$50.00	$335.90
2.	$35.00	12%	___	___	$186.40	$75.00	___
3.	$455.12	___	1.75%	___	$206.24	$125.00	___
4.	$2,390.00	___	$1\frac{1}{4}\%$	___	$1,233.38	$300.00	___
5.	$3,418.50	9%	___	___	$329.00	$1,200.00	___
6.	$857.25	___	2%	___	$166.70	$195.00	___

7. Anny Winslow has a Bank of America revolving credit account with an annual percentage rate of 12% calculated on the previous month's balance. Answer the questions that follow using the monthly statement below.

Statement of Account   Bank of America

NAME			
ANNY WINSLOW			

ACCOUNT NUMBER
2290-0090-4959

BILLING CYCLE
SEPTEMBER 1–30

DATE	DESCRIPTION OF TRANSACTIONS	CHARGES
09/01	Previous month's balance	$120.00
09/08	Radio Shack	65.52
09/11	Payment	70.00
09/14	Union Oil	23.25
09/22	Cash Advance	60.00
09/26	Safeway Supermarket	59.16

a. What is the finance charge?

b. What is Anny's new balance?

Kathy Hansen has a revolving credit account. The finance charge is calculated on the previous month's balance, and the annual percentage rate is 21%. Complete the following five-month account activity table for Kathy.

Month	Previous Month's Balance	Finance Charge	Purchases and Cash Advances	Payments and Credits	New Balance End of Month
8. March	$560.00	___	$121.37	$55.00	___
9. April	___	___	$46.45	$65.00	___
10. May	___	___	$282.33	$105.00	___
11. June	___	___	$253.38	$400.00	___
12. July	___	___	$70.59	$100.00	___

13. Calculate the average daily balance for November for a revolving credit account with a previous month's balance of $550 and the following activity.

Date	Activity	Amount
November 6	Purchase	$83.20
November 13	Payment	$150.00
November 19	Purchase	$348.50
November 24	Credit	$75.25
November 27	Cash advance	$200.00

$$\text{Average daily balance} = \frac{20,335.25}{30} = \$677.84$$

14. Calculate the average daily balance for October for a revolving credit account with a previous month's balance of $140 and the following activity.

Date	Activity	Amount
October 3	Cash advance	$50.00
October 7	Payment	$75.00
October 10	Purchase	$26.69
October 16	Credit	$40.00
October 25	Purchase	$122.70

15. Calculate the average daily balance for February for a revolving credit account with a previous month's balance of $69.50 and the following activity.

Date	Activity	Amount
February 6	Payment	$58.00
February 9	Purchase	$95.88
February 15	Purchase	$129.60
February 24	Credit	$21.15
February 27	Cash advance	$100.00

16. Carolyn Salkind has a Bank of America revolving credit account with a 15% annual percentage rate. The finance charge is calculated by using the average daily balance method. The billing date is the first day of each month, and the billing cycle is the number of days in that month. During March, Carolyn's account showed the following activity.

Statement of Account   Bank of America

NAME			
CAROLYN SALKIND	DATE	DESCRIPTION OF TRANSACTIONS	CHARGES
	03/01	**Previous month's balance**	**$324.45**
ACCOUNT NUMBER	03/05	**Crate and Barrel**	**156.79**
2967-39460	03/11	**Payment**	**150.00**
	03/15	**Starbucks**	**45.60**
BILLING CYCLE	03/17	**Gap**	**344.50**
MARCH 1–31			

a. What is the finance charge for March?

b. What is Carolyn's new balance?

Justin Kase zsixz/Alamy

Gap Inc. operates as a specialty retailer. The company offers clothing, accessories, and personal care products for men, women, children, and babies under the Gap, Old Navy, Banana Republic, Piperlime, and Athleta brand names.

The company offers its products through retail stores and catalogs as well as brand name websites. The Gap also franchises agreements with unaffiliated franchisees to operate Gap and Banana Republic stores worldwide. Typical annual sales exceed $14 billion.

17. The Freemont Bank offers a business line of credit that has an annual percentage rate of prime rate plus 5.4%, with a minimum of 11%. What is the APR if the prime rate is

    a. 7%   b. 10.1%   c. 9.25%   d. 5%

    7 + 5.4
    = 12.4%

18. The Jewelry Exchange has a $30,000 line of credit with Nations Bank. The annual percentage rate is the current prime rate plus 4.7%. The balance on March 1 was $8,400. On March 6, the company borrowed $6,900 to pay for a shipment of supplies, and on March 17, it borrowed another $4,500 for equipment repairs. On March 24, a $10,000 payment was made on the account. The billing cycle for March has 31 days. The current prime rate is 9%.

    a. What is the finance charge on the account?

    b. What is the company's new balance?

    c. On April 1, how much credit does the Jewelry Exchange have left on the account?

BUSINESS DECISION: PICK THE RIGHT PLASTIC

19. On October 22, you plan to purchase a $3,000 computer by using one of your two credit cards. The Silver Card charges 18% interest and calculates interest based on the balance on the first day of the previous month. The Gold Card charges 18% interest and calculates interest based on the average daily balance. Both cards have a $0 balance as of October 1. The closing date is the end of the month for each card.

    Your plan is to make a $1,000 payment in November, make a $1,000 payment in December, and pay off the remaining balance in January. All your payments will be received and posted on the 10th of each month. No other charges will be made on the account.

    a. Based on this information, calculate the interest charged by each card for this purchase.

    b. Which card is the better deal and by how much?

Top 6 Credit Card Issuers in the U.S.
In recent years the top six U.S. credit card issuers (based on outstanding balances) have been:

American Express
Chase
Bank of America
Citibank
Capital One
Discover

ICP/Alamy

CLOSED-END CREDIT—INSTALLMENT LOANS

13 SECTION II

Closed-end credit in the form of installment loans is used extensively today for the purchase of durable goods such as cars, boats, electronic equipment, furniture, and appliances, as well as services such as vacations and home improvements. An **installment loan** is a lump-sum loan whereby the borrower repays the principal plus interest in a specified number of equal monthly payments. These loans generally range from 6 months to 10 years depending on what is being financed.

When a home or another real estate property is financed, the installment loan is known as a **mortgage**. A mortgage may be for as long as 30 years on a home and even longer on commercial property such as an office building or a factory. These loans, along with home equity loans, are discussed in Chapter 14.

Many installment loans are secured by the asset for which the loan was made. For example, when a bank makes a car loan for three years, the consumer gets the car to use and monthly payments to make, but the lender still owns the car. Only after the final payment is made on the loan does the lender turn over the title (the proof of ownership document) to the borrower. An additional form of security for the lending institution is that borrowers are often asked to make a down payment as part of the loan agreement.

A **down payment** is a percentage of the purchase price that the buyer must pay in a lump sum at the time of purchase. Down payments on installment loans vary by category of merchandise and generally range from between 0% to 30% of the price of the item. Sometimes the amount of the down payment is based on the credit rating of the borrower. Usually, the better the credit, the lower the down payment.

installment loan Loan made for a specified number of equal monthly payments. A form of closed-end credit used for purchasing durable goods such as cars, boats, and furniture and services such as vacations and home improvements.

mortgage An installment loan made for homes and other real estate property.

down payment Portion of the purchase price that the buyer must pay in a lump sum at the time of purchase.

Until the loan on this vehicle is repaid, the lending institution is technically the owner.

CALCULATING THE TOTAL DEFERRED PAYMENT PRICE AND THE AMOUNT OF THE FINANCE CHARGE OF AN INSTALLMENT LOAN

13-4

Let's take a look at some of the terminology of installment loans. When a consumer buys goods or services without any financing, the price paid is known as the **cash price** or **purchase price**. When financing is involved, the **amount financed** is found by subtracting the down payment from the cash or purchase price. Sometimes the down payment will be listed as a dollar amount, and other times it will be expressed as a percent of the purchase price.

cash, or **purchase price** Price paid for goods and services without the use of financing.

amount financed After the down payment, the amount of money that is borrowed to complete a sale.

> **Amount financed = Purchase price − Down payment**

When the down payment is listed as a percent of the purchase price, it can be found by using

Down payment = Purchase price × Down payment percent

A finance charge, which includes simple interest and any loan origination fees, is then added to the amount financed to give the total amount of installment payments.

Total amount of installment payments = Amount financed + Finance charge

The finance charge can be found by subtracting the amount financed from the total amount of installment payments.

Finance charge = Total amount of installment payments − Amount financed

When the amount of the monthly payments is known, the total amount of installment payments can be found by multiplying the monthly payment amount by the number of payments.

$$\text{Total amount of installment payments} = \text{Monthly payment amount} \times \text{Number of monthly payments}$$

The total deferred payment price is the total amount of installment payments plus the down payment. This represents the total out-of-pocket expenses incurred by the buyer for an installment purchase.

Total deferred payment price = Total of installment payments + Down payment

EXAMPLE4   CALCULATING INSTALLMENT LOAN VARIABLES

Tracy Hall is interested in buying a computer. At Radio Shack, she picks out a computer and a printer for a total cash price of $2,550. The salesperson informs her that if she qualifies for an installment loan, she may pay 20% now as a down payment and finance the balance with payments of $110 per month for 24 months.

a. What is the finance charge on this loan?

b. What is the total deferred payment price of Tracy's computer?

▶SOLUTIONSTRATEGY

a. Finance charge:

To calculate the finance charge on this loan, we must first find the amount of the down payment, the amount financed, and the total amount of the installment payments.

Down payment = Purchase price × Down payment percent

Down payment = 2,550 × 20% = 2,550 × .2 = $510

Amount financed = Purchase price − Down payment

Amount financed = 2,550 − 510 = $2,040

$$\text{Total amount of installment payments} = \text{Monthly payment amount} \times \text{Number of monthly payments}$$

Total amount of installment payments = 110 × 24 = $2,640

Finance charge = Total amount of installment payments − Amount financed

Finance charge = 2,640 − 2,040

Finance charge = $600

b. Total deferred payment price:

Total deferred payment price = Total of installment payments + Down payment

Total deferred payment price = 2,640 + 510

Total deferred payment price = $3,150

►TRYITEXERCISE 4

Bob Johnson found a car he wanted to buy at Autorama Auto Sales. He had the option of paying $12,500 in cash or financing the car with a 4-year installment loan. The loan required a 15% down payment and equal monthly payments of $309.90 for 48 months.

a. What is the finance charge on the loan?

b. What is the total deferred payment price of Bob's car?

CHECK YOUR ANSWERS WITH THE SOLUTIONS ON PAGE 443.

CALCULATING THE REGULAR MONTHLY PAYMENTS OF AN INSTALLMENT LOAN BY THE ADD-ON INTEREST METHOD

13-5

One of the most common methods of calculating the finance charge on an installment loan is known as **add-on interest**. Add-on interest is essentially the simple interest that we studied in Chapter 10. The term gets its name from the fact that the simple interest is computed and then added to the amount financed to get the total of installment payments. The interest or finance charge is computed by using the simple interest formula

add-on interest Popular method of calculating the interest on an installment loan. Found by adding the simple interest ($I = PRT$) to the amount financed.

$$\underset{(\textit{finance charge})}{\textbf{Interest}} = \underset{(\textit{amount financed})}{\textbf{Principal}} \times \textbf{Rate} \times \textbf{Time}$$

STEPS TO CALCULATE THE REGULAR MONTHLY PAYMENT OF AN INSTALLMENT LOAN USING ADD-ON INTEREST

STEP 1. Calculate the amount to be financed by subtracting the down payment from the purchase price. *Note:* When the down payment is expressed as a percent, the amount financed can be found by the complement method because the percent financed is 100% minus the down payment percent.

Amount financed = Purchase price(100% − Down payment percent)

STEP 2. Compute the add-on interest finance charge by using $I = PRT$, with the amount financed as the principal.

STEP 3. Find the total of installment payments by adding the finance charge to the amount financed.

Total of installment payments = Amount financed + Finance charge

STEP 4. Find the regular monthly payments by dividing the total of installment payments by the number of months of the loan.

$$\textbf{Regular monthly payments} = \frac{\textbf{Total of installment payments}}{\textbf{Number of months of the loan}}$$

EXAMPLE5 CALCULATING MONTHLY PAYMENTS

David Kendall bought a new boat with a 7% add-on interest installment loan from his credit union. The purchase price of the boat was $19,500. The credit union required a 20% down payment and equal monthly payments for 5 years (60 months). What are David's monthly payments?

▶SOLUTIONSTRATEGY

Step 1. Amount financed = Purchase price(100% − Down payment percent)

Amount financed = 19,500(100% − 20%) = 19,500 × .8

Amount financed = $15,600

Step 2.
$$\underset{(\textit{finance charge})}{\text{Interest}} = \underset{(\textit{amount financed})}{\text{Principal}} \times \text{Rate} \times \text{Time}$$

Finance charge = 15,600 × .07 × 5

Finance charge = $5,460

Step 3. Total of installment payments = Amount financed + Finance charge

Total of installment payments = 15,600 + 5,460

Total of installment payments = $21,060

Step 4. Regular monthly payments = $\dfrac{\text{Total of installment payments}}{\text{Number of months of the loan}}$

Regular monthly payments = $\dfrac{21,060}{60}$

Regular monthly payments = $351

▶TRYITEXERCISE 5

Eileen Townsend bought a bedroom set from El Dorado Furniture with a 6% add-on interest installment loan from her bank. The purchase price of the furniture was $1,500. The bank required a 10% down payment and equal monthly payments for 2 years. What are Eileen's monthly payments?

CHECK YOUR ANSWER WITH THE SOLUTION ON PAGE 443.

13-6 CALCULATING THE ANNUAL PERCENTAGE RATE OF AN INSTALLMENT LOAN BY APR TABLES AND BY FORMULA

As we learned in Objective 13-5, the add-on interest calculation for an installment loan is the same as the procedure we used on the simple interest promissory note. Although the interest is calculated the same way, the manner in which the loans are repaid is different. With promissory notes, the principal plus interest is repaid at the end of the loan period. The borrower has the use of the principal for the full time period of the loan. With an installment loan, the principal plus interest is repaid in equal regular payments. Each month in which a payment is made, the borrower has less and less use of the principal.

For this reason, the effective or true interest rate on an installment loan is considerably higher than the simple add-on rate. As we learned in Section I of this chapter, the effective or true annual interest rate being charged on open- and closed-end credit is known as the APR.

The Federal Reserve Board has published APR tables that can be used to find the APR of an installment loan. APR tables, such as Table 13-1, have values representing the finance charge per $100 of the amount financed. To look up the APR of a loan, we must first calculate the finance charge per $100.

TABLE 13-1 Annual Percentage Rate (APR) Finance Charge per $100

ANNUAL PERCENTAGE RATE TABLE FOR MONTHLY PAYMENT PLANS
SEE INSTRUCTIONS FOR USE OF TABLES   FRB-103-M

NUMBER OF PAYMENTS	10.00%	10.25%	10.50%	10.75%	11.00%	11.25%	11.50%	11.75%	12.00%	12.25%	12.50%	12.75%	13.00%	13.25%	13.50%	13.75%
					(FINANCE CHARGE PER $100 OF AMOUNT FINANCED)											
1	0.83	0.85	0.87	0.90	0.92	0.94	0.96	0.98	1.00	1.02	1.04	1.06	1.08	1.10	1.12	1.15
2	1.25	1.28	1.31	1.35	1.38	1.41	1.44	1.47	1.50	1.53	1.57	1.60	1.63	1.66	1.69	1.72
3	1.67	1.71	1.76	1.80	1.84	1.88	1.92	1.96	2.01	2.05	2.09	2.13	2.17	2.22	2.26	2.30
4	2.09	2.14	2.20	2.25	2.30	2.35	2.41	2.46	2.51	2.57	2.62	2.67	2.72	2.78	2.83	2.88
5	2.51	2.58	2.64	2.70	2.77	2.83	2.89	2.96	3.02	3.08	3.15	3.21	3.27	3.34	3.40	3.46
6	2.94	3.01	3.08	3.16	3.23	3.31	3.38	3.45	3.53	3.60	3.68	3.75	3.83	3.90	3.97	4.05
7	3.36	3.45	3.53	3.62	3.70	3.78	3.87	3.95	4.04	4.12	4.21	4.29	4.38	4.47	4.55	4.64
8	3.79	3.88	3.98	4.07	4.17	4.26	4.36	4.46	4.55	4.65	4.74	4.84	4.94	5.03	5.13	5.22
9	4.21	4.32	4.43	4.53	4.64	4.75	4.85	4.96	5.07	5.17	5.28	5.39	5.49	5.60	5.71	5.82
10	4.64	4.76	4.88	4.99	5.11	5.23	5.35	5.46	5.58	5.70	5.82	5.94	6.05	6.17	6.29	6.41
11	5.07	5.20	5.33	5.45	5.58	5.71	5.84	5.97	6.10	6.23	6.36	6.49	6.62	6.75	6.88	7.01
12	5.50	5.64	5.78	5.92	6.06	6.20	6.34	6.48	6.62	6.76	6.90	7.04	7.18	7.32	7.46	7.60
13	5.93	6.08	6.23	6.38	6.53	6.68	6.84	6.99	7.14	7.29	7.44	7.59	7.75	7.90	8.05	8.20
14	6.36	6.52	6.69	6.85	7.01	7.17	7.34	7.50	7.66	7.82	7.99	8.15	8.31	8.48	8.64	8.81
15	6.80	6.97	7.14	7.32	7.49	7.66	7.84	8.01	8.19	8.36	8.53	8.71	8.88	9.06	9.23	9.41
16	7.23	7.41	7.60	7.78	7.97	8.15	8.34	8.53	8.71	8.90	9.08	9.27	9.46	9.64	9.83	10.02
17	7.67	7.86	8.06	8.25	8.45	8.65	8.84	9.04	9.24	9.44	9.63	9.83	10.03	10.23	10.43	10.63
18	8.10	8.31	8.52	8.73	8.93	9.14	9.35	9.56	9.77	9.98	10.19	10.40	10.61	10.82	11.03	11.24
19	8.54	8.76	8.98	9.20	9.42	9.64	9.86	10.08	10.30	10.52	10.74	10.96	11.18	11.41	11.63	11.85
20	8.98	9.21	9.44	9.67	9.90	10.13	10.37	10.60	10.83	11.06	11.30	11.53	11.76	12.00	12.23	12.46
21	9.42	9.66	9.90	10.15	10.39	10.63	10.88	11.12	11.36	11.61	11.85	12.10	12.34	12.59	12.84	13.08
22	9.86	10.12	10.37	10.62	10.88	11.13	11.39	11.64	11.90	12.16	12.41	12.67	12.93	13.19	13.44	13.70
23	10.30	10.57	10.84	11.10	11.37	11.63	11.90	12.17	12.44	12.71	12.97	13.24	13.51	13.78	14.05	14.32
24	10.75	11.02	11.30	11.58	11.86	12.14	12.42	12.70	12.98	13.26	13.54	13.82	14.10	14.38	14.66	14.95
25	11.19	11.48	11.77	12.06	12.35	12.64	12.93	13.22	13.52	13.81	14.10	14.40	14.69	14.98	15.28	15.57
26	11.64	11.94	12.24	12.54	12.85	13.15	13.45	13.75	14.06	14.36	14.67	14.97	15.28	15.59	15.89	16.20
27	12.09	12.40	12.71	13.03	13.34	13.66	13.97	14.29	14.60	14.92	15.24	15.56	15.87	16.19	16.51	16.83
28	12.53	12.86	13.18	13.51	13.84	14.16	14.49	14.82	15.15	15.48	15.81	16.14	16.47	16.80	17.13	17.46
29	12.98	13.32	13.66	14.00	14.33	14.67	15.01	15.35	15.70	16.04	16.38	16.72	17.07	17.41	17.75	18.10
30	13.43	13.78	14.13	14.48	14.83	15.19	15.54	15.89	16.24	16.60	16.95	17.31	17.66	18.02	18.38	18.74
31	13.89	14.25	14.61	14.97	15.33	15.70	16.06	16.43	16.79	17.16	17.53	17.90	18.27	18.63	19.00	19.38
32	14.34	14.71	15.09	15.46	15.84	16.21	16.59	16.97	17.35	17.73	18.11	18.49	18.87	19.25	19.63	20.02
33	14.79	15.18	15.57	15.95	16.34	16.73	17.12	17.51	17.90	18.29	18.69	19.08	19.47	19.87	20.26	20.66
34	15.25	15.65	16.05	16.44	16.85	17.25	17.65	18.05	18.46	18.86	19.27	19.67	20.08	20.49	20.90	21.31
35	15.70	16.11	16.53	16.94	17.35	17.77	18.18	18.60	19.01	19.43	19.85	20.27	20.69	21.11	21.53	21.95
36	16.16	16.58	17.01	17.43	17.86	18.29	18.71	19.14	19.57	20.00	20.43	20.87	21.30	21.73	22.17	22.60
37	16.62	17.06	17.49	17.93	18.37	18.81	19.25	19.69	20.13	20.58	21.02	21.46	21.91	22.36	22.81	23.25
38	17.08	17.53	17.98	18.43	18.88	19.33	19.78	20.24	20.69	21.15	21.61	22.07	22.52	22.99	23.45	23.91
39	17.54	18.00	18.46	18.93	19.39	19.86	20.32	20.79	21.26	21.73	22.20	22.67	23.14	23.61	24.09	24.56
40	18.00	18.48	18.95	19.43	19.90	20.38	20.86	21.34	21.82	22.30	22.79	23.27	23.76	24.25	24.73	25.22
41	18.47	18.95	19.44	19.93	20.42	20.91	21.40	21.89	22.39	22.88	23.38	23.88	24.38	24.88	25.38	25.88
42	18.93	19.43	19.93	20.43	20.93	21.44	21.94	22.45	22.96	23.47	23.98	24.49	25.00	25.51	26.03	26.55
43	19.40	19.91	20.42	20.94	21.45	21.97	22.49	23.01	23.53	24.05	24.57	25.10	25.62	26.15	26.68	27.21
44	19.86	20.39	20.91	21.44	21.97	22.50	23.03	23.57	24.10	24.64	25.17	25.71	26.25	26.79	27.33	27.88
45	20.33	20.87	21.41	21.95	22.49	23.03	23.58	24.12	24.67	25.22	25.77	26.32	26.88	27.43	27.99	28.55
46	20.80	21.35	21.90	22.46	23.01	23.57	24.13	24.69	25.25	25.81	26.37	26.94	27.51	28.08	28.65	29.22
47	21.27	21.83	22.40	22.97	23.53	24.10	24.68	25.25	25.82	26.40	26.98	27.56	28.14	28.72	29.31	29.89
48	21.74	22.32	22.90	23.48	24.06	24.64	25.23	25.81	26.40	26.99	27.58	28.18	28.77	29.37	29.97	30.57
49	22.21	22.80	23.39	23.99	24.58	25.18	25.78	26.38	26.98	27.59	28.19	28.80	29.41	30.02	30.63	31.24
50	22.69	23.29	23.89	24.50	25.11	25.72	26.33	26.95	27.56	28.18	28.80	29.42	30.04	30.67	31.29	31.92
51	23.16	23.78	24.40	25.02	25.64	26.26	26.89	27.52	28.15	28.78	29.41	30.05	30.68	31.32	31.96	32.60
52	23.64	24.27	24.90	25.53	26.17	26.81	27.45	28.09	28.73	29.38	30.02	30.67	31.32	31.98	32.63	33.29
53	24.11	24.76	25.40	26.05	26.70	27.35	28.00	28.66	29.32	29.98	30.64	31.30	31.97	32.63	33.30	33.97
54	24.59	25.25	25.91	26.57	27.23	27.90	28.56	29.23	29.91	30.58	31.25	31.93	32.61	33.29	33.98	34.66
55	25.07	25.74	26.41	27.09	27.77	28.44	29.13	29.81	30.50	31.18	31.87	32.56	33.26	33.95	34.65	35.35
56	25.55	26.23	26.92	27.61	28.30	28.99	29.69	30.39	31.09	31.79	32.49	33.20	33.91	34.62	35.33	36.04
57	26.03	26.73	27.43	28.13	28.84	29.54	30.25	30.97	31.68	32.39	33.11	33.83	34.56	35.28	36.01	36.74
58	26.51	27.23	27.94	28.66	29.37	30.10	30.82	31.55	32.27	33.00	33.74	34.47	35.21	35.95	36.69	37.43
59	27.00	27.72	28.45	29.18	29.91	30.65	31.39	32.13	32.87	33.61	34.36	35.11	35.86	36.62	37.37	38.13
60	27.48	28.22	28.96	29.71	30.45	31.20	31.96	32.71	33.47	34.23	34.99	35.75	36.52	37.29	38.06	38.83

continued

TABLE 13-1 Annual Percentage Rate (APR) Finance Charge per $100   (*continued*)

ANNUAL PERCENTAGE RATE TABLE FOR MONTHLY PAYMENT PLANS
SEE INSTRUCTIONS FOR USE OF TABLES

FRB-104-M

NUMBER OF PAYMENTS	14.00%	14.25%	14.50%	14.75%	15.00%	15.25%	15.50%	15.75%	16.00%	16.25%	16.50%	16.75%	17.00%	17.25%	17.50%	17.75%
							(FINANCE CHARGE PER $100 OF AMOUNT FINANCED)									
1	1.17	1.19	1.21	1.23	1.25	1.27	1.29	1.31	1.33	1.35	1.37	1.40	1.42	1.44	1.46	1.48
2	1.75	1.78	1.82	1.85	1.88	1.91	1.94	1.97	2.00	2.04	2.07	2.10	2.13	2.16	2.19	2.22
3	2.34	2.38	2.43	2.47	2.51	2.55	2.59	2.64	2.68	2.72	2.76	2.80	2.85	2.89	2.93	2.97
4	2.93	2.99	3.04	3.09	3.14	3.20	3.25	3.30	3.36	3.41	3.46	3.51	3.57	3.62	3.67	3.73
5	3.53	3.59	3.65	3.72	3.78	3.84	3.91	3.97	4.04	4.10	4.16	4.23	4.29	4.35	4.42	4.48
6	4.12	4.20	4.27	4.35	4.42	4.49	4.57	4.64	4.72	4.79	4.87	4.94	5.02	5.09	5.17	5.24
7	4.72	4.81	4.89	4.98	5.06	5.15	5.23	5.32	5.40	5.49	5.58	5.66	5.75	5.83	5.92	6.00
8	5.32	5.42	5.51	5.61	5.71	5.80	5.90	6.00	6.09	6.19	6.29	6.38	6.48	6.58	6.67	6.77
9	5.92	6.03	6.14	6.25	6.35	6.46	6.57	6.68	6.78	6.89	7.00	7.11	7.22	7.32	7.43	7.54
10	6.53	6.65	6.77	6.88	7.00	7.12	7.24	7.36	7.48	7.60	7.72	7.84	7.96	8.08	8.19	8.31
11	7.14	7.27	7.40	7.53	7.66	7.79	7.92	8.05	8.18	8.31	8.44	8.57	8.70	8.83	8.96	9.09
12	7.74	7.89	8.03	8.17	8.31	8.45	8.59	8.74	8.88	9.02	9.16	9.30	9.45	9.59	9.73	9.87
13	8.36	8.51	8.66	8.81	8.97	9.12	9.27	9.43	9.58	9.73	9.89	10.04	10.20	10.35	10.50	10.66
14	8.97	9.13	9.30	9.46	9.63	9.79	9.96	10.12	10.29	10.45	10.62	10.78	10.95	11.11	11.28	11.45
15	9.59	9.76	9.94	10.11	10.29	10.47	10.64	10.82	11.00	11.17	11.35	11.53	11.71	11.88	12.06	12.24
16	10.20	10.39	10.58	10.77	10.95	11.14	11.33	11.52	11.71	11.90	12.09	12.28	12.46	12.65	12.84	13.03
17	10.82	11.02	11.22	11.42	11.62	11.82	12.02	12.22	12.42	12.62	12.83	13.03	13.23	13.43	13.63	13.83
18	11.45	11.66	11.87	12.08	12.29	12.50	12.72	12.93	13.14	13.35	13.57	13.78	13.99	14.21	14.42	14.64
19	12.07	12.30	12.52	12.74	12.97	13.19	13.41	13.64	13.86	14.09	14.31	14.54	14.76	14.99	15.22	15.44
20	12.70	12.93	13.17	13.41	13.64	13.88	14.11	14.35	14.59	14.82	15.06	15.30	15.54	15.77	16.01	16.25
21	13.33	13.58	13.82	14.07	14.32	14.57	14.82	15.06	15.31	15.56	15.81	16.06	16.31	16.56	16.81	17.07
22	13.96	14.22	14.48	14.74	15.00	15.26	15.52	15.78	16.04	16.30	16.57	16.83	17.09	17.36	17.62	17.88
23	14.59	14.87	15.14	15.41	15.68	15.96	16.23	16.50	16.78	17.05	17.32	17.60	17.88	18.15	18.43	18.70
24	15.23	15.51	15.80	16.08	16.37	16.65	16.94	17.22	17.51	17.80	18.09	18.37	18.66	18.95	19.24	19.53
25	15.87	16.17	16.46	16.76	17.06	17.35	17.65	17.95	18.25	18.55	18.85	19.15	19.45	19.75	20.05	20.36
26	16.51	16.82	17.13	17.44	17.75	18.06	18.37	18.68	18.99	19.30	19.62	19.93	20.24	20.56	20.87	21.19
27	17.15	17.47	17.80	18.12	18.44	18.76	19.09	19.41	19.74	20.06	20.39	20.71	21.04	21.37	21.69	22.02
28	17.80	18.13	18.47	18.80	19.14	19.47	19.81	20.15	20.48	20.82	21.16	21.50	21.84	22.18	22.52	22.86
29	18.45	18.79	19.14	19.49	19.83	20.18	20.53	20.88	21.23	21.58	21.94	22.29	22.64	22.99	23.35	23.70
30	19.10	19.45	19.81	20.17	20.54	20.90	21.26	21.62	21.99	22.35	22.72	23.08	23.45	23.81	24.18	24.55
31	19.75	20.12	20.49	20.87	21.24	21.61	21.99	22.37	22.74	23.12	23.50	23.88	24.26	24.64	25.02	25.40
32	20.40	20.79	21.17	21.56	21.95	22.33	22.72	23.11	23.50	23.89	24.28	24.68	25.07	25.46	25.86	26.25
33	21.06	21.46	21.85	22.25	22.65	23.06	23.46	23.86	24.26	24.67	25.07	25.48	25.88	26.29	26.70	27.11
34	21.72	22.13	22.54	22.95	23.37	23.78	24.19	24.61	25.03	25.44	25.86	26.28	26.70	27.12	27.54	27.97
35	22.38	22.80	23.23	23.65	24.08	24.51	24.94	25.36	25.79	26.23	26.66	27.09	27.52	27.96	28.39	28.83
36	23.04	23.48	23.92	24.35	24.80	25.24	25.68	26.12	26.57	27.01	27.46	27.90	28.35	28.80	29.25	29.70
37	23.70	24.16	24.61	25.06	25.51	25.97	26.42	26.88	27.34	27.80	28.26	28.72	29.18	29.64	30.10	30.57
38	24.37	24.84	25.30	25.77	26.24	26.70	27.17	27.64	28.11	28.59	29.06	29.53	30.01	30.49	30.96	31.44
39	25.04	25.52	26.00	26.48	26.96	27.44	27.92	28.41	28.89	29.38	29.87	30.36	30.85	31.34	31.83	32.32
40	25.71	26.20	26.70	27.19	27.69	28.18	28.68	29.18	29.68	30.18	30.68	31.18	31.68	32.19	32.69	33.20
41	26.39	26.89	27.40	27.91	28.41	28.92	29.44	29.95	30.46	30.97	31.49	32.01	32.52	33.04	33.56	34.08
42	27.06	27.58	28.10	28.62	29.15	29.67	30.19	30.72	31.25	31.78	32.31	32.84	33.37	33.90	34.44	34.97
43	27.74	28.27	28.81	29.34	29.88	30.42	30.96	31.50	32.04	32.58	33.13	33.67	34.22	34.76	35.31	35.86
44	28.42	28.97	29.52	30.07	30.62	31.17	31.72	32.28	32.83	33.39	33.95	34.51	35.07	35.63	36.19	36.76
45	29.11	29.67	30.23	30.79	31.36	31.92	32.49	33.06	33.63	34.20	34.77	35.35	35.92	36.50	37.08	37.66
46	29.79	30.36	30.94	31.52	32.10	32.68	33.26	33.84	34.43	35.01	35.60	36.19	36.78	37.37	37.96	38.56
47	30.48	31.07	31.66	32.25	32.84	33.44	34.03	34.63	35.23	35.83	36.43	37.04	37.64	38.25	38.86	39.46
48	31.17	31.77	32.37	32.98	33.59	34.20	34.81	35.42	36.03	36.65	37.27	37.88	38.50	39.13	39.75	40.37
49	31.86	32.48	33.09	33.71	34.34	34.96	35.59	36.21	36.84	37.47	38.10	38.74	39.37	40.01	40.65	41.29
50	32.55	33.18	33.82	34.45	35.09	35.73	36.37	37.01	37.65	38.30	38.94	39.59	40.24	40.89	41.55	42.20
51	33.25	33.89	34.54	35.19	35.84	36.49	37.15	37.81	38.46	39.12	39.79	40.45	41.11	41.78	42.45	43.12
52	33.95	34.61	35.27	35.93	36.60	37.27	37.94	38.61	39.28	39.96	40.63	41.31	41.99	42.67	43.36	44.04
53	34.65	35.32	36.00	36.68	37.36	38.04	38.72	39.41	40.10	40.79	41.48	42.17	42.87	43.57	44.27	44.97
54	35.35	36.04	36.73	37.42	38.12	38.82	39.52	40.22	40.92	41.63	42.33	43.04	43.75	44.47	45.18	45.90
55	36.05	36.76	37.46	38.17	38.88	39.60	40.31	41.03	41.74	42.47	43.19	43.91	44.64	45.37	46.10	46.83
56	36.76	37.48	38.20	38.92	39.65	40.38	41.11	41.84	42.57	43.31	44.05	44.79	45.53	46.27	47.02	47.77
57	37.47	38.20	38.94	39.68	40.42	41.16	41.91	42.65	43.40	44.15	44.91	45.66	46.42	47.18	47.94	48.71
58	38.18	38.93	39.68	40.43	41.19	41.95	42.71	43.47	44.23	45.00	45.77	46.54	47.32	48.09	48.87	49.65
59	38.89	39.66	40.42	41.19	41.96	42.74	43.51	44.29	45.07	45.85	46.64	47.42	48.21	49.01	49.80	50.60
60	39.61	40.39	41.17	41.95	42.74	43.53	44.32	45.11	45.91	46.71	47.51	48.31	49.12	49.92	50.73	51.55

TABLE 13-1 Annual Percentage Rate (APR) Finance Charge per $100 *(continued)*

ANNUAL PERCENTAGE RATE TABLE FOR MONTHLY PAYMENT PLANS
SEE INSTRUCTIONS FOR USE OF TABLES   FRB-105-M

NUMBER OF PAYMENTS	18.00%	18.25%	18.50%	18.75%	19.00%	19.25%	19.50%	19.75%	20.00%	20.25%	20.50%	20.75%	21.00%	21.25%	21.50%	21.75%
	(FINANCE CHARGE PER $100 OF AMOUNT FINANCED)															
1	1.50	1.52	1.54	1.56	1.58	1.60	1.62	1.65	1.67	1.69	1.71	1.73	1.75	1.77	1.79	1.81
2	2.26	2.29	2.32	2.35	2.38	2.41	2.44	2.48	2.51	2.54	2.57	2.60	2.63	2.66	2.70	2.73
3	3.01	3.06	3.10	3.14	3.18	3.23	3.27	3.31	3.35	3.39	3.44	3.48	3.52	3.56	3.60	3.65
4	3.78	3.83	3.88	3.94	3.99	4.04	4.10	4.15	4.20	4.25	4.31	4.36	4.41	4.47	4.52	4.57
5	4.54	4.61	4.67	4.74	4.80	4.86	4.93	4.99	5.06	5.12	5.18	5.25	5.31	5.37	5.44	5.50
6	5.32	5.39	5.46	5.54	5.61	5.69	5.76	5.84	5.91	5.99	6.06	6.14	6.21	6.29	6.36	6.44
7	6.09	6.18	6.26	6.35	6.43	6.52	6.60	6.69	6.78	6.86	6.95	7.04	7.12	7.21	7.29	7.38
8	6.87	6.96	7.06	7.16	7.26	7.35	7.45	7.55	7.64	7.74	7.84	7.94	8.03	8.13	8.23	8.33
9	7.65	7.76	7.87	7.97	8.08	8.19	8.30	8.41	8.52	8.63	8.73	8.84	8.95	9.06	9.17	9.28
10	8.43	8.55	8.67	8.79	8.91	9.03	9.15	9.27	9.39	9.51	9.63	9.75	9.88	10.00	10.12	10.24
11	9.22	9.35	9.49	9.62	9.75	9.88	10.01	10.14	10.28	10.41	10.54	10.67	10.80	10.94	11.07	11.20
12	10.02	10.16	10.30	10.44	10.59	10.73	10.87	11.02	11.16	11.31	11.45	11.59	11.74	11.88	12.02	12.17
13	10.81	10.97	11.12	11.28	11.43	11.59	11.74	11.90	12.05	12.21	12.36	12.52	12.67	12.83	12.99	13.14
14	11.61	11.78	11.95	12.11	12.28	12.45	12.61	12.78	12.95	13.11	13.28	13.45	13.62	13.79	13.95	14.12
15	12.42	12.59	12.77	12.95	13.13	13.31	13.49	13.67	13.85	14.03	14.21	14.39	14.57	14.75	14.93	15.11
16	13.22	13.41	13.60	13.80	13.99	14.18	14.37	14.56	14.75	14.94	15.13	15.33	15.52	15.71	15.90	16.10
17	14.04	14.24	14.44	14.64	14.85	15.05	15.25	15.46	15.66	15.86	16.07	16.27	16.48	16.68	16.89	17.09
18	14.85	15.07	15.28	15.49	15.71	15.93	16.14	16.36	16.57	16.79	17.01	17.22	17.44	17.66	17.88	18.09
19	15.67	15.90	16.12	16.35	16.58	16.81	17.03	17.26	17.49	17.72	17.95	18.18	18.41	18.64	18.87	19.10
20	16.49	16.73	16.97	17.21	17.45	17.69	17.93	18.17	18.41	18.66	18.90	19.14	19.38	19.63	19.87	20.11
21	17.32	17.57	17.82	18.07	18.33	18.58	18.83	19.09	19.34	19.60	19.85	20.11	20.36	20.62	20.87	21.13
22	18.15	18.41	18.68	18.94	19.21	19.47	19.74	20.01	20.27	20.54	20.81	21.08	21.34	21.61	21.88	22.15
23	18.98	19.26	19.54	19.81	20.09	20.37	20.65	20.93	21.21	21.49	21.77	22.05	22.33	22.61	22.90	23.18
24	19.82	20.11	20.40	20.69	20.98	21.27	21.56	21.86	22.15	22.44	22.74	23.03	23.33	23.62	23.92	24.21
25	20.66	20.96	21.27	21.57	21.87	22.18	22.48	22.79	23.10	23.40	23.71	24.02	24.32	24.63	24.94	25.25
26	21.50	21.82	22.14	22.45	22.77	23.09	23.41	23.73	24.04	24.36	24.68	25.01	25.33	25.65	25.97	26.29
27	22.35	22.68	23.01	23.34	23.67	24.00	24.33	24.67	25.00	25.33	25.67	26.00	26.34	26.67	27.01	27.34
28	23.20	23.55	23.89	24.23	24.58	24.92	25.27	25.61	25.96	26.30	26.65	27.00	27.35	27.70	28.05	28.40
29	24.06	24.41	24.77	25.13	25.49	25.84	26.20	26.56	26.92	27.28	27.64	28.00	28.37	28.73	29.09	29.46
30	24.92	25.29	25.66	26.03	26.40	26.77	27.14	27.52	27.89	28.26	28.64	29.01	29.39	29.77	30.14	30.52
31	25.78	26.16	26.55	26.93	27.32	27.70	28.09	28.47	28.86	29.25	29.64	30.03	30.42	30.81	31.20	31.59
32	26.65	27.04	27.44	27.84	28.24	28.64	29.04	29.44	29.84	30.24	30.64	31.05	31.45	31.85	32.26	32.67
33	27.52	27.93	28.34	28.75	29.16	29.57	29.99	30.40	30.82	31.23	31.65	32.07	32.49	32.91	33.33	33.75
34	28.39	28.81	29.24	29.66	30.09	30.52	30.95	31.37	31.80	32.23	32.67	33.10	33.53	33.96	34.40	34.83
35	29.27	29.71	30.14	30.58	31.02	31.47	31.91	32.35	32.79	33.24	33.68	34.13	34.58	35.03	35.47	35.92
36	30.15	30.60	31.05	31.51	31.96	32.42	32.87	33.33	33.79	34.25	34.71	35.17	35.63	36.09	36.56	37.02
37	31.03	31.50	31.97	32.43	32.90	33.37	33.84	34.32	34.79	35.26	35.74	36.21	36.69	37.16	37.64	38.12
38	31.92	32.40	32.88	33.37	33.85	34.33	34.82	35.30	35.79	36.28	36.77	37.26	37.75	38.24	38.73	39.23
39	32.81	33.31	33.80	34.30	34.80	35.30	35.80	36.30	36.80	37.30	37.81	38.31	38.82	39.32	39.83	40.34
40	33.71	34.22	34.73	35.24	35.75	36.26	36.78	37.29	37.81	38.33	38.85	39.37	39.89	40.41	40.93	41.46
41	34.61	35.13	35.66	36.18	36.71	37.24	37.77	38.30	38.83	39.36	39.89	40.43	40.96	41.50	42.04	42.58
42	35.51	36.05	36.59	37.13	37.67	38.21	38.76	39.30	39.85	40.40	40.95	41.50	42.05	42.60	43.15	43.71
43	36.42	36.97	37.52	38.08	38.63	39.19	39.75	40.31	40.87	41.44	42.00	42.57	43.13	43.70	44.27	44.84
44	37.33	37.89	38.46	39.03	39.60	40.18	40.75	41.33	41.90	42.48	43.06	43.64	44.22	44.81	45.39	45.98
45	38.24	38.82	39.41	39.99	40.58	41.17	41.75	42.35	42.94	43.53	44.13	44.72	45.32	45.92	46.52	47.12
46	39.16	39.75	40.35	40.95	41.55	42.16	42.76	43.37	43.98	44.58	45.20	45.81	46.42	47.03	47.65	48.27
47	40.08	40.69	41.30	41.92	42.54	43.15	43.77	44.40	45.02	45.64	46.27	46.90	47.53	48.16	48.79	49.42
48	41.00	41.63	42.26	42.89	43.52	44.15	44.79	45.43	46.07	46.71	47.35	47.99	48.64	49.28	49.93	50.58
49	41.93	42.57	43.22	43.86	44.51	45.16	45.81	46.47	47.12	47.77	48.43	49.09	49.75	50.41	51.08	51.74
50	42.86	43.52	44.18	44.84	45.50	46.17	46.83	47.50	48.17	48.84	49.52	50.19	50.87	51.55	52.23	52.91
51	43.79	44.47	45.14	45.82	46.50	47.18	47.86	48.55	49.23	49.92	50.61	51.30	51.99	52.69	53.38	54.08
52	44.73	45.42	46.11	46.80	47.50	48.20	48.89	49.59	50.30	51.00	51.71	52.41	53.12	53.83	54.55	55.26
53	45.67	46.38	47.08	47.79	48.50	49.22	49.93	50.65	51.37	52.09	52.81	53.53	54.26	54.98	55.71	56.44
54	46.62	47.34	48.06	48.79	49.51	50.24	50.97	51.70	52.44	53.17	53.91	54.65	55.39	56.14	56.88	57.63
55	47.57	48.30	49.04	49.78	50.52	51.27	52.02	52.76	53.52	54.27	55.02	55.78	56.54	57.30	58.06	58.82
56	48.52	49.27	50.03	50.78	51.54	52.30	53.06	53.83	54.60	55.37	56.14	56.91	57.68	58.46	59.24	60.02
57	49.47	50.24	51.01	51.79	52.56	53.34	54.12	54.90	55.68	56.47	57.25	58.04	58.84	59.63	60.43	61.22
58	50.43	51.22	52.00	52.79	53.58	54.38	55.17	55.97	56.77	57.57	58.38	59.18	59.99	60.80	61.62	62.43
59	51.39	52.20	53.00	53.80	54.61	55.42	56.23	57.05	57.87	58.68	59.51	60.33	61.15	61.98	62.81	63.64
60	52.36	53.18	54.00	54.82	55.64	56.47	57.30	58.13	58.96	59.80	60.64	61.48	62.32	63.17	64.01	64.86

STEPS TO FIND THE ANNUAL PERCENTAGE RATE OF AN INSTALLMENT LOAN BY USING APR TABLES

STEP 1. Calculate the finance charge per $100.

$$\text{Finance charge per \$100} = \frac{\text{Finance charge} \times 100}{\text{Amount financed}}$$

STEP 2. From Table 13-1, scan down the Number of Payments column to the number of payments for the loan in question.

STEP 3. Scan to the right in that Number of Payments row to the table factor that most closely corresponds to the finance charge per $100 calculated in Step 1.

STEP 4. Look to the top of the column containing the finance charge per $100 to find the APR of the loan.

EXAMPLE6 CALCULATING APR BY TABLES

Gary Robbins purchased a used motorcycle for $7,000. He made a down payment of $1,000 and financed the remaining $6,000 for 36 months. With monthly payments of $200 each, the total finance charge on the loan was $1,200 ($200 × 36 = $7,200 − $6,000 = $1,200). Use Table 13-1 to find what annual percentage rate was charged on Gary's loan.

▶ SOLUTIONSTRATEGY

Step 1. Finance charge per $100 $= \dfrac{\text{Finance charge} \times 100}{\text{Amount financed}}$

Finance charge per $100 $= \dfrac{1{,}200 \times 100}{6{,}000} = \dfrac{120{,}000}{6{,}000}$

Finance charge per $100 = $20

Step 2. Using Table 13-1, scan down the Number of Payments column to 36 payments.

Step 3. Scan to the right in that Number of Payments row until you find $20, the finance charge per $100.

Step 4. Looking at the top of the column containing the $20, you will find the annual percentage rate for the loan to be 12.25%.

▶ TRYITEXERCISE 6

Erica Larsen purchased a living room set for $4,500 from Century Designs. She made a $500 down payment and financed the balance with an installment loan for 24 months. If her payments are $190 per month, what APR is she paying on the loan?

CHECK YOUR ANSWER WITH THE SOLUTION ON PAGE 443.

CALCULATING APR BY FORMULA

When APR tables are not available, the annual percentage rate can be closely approximated by the formula

$$APR = \frac{72I}{3P(n+1) + I(n-1)}$$

where:

I = finance charge on the loan
P = principal, or amount financed
n = number of months of the loan

EXAMPLE7 CALCULATING APR BY FORMULA

Refer to Example 6, Gary Robbins' motorcycle purchase. This time use the APR formula to find the annual percentage rate. How does it compare with the APR from the table?

SOLUTIONSTRATEGY

$$APR = \frac{72I}{3P(n + 1) + I(n - 1)}$$

$$APR = \frac{72(1,200)}{3(6,000)(36 + 1) + 1,200(36 - 1)} = \frac{86,400}{666,000 + 42,000} = \frac{86,400}{708,000}$$

$$APR = .1220338 = \underline{12.20\%}$$

Note: In comparing the two answers, we can see that using the formula gives a close approximation of the Federal Reserve Board's APR table value of 12.25%.

▶TRYITEXERCISE 7

Christina Pitt repaid a $2,200 installment loan with 18 monthly payments of $140 each. Use the APR formula to determine the annual percentage rate of Christina's loan.

CHECK YOUR ANSWER WITH THE SOLUTION ON PAGE 443.

CALCULATING THE FINANCE CHARGE AND MONTHLY PAYMENT OF AN INSTALLMENT LOAN BY USING THE APR TABLES

13-7

When the annual percentage rate and number of months of an installment loan are known, the APR tables can be used in reverse to find the amount of the finance charge. Once the finance charge is known, the monthly payment required to amortize the loan can be calculated as before.

STEPS TO FIND THE FINANCE CHARGE AND THE MONTHLY PAYMENT OF AN INSTALLMENT LOAN BY USING THE APR TABLES

STEP 1. Using the APR and the number of payments of the loan, locate the table factor at the intersection of the APR column and the Number of Payments row. This factor represents the finance charge per $100 financed.

STEP 2. Calculate the total finance charge of the loan.

$$\text{Finance charge} = \frac{\text{Amount financed} \times \text{Table factor}}{100}$$

STEP 3. Calculate the monthly payment.

$$\text{Monthly payment} = \frac{\text{Amount financed} + \text{Finance charge}}{\text{Number of months of the loan}}$$

EXAMPLE 8 — CALCULATING FINANCE CHARGE BY APR TABLES

Classic Motors uses Regal Bank to finance automobile and truck sales. This month Regal is offering up to 48-month installment loans with an APR of 15.5%. For qualified buyers, no down payment is required. If Todd Martin wants to finance a new truck for $17,500, what are the finance charge and the monthly payment on Todd's loan?

SOLUTIONSTRATEGY

Step 1. The table factor at the intersection of the 15.5% APR column and the 48 Payments row is $34.81.

Step 2.
$$\text{Finance charge} = \frac{\text{Amount financed} \times \text{Table factor}}{100}$$

$$\text{Finance charge} = \frac{17,500 \times 34.81}{100} = \frac{609,175}{100}$$

$$\text{Finance charge} = \$6,091.75$$

Step 3.
$$\text{Monthly payment} = \frac{\text{Amount financed} + \text{Finance charge}}{\text{Number of months of the loan}}$$

$$\text{Monthly payment} = \frac{17,500 + 6,091.75}{48} = \frac{23,591.75}{48}$$

$$\text{Monthly payment} = \$491.49$$

TRYITEXERCISE 8

Computer Mart uses a finance company that is offering up to 24-month installment loans with an APR of 13.25%. For qualified buyers, no down payment is required. If Randy Salazar wants to finance a computer and printer for $3,550, what are the finance charge and the monthly payment on Randy's loan?

CHECK YOUR ANSWERS WITH THE SOLUTIONS ON PAGE 443.

Dollars AND Sense

Business and personal financial decisions involve a concept known as opportunity cost. Like time, money used in one way cannot be used in other ways. Financial choices are always a series of trade-offs.

If you buy a car with your savings, you give up the interest that money could earn. If you invest the money, you don't get the car. If you borrow money to buy the car, you have to pay interest for its use.

When making financial choices such as saving, spending, investing, or borrowing, you should consider the interest-earning ability of that money as an opportunity cost.

13-8 CALCULATING THE FINANCE CHARGE REBATE AND THE PAYOFF FOR LOANS PAID OFF EARLY BY USING THE SUM-OF-THE-DIGITS METHOD

finance charge rebate Unearned portion of the finance charge that the lender returns to the borrower when an installment loan is paid off early.

sum-of-the-digits method or **Rule of 78** Widely accepted method for calculating the finance charge rebate. Based on the assumption that more interest is paid in the early months of a loan, when a greater portion of the principal is available to the borrower.

Frequently, borrowers choose to repay installment loans before the full time period of the loan has elapsed. When loans are paid off early, the borrower is entitled to a **finance charge rebate** because the principal was not kept for the full amount of time on which the finance charge was calculated. At payoff, the lender must return, or rebate, to the borrower any unearned portion of the finance charge.

A widely accepted method for calculating the finance charge rebate is known as the **sum-of-the-digits method** or the **Rule of 78**. This method is based on the assumption that the lender earns more interest in the early months of a loan, when the borrower has the use of much of the principal, than in the later months, when most of the principal has already been paid back.

When using this method, the finance charge is assumed to be divided in parts equal to the sum of the digits of the months of the loan. Because the sum of the digits of a 12-month loan is 78, the technique has become known as the Rule of 78.

$$\text{Sum of the digits of } 12 = 1 + 2 + 3 + 4 + 5 + 6 + 7 + 8 + 9 + 10 + 11 + 12 = 78$$

The amount of finance charge in any given month is represented by a fraction whose numerator is the number of payments remaining, and the denominator is the sum of the digits of the number of months in the loan.

For a 12-month loan, for example, the fraction of the finance charge in the first month would be $\frac{12}{78}$. The numerator is 12 because in the first month, no payments have been made; therefore, 12 payments remain. The denominator is 78 because the sum of the digits of

12 payments is 78. In the second month, the lender earns $\frac{11}{78}$; in the third month, $\frac{10}{78}$. This decline continues until the last month when only $\frac{1}{78}$ remains. Exhibit 13-6 illustrates the distribution of a \$1,000 finance charge by using the sum-of-the-digits method.

With the sum-of-the-digits method, a **rebate fraction** is established based on when a loan is paid off. The numerator of the rebate fraction is the sum of the digits of the number of remaining payments, and the denominator is the sum of the digits of the total number of payments.

$$\text{Rebate fraction} = \frac{\text{Sum of the digits of the number of remaining payments}}{\text{Sum of the digits of the total number of payments}}$$

Although the sum of the digits is easily calculated by addition, it can become tedious for loans of 24, 36, or 48 months. For this reason, we will use the sum-of-the-digits formula to find the numerator and denominator of the rebate fraction. In the formula, n represents the number of payments.

$$\text{Sum of digits} = \frac{n(n+1)}{2}$$

rebate fraction Fraction used to calculate the finance charge rebate. The numerator is the sum of the digits of the number of payments remaining at the time the loan is paid off; the denominator is the sum of the digits of the total number of payments of the loan.

Installment financing is frequently used when consumers purchase big ticket items such as appliances and electronic equipment.

EXHIBIT 13-6 Distribution of a \$1,000 Finance Charge over 12 Months

Month Number	Finance Charge Fraction	×	\$1,000	=	Finance Charge
1	$\frac{12}{78}$	×	\$1,000	=	\$153.85
2	$\frac{11}{78}$	×	\$1,000	=	\$141.03
3	$\frac{10}{78}$	×	\$1,000	=	\$128.21
4	$\frac{9}{78}$	×	\$1,000	=	\$115.38
5	$\frac{8}{78}$	×	\$1,000	=	\$102.56
6	$\frac{7}{78}$	×	\$1,000	=	\$89.74
7	$\frac{6}{78}$	×	\$1,000	=	\$76.92
8	$\frac{5}{78}$	×	\$1,000	=	\$64.10
9	$\frac{4}{78}$	×	\$1,000	=	\$51.28
10	$\frac{3}{78}$	×	\$1,000	=	\$38.46
11	$\frac{2}{78}$	×	\$1,000	=	\$25.64
12	$\frac{1}{78}$	×	\$1,000	=	\$12.82

IN THE Business World

This table clearly illustrates that the majority of the finance charge on an installment loan is incurred in the first half of the loan.

STEPS TO CALCULATE THE FINANCE CHARGE REBATE AND LOAN PAYOFF

STEP 1. Calculate the rebate fraction.

$$\text{Rebate fraction} = \frac{\text{Sum of the digits of the number of remaining payments}}{\text{Sum of the digits of the total number of payments}}$$

STEP 2. Determine the finance charge rebate.

$$\text{Finance charge rebate} = \text{Rebate fraction} \times \text{Total finance charge}$$

STEP 3. Find the loan payoff.

$$\frac{\text{Loan}}{\text{payoff}} = \left(\frac{\text{Payment}}{\text{remaining}} \times \frac{\text{Payments}}{\text{amount}} \right) - \frac{\text{Finance charge}}{\text{rebate}}$$

EXAMPLE9   CALCULATING EARLY LOAN PAYOFF FIGURES

Suzie Starr financed a $1,500 health club membership with an installment loan for 12 months. The payments were $145 per month, and the total finance charge was $240. After 8 months, she decided to pay off the loan. What is the finance charge rebate, and what is her loan payoff?

▶SOLUTIONSTRATEGY

Step 1.   Rebate fraction:

Set up the rebate fraction by using the sum-of-the-digits formula. Because Suzie already made eight payments, she has four payments remaining ($12 - 8 = 4$).

The *numerator* will be the sum of the digits of the number of remaining payments, 4.

$$\text{Sum of the digits of } 4 = \frac{n(n + 1)}{2} = \frac{4(4 + 1)}{2} = \frac{4(5)}{2} = \frac{20}{2} = \underline{10}$$

The *denominator* will be the sum of the digits of the number of payments, 12.

$$\text{Sum of the digits of } 12 = \frac{n(n + 1)}{2} = \frac{12(12 + 1)}{2} = \frac{12(13)}{2} = \frac{156}{2} = \underline{78}$$

The rebate fraction is therefore $\frac{10}{78}$.

Step 2.   Finance charge rebate:

Finance charge rebate = Rebate fraction × Total finance charge

Finance charge rebate $= \frac{10}{78} \times 240$

Finance charge rebate $= 30.7692 = \underline{\underline{\$30.77}}$

Step 3.   Loan payoff:

Loan payoff = (Payments remaining × Payment amount) − Finance charge rebate

Loan payoff = (4 × 145) − 30.77

Loan payoff = 580.00 − 30.77

Loan payoff = $\underline{\underline{\$549.23}}$

▶TRYITEXERCISE 9

Mark Sanchez financed a $4,000 piano with an installment loan for 36 months. The payments were $141 per month, and the total finance charge was $1,076. After 20 months, Mark decided to pay off the loan. What is the finance charge rebate, and what is his loan payoff?

CHECK YOUR ANSWERS WITH THE SOLUTIONS ON PAGES 443–444.

SECTION II   13   REVIEW EXERCISES

Note: Round all answers to the nearest cent when necessary.

Calculate the amount financed, the finance charge, and the total deferred payment price for the following installment loans.

	Purchase (Cash) Price	Down Payment	Amount Financed	Monthly Payment	Number of Payments	Finance Charge	Total Deferred Payment Price
1.	$1,400	$350	$1,050.00	$68.00	24	$582.00	$1,982.00
2.	$3,500	20%	_____	$257.00	12	_____	_____

	Purchase (Cash) Price	Down Payment	Amount Financed	Monthly Payment	Number of Payments	Finance Charge	Total Deferred Payment Price
3.	$12,000	10%	_____	$375.00	36	_____	_____
4.	$2,900	0	_____	$187.69	18	_____	_____
5.	$8,750	15%	_____	$198.33	48	_____	_____
6.	$5,400	$1,500	_____	$427.50	12	_____	_____
7.	$20,000	25%	_____	$682.70	36	_____	_____

Calculate the amount financed, the finance charge, and the monthly payments for the following add-on interest loans.

	Purchase (Cash) Price	Down Payment	Amount Financed	Add-on Interest	Number of Payments	Finance Charge	Monthly Payment
8.	$788	10%	$709.20	8%	12	$56.74	$63.83
9.	$1,600	$250	_____	10%	24	_____	
10.	$4,000	15%	_____	$11\frac{1}{2}\%$	30	_____	_____
11.	$17,450	$2,000	_____	14%	48	_____	_____
12.	$50,300	25%	_____	12.4%	60	_____	_____
13.	$12,300	5%	_____	9%	36	_____	_____
14.	$5,225	$1,600	_____	7.8%	18	_____	_____

Calculate the finance charge, the finance charge per $100, and the annual percentage rate for the following installment loans by using the APR table, Table 13-1.

	Amount Financed	Number of Payments	Monthly Payment	Finance Charge	Finance Charge per $100	APR
15.	$2,300	24	$109.25	$322.00	$14.00	13%
16.	$14,000	36	$495.00	_____	_____	_____
17.	$1,860	18	$115.75	_____	_____	_____
18.	$35,000	60	$875.00	_____	_____	_____
19.	$6,550	24	$307.30	_____	_____	_____
20.	$17,930	48	$540.47	_____	_____	_____

Calculate the finance charge and the annual percentage rate for the following installment loans by using the APR formula.

	Amount Financed	Number of Payments	Monthly Payment	Finance Charge	APR
21.	$500	12	$44.25	$31.00	11.25%
22.	$2,450	36	$90.52	_____	_____
23.	$13,000	48	$373.75	_____	_____
24.	$100,000	72	$2,055.50	_____	_____
25.	$35,600	60	$845.50	_____	_____
26.	$8,850	30	$333.35	_____	_____

Calculate the finance charge and the monthly payment for the following loans by using the APR table, Table 13-1.

	Amount Financed	Number of Payments	APR	Table Factor	Finance Charge	Monthly Payment
27.	$5,000	48	13.5%	$29.97	$1,498.50	$135.39
28.	$7,500	36	12%	___	___	___
29.	$1,800	12	11.25%	___	___	___
30.	$900	18	14%	___	___	___
31.	$12,200	24	12.75%	___	___	___
32.	$3,875	30	16.5%	___	___	___

Calculate the missing information for the following installment loans that are being paid off early.

	Number of Payments	Payments Made	Payments Remaining	Sum-of-the-Digits Payments Remaining	Sum-of-the-Digits Number of Payments	Rebate Fraction
33.	12	4	8	36	78	36/78
34.	36	22	___	___	___	___
35.	24	9	___	___	___	___
36.	60	40	___	___	___	___
37.	48	8	___	___	___	___
38.	18	5	___	___	___	___

You are the loan department supervisor for the Pacific National Bank. The following install-ment loans are being paid off early, and it is your task to calculate the rebate fraction, the finance charge rebate, and the payoff for each loan.

	Amount Financed	Number of Payments	Monthly Payment	Payments Made	Rebate Fraction	Finance Charge Rebate	Loan Payoff
39.	$3,000	24	$162.50	9	120/300	$360.00	$2,077.50
40.	$1,600	18	$104.88	11	___	___	___
41.	$9,500	48	$267.00	36	___	___	___
42.	$4,800	36	$169.33	27	___	___	___
43.	$11,000	30	$440.00	20	___	___	___
44.	$6,200	12	$585.50	8	___	___	___

Solar Energy Although solar energy is a relatively new energy source, it may become the most important energy source of the future. Presently, available tax credits and incentives greatly reduce startup costs for solar power systems. Some of the major advantages of solar power include the fact that it is renewable, is nonpolluting, does not emit greenhouse gases, and provides free energy and heat from the sun.

According to www.sunworkssolar.com, by 2016, the U.S. solar industry is expected to support more than 440,000 permanent full-time jobs.

45. Belinda Raven is interested in buying a solar energy system for her home. At Sun-Catchers Inc., she picks out a system for a total cash price of $1,899. The salesperson informs her that if she qualifies for an installment loan, she may pay 10% now as a down payment and finance the balance with payments of $88.35 per month for 24 months.

   a. What is the finance charge on this loan?

   b. What is the total deferred payment price of the system?

46. Meghan Pease purchased a small sailboat for $8,350. She made a down payment of $1,400 and financed the balance with monthly payments of $239.38 for 36 months.

   a. What is the finance charge on the loan?

b. Use Table 13-1 to find what annual percentage rate was charged on Meghan's loan.

47. Valerie Ross financed a cruise to the Bahamas with a 5% add-on interest installment loan from her bank. The total price of the trip was $1,500. The bank required equal monthly payments for 2 years. What are Valerie's monthly payments?

48. Doug Black bought a jet ski with a 9% add-on interest installment loan from his credit union. The purchase price was $1,450. The credit union required a 15% down payment and equal monthly payments for 48 months. What are Doug's monthly payments?

Timeshare is a form of ownership that provides the right to the use of a property either directly or through a "points club." Each time sharer is allotted a period of time, typically a week or longer, for a great many years or in perpetuity. The timeshare industry is more than 30 years old and generates revenues of over $9.4 billion per annum. Today there are 6.7 million timeshare owners worldwide.

© Cengage Learning 2015

49. Olivia Fast found a timeshare offer entitling her to 3 weeks per year in a Rocky Mountain townhouse. She had the option of paying $7,600 in cash or financing the timeshare with a 2-year installment loan. The loan required a 20% down payment and equal monthly payments of $283.73.

a. What is the finance charge on Olivia's loan?

b. What is the total deferred payment price of the timeshare contract?

50. Tim Houston purchased a wall unit for $2,400. He made a $700 down payment and financed the balance with an installment loan for 48 months. If Tim's payments are $42.50 per month, use the APR formula to calculate what annual percentage rate he is paying on the loan.

51. Stereo Central uses the Second National Bank to finance customer purchases. This month the bank is offering 24-month installment loans with an APR of 15.25%. For qualified buyers, no down payment is required. If Nathan David wants to finance a complete stereo system for $1,300, use the APR tables to calculate the finance charge and the monthly payment on his loan.

52. At a recent boat show, Nautica Bank was offering boat loans for up to 5 years with APRs of 13.5%. On new boats, a 20% down payment was required. Scott Vaughn wanted to finance a $55,000 boat for 5 years.

    a. What would be the finance charge on the loan?

    b. What would be the monthly payment?

53. Find the sum of the digits of

    a. 24   b. 30

54. a. What is the rebate fraction of a 36-month loan paid off after the 14th payment?

    b. What is the rebate fraction of a 42-month loan paid off after the 19th payment?

Home Gym
Nautilus, Inc., is a fitness products company headquartered in Vancouver, Washington. Its principal business activities include designing, developing, sourcing, and marketing high-quality cardiovascular and strength fitness products and related accessories.

Nautilus products are sold under the brand names Nautilus, Bowflex, Universal, and Schwinn Fitness. Products offered include home gyms, free weight equipment, treadmills, indoor cycling equipment, ellipticals, and fitness accessories and apparel. Typical annual revenues for Nautilus, Inc., exceed $160 million.

55. Charlie Allen financed a $3,500 Nautilus home gym with an 8% add-on interest installment loan for 24 months. The loan required a 10% down payment.

    a. What is the finance charge on the loan?

    b. What are Charlie's monthly payments?

c. What annual percentage rate is being charged on the loan?

d. If Charlie decides to pay off the loan after 16 months, what is his loan payoff?

56. Chuck Wells is planning to buy a Winnebago motor home. The listed price is $165,000. Chuck can get a secured loan from his bank at 7.25% for as long as 60 months if he pays 15% down. Chuck's goal is to keep his payments below $3,800 per month and amortize the loan in 42 months.

    a. Can he pay off the loan in 42 months and keep his payments under $3,800?

Winnebago Industries, Inc., founded in 1958 and headquartered in Forest City, Iowa, manufactures motor homes, which are self-contained recreation vehicles used primarily in leisure travel and outdoor recreation activities.

    c. What are Chuck's options to get his payments closer to his goal?

    d. Chuck spoke with his bank's loan officer, who has agreed to finance the deal with a 6.95% loan if Chuck can pay 20% down. Will these conditions meet Chuck's goal?

The company markets its motor homes through independent dealers under the Winnebago, Itasca, and ERA brand names in the United States and Canada. Annual revenues for Winnebago vary depending on various factors, including the state of the U.S. economy and gas prices. They typically exceed $400 million.

    e. Chuck has told the seller he cannot buy the motor home at the listed price. If the seller agrees to reduce the listed price by $4,600 and Chuck pays the 20% down, will Chuck meet his goal?

BUSINESS DECISION: READING THE FINE PRINT

The advertisement for the 3-D TV at the Electronic Boutique shown below appeared in your local newspaper this morning. Answer the questions that follow based on the information in the ad.

57. a. If you purchased the TV on January 24 of this year and the billing date of the installment loan is the 15th of each month, when would your first payment be due?

b. What is the required amount of that payment?

c. If that payment is late or less than required, what happens and how much does that amount to?

d. If that payment is more than 30 days late, what happens and how much does that amount to?

e. Explain the advantages and disadvantages of this offer.

Electronic Boutique

NO INTEREST & NO PAYMENTS*
FOR 12 MONTHS
on all 3-D TVs

*Offer is subject to credit approval. No finance charges assessed and no monthly payment required on the promotional purchase if you pay this amount in full by the payment due date as shown on the twelfth (12th) billing statement after purchase date. If you do not, finance charges will be assessed on the promotional purchase amount from the purchase date and minimum monthly payment will be required on balance of amount. Standard account terms apply to non-promotional balances and, after the promotion ends, to promotional purchases. **APR = 22.73%**. **APR of 24.75%** applies if payment is more than 30 days late. Sales tax will be paid at the time of purchase.

$3,499 Optimax Plus
1080p true HD resolution for better picture quality. 120Hz refresh rate, dual core processor, content sharing and screen mirroring. Smart TV features let you interact and stream content from the web. Supports apps.

© spaxiax/Shutterstock.com

CHAPTER FORMULAS

Open-End Credit

$$\text{Periodic rate} = \frac{\text{Annual percentage rate}}{12}$$

Finance charge = Previous month's balance × Periodic rate

$$\text{Average daily balance} = \frac{\text{Sum of the daily balances}}{\text{Days in billing cycle}}$$

Finance charge = Average daily balance × Periodic rate

$$\frac{\text{New}}{\text{balance}} = \frac{\text{Previous}}{\text{balance}} + \frac{\text{Finance}}{\text{charge}} + \frac{\text{Purchases and}}{\text{cash advances}} - \frac{\text{Payments and}}{\text{credits}}$$

Closed-End Credit

Amount financed = Purchase price − Down payment

Down payment − Purchase price × Down payment percent

Amount financed = Purchase price(100% − Down payment percent)

Total amount of installment payments = Amount financed + Finance charge

Finance charge = Total amount of installment payments − Amount financed

$$\frac{\text{Total amount of}}{\text{installment payments}} = \frac{\text{Monthly payment}}{\text{amount}} \times \frac{\text{Number of monthly}}{\text{payments}}$$

Total deferred payment price = Total of installment payments + Down payment

$$\underset{(\textit{finance charge})}{\text{Interest}} = \underset{(\textit{amount financed})}{\text{Principal}} \times \text{Rate} \times \text{Time}$$

$$\text{Regular monthly payments} = \frac{\text{Total of installment payments}}{\text{Number of months of loan}}$$

$$\text{APR} = \frac{72I}{3P(n+1) + I(n-1)}$$

$$\text{Finance charge} = \frac{\text{Amount financed} \times \text{APR table factor}}{100}$$

$$\text{Sum of digits} = \frac{n(n+1)}{2}$$

$$\text{Rebate fraction} = \frac{\text{Sum of the digits of remaining payments}}{\text{Sum of the digits of total payment}}$$

Finance charge rebate = Rebate fraction × Total finance charge

Loan payoff = (Payments remaining × Payment amount) − Finance charge rebate

CHAPTER SUMMARY

Section I: Open-End Credit—Charge Accounts, Credit Cards, and Lines of Credit

Topic	Important Concepts	Illustrative Examples

Calculating the Finance Charge and New Balance by Using the Previous Month's Balance Method
 	
Performance Objective 13-1, Page 408
	1. Divide the annual percentage rate by 12 to find the monthly or periodic interest rate.
	2. Calculate the finance charge by multiplying the previous month's balance by the periodic interest rate from Step 1.
	3. Total all the purchases and cash advances for the month.
	4. Total all the payments and credits for the month.
	5. Use the following formula to determine the new balance:
	
	$$\begin{array}{l}\text{New} \\ \text{bal}\end{array} = \begin{array}{l}\text{Prev} \\ \text{bal}\end{array} + \begin{array}{l}\text{Fin} \\ \text{chg}\end{array} + \begin{array}{l}\text{Purch} \\ \text{\& csh}\end{array} - \begin{array}{l}\text{Pmts} \\ \text{\& crd}\end{array}$$
		Calculate the finance charge and the new balance of an account with an annual percentage rate of 15%.
		
		Previous month's balance = \$186.11
		Purchases = \$365.77
		Payments = \$200
		
		Periodic rate = $\dfrac{15}{12}$ = 1.25%
		
		Finance charge = 186.11 × .0125 = $\underline{\$2.33}$
		
		New balance
		    = 186.11 + 2.33 + 365.77 − 200.00
		    = $\underline{\$354.21}$

Calculating the Finance Charge and New Balance by Using the Average Daily Balance Method **Performance Objective 13-2, Page 412**	1. Starting with the previous month's balance, multiply each by the number of days that balance existed until the next account transaction. 2. At the end of the billing cycle, add all the daily balances × days figures. 3. $\begin{array}{l}\text{Average} \\ \text{daily} \\ \text{balance}\end{array} = \dfrac{\text{Sum of the daily balances}}{\text{Number of days of billing cycle}}$ 4. $\begin{array}{l}\text{Finance} \\ \text{charge}\end{array} = \begin{array}{l}\text{Periodic} \\ \text{rate}\end{array} \times \begin{array}{l}\text{Average daily} \\ \text{balance}\end{array}$ 5. $\begin{array}{l}\text{New} \\ \text{bal}\end{array} = \begin{array}{l}\text{Prev} \\ \text{bal}\end{array} + \begin{array}{l}\text{Fin} \\ \text{chg}\end{array} + \begin{array}{l}\text{Purch} \\ \text{\& csh}\end{array} - \begin{array}{l}\text{Pmts} \\ \text{\& crd}\end{array}$	Calculate the finance charge and the new balance of an account with a periodic rate of 1%, a previous balance of \$132.26, and the following activity. May 5 Purchase \$45.60 May 9 Cash advance 100.00 May 15 Credit 65.70 May 23 Purchase 75.62 May 26 Payment 175.00 \$132.26 × 4 days = \$529.04 177.86 × 4 days = 711.44 277.86 × 6 days = 1,667.16 212.16 × 8 days = 1,697.28 287.78 × 3 days = 863.34 112.78 × 6 days = 676.68 31 days \$6,144.94 Average daily balance = $\dfrac{6,144.94}{31}$ = \$198.22 Finance charge = 1% × 198.22 = $\underline{\$1.98}$ New balance = 132.26 + 1.98 + 221.22 − 240.70 = $\underline{\$114.76}$
Calculating the Finance Charge and New Balance of Business and Personal Lines of Credit **Performance Objective 13-3, Page 414**	With business and personal lines of credit, the annual percentage rate is quoted as the current prime rate plus a fixed percent. Once the APR rate is determined, the finance charge and new balance are calculated as before using the average daily balance method. $\begin{array}{l}\text{New} \\ \text{bal}\end{array} = \begin{array}{l}\text{Previous} \\ \text{balance}\end{array} + \begin{array}{l}\text{Finance} \\ \text{charge}\end{array} + \text{Loans} - \text{Payments}$	What are the finance charge and new balance of a line of credit with an APR of the current prime rate plus 4.6%? Previous balance = \$2,000 Average daily balance = \$3,200 Payments = \$1,500 Loans = \$3,600 Current prime rate = 7% APR = 7% + 4.6% = 11.6% Periodic rate = $\dfrac{11.6}{12}$ = .97% Finance charge = 3,200 × .0097 = $\underline{\$31.04}$ New balance = 2,000 + 31.04 + 3,600 − 1,500 = $\underline{\$4,131.04}$

Section II: Closed-End Credit—Installment Loans

Topic	Important Concepts	Illustrative Examples
Calculating the Total Deferred Payment Price and the Amount of the Finance Charge of an Installment Loan **Performance Objective 13-4, Page 421**	$\text{Finance charge} = \text{Total amount of installment payments} - \text{Amount financed}$ $\text{Total deferred payment price} = \text{Total of installment payments} + \text{Down payment}$	Value City Furniture sold a $1,900 bedroom set to Jeremy Jackson. Jeremy put down $400 and financed the balance with an installation loan of 24 monthly payments of $68.75 each. What are the finance charge and total deferred payment price of the bedroom set? Total amount of payments = $68.75 × 24 = $1,650 Finance charge = 1,650 − 1,500 = $150 Total deferred payment price = 1,650 + 400 = $2,050
Calculating the Regular Monthly Payments of an Installment Loan by the Add-on Interest Method **Performance Objective 13-5, Page 423**	1. Calculate the amount financed by subtracting the down payment from the purchase price. 2. Compute the add-on interest finance charge by using $I = PRT$, with the amount financed as the principal. 3. Find the total of the installment payments by adding the interest to the amount financed. 4. Calculate the monthly payment by dividing the total of the installment payments by the number of months of the loan.	Diane Barber financed a new car with an 8% add-on interest loan. The purchase price of the car was $13,540. The bank required a $1,500 down payment and equal monthly payments for 48 months. What are Diane's monthly payments? Amount financed = 13,540 − 1,500 = $12,040 Interest = 12,040 × .08 × 4 = $3,852.80 Total of installment payments = 12,040.00 + 3,852.80 = $15,892.80 $\text{Monthly payment} = \dfrac{15{,}892.80}{48} = \$331.10$
Calculating the Annual Percentage Rate by APR Tables **Performance Objective 13-6, Page 424**	1. Calculate the finance charge per $100 by $$\dfrac{\text{Finance charge} \times 100}{\text{Amount financed}}$$ 2. From Table 13-1, scan down the Payments column to the number of payments of the loan. 3. Scan to the right in that row to the table factor that most closely corresponds to the finance charge per $100. 4. Look to the top of the column containing the finance charge per $100 to find the APR of the loan.	Steve Moran purchased a home gym for $8,000. He made a $1,500 down payment and financed the remaining $6,500 for 30 months. If Steve's total finance charge is $1,858, what APR is he paying on the loan? $\text{Finance charge per } \$100 = \dfrac{1{,}858 \times 100}{6{,}500} = \$28.58$ From Table 13-1, scan down the Payments column to 30. Then scan right to the table factor closest to 28.58, which is 28.64. The top of that column shows the APR to be 20.5%.
Calculating the Annual Percentage Rate of an Installment Loan by Formula **Performance Objective 13-6, Page 428**	When APR tables are not available, the annual percentage rate can be approximated by the formula $$\text{APR} = \dfrac{72I}{3P(n + 1) + I(n - 1)}$$ where I = finance charge on the loan P = principal; amount financed n = number of months of the loan	Using the APR formula, verify the 20.5% found in the table in the previous example. $\text{APR} = \dfrac{72(1{,}858)}{3(6{,}500)(30 + 1) + 1{,}858(30 - 1)}$ $= \dfrac{133{,}776}{658{,}382} = .2031 = 20.3\%$
Calculating the Finance Charge and Monthly Payment of an Installment Loan by Using the APR Tables **Performance Objective 13-7, Page 429**	1. From Table 13-1, locate the table factor at the intersection of the APR and number of payments of the loan. This table factor is the finance charge per $100. 2. Total finance charge $$= \dfrac{\text{Amount financed} \times \text{Table factor}}{100}$$ 3. Monthly payment $$= \dfrac{\text{Amount financed} + \text{Finance charge}}{\text{Number of months of the loan}}$$	Appliance Mart uses Galaxy Bank to finance customer purchases. This month Galaxy is offering loans up to 36 months with an APR of 13.25%. For qualified buyers, no down payment is required. If Clark Shaw wants to purchase a $2,350 stove using a 36-month loan, what are the finance charge and monthly payment of the loan? From Table 13-1, the table factor for 36 payments, 13.25% = 21.73 $\text{Total finance charge} = \dfrac{2{,}350 \times 21.73}{100} = \$510.66$ $\text{Monthly payment} = \dfrac{2{,}350.00 + 510.66}{36} = \$79.46$

Section II (continued)

Topic	Important Concepts	Illustrative Examples
Calculating the Finance Charge Rebate and the Payoff for Loans Paid Off Early by Using the Sum-of-the-Digits, or Rule of 78, Method **Performance Objective 13-8, Page 430**	1. Calculate the rebate fraction by $$\text{Rebate fraction} = \frac{\text{Sum of the digits of the number of remaining payments}}{\text{Sum of the digits of the total number of payments}}$$ 2. Determine the finance charge rebate by Finance charge rebate $= \text{Rebate fraction} \times \text{Total finance charge}$ 3. Find the loan payoff by Loan payoff $= \left(\begin{array}{c}\text{Payments} \\ \text{remaining}\end{array} \times \begin{array}{c}\text{Payments} \\ \text{amount}\end{array} - \begin{array}{c}\text{Finance charge} \\ \text{rebate}\end{array} \right)$	Jill Otis financed a $2,000 riding lawn mower with an installment loan for 24 months. The payments are $98 per month, and the total finance charge is $352. After 18 months, Jill decides to pay off the loan. What is the finance charge rebate, and what is the loan payoff? $\text{Rebate fraction} = \dfrac{\text{Sum of the digits of 6}}{\text{Sum of the digits of 24}}$ Sum of the digits $6 = \dfrac{6(7)}{2} = 21$ Sum of the digits $24 = \dfrac{24(25)}{2} = 300$ $\text{Rebate fraction} = \dfrac{21}{300}$ $\text{Finance charge rebate} = \dfrac{21}{300} \times 352 = \underline{\underline{\$24.64}}$ $\text{Loan payoff} = (6 \times 98) - 24.64$ $\qquad\qquad = 588.00 - 24.64 = \underline{\underline{\$563.36}}$

Try It: Exercise Solutions for Chapter 13

1. $\text{Periodic rate} = \dfrac{\text{APR}}{12} = \dfrac{15\%}{12} = 1.25\%$

Finance charge = Previous balance × Periodic rate

Finance charge = $214.90 \times .0125 = \underline{\$2.69}$

New balance = Previous balance + Finance charge + Purchases and cash advance − Payments and credits

New balance = $214.90 + 2.69 + 238.85 − 49.12 = \underline{\$407.32}$

2. $\text{Periodic rate} = \dfrac{\text{APR}}{12} = \dfrac{18\%}{12} = 1.5\%$

Dates	Days	Activity/Amount		Unpaid Balance	Daily Balances
Aug. 1–4	4	Previous balance	$158.69	$158.69	$634.76
Aug. 5–10	6	Charge	55.00	213.69	1,282.14
Aug. 11–14	4	Payment	−100.00	113.69	454.76
Aug. 15–16	2	Charge	43.22	156.91	313.82
Aug. 17–19	3	Charge	54.10	211.01	633.03
Aug. 20–25	6	Charge	224.50	435.51	2,613.06
Aug. 26–31	6	Cash advance	75.00	510.51	3,063.06
	31				$8,994.63

$\text{Average daily balance} = \dfrac{\text{Sum of the daily balances}}{\text{Days in billing cycle}} = \dfrac{8,994.63}{31} = \$290.15$

Finance charge = Average daily balance × Periodic rate

Finance charge = $290.15 \times .015 = \underline{\$4.35}$

New balance = Previous balance + Finance charge + Purchases and cash advance − Payments and credits

New balance = $158.69 + 4.35 + 451.82 − 100.00 = \underline{\$514.86}$

3. APR = Prime rate + 4.5%

APR = 8.5 + 4.5 = 13%

$\text{Periodic rate} = \dfrac{13\%}{12} = 1.08\%$

Dates	Days	Activity/Amount		Unpaid Balance	Daily Balances
Nov. 1–6	6	Previous balance	$12,300	$12,300	$73,800
Nov. 7–20	14	Borrowed	16,700	29,000	406,000
Nov. 21–25	5	Borrowed	8,800	37,800	189,000
Nov. 26–30	5	Payment	−20,000	17,800	89,000
	30				$757,800

Average daily balance $= \dfrac{757,800}{30} = \$25,260$

Finance charge $= 25,260 \times .0108 = \underline{\$272.81}$

New balance = Previous balance + Finance charge + Loan amounts − Payments

New balance $= 12,300.00 + 272.81 + 25,500.00 - 20,000.00 = \underline{\$18,072.81}$

4. **a.** Down payment = Purchase price × Down payment percent

   Down payment $= 12,500 \times .15 = \$1,875$

   Amount financed = Purchase price − Down payment

   Amount financed $= 12,500 - 1,875 = \$10,625$

   Total amount of installment payments = Monthly payment × Number of payments

   Total amount of installment payments $= 309.90 \times 48 = \$14,875.20$

   Finance charge = Total amount of installment payments − Amount financed

   Finance charge $= 14,875.20 - 10,625.00 = \underline{\$4,250.20}$

   b. Total deferred payment price = Total amount of installment payments + Down payment

   Total deferred payment price $= 14,875.20 + 1,875.00 = \underline{\$16,750.20}$

5. Amount financed = Purchase price(100% − Down payment %)

   Amount financed $= 1,500 \times .9 = \$1,350$

   Finance charge = Amount financed × Rate × Time

   Finance charge $= 1,350 \times .06 \times 2 = \$162$

   Total of installment payments = Amount financed + Finance charge

   Total of installment payments $= 1,350 + 162 = \$1,512$

   Monthly payments $= \dfrac{\text{Total of installment payments}}{\text{Number of months of loan}}$

   Monthly payments $= \dfrac{1,512}{24} = \underline{\$63}$

6. Amount financed $= 4,500 - 500 = \$4,000$

   Total payments $= 190 \times 24 = 4,560$

   Finance charge $= 4,560 - 4,000 = \$560$

   Finance charge per 100 $= \dfrac{\text{Finance charge} \times 100}{\text{Amount financed}} = \dfrac{560 \times 100}{4,000} = \$14$

   From Table 13-1 APR for \$14 = $\underline{13\%}$

7. Total payments $= 140 \times 18 = 2,520$

   Finance charge $= 2,520 - 2,200 = \$320$

   $\text{APR} = \dfrac{72I}{3P(n+1) + I(n-1)}$

   $\text{APR} = \dfrac{72(320)}{3(2,200)(18+1) + 320(18-1)} = \dfrac{23,040}{125,400 + 5,440}$

   $\text{APR} = \dfrac{23,040}{130,840} = .17609 = \underline{17.6\%}$

8. 13.25%, 24-month table factor = \$14.38

   Finance charge $= \dfrac{\text{Amount financed} \times \text{Table factor}}{100}$

   Finance charge $= \dfrac{3,550.00 \times 14.38}{100} = \dfrac{51,049}{100} = \underline{\$510.49}$

   Monthly payment $= \dfrac{\text{Amount financed} + \text{Finance charge}}{\text{Number of months of loan}}$

   Monthly payment $= \dfrac{3,550.00 + 510.49}{24} = \dfrac{4,060.49}{24}$

   Monthly payment $= \underline{\$169.19}$

9. 16 months remaining; total of 36 months

   Sum of the digits 16 $= \dfrac{n(n+1)}{2} = \dfrac{16(16+1)}{2} = \dfrac{272}{2} = 136$

   Sum of the digits 36 $= \dfrac{n(n+1)}{2} = \dfrac{36(36+1)}{2} = \dfrac{1,332}{2} = 666$

$$\text{Rebate fraction} = \frac{136}{666}$$

$$\text{Finance charge rebate} = \text{Rebate fraction} \times \text{Total finance charge} = \frac{136}{666} \times 1,076$$

Finance charge rebate = $219.72
Loan payoff = (Payments remaining × Payment amount) − Finance charge rebate
Loan payoff = (16 × 141) − 219.72 = 2,256.00 − 219.72
Loan payoff = $2,036.28

CONCEPT REVIEW

1. _____ credit is a loan arrangement in which there is no set number of payments. (13-1)

2. The effective or true annual interest rate being charged for credit is known as the _____ _____ _____ and is abbreviated _____. (13-1)

3. Loans that are backed by the borrower's "promise" to repay are known as _____ loans, whereas loans that are backed by a tangible asset are known as _____ loans. (13-1)

4. Loans made on a continuous basis and billed periodically are known as _____ credit. (13-1)

5. Name the two most common methods used to calculate the finance charge of a revolving credit account. (13-1, 13-2)

6. Write the formula for calculating the average daily balance of a revolving credit account. (13-2)

7. A pre-approved amount of open-end credit is known as a(n) _____ of credit. (13-3)

8. The interest rate of most lines of credit is tied to the movement of the _____ rate. (13-3)

9. A loan made for a specified number of equal monthly payments is known as a(n) _____ loan. (13-4)

10. The portion of the purchase price of an asset paid in a lump sum at the time of purchase is known as the _____ payment. (13-4)

11. A popular method for calculating the interest on an installment loan is known as _____ interest. (13-5)

12. Write the formula for calculating the APR of an installment loan. (13-6)

13. The finance charge _____ is the unearned portion of the finance charge that is returned to a borrower when an installment loan is paid off early. (13-8)

14. The most common method for calculating the finance charge rebate of an installment loan is known as the sum-of-the- _____ method or the Rule of _____. (13-8)

ASSESSMENT TEST

1. Heather MacMaster's revolving credit account has an annual percentage rate of 16%. The previous month's balance was $345.40. During the current month, Heather's purchases and cash advances amounted to $215.39 and her payments and credits totaled $125.00.

   a. What is the monthly periodic rate of the account?

   b. What is the finance charge?

   c. What is Heather's new balance?

2. Daniel Noguera has a Bank of America revolving credit account with an annual percentage rate of 12% calculated on the previous month's balance. In April, the account had the following activity.

Statement of Account — Bank of America

NAME		
DANIEL NOGUERA		

ACCOUNT NUMBER		
9595-55-607		

BILLING CYCLE		
APRIL 1–30		

DATE	DESCRIPTION OF TRANSACTIONS	CHARGES
04/01	Previous month's balance	$301.98
04/08	Mason Gym & Health Club	250.00
04/09	Payment	75.00
04/15	Nordstrom	124.80
04/25	Cash Advance	100.00
04/28	Rimrock Hotel	178.90

a. What is the finance charge?

b. What is Daniel's new balance?

3. Charlotte Williams has a Visa account. The finance charge is calculated on the previous month's balance, and the annual percentage rate is 20%. Complete the following three-month account activity table for Charlotte.

	Month	Previous Month's Balance	Finance Charge	Purchases and Cash Advances	Payments and Credits	New Balance End of Month
a.	December	$267.00	_____	$547.66	$95.00	_____
b.	January	_____	_____	$213.43	$110.00	_____
c.	February	_____	_____	$89.95	$84.00	_____

4. Calculate the average daily balance for January of a charge account with a previous month's balance of $480.94 and the following activity.

Date	Activity	Amount
January 7	Cash advance	$80.00
January 12	Payment	$125.00
January 18	Purchase	$97.64
January 24	Credit	$72.00
January 29	Purchase	$109.70
January 30	Purchase	$55.78

5. Mel Arrandt has a Bank of America account with a 13% annual percentage rate calculated on the average daily balance. The billing date is the first day of each month, and the billing cycle is the number of days in that month.

Statement of Account — Bank of America

NAME		
MEL ARRANDT		

ACCOUNT NUMBER		
4495-5607		

BILLING CYCLE		
SEPTEMBER 1–30		

DATE	DESCRIPTION OF TRANSACTIONS	CHARGES
09/01	Previous month's balance	$686.97
09/04	eBay.com	223.49
09/08	Payment	350.00
09/12	Staples	85.66
09/21	Delta Air Lines (credit)	200.00
09/24	Barnes and Noble Books	347.12
09/28	Milam's Supermarket	64.00

Credit Card Fees Decline As a result of the Credit Card Accountability, Responsibility, and Disclosure Act and the improving economy, the number of households paying late and over-the-limit fees has significantly declined. Approximately 52% of households paid late fees in 2008, compared with 28% in 2012. Likewise, in 2008, 53% of households experienced an increase in their rates as a result of late payments as compared with 29% in 2012.

a. What is the average daily balance for September?

b. What is the finance charge for September?

c. What is Mel's new balance?

6. Alpine Construction, Inc., has a $100,000 line of credit with the Bow Valley Bank. The annual percentage rate is the current prime rate plus $3\frac{1}{4}\%$. The balance on June 1 was $52,900. On June 8, Alpine borrowed $30,600 to pay for a shipment of lumber and roofing materials and on June 18 borrowed another $12,300 for equipment repairs. On June 28, a $35,000 payment was made on the account. The billing cycle for June has 30 days. The current prime rate is $7\frac{3}{4}\%$.

a. What is the finance charge on the account?

b. What is Alpine's new balance?

7. George Bell bought an ultralight airplane for $29,200. He made a 15% down payment and financed the balance with payments of $579 per month for 60 months.

a. What is the finance charge on George's loan?

b. What is the total deferred payment price of the airplane?

8. David Sporn bought a saddle from Linville Western Gear with a 9.3% add-on interest installment loan. The purchase price of the saddle was $1,290. The loan required a 15% down payment and equal monthly payments for 24 months.

a. What is the total deferred payment price of the saddle?

b. What are David's monthly payments?

9. Sound Blaster Recording Studio purchased a new digital recording console for $28,600. A down payment of $5,000 was made and the balance financed with monthly payments of $708 for 48 months.

a. What is the finance charge on the loan?

b. Use Table 13-1 to find what annual percentage rate was charged on the equipment loan.

Up, Up, and Away!
Ultralight aircraft provide an exciting and affordable flying solution for many people. They allow you to own an aircraft that doesn't require an expensive hangar or a special pilot license; and, best of all, you can haul it with your car or truck.

Ultralights are defined by the U.S. FAA as a single-seat vehicle of less than 5 U.S. gallons of fuel capacity, empty weight of less than 254 pounds, and a top speed of 64 mph. Restrictions include flying only during daylight hours over unpopulated areas. Quicksilver and Buckeye Corporations are the industry leaders in ultralight and powered parachute-type aircraft.

© iStockphoto.com/Nancy Nehring

10. Chris Manning purchased a $7,590 motorcycle with a 36-month installment loan. The monthly payments are $261.44 per month.

    a. Use the APR formula to calculate the annual percentage rate of the loan. Round to the nearest hundredth of a percent.

    b. Use the APR tables to verify your answer from part a.

11. SkyHigh Aircraft Sales uses the Executive National Bank to finance customer aircraft purchases. This month Executive National is offering 60-month installment loans with an APR of 11.25%. A 15% down payment is required. The president of Vista Industries wants to finance the purchase of a company airplane for $250,000.

    a. Use the APR tables to calculate the finance charge.

    b. What are the monthly payments on Vista's aircraft loan?

12. After making 11 payments on a 36-month loan, you pay it off.

    a. What is your rebate fraction?

    b. If the finance charge was $1,300, what is your finance charge rebate?

13. An Auntie Anne's franchise financed a $68,000 pretzel oven with a $6\frac{1}{2}\%$ add-on interest installment loan for 48 months. The loan required a 20% down payment.

    a. What is the finance charge on the loan?

    b. What are the monthly payments?

    c. What annual percentage rate is being charged on the loan?

Auntie Anne's, Inc., Is a leading franchisor of snack outlets, with more than 1,050 pretzel stores located in some 45 states and 23 other countries. The stores are found primarily in high-traffic areas such as malls, airports, train stations, and stadiums.

    Back in June 2006, Auntie Anne's sold its billionth pretzel! Total initial investment to purchase a franchise ranges from $197,875 to $439,100.

d. If the company decides to pay off the loan after 22 months, what is the loan payoff?

14. You are a salesperson for Mega Marine Boat Sales. A customer is interested in purchasing the Donzi Classic shown in the accompanying ad and has asked you the following questions.

    a. What is the APR of the loan? (Use the formula.)

    b. What is the total deferred payment price of the boat?

    c. If the loan is paid off after 7 years, what would be the payoff?

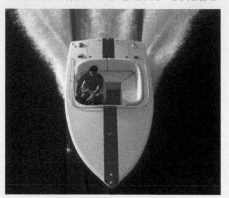

MEGA MARINE BOAT SALES

Donzi Classic
Sale price $29,000
Now $379 per month
$6,000 Down – 120 Months

Winston Luzier/Transtock Inc./Alamy

15. Joe Keener found the accompanying ad for a Ford Mustang in his local newspaper. If the sales tax in his state is 7% and the tag and title fees are $165, calculate the following information for Joe.

    a. The total cost of the car, including tax, tag, and title

    b. The amount financed

    c. The finance charge

    d. The total deferred price of the car

    e. The annual percentage rate of the loan rounded to the nearest hundredth

FORD MUSTANG

$6,000 DOWN - PLUS TAX, TAG, TITLE
60-MONTHS WITH APPROVED
CREDIT

INCLUDES: AUTO TRANS., AIR
COND., 2-DOOR, AM/FM WITH CD &
SIRIUS XM RADIO, POWER WINDOWS AND
LOCKS, POWER STEERING

$28,525

$557 PER MO.

Winston Luzier/Transtock Inc./Alamy

BUSINESS DECISION: PURCHASE VS. LEASE

16. You are interested in getting a Nissan Rogue. You have decided to look into leasing to see how it compares with buying. In recent years, you have noticed that advertised lease payments are considerably lower than those advertised for financing a purchase. It always seemed as if you would be getting "more car for the money!"

In your research, you have found that a closed-end vehicle lease is an agreement in which you make equal monthly payments based on your estimated usage for a set period of time. Then you turn the vehicle back in to the leasing dealer. No equity, no ownership, no asset at the end! You also have the option of purchasing the vehicle at an agreed-upon price. Leasing terminology is different from that of purchasing, but they are related.

Purchase		**Lease**
Purchase price	=	Capitalized cost
Down payment	=	Capitalized cost reduction
Interest rate	=	Money factor
End-of-lease market price	=	Residual value

Use the advertisement below and the Purchase vs. Lease Worksheet on page 450 to compare the total cost of each option. The residual value of the car is estimated to be $13,650. The lease has no termination fees or charges. If you decide to purchase, your bank requires a down payment of $3,800 and will finance the balance with a 10.25% APR loan for 36 months. The sales tax in your state is 6.5%, and the tag and title charges are $75. The *opportunity cost* is the interest your down payment could have earned if you didn't purchase the vehicle. Currently, your money earns 4.5% in a savings account.

a. What is the total purchase price of the vehicle, including tax, tag, and title?

b. What are the monthly payments on the loan?

c. What is the total cost of purchasing?

d. What is the total cost of leasing?

e. In your own words, explain which of these financing choices is a better deal and why.

Nissan Rogue

$19,995

$249

LEASE PER MO.

36 mos.
No security deposit.
$2,500 at signing.
Plus tax, tag & title
with approved
credit.

Car Culture/Corbis

f. Choose an ad from your local newspaper for a lease offer on a vehicle you would like to have. Gather the necessary information needed to complete a Purchase vs. Lease Worksheet. Use local dealers and banks to find the information you need or do some research on the Internet. Report your findings and conclusions to the class.

Purchase vs. Lease Worksheet

Cost of Purchasing

1. Total purchase price, including tax, tag, and title   _____

2. Down payment   _____

3. Total of loan payments (monthly payment _____ × _____ months)   _____

4. Opportunity cost on down payment (_____ % × _____ years × line 2)   _____

5. Less: Expected market value of vehicle at the end of the loan   _____

6. **Total cost of purchasing (lines 2 + 3 + 4 − 5)**   _____

Cost of Leasing

1. Capitalized cost, including tax, tag, and title.   _____

2. Down payment (capitalized cost reduction
   _____ + security deposit _____)   _____

3. Total of lease payments (monthly payments_____ × _____ months)   _____

4. Opportunity cost on down payment (_____ % × _____ years × line 2)   _____

5. End-of-lease termination fees and charges (excess mileage or damage)   _____

6. Less: Refund of security deposit   _____

7. **Total cost of leasing (lines 2 + 3 + 4 + 5 − 6)**   _____

COLLABORATIVE LEARNING ACTIVITY

Plastic Choices

1. Have each member of the team contact a bank, credit union, or retail store in your area that offers a credit card. Get a brochure and/or a copy of the credit agreement.

   a. For each card, determine the following:

   - Annual interest rate
   - Method used for computing interest
   - Credit limit
   - Annual fee
   - "Fine-print" features

   b. Based on your research, which cards are the best and worst deals?

2. Go to www.cardtrak.com or www.bankrate.com.

   a. Research and list the best credit card deals being offered around the country.

   b. Compare your local banks' offers with those found on the Internet.

3. Research the Internet for recent changes to the following:

   a. The Credit Card Accountability, Responsibility, and Disclosure Act (the Credit Card Act)

   b. Other financial regulations relating to consumer credit and credit cards

   c. Laws in your state relating to consumer credit and credit cards

CHAPTER 14 Mortgages

PERFORMANCE OBJECTIVES

SECTION I 14 MORTGAGES—FIXED-RATE AND ADJUSTABLE-RATE

real estate Land, including any permanent improvements such as homes, apartment buildings, factories, hotels, shopping centers, or any other "real" structures.

Mortgage A loan in which real property is used as security for a debt.

Federal Housing Administration (FHA) A government agency within the U.S. Department of Housing and Urban Development (HUD) that sets construction standards and insures residential mortgage loans made by approved lenders.

VA mortgages or **GI Loans** Long-term, low-down-payment home loans made by private lenders to eligible veterans, the payment of which is guaranteed by the Veterans Administration in the event of a default.

conventional loans Real estate loans made by private lenders that are not FHA-insured or VA-guaranteed.

private mortgage insurance (PMI) A special form of insurance primarily on mortgages for single-family homes, allowing the buyer to borrow more by putting down a smaller down payment.

adjustable-rate mortgage (ARM) A mortgage loan in which the interest rate changes periodically, usually in relation to a predetermined economic index.

Real estate is defined as "land, including the air above and the earth below, plus any permanent improvements to the land, such as homes, apartment buildings, factories, hotels, shopping centers, or any other 'real' property." Whether for commercial or residential property, practically all real estate transactions today involve some type of financing. The mortgage loan is the most popular method of financing real estate purchases.

A **mortgage** is any loan in which real property is used as security for a debt. During the term of the loan, the property becomes security, or collateral, for the lender, sufficient to ensure recovery of the amount loaned.

Mortgages today fall into one of three categories: FHA-insured, VA-guaranteed, and conventional. The National Housing Act of 1934 created the **Federal Housing Administration (FHA)** to encourage reluctant lenders to invest their money in the mortgage market, thereby stimulating the depressed construction industry. Today the FHA is a government agency within the Department of Housing and Urban Development (HUD). The FHA insures private mortgage loans made by approved lenders.

In 1944, the Servicemen's Readjustment Act (GI Bill of Rights) was passed to help returning World War II veterans purchase homes. Special mortgages were established known as **Veterans Affairs (VA) mortgages** or **GI Loans**. Under this and subsequent legislation, the government guarantees payment of a mortgage loan made by a private lender to a veteran/buyer should the veteran default on the loan.

VA loans may be used by eligible veterans, surviving spouses, and active service members to buy, construct, or refinance homes, farm residences, or condominiums. Down payments by veterans are not required but are left to the discretion of lenders, whereas FHA and conventional loans require a down payment from all buyers.

Conventional loans are made by private lenders and generally have a higher interest rate than either an FHA or VA loan. Most conventional lenders are restricted to loaning 80% of the appraised value of a property, thus requiring a 20% down payment. If the borrower agrees to pay the premium for **private mortgage insurance (PMI)**, the conventional lender can lend up to 95% of the appraised value of the property.

Historically, high interest rates in the early 1980s caused mortgage payments to skyrocket beyond the financial reach of the average home buyer. To revitalize the slumping mortgage industry, the **adjustable-rate mortgage (ARM)** was created. These are mortgage loans under which the interest rate is periodically adjusted to more closely coincide with changing

Mortgage loans are the most common form of loan made for real estate property purchases.

Photo by Robert Brechner

economic conditions. ARMs are very attractive, particularly to first-time buyers, because a low teaser rate may be offered for the first few years and then adjusted upward to a higher rate later in the loan. Today the adjustable-rate mortgage has become the most widely accepted option to the traditional 15- and 30-year fixed-rate mortgages.

Extra charges known as **mortgage discount points** are frequently added to the cost of a loan as a rate adjustment factor. This allows lenders to increase their yield without showing an increase in the mortgage interest rate. Each discount point is equal to 1% of the amount of the loan.

By their nature, mortgage loans involve large amounts of money and long periods of time. Consequently, the monthly payments and the amount of interest paid over the years can be considerable. Exhibit 14-1 illustrates the 30-year mortgage rates in the United States from 1974 to 2010 and the monthly payment on a $100,000 mortgage at various interest rate levels.

In reality, the higher interest mortgages would have been refinanced as rates declined, but consider the "housing affordability" factor. In 1982, payments on a $100,000 mortgage were $1,548 per month, compared with $457 in 2010!

In this section, you learn to calculate the monthly payments of a mortgage and prepare a partial amortization schedule of that loan. You also calculate the amount of property tax and insurance required as part of each monthly payment. In addition, you learn about the **closing**, the all-important final step in a real estate transaction, and the calculation of the closing costs. Finally, you learn about the important components of an adjustable-rate mortgage: the index, the lender's margin, the interest rate, and the cost caps.

mortgage discount points Extra charges frequently added to the cost of a mortgage, allowing lenders to increase their yield without showing an increase in the mortgage interest rate.

closing A meeting at which the buyer and seller of real estate conclude all matters pertaining to the transaction. At the closing, the funds are transferred to the seller and the ownership or title is transferred to the buyer.

CALCULATING THE MONTHLY PAYMENT AND TOTAL INTEREST PAID ON A FIXED-RATE MORTGAGE

14-1

In Chapter 12, we learned that amortization is the process of paying off a financial obligation in a series of equal, regular payments over a period of time. We calculated the amount of an amortization payment by using the present value of an annuity table or the optional amortization formula.

Because mortgages run for relatively long periods of time, we can also use a special present-value table in which the periods are listed in years. The table factors represent the monthly payment required per $1,000 of debt to amortize a mortgage. The monthly payment includes mortgage interest and an amount to reduce the principal. (See Table 14-1.)

Dollars AND Sense

As a result of declining mortgage rates in recent years, a record 68.8% of families own their own homes today. That amounts to nearly 76 million households.

Purchasing and financing a home is one of the most important financial decisions a person will ever make. Substantial research should be done and much care taken in choosing the correct time to buy, the right property to buy, and the best financial offer to accept. (See Exhibit 14-2, "Mortgage Shopping Worksheet," pages 459–460.)

EXHIBIT 14-1 Historical Mortgage Rates and Monthly Payments

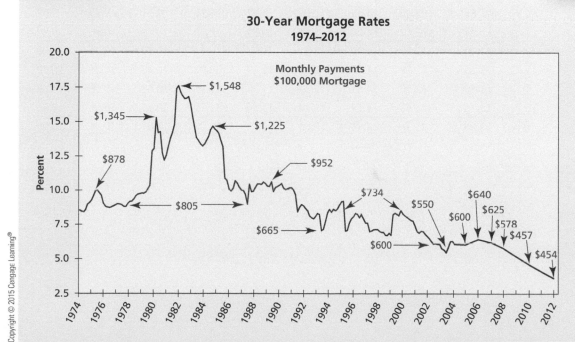

TABLE 14-1 Monthly Payments to Amortize Principal and Interest per $1,000 Financed

Monthly Payments
(Necessary to amortize a loan of $1,000)

Interest Rate (%)	5 Years	10 Years	15 Years	20 Years	25 Years	30 Years	35 Years	40 Years
3.50	$18.19	$9.89	$7.15	$5.80	$5.01	$4.49	$4.13	$3.87
3.75	18.30	10.01	7.27	5.93	5.14	4.63	4.28	4.03
4.00	18.42	10.12	7.40	6.06	5.28	4.77	4.43	4.18
4.25	18.53	10.24	7.52	6.19	5.42	4.92	4.58	4.34
4.50	18.64	10.36	7.65	6.33	5.56	5.07	4.73	4.50
4.75	18.76	10.48	7.78	6.46	5.70	5.22	4.89	4.66
5.00	18.88	10.61	7.91	6.60	5.85	5.37	5.05	4.83
5.25	18.99	10.73	8.04	6.74	6.00	5.53	5.21	4.99
5.50	19.11	10.86	8.18	6.88	6.15	5.68	5.38	5.16
5.75	19.22	10.98	8.31	7.03	6.30	5.84	5.54	5.33
6.00	19.34	11.11	8.44	7.17	6.45	6.00	5.71	5.51
6.25	19.45	11.23	8.58	7.31	6.60	6.16	5.88	5.68
6.50	19.57	11.36	8.72	7.46	6.76	6.33	6.05	5.86
6.75	19.69	11.49	8.85	7.61	6.91	6.49	6.22	6.04
7.00	19.81	11.62	8.99	7.76	7.07	6.66	6.39	6.22
7.25	19.92	11.75	9.13	7.91	7.23	6.83	6.57	6.40
7.50	20.04	11.88	9.28	8.06	7.39	7.00	6.75	6.59
7.75	20.16	12.01	9.42	8.21	7.56	7.17	6.93	6.77
8.00	20.28	12.14	9.56	8.37	7.72	7.34	7.11	6.96
8.25	20.40	12.27	9.71	8.53	7.89	7.52	7.29	7.15
8.50	20.52	12.40	9.85	8.68	8.06	7.69	7.47	7.34
8.75	20.64	12.54	10.00	8.84	8.23	7.87	7.66	7.53
9.00	20.76	12.67	10.15	9.00	8.40	8.05	7.84	7.72
9.25	20.88	12.81	10.30	9.16	8.57	8.23	8.03	7.91
9.50	21.01	12.94	10.45	9.33	8.74	8.41	8.22	8.11
9.75	21.13	13.08	10.60	9.49	8.92	8.60	8.41	8.30
10.00	21.25	13.22	10.75	9.66	9.09	8.78	8.60	8.50
10.25	21.38	13.36	10.90	9.82	9.27	8.97	8.79	8.69
10.50	21.50	13.50	11.06	9.99	9.45	9.15	8.99	8.89
10.75	21.62	13.64	11.21	10.16	9.63	9.34	9.18	9.09
11.00	21.75	13.78	11.37	10.33	9.81	9.53	9.37	9.29
11.25	21.87	13.92	11.53	10.50	9.99	9.72	9.57	9.49
11.50	22.00	14.06	11.69	10.67	10.17	9.91	9.77	9.69
11.75	22.12	14.21	11.85	10.84	10.35	10.10	9.96	9.89
12.00	22.25	14.35	12.01	11.02	10.54	10.29	10.16	10.09
12.25	22.38	14.50	12.17	11.19	10.72	10.48	10.36	10.29
12.50	22.50	14.64	12.33	11.37	10.91	10.68	10.56	10.49
12.75	22.63	14.79	12.49	11.54	11.10	10.87	10.76	10.70
13.00	22.76	14.94	12.66	11.72	11.28	11.07	10.96	10.90

Learning Tip

Remember that the table values represent monthly payments "per $1,000" financed. When calculating the amount of the monthly payment, you must first determine the number of $1,000s being financed, then multiply that figure by the table factor.

STEPS TO FIND THE MONTHLY MORTGAGE PAYMENT BY USING AN AMORTIZATION TABLE AND TO FIND TOTAL INTEREST

STEP 1. Find the number of $1,000s financed.

$$\text{Number of \$1,000s financed} = \frac{\text{Amount financed}}{1,000}$$

STEP 2. Using Table 14-1, locate the table factor, monthly payment per $1,000 financed, at the intersection of the number-of-years column and the interest-rate row.

STEP 3. Calculate the monthly payment.

Monthly payment = Number of $1,000s financed × Table factor

STEP 4. Find the total interest of the loan.

Total interest = (Monthly payment × Number of payments) − Amount financed

EXAMPLE1 CALCULATING MONTHLY PAYMENT AND TOTAL INTEREST

What is the monthly payment and total interest on a $150,000 mortgage at 5% for 30 years?

SOLUTIONSTRATEGY

Step 1. Number of $1,000s financed $= \dfrac{\text{Amount financed}}{1,000} = \dfrac{150,000}{1,000} = 150$

Step 2. Table factor for 5%, 30 years is 5.37.

Step 3. Monthly payment = Number of $1,000s financed × Table factor
Monthly payment = 150 × 5.37
Monthly payment = $805.50

Step 4. Total interest = (Monthly payment × Number of payments) − Amount financed
Total interest = (805.50 × 360) − 150,000
Total interest = 289,980 − 150,000
Total interest = $139,980

TRYITEXERCISE 1

What is the monthly payment and total interest on an $85,500 mortgage at 4.5% for 25 years?

CHECK YOUR ANSWERS WITH THE SOLUTIONS ON PAGE 475.

PREPARING A PARTIAL AMORTIZATION SCHEDULE OF A MORTGAGE

14-2

Mortgages used to purchase residential property generally require regular, equal payments. A portion of the payment is used to pay interest on the loan; the balance of the payment is used to reduce the principal. This type of mortgage is called a **level-payment plan** because the amount of the payment remains the same for the duration of the loan. The amount of the payment that is interest gradually decreases, while the amount that reduces the debt gradually increases.

level-payment plan Mortgages with regular, equal payments over a specified period of time.

amortization schedule A chart that shows the month-by-month breakdown of each mortgage payment into interest and principal and the outstanding balance of the loan.

An **amortization schedule** is a chart that shows the status of the mortgage loan after each payment. The schedule illustrates month by month how much of the mortgage payment is interest and how much is left to reduce to principal. The schedule also shows the outstanding balance of the loan after each payment.

In reality, amortization schedules are long because they show the loan status for each month. A 30-year mortgage, for example, would require a schedule with 360 lines (12 months × 30 years = 360 payments).

Dollars AND Sense

In most cases, mortgage interest expense is tax-deductible. To increase your deductions for the current year, make your January mortgage payment by December 20. This will allow time for the payment to be credited to your account in December, giving you an extra month of interest deduction this year.

STEPS TO CREATE AN AMORTIZATION SCHEDULE FOR A LOAN

STEP 1. Use Table 14-1 to calculate the amount of the monthly payment.

STEP 2. Calculate the amount of interest for the current month using $I = PRT$, where P is the current outstanding balance of the loan, R is the annual interest rate, and T is $\frac{1}{12}$.

STEP 3. Find the portion of the payment used to reduce principal.

Portion of payment reducing principal = Monthly payment − Interest

STEP 4. Calculate the outstanding balance of the mortgage loan.

Outstanding balance = Previous balance − Portion of payment reducing principal

STEP 5. Repeat Steps 2, 3, and 4 for each succeeding month and enter the values on a schedule with columns labeled as follows.

Payment Number	Monthly Payment	Monthly Interest	Portion Used to Reduce Principal	Loan Balance

EXAMPLE2   PREPARING A PARTIAL AMORTIZATION SCHEDULE

Prepare an amortization schedule for the first three months of the $150,000 mortgage at 5% for 30 years from Example 1. Remember, you have already calculated the monthly payment to be $805.50.

SOLUTIONSTRATEGY

Step 1. $805.50 (from Example 1, page 455)

Step 2. **Month 1:**
Interest = Principal × Rate × Time
Interest = $150,000 \times .05 \times \frac{1}{12}$
Interest = $625.00

Step 3. Portion of payment reducing principal = Monthly payment − Interest
Portion of payment reducing principal = 805.50 − 625.00
Portion of payment reducing principal = $180.50

Step 4. Outstanding balance = Previous balance − Portion of payment reducing principal
Outstanding balance = 150,000.00 − 180.50
Outstanding balance after one payment = $149,819.50

Step 5. Repeat Steps 2, 3, and 4, for two more payments and enter the values on the schedule.
Month 2:
Interest = $149,819.50 \times .05 \times \frac{1}{12} = \$624.25$
(*Note:* Although very slightly, interest decreased.)

Portion reducing principal = 805.50 − 624.25 = $181.25

Outstanding balance after two payments = 149,819.50 − 181.25 = $149,638.25

Month 3:

Interest = 149,638.25 × .05 × $\frac{1}{12}$ = $623.49

Portion reducing principal = 805.50 − 623.49 = $182.01

Outstanding balance after three payments = 149,638.25 − 182.01 = $149,456.24

Amortization Schedule
$150,000 Loan, 5%, 30 years

Payment Number	Monthly Payment	Monthly Interest	Portion Used to Reduce Principal	Loan Balance
0				$150,000.00
1	$805.50	$625.00	$180.50	$149,819.50
2	$805.50	$624.25	$181.25	$149,638.25
3	$805.50	$623.49	$182.01	$149,456.24

▶TRYITEXERCISE 2

Prepare an amortization schedule of the first four payments of a $125,000 mortgage at 6% for 15 years. Use Table 14-1 to calculate the amount of the monthly payment.

CHECK YOUR ANSWERS WITH THE SOLUTIONS ON PAGES 475–476.

CALCULATING THE MONTHLY PITI OF A MORTGAGE LOAN

14-3

In reality, mortgage payments include four parts: principal, interest, taxes, and insurance—thus the abbreviation PITI. VA, FHA, and most conventional loans require borrowers to pay $\frac{1}{12}$ of the estimated annual property taxes and hazard insurance with each month's mortgage payment. Each month the taxes and insurance portions of the payment are placed in a type of savings account for safekeeping known as an **escrow account**. Each year when the property taxes and hazard insurance premiums are due, the lender disburses those payments from the borrower's escrow account. During the next 12 months, the account again builds up to pay the next year's taxes and insurance.

PITI An abbreviation for the total amount of a mortgage payment; includes principal, interest, property taxes, and hazard insurance.

escrow account Bank account used by mortgage lenders for the safekeeping of the funds accumulating to pay next year's property taxes and hazard insurance.

STEPS TO CALCULATE THE PITI OF A MORTGAGE

STEP 1. Calculate the principal and interest portion, PI, of the payment as before, using the amortization table, Table 14-1.

STEP 2. Calculate the monthly tax and insurance portion, TI.

$$\text{Monthly TI} = \frac{\text{Estimated property tax} + \text{Hazard insurance}}{12}$$

STEP 3. Calculate the total monthly PITI.

$$\text{Monthly PITI} = \text{Monthly PI} + \text{Monthly TI}$$

IN THE
Business World

Typically, over the years of a mortgage, property taxes and insurance premiums rise. When this happens, the lender must increase the portion set aside in the escrow account by increasing the taxes and insurance parts of the monthly payment.

EXAMPLE3 CALCULATING THE MONTHLY PITI OF A MORTGAGE

Lorie Kojian purchased a home with a mortgage of $87,500 at 7.5% for 30 years. The property taxes are $2,350 per year, and the hazard insurance premium is $567.48. What is the monthly PITI payment of Lorie's loan?

▶SOLUTIONSTRATEGY

Step 1. From the amortization table, Table 14-1, the factor for 7.5%, 30 years is 7.00. When we divide the amount of Lorie's loan by 1,000, we get 87.5 as the number of 1,000s financed. The principal and interest portion, PI, is therefore 87.5 × 7.00 = $612.50.

Step 2. Monthly TI $= \dfrac{\text{Estimated property tax} + \text{Hazard insurance}}{12}$

Monthly TI $= \dfrac{2{,}350.00 + 567.48}{12} = \dfrac{2{,}917.48}{12} = \$243.12$

Step 3. Monthly PITI = PI + TI
Monthly PITI = 612.50 + 243.12
Monthly PITI = $855.62

▶TRYITEXERCISE 3

Michael Veteramo purchased a home with a mortgage of $125,600 at 6.25% for 20 years. The property taxes are $3,250 per year, and the hazard insurance premium is $765. What is the monthly PITI payment of Michael's loan?

CHECK YOUR ANSWER WITH THE SOLUTION ON PAGE 476.

14-4 UNDERSTANDING CLOSING COSTS AND CALCULATING THE AMOUNT DUE AT CLOSING

title or **deed** The official document representing the right of ownership of real property.

closing costs Expenses incurred in conjunction with the sale of real estate, including loan origination fees, credit reports, appraisal fees, title search, title insurance, inspections, attorney's fees, recording fees, and broker's commission.

settlement or **closing statement** A document that provides a detailed accounting of payments, credits, and closing costs of a real estate transaction.

The term *closing* or *settlement* is used to describe the final step in a real estate transaction. This is a meeting at which time documents are signed; the buyer pays the agreed-upon purchase price; and the seller delivers the **title**, or right of ownership, to the buyer. The official document conveying ownership is known as the **deed**.

Closing costs are the expenses incurred in conjunction with the sale of real estate. In the typical real estate transaction, both the buyer and the seller are responsible for a number of costs that are paid for at the time of closing. The party obligated for paying a particular closing cost is often determined by local custom or by negotiation. Some closing costs are expressed as dollar amounts, whereas others are a percent of the amount financed or amount of the purchase price.

At closing, the buyer is responsible for the purchase price (mortgage + down payment) plus closing costs. The amount received by the seller after all expenses have been paid is known as the proceeds. The **settlement statement** or **closing statement** is a document, usually prepared by an attorney, that provides a detailed breakdown of the real estate transaction. This document itemizes closing costs and indicates how they are allocated between the buyer and the seller.

Exhibit 14-2, "Mortgage Shopping Worksheet," can be used to compare mortgage offers from various lenders. It provides a comprehensive checklist of important loan information, typical fees, closing and settlement costs, and other questions and considerations people should be aware of when shopping for a mortgage loan.

EXHIBIT 14-2 Mortgage Shopping Worksheet

Mortgage Shopping Worksheet

	Lender 1	Lender 2
Name of Lender		
Name of Contact		
Date of Contact		
Mortgage Amount		
Basic Information on the Loans		
Type of mortgage: fixed rate, adjustable rate, conventional, FHA, other? If adjustable, see page 460.		
Minimum down payment required		
Loan term (length of loan)		
Contract interest rate		
Annual percentage rate (APR)		
Points (may be called loan discount points)		
Monthly private mortgage insurance (PMI) premiums		
How long must you keep PMI?		
Estimated monthly escrow for taxes and hazard insurance		
Estimated monthly payment (principal, interest, taxes, insurance, PMI)		
Fees		
Different institutions may have different names for some fees and may charge different fees. We have listed some typical fees you may see on loan documents.		
Appraisal fee or loan processing fee		
Origination fee or underwriting fee		
Lender fee or funding fee		
Appraisal fee		
Attorney's fees		
Document preparation and recording fees		
Broker's fees (may be quoted as points, origination fees, or interest rate add-on)		
Credit report fee		
Other fees		
Name of Lender		
Other Costs at Closing/Settlement		
Title search/title insurance		
For lender		
For you		
Estimated prepaid amounts for interest, taxes, hazard insurance, payments to escrow		
State and local taxes, stamp taxes, transfer taxes		
Flood determination		
Prepaid private mortgage insurance (PMI)		
Surveys and home inspections		
Total Fees and Other Closing/Settlement Cost Estimates		
Other Questions and Considerations about the Loan		
Are any of the fees or costs waivable?		
Prepayment penalties		
Is there a prepayment penalty?		
If so, how much is it?		
How long does the penalty period last? (for example, three years? five years?)		
Are extra principal payments allowed?		

(Continued)

EXHIBIT 14-2   Mortgage Shopping Worksheet *(Continued)*

Mortgage Shopping Worksheet

	Lender 1	Lender 2
Lock-ins		
Is the lock-in agreement in writing?.............................	_____	_____
Is there a fee to lock in?....................................	_____	_____
When does the lock-in occur—at application, approval, or another time?.............................	_____	_____
How long will the lock-in last?...............................	_____	_____
If the rate drops before closing, can you lock in at a lower rate?...............	_____	_____
If the loan is an adjustable rate mortgage:		
What is the initial rate?.....................................	_____	_____
What is the maximum the rate could be next year?....................	_____	_____
What are the rate and payment caps for each year and over the life of the loan?............................	_____	_____
What is the frequency of rate change and of any changes to the monthly payment?......................	_____	_____
What index will the lender use?..............................	_____	_____
What margin will the lender add to the index?.....................	_____	_____
Credit life insurance		
Does the monthly amount quoted to you include a charge for credit life insurance?......................	_____	_____
If so, does the lender require credit life insurance as a condition of the loan?........................	_____	_____
How much does the credit life insurance cost?.....................	_____	_____
How much lower would your monthly payment be without the credit life insurance?......................	_____	_____
If the lender does not require credit life insurance and you still want to buy it, what rates can you get from other insurance providers?...................	_____	_____

Dollars AND Sense

The amount of interest paid and the length of a mortgage can be dramatically reduced by making **biweekly payments** (every two weeks) instead of monthly. By choosing this mortgage payment option, you are taking advantage of the all-important "time value of money" concept.

Here's an example. A 30-year, 7% mortgage for $100,000 has monthly payments of $666. The total interest you will pay on the loan is $139,509. If, instead, you make biweekly payments of $333, you would pay off the loan in 23 years and the total interest would be $103,959. The biweekly option saves you $35,550 in interest and seven years of payments!

To see how this option can be applied to your mortgage, go to www.bankrate.com and type *biweekly mortgage calculator* in the search box.

EXAMPLE4   CALCULATING MORTGAGE CLOSING COSTS

Barry and Donna Rae Schwartz are purchasing a $180,000 home. The down payment is 25%, and the balance will be financed with a 25-year fixed-rate mortgage at 6.5% and 2 discount points (each point is 1% of the amount financed). When Barry and Donna Rae signed the sales contract, they put down a deposit of $15,000, which will be credited to their down payment at the time of the closing. In addition, they must pay the following expenses: credit report, $80; appraisal fee, $150; title insurance premium, $\frac{1}{2}$% of amount financed; title search, $200; and attorney's fees, $450.

a. Calculate the amount due from Barry and Donna Rae at the closing.

b. If the sellers are responsible for the broker's commission, which is 6% of the purchase price, $900 in other closing costs, and the existing mortgage with a balance of $50,000, what proceeds will they receive on the sale of the property?

▶ SOLUTIONSTRATEGY

a. Down payment = 180,000 × 25% = $45,000

    Amount financed = 180,000 − 45,000 = $135,000

Closing Costs, Buyer	
Discount points (135,000 × 2%)	$ 2,700
Down payment (45,000 − 15,000 deposit)	30,000
Credit report	80
Appraisal fee	150
Title insurance (135,000 × $\frac{1}{2}$%)	675
Title search	200
Attorney's fees	450
Due at closing	$34,255

b.

Proceeds, Seller		
Sale price		$180,000
Less: Broker's commission:		
180,000 × 6%	$10,800	
Closing costs	900	
Mortgage payoff	50,000	
		−61,700
Proceeds to seller		$118,300

►TRYITEXERCISE 4

Jonathan Monahan is purchasing a townhouse for $120,000. The down payment is 20%, and the balance will be financed with a 15-year fixed-rate mortgage at 9% and 3 discount points (each point is 1% of the amount financed). When Jonathan signed the sales contract, he put down a deposit of $10,000, which will be credited to his down payment at the time of the closing. In addition, he must pay the following expenses: loan application fee, $100; property transfer fee, $190; title insurance premium, $\frac{3}{4}$% of amount financed; hazard insurance premium, $420; prepaid taxes, $310; and attorney's fees, $500.

a. Calculate the amount due from Jonathan at the closing.

b. If the seller is responsible for the broker's commission, which is $5\frac{1}{2}$% of the purchase price, $670 in other closing costs, and the existing mortgage balance of $65,000, what proceeds will the seller receive on the sale of the property?

CHECK YOUR ANSWERS WITH THE SOLUTIONS ON PAGE 476.

CALCULATING THE INTEREST RATE OF AN ADJUSTABLE-RATE MORTGAGE (ARM)

14-5

With a fixed-rate mortgage, the interest rate stays the same during the life of the loan. With an adjustable-rate mortgage (ARM), the interest rate changes periodically, usually in relation to an index, and payments may go up or down accordingly. In recent years, the ARM has become the most widely accepted alternative to the traditional 30-year fixed-rate mortgage.

The primary components of an ARM are the index, lender's margin, calculated interest rate, initial interest rate, and cost caps. With most ARMs, the interest rate and monthly payment change every year, every three years, or every five years. The period between one rate change and the next is known as the **adjustment period**. A loan with an adjustment period of one year, for example, is called a one-year ARM.

Most lenders tie ARM interest rate changes to changes in an **index rate**. These indexes usually go up and down with the general movement of interest rates in the nation's economy. When the index goes up, so does the mortgage rate, resulting in higher monthly payments. When the index goes down, the mortgage rate may or may not go down.

adjustment period The amount of time between one rate change and the next on an adjustable-rate mortgage; generally one, two, or three years.

index rate The economic index to which the interest rate on an adjustable-rate mortgage is tied.

lender's margin or **spread** The percentage points added to an index rate to get the interest rate of an adjustable-rate mortgage.

calculated or **initial ARM interest rate** The interest rate of an adjustable-rate mortgage to which all future adjustments and caps apply.

teaser rate A discounted interest rate for the first adjustment period of an adjustable-rate mortgage that is below the current market rate of interest.

interest-rate caps Limits on the amount the interest rate can increase on an ARM.

periodic rate caps Limits on the amount the interest rate of an ARM can increase per adjustment period.

overall rate caps Limits on the amount the interest rate of an ARM can increase over the life of the loan.

To calculate the interest rate on an ARM, lenders add a few points called the **lender's margin** or **spread** to the index rate. The amount of the margin can differ among lenders and can make a significant difference in the amount of interest paid over the life of a loan.

> **Calculated ARM interest rate = Index rate + Lender's margin**

The **calculated** or **initial ARM interest rate** is usually the rate to which all future adjustments and caps apply, although this rate may be discounted by the lender during the first payment period to attract and qualify more potential borrowers. This low initial interest rate, sometimes known as a **teaser rate**, is one of the main appeals of the ARM; however, without some protection from rapidly rising interest rates, borrowers might be put in a position of not being able to afford the rising mortgage payments. To prevent this situation, standards have been established requiring limits or caps on increases.

Interest-rate caps place a limit on the amount the interest rate can increase. These may come in the form of **periodic rate caps**, which limit the increase from one adjustment period to the next, and **overall rate caps**, which limit the increase over the life of the mortgage. The following formulas can be used to find the maximum interest rates of an ARM:

> **Maximum rate per adjustment period = Previous rate + Periodic rate cap**
>
> **Maximum overall ARM rate = Initial rate + Overall rate cap**

EXAMPLE5 CALCULATING ARM RATES

Florence Powers bought a home with an adjustable-rate mortgage. The lender's margin on the loan is 2.5%, and the overall rate cap is 6% over the life of the loan.

a. If the current index rate is 4.9%, what is the calculated interest rate of the ARM?

b. What is the maximum overall rate of the loan?

►SOLUTIONSTRATEGY

a. Because the loan interest rate is tied to an index, we use the formula

> Calculated ARM interest rate = Index rate + Lender's margin
> Calculated ARM interest rate = 4.9% + 2.5%
> Calculated ARM interest rate = 7.4%

b.
> Maximum overall rate = Calculated rate + Overall rate cap
> Maximum overall rate = 7.4% + 6%
> Maximum overall rate = 13.4%

►TRYITEXERCISE 5

Kate Fitzgerald bought a home with an adjustable-rate mortgage. The lender's margin on the loan is 3.4%, and the overall rate cap is 7% over the life of the loan. The current index rate is 3.2%.

a. What is the initial interest rate of the ARM?

b. What is the maximum overall rate of the loan?

CHECK YOUR ANSWERS WITH THE SOLUTIONS ON PAGE 476.

REVIEW EXERCISES

14 | SECTION I

Using Table 14-1 as needed, calculate the required information for the following mortgages.

	Amount Financed	Interest Rate	Term of Loan (years)	Number of $1,000s Financed	Table Factor	Monthly Payment	Total Interest
1.	$80,000	9.00%	20	80	9.00	$720.00	$92,800.00
2.	$72,500	6.00%	30				
3.	$130,900	8.50%	25				
4.	$154,300	4.75%	15				
5.	$96,800	7.75%	30				
6.	$422,100	5.50%	20				
7.	$184,300	6.25%	15				

8. Marc Bove purchased a home with a $78,500 mortgage at 9% for 15 years. Calculate the monthly payment and prepare an amortization schedule for the first four months of Marc's loan.

Payment Number	Monthly Payment	Monthly Interest	Portion Used to Reduce Principal	Loan Balance
0				$78,500.00
1				
2				
3				
4				

As one of the loan officers for Grove Gate Bank, calculate the monthly principal and interest, PI, using Table 14-1 and the monthly PITI for the following mortgages.

	Amount Financed	Interest Rate	Term of Loan (years)	Monthly PI	Annual Property Tax	Annual Insurance	Monthly PITI
9.	$76,400	8.00%	20	$639.47	$1,317	$866	$821.39
10.	$128,800	4.75%	15		$2,440	$1,215	
11.	$174,200	7.25%	30		$3,505	$1,432	
12.	$250,000	4.50%	25		$6,553	$2,196	
13.	$164,500	6.75%	30		$3,125	$1,569	
14.	$98,200	7.50%	10		$1,688	$935	

15. Ben and Mal Scott plan to buy a home for $272,900. They will make a 10% down payment and qualify for a 25-year, 7% mortgage loan.

 a. What is the amount of their monthly payment?

 b. How much interest will they pay over the life of the loan?

16. Michael Sanchez purchased a condominium for $88,000. He made a 20% down payment and financed the balance with a 30-year, 9% fixed-rate mortgage.

    a. What is the amount of the monthly principal and interest portion, PI, of Michael's loan?

    b. Construct an amortization schedule for the first four months of Michael's mortgage.

Payment Number	Monthly Payment	Monthly Interest	Portion Used to Reduce Principal	Loan Balance
0				_____
1	_____	_____	_____	_____
2	_____	_____	_____	_____
3	_____	_____	_____	_____
4	_____	_____	_____	_____

    c. If the annual property taxes are $1,650 and the hazard insurance premium is $780 per year, what is the total monthly PITI of Michael's loan?

17. Luis Schambach is shopping for a 15-year mortgage for $150,000. Currently, the Fortune Bank is offering an 8.5% mortgage with 4 discount points and the Northern Trust Bank is offering an 8.75% mortgage with no points. Luis is unsure which mortgage is a better deal and has asked you to help him decide. (Remember, each discount point is equal to 1% of the amount financed.)

    a. What is the total interest paid on each loan?

    b. Taking into account the closing points, which bank is offering a better deal and by how much?

18. Phil Pittman is interested in a fixed-rate mortgage for $100,000. He is undecided whether to choose a 15- or 30-year mortgage. The current mortgage rate is 5.5% for the 15-year mortgage and 6.5% for the 30-year mortgage.

    a. What are the monthly principal and interest payments for each loan?

    b.   What is the total amount of interest paid on each loan?

    c.   Overall, how much more interest is paid by choosing the 30-year mortgage?

19. Larry and Cindy Lynden purchased a townhome in Alison Estates with an adjustable-rate
mortgage. The lender's margin on the loan is 4.1%, and the overall rate cap is 5% over the life
of the loan. The current index rate is the prime rate, 3.25%.

    a.   What is the calculated interest rate of the ARM?

        Calculated ARM interest rate = Index rate + Lender's margin

        Calculated ARM interest rate = 3.25 + 4.1 = 7.35%

    b.   What is the maximum overall rate of the loan?

        Maximum overall ARM rate = Initial rate + Overall rate cap

        Maximum overall ARM rate = 7.35 + 5.0 = 12.35%

20. Heather Gott bought a home with an adjustable-rate mortgage. The lender's margin on the loan
is 3.5%, and the overall rate cap is 8% over the life of the loan.

    a.   If the current index rate is 3.75%, what is the calculated interest rate of the ARM?

    b.   What is the maximum overall ARM rate of Heather's loan?

21. Joe and Gloria Moutran are purchasing a house in Winter Springs financed with an adjustable-
rate mortgage. The lender's margin on the loan is 2.75%, and the overall rate cap is 6.2% over
the life of the loan. The current index rate is 5.8%.

    a.   What is the calculated interest rate of the ARM?

    b.   What is the maximum overall ARM rate of the loan?

22. You are a real estate broker for Aurora Realty. One of your clients, Erica Heston, has agreed
to purchase one of the homes your office has listed for sale for a negotiated price of $235,000.
The down payment is 20%, and the balance will be financed with a 15-year fixed-rate mortgage
at 8.75% and $3\frac{1}{2}$ discount points. The annual property tax is $5,475, and the hazard insurance
premium is $2,110. When Erica signed the original contract, she put down a deposit of $5,000,
which will be credited to her down payment. In addition, at the time of closing, Dawn must pay
the following expenses:

Appraisal fee	$215
Credit report	$65
Roof inspection	$50
Mortgage insurance premium	$\frac{1}{2}$% of amount financed
Title search	$125
Attorney's fees	$680
Escrow fee	$210
Prepaid interest	$630

► TRYITEXERCISE 6

Justin Schaefer owns a home that was recently appraised for $92,900. The balance on his existing first mortgage is $32,440. If his credit union is willing to loan up to 80% of the appraised value, what is the potential amount of credit available to Justin on a home equity line of credit?

CHECK YOUR ANSWER WITH THE SOLUTION ON PAGE 476.

EXHIBIT 14-3

Home Equity Lending

Dollars AND Sense

In 2010, the signing of the financial reform bill into law meant real financial reform had finally become a reality. Almost two years after the near collapse of the financial system, Congress put new rules in place to prevent the abusive lending practices responsible for the crisis. Highlights of the new law include:

- A Consumer Financial Protection Bureau (CFPB) to stop unfair lending practices

- Governmental authority to step in and safely shut down failing financial firms

- Prohibitions on abusive mortgage lending practices such as kickbacks for steering people into high-rate loans when they qualify for lower rates

- Stronger foreclosure prevention, including an emergency loan fund to help families at risk of losing their home because of unemployment or illness

Source: www.responsiblelending.org

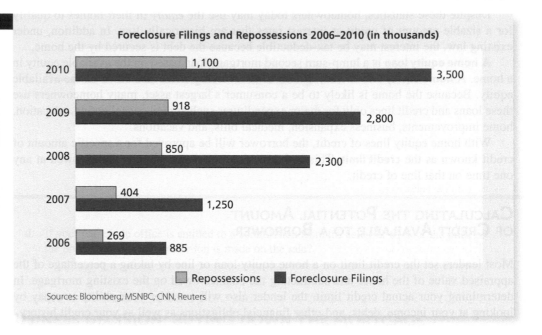

Foreclosure Filings and Repossessions 2006–2010 (in thousands)

Year	Repossessions	Foreclosure Filings
2010	1,100	3,500
2009	918	2,800
2008	850	2,300
2007	404	1,250
2006	269	885

Sources: Bloomberg, MSNBC, CNN, Reuters

14-7 CALCULATING THE HOUSING EXPENSE RATIO AND THE TOTAL OBLIGATIONS RATIO OF A BORROWER

qualifying ratios Ratios used by lenders to determine whether borrowers have the economic ability to repay loans.

housing expense ratio The ratio of a borrower's monthly housing expense (PITI) to monthly gross income.

total obligations ratio The ratio of a borrower's total monthly financial obligations to monthly gross income.

Mortgage lenders use ratios to determine whether borrowers have the economic ability to repay the loan. FHA, VA, and conventional lenders all use monthly gross income as the base for calculating these **qualifying ratios**. Two important ratios used for this purpose are the **housing expense ratio** and the **total obligations ratio**. These ratios are expressed as percents and are calculated by using the following formulas:

$$\text{Housing expense ratio} = \frac{\text{Monthly housing expense (PITI)}}{\text{Monthly gross income}}$$

$$\text{Total obligations ratio} = \frac{\text{Total monthly financial obligations}}{\text{Monthly gross income}}$$

The mortgage business uses widely accepted guidelines for these ratios that should not be exceeded. The ratio guidelines are shown in Exhibit 14-4.

EXHIBIT 14-4

Lending Ratio Guidelines

Mortgage Type	Housing Expense Ratio	Total Obligations Ratio
FHA	29%	41%
Conventional	28%	36%

Note that the ratio formulas are an application of the percentage formula; the ratio is the rate, the PITI or total obligations are the portion, and the monthly gross income is the base. With this in mind, we are able to solve for any of the variables.

EXAMPLE7 CALCULATING MORTGAGE LENDING RATIOS

Sue Harper earns a gross income of $2,490 per month. She has applied for a mortgage with a monthly PITI of $556. Sue has other financial obligations totaling $387.50 per month.

a. What is Sue's housing expense ratio?

b. What is Sue's total obligations ratio?

c. According to the Lending Ratio Guidelines in Exhibit 14-4, for what type of mortgage would she qualify, if any?

SOLUTIONSTRATEGY

a. $\text{Housing expense ratio} = \dfrac{\text{Monthly housing expense (PITI)}}{\text{Monthly gross income}}$

$\text{Housing expense ratio} = \dfrac{556}{2,490}$

$\text{Housing expense ratio} = .2232 = \underline{\underline{22.3\%}}$

b. $\text{Total obligations ratio} = \dfrac{\text{Total monthly financial obligations}}{\text{Monthly gross income}}$

$\text{Total obligations ratio} = \dfrac{556.00 + 387.50}{2,490} = \dfrac{943.50}{2,490}$

$\text{Total obligations ratio} = .3789 = \underline{\underline{37.9\%}}$

c. According to the Lending Ratio Guidelines, Sue would qualify for an FHA mortgage but not a conventional mortgage; her total obligations ratio is 37.9%, which is above the limit for conventional mortgages.

TRYITEXERCISE 7

Roman Bass earns a gross income of $3,100 per month. He has made application at the Golden Gables Bank for a mortgage with a monthly PITI of $669. Roman has other financial obligations totaling $375 per month.

a. What is Roman's housing expense ratio?

b. What is Roman's total obligations ratio?

c. According to the Lending Ratio Guidelines in Exhibit 14-4, for what type of mortgage would he qualify, if any?

CHECK YOUR ANSWERS WITH THE SOLUTIONS ON PAGE 477.

SECTION II

14

REVIEW EXERCISES

Note: Round all answers to the nearest cent when necessary.

For the following second mortgage applications, calculate the percentage of appraised value and the potential credit.

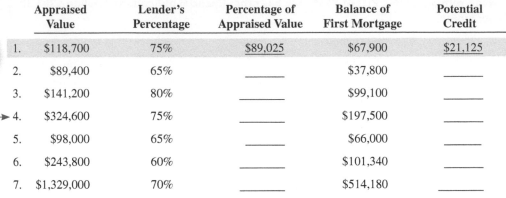

	Appraised Value	Lender's Percentage	Percentage of Appraised Value	Balance of First Mortgage	Potential Credit
1.	$118,700	75%	$89,025	$67,900	$21,125
2.	$89,400	65%	_____	$37,800	_____
3.	$141,200	80%	_____	$99,100	_____
4.	$324,600	75%	_____	$197,500	_____
5.	$98,000	65%	_____	$66,000	_____
6.	$243,800	60%	_____	$101,340	_____
7.	$1,329,000	70%	_____	$514,180	_____

Calculate the housing expense ratio and the total obligations ratio for the following mortgage applications.

	Applicant	Monthly Gross Income	Monthly PITI Expense	Other Monthly Financial Obligations	Housing Expense Ratio (%)	Total Obligations Ratio (%)
8.	Parker	$2,000	$455	$380	22.75	41.75
9.	Forman	$3,700	$530	$360		
10.	Martin	$3,100	$705	$720		
11.	Panko	$4,800	$1,250	$430		
12.	Emerson	$2,900	$644	$290		
13.	Jameson	$4,250	$1,150	$475		
14.	Renquest	$6,725	$1,648	$580		

15. Use Exhibit 14-4, Lending Ratio Guidelines, on page 468 to answer the following questions:

   a. Which of the applicants in Exercises 8–14 would *not* qualify for a conventional mortgage?

   b. Which of the applicants in Exercises 8–14 would *not* qualify for any mortgage?

IN THE Business World

To help home buyers estimate mortgage expenses, various companies provide online calculators that are free to use. To try these out, use your browser to search for "Mortgage Calculator."

16. Ronald and Samantha Brady recently had their condominium in Port Isaac appraised for $324,600. The balance on their existing first mortgage is $145,920. If their bank is willing to loan up to 75% of the appraised value, what is the amount of credit available to the Bradys on a home equity line of credit?

$$324,600 \times .75 = \$243,450$$
$$ -145,920$$

Available credit $\quad \$97,530$

17. The Barclays own a home that was recently appraised for $219,000. The balance on their existing first mortgage is $143,250. If their bank is willing to loan up to 65% of the appraised value, what is the potential amount of credit available to the Barclays on a home equity loan?

18. Ransford and Alda Mariano own a home recently appraised for $418,500. The balance on their existing mortgage is $123,872. If their bank is willing to loan up to 80% of the appraised value, what is the amount of credit available to them?

19. Michelle Heaster is thinking about building an addition on her home. The house was recently appraised at $154,000, and the balance on her existing first mortgage is $88,600. If Michelle's bank is willing to loan 70% of the appraised value, does she have enough equity in the house to finance a $25,000 addition?

20. Jamie and Alice Newmark have a combined monthly gross income of $9,702 and monthly expenses totaling $2,811. They plan to buy a home with a mortgage whose monthly PITI will be $2,002.

   a. What is Jamie and Alice's combined housing expense ratio?

   b. What is their total obligations ratio?

   c. For what kind of mortgage can they qualify, if any?

   d. (Optional challenge) By how much would they need to reduce their monthly expenses in order to qualify for an FHA mortgage?

Mortgage brokers are real estate financing professionals acting as the intermediary between consumers and lenders during mortgage transactions. A mortgage broker works with consumers to help them through the complex mortgage origination process.

Brokers earn commissions in exchange for bringing borrowers and lenders together and receive payment when the mortgage loan is closed.

21. You are a mortgage broker at Interamerican Bank. One of your clients, Bill Cramer, has submitted an application for a mortgage with a monthly PITI of $1,259. His other financial obligations total $654.50 per month. Bill earns a gross income of $4,890 per month.

   a. What is his housing expense ratio?

   b. What is his total obligations ratio?

c. According to the Lending Ratio Guidelines on page 468, for what type of mortgage would Bill qualify, if any?

d. If Bill decided to get a part-time job so that he could qualify for a conventional mortgage, how much additional monthly income would he need?

BUSINESS DECISION: DOES IT PAY TO REFINANCE YOUR MORTGAGE?

22. According to money.CNN.com, with mortgage rates near 35-year lows, you may be able to cut your payments sharply by refinancing your loan. To qualify for the best rates, you need a credit score of 740 or higher and usually at least 20% equity.

Even if you have to settle for a higher rate, a new loan may save you money. The main consideration is whether you will live in your home long enough to offset the refinance closing costs.

Your current mortgage payment is $1,458.50 per month, with a balance of $214,800. You have a chance to refinance at the Biltmore Bank with a 30-year, 5.5% mortgage. The closing costs of the loan are application fee, $90; credit report, $165; title insurance, .4% of the amount financed; title search, $360; and attorney's fees, $580.

You plan to live in your home for at least four more years. Use the Mortgage Refinancing Worksheet below to see if it makes sense to refinance your mortgage.

MORTGAGE REFINANCING WORKSHEET

STEP 1. Current monthly mortgage payment.. ☐

STEP 2. New monthly mortgage payment if you refinance......................... ☐

New rate ____   Current mortgage balance ____

| Table 14-1 factor ____ | × | # of 1,000s to borrow ____ |

STEP 3. Monthly savings... ☐

| Step 1. ____ | − | Step 2. ____ |

STEP 4. Total refinance closing costs (appraisal, title search, etc.)............... ☐

STEP 5. Total months needed to recoup your costs..................................... ☐

| Step 4 result | ÷ | Step 3 result |

STEP 6. Total months you plan to live in your home.................................... ☐

The Bottom Line – If you plan to live in your home longer than the result in Step 5, it makes sense to refinance.

CHAPTER FORMULAS

Fixed-Rate Mortgages

Monthly payment = Number of $1,000s financed × Table 14-1 factor

Total interest = (Monthly payment × Number of payments) − Amount financed

$$\text{Monthly taxes and Insurance (TI)} = \frac{\text{Estimated property tax} + \text{Hazard insurance}}{12}$$

Monthly PITI = Monthly PI + Monthly TI

Adjustable-Rate Mortgages

Calculated interest rate = Index rate + Lender's margin

Maximum rate per adjustment period = Previous rate + Periodic rate cap

Maximum overall rate = Initial rate + Overall rate cap

Home Equity Loans and Lines of Credit

Percentage of appraised value = Appraised value × Lender's percentage

Second mortgage potential credit = Percentage of appraised value − First mortgage balance

$$\text{Housing expense ratio} = \frac{\text{Monthly housing expense (PITI)}}{\text{Monthly gross income}}$$

$$\text{Total obligations ratio} = \frac{\text{Total monthly financial obligations}}{\text{Monthly gross income}}$$

CHAPTER SUMMARY

Section I: Mortgages—Fixed-Rate and Adjustable-Rate

Topic	Important Concepts	Illustrative Examples
Calculating the Monthly Payment and Total Interest Paid on a Fixed-Rate Mortgage **Performance Objective 14-1, Page 453**	1. Find the number of $1,000s financed by $$\text{Number of \$1,000s} = \frac{\text{Amount financed}}{1,000}$$ 2. From Table 14-1, locate the table factor, monthly payment per $1,000 financed, at the intersection of the number-of-years column and the interest-rate row. 3. Calculate the monthly payment by Monthly payment = Number of 1,000s financed × Table factor 4. Find the total interest of the loan by $$\text{Total interest} = \left(\text{Monthly payments} \times \text{Number of payments}\right) - \text{Amount financed}$$	What is the monthly payment and total interest on a $100,000 mortgage at 9.5% for 30 years? $$\text{Number of 1,000s} = \frac{100,000}{1,000} = 100$$ Table factor: $9\frac{1}{2}\%$, 30 years = 8.41 Monthly payment = 100 × 8.41 = $841 Total interest of the loan = (841 × 360) − 100,000 = 302,760 − 100,000 = $202,760
Preparing a Partial Amortization Schedule of a Mortgage **Performance Objective 14-2, Page 455**	1. Calculate the monthly payment of the loan as before. 2. Calculate the amount of interest for the current month using $I = PRT$, where P is the current outstanding balance of the loan, R is the annual interest rate, and T is $\frac{1}{12}$. 3. Find the portion of the payment used to reduce principal by $$\text{Portion of payment reducing principal} = \text{Monthly payment} - \text{Interest}$$ 4. Calculate outstanding balance of the loan by $$\text{Outstanding balance} = \text{Previous balance} - \text{Portion of payment reducing principal}$$ 5. Repeat Steps 2, 3, and 4 for each succeeding month and enter the values on a schedule labeled appropriately.	Prepare an amortization schedule for the first month of a $70,000 mortgage at 9% for 20 years. Using Table 14-1, we find the monthly payment of the mortgage to be $630. *Month 1:* Interest = Principal × Rate × Time Interest = 70,000 × .09 × $\frac{1}{12}$ Interest = $525 Portion of payment reducing principal 630 − 525 = $105 Outstanding balance after one payment 70,000 − 105 = $69,895 An amortization schedule can now be prepared from these data.

Section I (continued)

Topic	Important Concepts	Illustrative Examples
Calculating the Monthly PITI of a Mortgage Loan **Performance Objective 14-3, Page 457**	In reality, mortgage payments include four elements: principal, interest, taxes, and insurance—thus the abbreviation PITI. *Monthly PITI of a mortgage:* 1. Calculate the principal and interest portion (PI) of the payment as before using Table 14-1. 2. Calculate the monthly tax and insurance portion (TI) by $$\text{Monthly TI} = \frac{\text{Estimated properly tax} + \text{Hazard insurance}}{12}$$ 3. Calculate the total monthly PITI by Monthly PITI = Monthly PI + Monthly TI	Maureen Cassidy purchased a home for \$97,500 with a mortgage at 8.5% for 15 years. The property taxes are \$1,950 per year, and the hazard insurance premium is \$466. What is the monthly PITI payment of Maureen's loan? Using a table factor of 9.85 from Table 14-1, we find the monthly PI for this 8.5%, 15-year mortgage to be \$960.38. $$\text{Monthly TI} = \frac{1,950 + 466}{12}$$ $$= \frac{2,416}{12} = \$201.33$$ Monthly PITI = PI + TI $= 960.38 + 201.33 = \underline{\underline{\$1,161.71}}$

Calculating the Amount Due at Closing
 	
Performance Objective 14-4, Page 458
	Closing costs are the expenses incurred in conjunction with the sale of real estate. Both buyer and seller are responsible for specific costs.
	  The party responsible for paying a particular closing cost is often determined by local custom or by negotiation.
	  Some closing costs are expressed as dollar amounts, whereas others are a percent of the amount financed or amount of the purchase price.
	  At closing, the buyer is responsible for the purchase price (mortgage and down payment) plus closing costs.
	  The amount received by the seller after all expenses have been paid is known as the proceeds.
		Typical Closing Costs
		Buyer: Attorney's fee, inspections, credit report, appraisal fee, hazard insurance premium, title exam and insurance premium, escrow fee, prepaid taxes, and interest
		Seller: Attorney's fee, broker's commission, survey expense, inspections, abstract of title, certificate of title, escrow fee, prepayment penalty—existing loan, documentary stamps

Calculating the Interest Rate of an Adjustable-Rate Mortgage (ARM) **Performance Objective 14-5, Page 461**	Use the following formulas to find the various components of an ARM: $\text{Calculated interest rate} = \text{Index rate} + \text{Lender's margin}$ $\text{Max rate per period} = \text{Previous rate} + \text{Periodic cap}$ $\text{Maximum overall rate of ARM} = \text{Initial rate} + \text{Overall cap}$	Howard Gold bought a home with an adjustable-rate mortgage. The margin on the loan is 3.5%, and the rate cap is 8% over the life of the loan. If the current index rate is 3.6%, what is the calculated interest rate and the maximum overall rate of the loan? Calculated interest rate = 3.6% + 3.5% = $\underline{7.1\%}$ Maximum overall rate = 7.1% + 8% = $\underline{\underline{15.1\%}}$

Section II: Second Mortgages—Home Equity Loans and Lines of Credit

Topic	Important Concepts	Illustrative Examples
Calculating the Potential Amount of Credit Available to a Borrower **Performance Objective 14-6, Page 467**	Most lenders set the credit limit on a home equity loan or line by taking a percentage of the appraised value of the home and subtracting the balance owed on the existing first mortgage. In determining your actual credit limit, the lender also will consider your ability to repay by looking at your income, debts, and other financial obligations, as well as your credit history. *Potential amount of credit available to borrower:* 1. Calculate the percentage of appraised value by $\dfrac{\text{Percentage of}}{\text{appraised value}} = \dfrac{\text{Appraised}}{\text{value}} \times \dfrac{\text{Lender's}}{\text{percentage}}$ 2. Find the potential amount of credit available by $\dfrac{\text{Potential}}{\text{credit}} = \dfrac{\text{Percentage of}}{\text{appraised value}} - \dfrac{\text{First mortgage}}{\text{debt}}$	The McCartneys own a home that was recently appraised for \$134,800. The balance on their existing first mortgage is \$76,550. If their bank is willing to loan up to 70% of the appraised value, what is the amount of credit available to the McCartneys on a home equity loan? Percentage of appraisal value = 134,800 × .70 $\qquad\qquad\qquad\qquad = \$94,360$ Available credit = 94,360 − 76,550 = $\underline{\underline{\$17,810}}$

Section II (continued)

Topic	Important Concepts	Illustrative Examples
Calculating the Housing Expense Ratio and the Total Obligations Ratio of a Borrower **Performance Objective 14-7, Page 468**	Mortgage lenders use ratios to determine whether borrowers have the economic ability to repay the loan. Two important ratios used for this purpose are the housing expense ratio and the total obligations ratio. These ratios are expressed as percents and are calculated by using the following formulas: $$\text{Housing expense ratio} = \frac{\text{Monthly housing expense (PITI)}}{\text{Monthly gross income}}$$ $$\text{Total obligations ratio} = \frac{\text{Total monthly financial obligations}}{\text{Monthly gross income}}$$	Vickie Howard earns a gross income of \$3,750 per month. She has made application for a mortgage with a monthly PITI of \$956. Vickie has other financial obligations totaling \$447 per month. a. What is her housing expense ratio? b. What is her total obligations ratio? c. According to the Lending Ratio Guidelines on page 468, for what type of mortgage would Vickie qualify, if any? $$\text{Housing expense ratio} = \frac{956}{3,750} = 25.5\%$$ $$\text{Total obligation ratio} = \frac{1,403}{3,750} = 37.4\%$$ According to the Lending Ratio Guidelines, Vickie would qualify for an FHA mortgage but not a conventional mortgage; her total obligations ratio is 37.4%, which is above the limit for conventional mortgages.

TRY IT: EXERCISE SOLUTIONS FOR CHAPTER 14

1. $\text{Number of 1,000s financed} = \dfrac{\text{Amount financed}}{1,000}$

    $\text{Number of 1,000s financed} = \dfrac{85,500}{1,000} = 85.5$

    Table factor 4.5%, 25 years = 5.56

    Monthly payment = Number of 1,000s financed × Table factor

    Monthly payment = 85.5 × 5.56 = $\underline{\underline{\$475.38}}$

    Total interest = (Monthly payment × Number of payments) − Amount financed

    Total interest = (475.38 × 300) − 85,500

    Total interest = 142,614 − 85,500 = $\underline{\underline{\$57,114}}$

2. $\text{Number of 1,000s financed} = \dfrac{125,000}{1,000} = 125$

    Table factor 6%, 15 years = 8.44

    Monthly payment = 125 × 8.44 = $1055.00

    Month 1

    $I = PRT = 125,000 \times .06 \times \dfrac{1}{12} = \$625.00$

    Portion of payment reducing principal = $1055.00 − 625.00 = $430.00

    Outstanding balance = 125,000.00 − 430.00 = $124,570.00

    Month 2

    $I = PRT = 124,570.00 \times .06 \times \dfrac{1}{12} = \$622.85$

    Portion of payment reducing principal = $1055.00 − 622.85 = $432.15

    Outstanding balance = 124,570.00 − 432.15 = $124,137.85

    Month 3

    $I = PRT = 124,137.85 \times .06 \times \dfrac{1}{12} = \$620.69$

    Portion of payment reducing principal = 1055.00 − 620.69 = $434.31

    Outstanding balance = 124,137.85 − 434.31 = $123,703.54

GO ONLINE FOR MORE ACTIVITIES • www.cengagebrain.com

Month 4

$$I = PRT = 123{,}703.54 \times .06 \times \frac{1}{12} = \$618.52$$

Portion of payment reducing principal $= 1055.00 - 618.52 = \$436.48$

Outstanding balance $= 123{,}703.54 - 436.48 = \$123{,}267.06$

Amortization Schedule
$125,000, 6%, 15 years

Payment Number	Monthly Payment	Monthly Interest	Portion Used to Reduce Principal	Loan Balance
0				$125,000.00
1	$1055.00	$625.00	$430.00	$124,570.00
2	$1055.00	$622.85	$432.15	$124,137.85
3	$1055.00	$620.69	$434.31	$123,703.54
4	$1055.00	$618.52	$436.48	$123,267.06

3.

Number of 1,000s $= \dfrac{125{,}600}{1{,}000} = 125.6$

Table factor 6.25%, 20 years $= 7.31$

Monthly payment (PI) $= 125.6 \times 7.31 = \$918.14$

$$\text{Monthly TI} = \frac{\text{Property tax} + \text{Hazard insurance}}{12}$$

$$\text{Monthly TI} = \frac{3{,}250 + 765}{12} = \frac{4{,}015}{12} = \$334.58$$

Monthly PITI $= $ PI $+$ TI $= 918.14 + 334.58 = \underline{\$1{,}252.72}$

4. a. Down payment $= 120{,}000 \times 20\% = \$24{,}000$

Amount financed $= 120{,}000 - 24{,}000 = \$96{,}000$

Closing Costs, Buyer:

Discount points (96,000 × 3%)	$ 2,880
Down payment (24,000 − 10,000)	14,000
Application fee	100
Condominium transfer fee	190
Title insurance (96,000 × $\frac{3}{4}$%)	720
Hazard insurance	420
Prepaid taxes	310
Attorney's fees	500
Due at closing	$19,120

b. *Proceeds, Seller:*

Purchase price $120,000

Less: Broker's commission

120,000 × $5\frac{1}{2}$%	$ 6,600
Closing costs	670
Mortgage payoff	65,000

$-72{,}270$

Proceeds to seller $\underline{\$47{,}730}$

5. a. Calculated ARM rate = Index rate + Lender's margin

Calculated ARM rate $= 3.2 + 3.4 = \underline{6.6\%}$

b. Maximum overall rate = Calculated ARM rate + Overall rate cap

Maximum overall rate $= 6.6 + 7.0 = \underline{13.6\%}$

6. Percentage of appraised value = Appraised value × Lender's percentage

Percentage of appraised value $= 92{,}900 \times 80\% = \$74{,}320$

Potential credit = Percentage of appraised value − First mortgage balance

Potential credit $= 74{,}320 - 32{,}440 = \underline{\$41{,}880}$

7. a. Housing expense ratio $= \dfrac{\text{Monthly housing expense (PITI)}}{\text{Monthly gross income}}$

Housing expense ratio $= \dfrac{669}{3,100} = 21.6\%$

b. Total obligations ratio $= \dfrac{\text{Total monthly financial obligation}}{\text{Monthly gross income}}$

Total obligations ratio $= \dfrac{669 + 375}{3,100} = \dfrac{1,044}{3,100} = 33.7\%$

c. According to the guidelines, Roman qualifies for both FHA and conventional mortgages.

CONCEPT REVIEW

1. Land, including permanent improvements on that land, is known as
_____. (14-1)

2. A(n) _____ is a loan in which real property is used as
security for a debt. (14-1)

3. Mortgage _____ points are an extra charge frequently added
to the cost of a mortgage. (14-1, 14-4)

4. A chart that shows the month-by-month breakdown of each
mortgage payment into interest and principal is known as a(n)
_____ schedule. (14-2)

5. A(n) _____ account is a bank account used by mortgage
lenders to accumulate next year's property taxes and hazard
insurance. (14-3)

6. Today most mortgage payments include four parts, abbreviated PITI.
Name these parts. (14-3)

7. The final step in a real estate transaction is a meeting at which
time the buyer pays the agreed-upon purchase price and the seller
delivers the ownership documents. This meeting is known as
the _____. (14-4)

8. The official document representing the right of ownership of real
property is known as the _____ or the _____. (14-4)

9. List four mortgage loan closing costs. (14-4)

10. A mortgage in which the interest rate changes periodically, usually
in relation to a predetermined economic index, is known as a(n)
_____ rate mortgage. (14-5)

11. A home equity _____ is a lump-sum second mortgage based
on the available equity in a home. (14-6)

12. A home equity _____ of credit is a revolving credit second
mortgage loan on the equity in a home. (14-6)

13. Write the formula for the housing expense ratio. (14-7)

14. Write the formula for the total obligations ratio. (14-7)

ASSESSMENT TEST

You are one of the branch managers of the Insignia Bank. Today two loan applications were submitted to your office. Calculate the requested information for each loan.

	Amount Financed	Interest Rate	Term of Loan	Number of $1,000s Financed	Table Factor	Monthly Payment	Total Interest
1.	$134,900	7.75%	25 years	____	____	____	____
2.	$79,500	8.25%	20 years	____	____	____	____

3. Suzanne Arthurs purchased a home with a $146,100 mortgage at 6.5% for 30 years. Calculate the monthly payment and prepare an amortization schedule for the first three months of Suzanne's loan.

Payment Number	Monthly Payment	Monthly Interest	Portion Used to Reduce Principal	Loan Balance
0				$146,100.00
1	_____	_____	_____	_____
2	_____	_____	_____	_____
3	_____	_____	_____	_____

Use Table 14-1 to calculate the monthly principal and interest and calculate the monthly PITI for the following mortgages.

	Amount Financed	Interest Rate	Term of Loan	Monthly PI	Annual Property Tax	Annual Insurance	Monthly PITI
4.	$54,200	4.75%	25 years	_____	$719	$459	_____
5.	$132,100	8.75%	15 years	_____	$2,275	$1,033	_____

For the following second mortgage applications, calculate the percentage of appraised value and the potential credit.

	Appraised Value	Lender's Percentage	Percentage of Appraised Value	Balance of First Mortgage	Potential Credit
6.	$114,500	65%	_____	$77,900	_____
7.	$51,500	80%	_____	$27,400	_____
8.	$81,200	70%	_____	$36,000	_____

For the following mortgage applications, calculate the housing expense ratio and the total expense ratio.

Applicant	Monthly Gross Income	Monthly PITI Expense	Other Monthly Financial Obligations	Housing Expense Ratio (%)	Total Obligations Ratio (%)
9. Morton	$5,300	$1,288	$840	_____	_____
10. Hauser	$3,750	$952	$329	_____	_____

11. As a loan officer using the Lending Ratio Guidelines on page 468, what type of mortgage can you offer Morton and Hauser from Exercises 9 and 10?

12. Dale Evans bought the Lazy D Ranch with an adjustable-rate mortgage. The lender's margin on the loan is 3.9%, and the overall rate cap is 6% over the life of the loan.

    a. If the current index rate is 4.45%, what is the calculated interest rate of the ARM?

    b. What is the maximum overall rate of Dale's loan?

13. Diversified Investments purchased a 24-unit apartment building for $650,000. After a 20% down payment, the balance was financed with a 20-year, 7.75% fixed-rate mortgage.

    a. What is the amount of the monthly principal and interest portion of the loan?

CHAPTER
14

b. As Diversified's loan officer, construct an amortization schedule for the first two months of the mortgage.

Payment Number	Monthly Payment	Monthly Interest	Portion Used to Reduce Principal	Loan Balance
0				_____
1	_____	_____	_____	_____
2	_____	_____	_____	_____

c. If the annual property taxes are $9,177 and the hazard insurance premium is $2,253 per year, what is the total monthly PITI of the loan?

d. If each apartment rents for $825 per month, how much income will Diversified make per month after the PITI is paid on the building?

14. Larry Mager purchased a ski lodge in Telluride for $850,000. His bank is willing to finance 70% of the purchase price. As part of the mortgage closing costs, Larry had to pay $4\frac{1}{4}$ discount points. How much did this amount to?

Denny's Corporation, through its subsidiaries, engages in the ownership and operation of a chain of family-style restaurants primarily in the United States. Its restaurants offer traditional American-style food. The company owns and operates its restaurants under the Denny's brand name.

In a typical year, total revenue from company restaurant sales and franchise and license sales exceeds $530 million.

Source: www.dennys.com

15. A Denny's Restaurant franchisee is looking for a 20-year mortgage with 90% financing to build a new location costing $775,000. The Spring Creek Bank is offering an 8% mortgage with $1\frac{1}{2}$ discount points; Foremost Savings & Loan is offering a 7.5% mortgage with 4 discount points. The franchisee is unsure which mortgage is the better deal and has asked for your help.

a. What is the total interest paid on each loan?

b. Taking into account the discount points, which lender is offering a better deal and by how much?

16. How much more total interest will be paid on a 30-year fixed-rate mortgage for $100,000 at 9.25% compared with a 15-year mortgage at 8.5%?

CHAPTER 14

17. Adam Marsh is purchasing a $134,000 condominium apartment. The down payment is 20%, and the balance will be financed with a 20-year fixed-rate mortgage at 8.75% and 3 discount points. The annual property tax is $1,940, and the hazard insurance premium is $1,460. When Adam signed the original sales contract, he put down a deposit of $10,000, which will be credited to his down payment. In addition, at the time of closing, he must pay the following expenses:

Appraisal fee	$165
Credit report	$75
Attorney's fees	$490
Roof inspection	$50
Termite inspection	$88
Title search	$119
Mortgage insurance premium	1.2% of amount financed
Documentary stamps	$\frac{1}{4}$% of amount financed

As Adam's real estate agent, he has asked you the following questions:

a. What is the total monthly PITI of the mortgage loan?

b. What is the total amount of interest that Adam will pay on the loan?

c. How much is due at the time of the closing?

d. If the sellers are responsible for the 6% broker's commission, $900 in closing costs, and the existing first mortgage with a balance of $45,000, what proceeds will be received on the sale of the property?

18. Martin Ellingham is negotiating to buy a vacation cottage in Port Wenn. The seller of the cottage is asking $186,000. Martin offered him a cash deal, owner-seller (no broker) only if the seller would reduce the price by 12%. The seller agreed. Martin must pay a 10% down payment upon signing the agreement of sale. At closing, he must pay the balance of the agreed-upon sale price, a $500 attorney's fee, a $68 utility transfer fee, a title search and transfer fee of $35 plus $\frac{3}{4}$% of the selling price, and the first six months of the annual insurance of $1,460 per year. How much does Martin owe at closing?

19. The Randolphs own a home that recently appraised for $161,400. The balance on their existing first mortgage is $115,200. If their bank is willing to loan up to 70% of the appraised value, what is the amount of credit available to the Randolphs on a home equity line of credit?

20. Jonathan and Kimberly Schwartz live in a home to which they want to make major improvements. They plan to replace the existing heating and cooling system, remodel the kitchen, and add a room above the garage. To pay for this renovation, they plan to get a home equity line of credit. Their home currently appraises for $298,000. They owe $68,340 on the first mortgage. How much credit will their bank provide if the limit is 75% of their home's value?

21. Phil Armstrong earns a gross income of $5,355 per month. He has submitted an application for a fixed-rate mortgage with a monthly PITI of $1,492. Phil has other financial obligations totaling $625 per month.

    a. What is his housing expense ratio?

    b. What is his total obligations ratio?

    c. According to the Lending Ratio Guidelines on page 468, for what type of mortgage would Phil qualify, if any?

22. Magda Leon is applying for a home mortgage with a monthly PITI of $724. She currently has a gross income of $2,856 and other monthly expenses of $411.

    a. What is Magda's housing expense ratio?

    b. What is her total obligations ratio?

    c. According to the lending ratio guidelines, for what type of mortgage would Magda qualify, if any?

BUSINESS DECISION: FOR WHAT SIZE MORTGAGE CAN YOU QUALIFY?

23. You are applying for a conventional mortgage from the Americana Bank. Your monthly gross income is $3,500, and the bank uses the 28% housing expense ratio guideline.

    a. What is the highest PITI for which you can qualify? *Hint:* Solve the housing expense ratio formula for PITI. Remember, this is an application of the percentage formula, Portion = Rate × Base, where PITI is the portion, the expense ratio is the rate, and your monthly gross income is the base.

b. Based on your answer from part a, if you are applying for a 30-year, 9% mortgage and the taxes and insurance portion of PITI is $175 per month, use Table 14-1 to calculate the size of the mortgage for which you qualify. *Hint:* Subtract TI from PITI. Divide the PI by the appropriate table factor to determine the number of $1,000s for which you qualify.

c. Based on your answer from part b, if you are planning on a 20% down payment, what is the most expensive house you can afford? *Hint:* Use the percentage formula again. The purchase price of the house is the base, the amount financed is the portion, and the percent financed is the rate.

COLLABORATIVE LEARNING ACTIVITY

The Hypothetical Mortgage

Speak with the loan officers at mortgage lending institutions in your area and ask for their help with a business math class project.

Your assignment is to research the various types of financing deals currently being offered for a hypothetical condominium you plan to buy. The following assumptions apply to this project:

- The purchase price of the condo you plan to buy is $200,000.
- The condo was recently appraised for $220,000.
- You plan to make a 25% down payment ($50,000) and are seeking a $150,000 mortgage.
- You have a job that qualifies you for that size mortgage.

As a team, your assignment is to compare the current interest rates, costs, and features associated with a 15-year fixed-rate mortgage, a 30-year fixed-rate mortgage, and an adjustable-rate mortgage.

a. What are the current interest rates and discount points of the 15- and 30-year fixed-rate mortgages?

b. What are the monthly payments of the fixed-rate mortgages?

c. What is the initial (teaser) rate, discount points, adjustment period, rate caps, margin, and index for the adjustable-rate mortgage?

d. What are the fees or charges for the loan application, property appraisal, survey, credit report, inspections, title search, title insurance, and document preparation?

e. What other charges or fees can be expected at closing?

f. Which type of mortgage does your team think is the best deal at this time? Why?

g. Which bank would you choose for the mortgage? Why?

Insurance

PERFORMANCE OBJECTIVES

SECTION I: Life Insurance

19-1: Understanding life insurance and calculating typical premiums for various types of policies (p. 642)

19-2: Calculating the value of various nonforfeiture options (p. 645)

19-3: Calculating the amount of life insurance needed to cover dependents' income shortfall (p. 647)

SECTION II: Property Insurance

19-4: Understanding property insurance and calculating typical fire insurance premiums (p. 650)

19-5: Calculating premiums for short-term policies and the refunds due on canceled policies (p. 652)

19-6: Understanding coinsurance and computing compensation due in the event of a loss (p. 654)

19-7: Determining each company's share of a loss when liability is divided among multiple carriers (p. 655)

SECTION III: Motor Vehicle Insurance

19-8: Understanding motor vehicle insurance and calculating typical premiums (p. 658)

19-9: Computing the compensation due following an accident (p. 661)

LIFE INSURANCE

Insurance is the promise to substitute future economic certainty for uncertainty and to replace the unknown with a sense of security. It is a mechanism for reducing financial risk and spreading financial loss due to unexpected events such as the death or disability of an individual, a home or business fire, a flood, an earthquake, an automobile accident, a negligence lawsuit, or an illness. These are only a few of the uncertainties that businesses and individuals can protect against by purchasing insurance. Companies may even purchase business interruption insurance, which covers the loss of income that may occur as a result of a multitude of perils.

Insurance is a very large and important segment of the U.S. economic system. Today there are more than 6,000 insurance companies employing more than 2.3 million persons and collecting close to $240 billion in annual premiums. The insurance industry is second only to commercial banking as a source of investment funds because insurance companies invest the billions of premium dollars they receive each year in a wide range of investments.

Insurance is based on the theory of **shared risk**, which means that insurance protection is purchased by many whose total payments are pooled together to pay off those few who actually incur a particular loss. Insurance companies use statisticians known as **actuaries** to calculate the probability, or chance, of a certain insurable event occurring. Based on a series of complicated calculations, insurance rates are then set. The rates are high enough to cover the cost of expected loss payments in the future and to provide a profit for the insurance company.

This chapter covers three major categories of insurance: life insurance, property insurance, and motor vehicle insurance. Within these three categories are several hundred different products or lines. Each year companies market new insurance products to meet the needs of a changing society. Recently, for example, insurance was made available to cover the loss of communication satellites during launch, space travel, and reentry.

Let's start with some basic terminology of the insurance industry. The company offering the insurance protection and ensuring payment in the event of a loss is known as the **insurer, carrier,** or **underwriter**. The individual or business purchasing the protection is the **insured, or policyholder**. The document stipulating the terms of the contract between the insurer and the insured is the **policy**. The amount of protection provided by the policy is the **face value**, and the amount paid at regular intervals to purchase this protection is known as the **premium**. The **beneficiary** is the person or institution to whom the proceeds of the policy are paid in the event that a loss occurs.

The insurance industry is regulated by a number of authorities, including federal, state, and some inside the industry itself. This regulation is designed to promote the public welfare by maintaining the solvency of insurance companies, providing consumer protection, and ensuring fair trade practices as well as fair contracts at fair prices.

insurance A mechanism for reducing financial risk and spreading financial loss due to unexpected events.

shared risk The theory on which insurance is based; protection is purchased by many whose total payments are pooled together to pay off those few who actually incur a particular loss.

actuaries Statisticians employed by insurance companies who calculate the probability, or chance, of a certain insurable event occurring.

insurer, carrier, or **underwriter** The company offering the insurance protection and ensuring payment in the event of a loss.

insured, or **policyholder** The person or business purchasing the insurance protection.

policy The document stipulating the terms of the contract between the insurer and the insured.

face value The amount of protection provided by the policy.

premium The amount paid at regular intervals to purchase insurance protection.

beneficiary The person or institution to whom the proceeds of the policy are paid in the event that a loss occurs.

According to statistics from industry research and consulting firm LIMRA International, the average American household carries just $126,000 in life insurance—approximately $300,000 less than they actually need. Only 61% of adult Americans have life insurance protection.

Insurance regulations, procedures, and laws vary widely from state to state. Most states have insurance commissions, departments, divisions, or boards that regulate all aspects of the insurance industry. Some of their responsibilities include premium structure and computation, insurance requirements, and salesperson education and licensing. This chapter focuses on calculating the premiums and the payouts of typical life, property, and motor vehicle insurance policies.

19-1 UNDERSTANDING LIFE INSURANCE AND CALCULATING TYPICAL PREMIUMS FOR VARIOUS TYPES OF POLICIES

life insurance A type of insurance that guarantees a specified sum of money to the surviving beneficiaries upon the death of the person who is insured.

Most individuals enjoy feeling that they are in control of their financial destiny. Few products are more important to that sense of security than life insurance. **Life insurance** guarantees a specified sum of money to the surviving beneficiaries upon the death of the person who is insured. Over the years, the average amount of life insurance per insured household has been steadily increasing. In 1960, for example, each insured household had an average of $13,000 in life insurance. By 1970, the average had doubled to about $26,000. By 1980, it had doubled again to more than $50,000. Today the average insured household has more than $125,000 in life insurance coverage. Exhibit 19-1 lists the top 10 life insurance companies by revenue.

term insurance A type of life insurance that offers pure insurance protection, paying the face value of the policy to the beneficiaries upon the death of the insured.

There are two basic types of policies: those that pay only if the policyholder dies (**term insurance**) and those that pay whether the policyholder lives or dies (**permanent insurance**). Today many insurance policies combine an investment component with risk protection to provide the policyholder with both a death benefit if he or she dies and attractive investment returns if he or she lives. In this section, we examine five popular types of life insurance policies: term, whole life, limited payment life, endowment, and nontraditional.

permanent insurance A type of insurance that combines an investment component with risk protection to provide the policyholder with both a death benefit and attractive investment returns.

TYPES OF LIFE INSURANCE

Term Insurance. This type of life insurance offers pure insurance protection, paying the face value of the policy to the beneficiaries upon the death of the insured. With term insurance, there is no investment component. All the premium goes toward purchasing the risk coverage. With most term policies, the premium increases periodically because the risk of death of the insured increases with age. Term policies may be purchased with premiums increasing every year, every 5 years, every 10 years, and so on.

Renewable term insurance allows the policyholder the option of renewing the policy for another 5- or 10-year period regardless of his or her health. The premiums on these policies

EXHIBIT 19-1

Top 10 Life Insurance Companies by Revenue

Dollars AND Sense

Should you purchase insurance from an *agent* or a *broker*? Insurance agents are employees of one specific company, such as MetLife, Prudential, or AFLAC. They can sell policies only from the company they represent.

Insurance brokers, on the other hand, are "independent" agents who represent many insurance companies. They have the advantage of being able to "shop" numerous companies to find the one that offers the best policy at the best price for you. When purchasing any form of insurance, you should deal with one broker or do the shopping yourself with several agents.

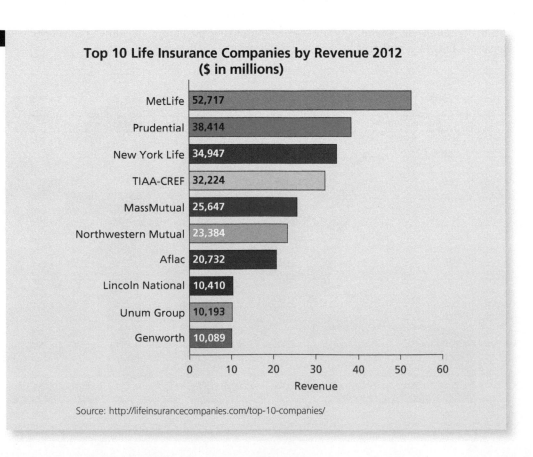

Source: http://lifeinsurancecompanies.com/top-10-companies/

are higher than nonrenewable term insurance. Because it is impossible to predict one's future health, many persons opt for the renewable policy. Another common type of insurance, known as convertible term, allows the policyholder to trade in or convert the term policy for permanent insurance with an investment element and cash value, without having to prove his or her health status.

Whole Life Insurance. Whole life, also known as ordinary life and straight life, is the most common type of permanent insurance. With whole life insurance, policyholders agree to pay premiums for their entire lives. Whole life insurance offers a guaranteed premium and death benefit as well as a guaranteed minimum cash value, which can be borrowed against if necessary. When the insured dies, the beneficiaries receive the face value of the policy. Having cash value is like having a savings account within the policy that grows each year. If the policyholder lives long enough, the cash value can be received as an annuity to supplement retirement income in later years.

Limited Payment Life Insurance. Limited payment life policies have level premiums that are limited to a certain period of time. After this period, usually 10, 20, or 30 years, the policy is paid up and the insured is covered for the rest of his or her life. The premiums charged for limited payment policies are higher than premiums for whole life policies because they are paid for a shorter period of time. A variation of the limited payment policy is the Life Paid-Up at 65 policy. With this policy, the premiums are payable until the insured reaches age 65, after which no more premiums are owed.

Endowment Insurance. Endowment insurance is a combination of life insurance and an accelerated savings plan. The emphasis of the endowment policy is the accumulation of money. Endowment insurance pays the face amount of the policy upon the death of the insured. It also pays the face amount if the insured is alive as of a specified date, known as the maturity date. Typical endowment periods are 10, 15, or 20 years or to a specified age such as 65 or 70. Traditionally, this type of insurance has been purchased by families with young children to save money for college education or by those who want to set up a retirement fund with immediate life insurance protection. Because they are designed to build cash values quickly, endowment policies have comparatively high premiums.

Nontraditional Insurance. In recent years, certain nontraditional policies have been introduced by insurance companies. Most of these interest-sensitive products are more flexible in design and provisions than their traditional counterparts. With these policies, the basic components of a life insurance policy, insurance (protection) and savings (investment), are separated. When premium payments are made, a portion known as the *mortality charge* is deducted to pay for the insurance coverage. This mortality charge increases with the age of the policyholder each year because the probability of death increases with age. The remaining amount, after other fees are deducted, goes to the investment *side fund*.

- *Universal life* is the most popular interest-sensitive policy. It features a minimum guaranteed death benefit and flexible premiums and face amounts. The insurance company decides on the type of investments to make, with the earnings credited to the side fund.
- *Variable life* is a higher-risk interest-sensitive policy that allows the policyholder to choose how the side fund will be invested. Typical choices include stocks, bonds, money market accounts, and real estate funds. Although this policy has a guaranteed death benefit, it does not have a guaranteed cash value like universal life does.
- *Variable/universal life* is a recently introduced policy that combines features of both variable life and universal life. These policies offer flexible premiums and guaranteed death benefits, both of which can be adjusted by the policyholder. The cash value is not guaranteed and depends on the investment performance of the funds selected by the policyholder.

CALCULATING PREMIUMS

Insurance premiums are based on the age and sex of the insured as well as the type of policy being purchased. Premiums are less expensive for younger people because their probability of dying is lower than for older people. Females pay lower rates than do males of the same age because females have a longer life expectancy than males.

Life insurance is purchased in increments of $1,000 of face value. The actuaries at insurance companies generate comprehensive rate tables listing the premiums per $1,000 of insurance for males and females of all ages. Table 19-1 is a typical example of such a table.

Annual life insurance premiums are calculated by determining the number of $1,000 of insurance desired and then multiplying the number of $1,000 by the rate per $1,000 found in Table 19-1. When the insured desires to pay the premiums more frequently than annually, such as semiannually, quarterly, or monthly, a small surcharge is added to account for the increased cost of billing, handling, and bookkeeping. Table 19-2 illustrates typical **premium factors** used by insurance companies for this purpose.

premium factors Small surcharges added to the cost of insurance policies when the insured chooses to pay the premiums more frequently than annually; takes into account the increased cost of billing, handling, and bookkeeping.

TABLE 19-1 Annual Life Insurance Premiums (per $1,000 of Face Value)

| | Term Insurance | | | | Permanent Insurance | | | | | |
| | 5-Year Term | | 10-Year Term | | Whole Life | | 20-Payment Life | | 20-Year Endowment | |
Age	Male	Female	Male	Female	Male	Female	Male	Female	Male	Female
18	$ 2.32	$ 1.90	$ 4.33	$ 4.01	$13.22	$11.17	$23.14	$19.21	$33.22	$29.12
19	2.38	1.96	4.42	4.12	13.60	11.68	24.42	20.92	33.68	30.04
20	2.43	2.07	4.49	4.20	14.12	12.09	25.10	21.50	34.42	31.28
21	2.49	2.15	4.57	4.29	14.53	12.53	25.83	22.11	34.90	31.79
22	2.55	2.22	4.64	4.36	14.97	12.96	26.42	22.89	35.27	32.40
23	2.62	2.30	4.70	4.42	15.39	13.41	27.01	23.47	35.70	32.93
24	2.69	2.37	4.79	4.47	15.90	13.92	27.74	24.26	36.49	33.61
25	2.77	2.45	4.85	4.51	16.38	14.38	28.40	25.04	37.02	34.87
26	2.84	2.51	4.92	4.60	16.91	14.77	29.11	25.96	37.67	35.30
27	2.90	2.58	5.11	4.69	17.27	15.23	29.97	26.83	38.23	35.96
28	2.98	2.64	5.18	4.77	17.76	15.66	30.68	27.54	38.96	36.44
29	3.07	2.70	5.23	4.84	18.12	16.18	31.52	28.09	39.42	37.21
30	3.14	2.78	5.30	4.93	18.54	16.71	32.15	28.73	40.19	37.80
35	3.43	2.92	6.42	5.35	24.19	22.52	37.10	33.12	43.67	39.19
40	4.23	3.90	7.14	6.24	27.21	25.40	42.27	36.29	48.20	42.25
45	6.12	5.18	8.81	7.40	33.02	29.16	48.73	39.08	51.11	46.04
50	9.72	8.73	14.19	9.11	37.94	33.57	56.31	44.16	58.49	49.20
55	16.25	12.82	22.03	13.17	45.83	37.02	61.09	49.40	71.28	53.16
60	24.10	19.43	37.70	24.82	53.98	42.24	70.43	52.55	79.15	58.08

Copyright © Cengage Learning®

TABLE 19-2
Life Insurance—Premium Factors

Premium Paid	Percent of Annual Premium
Semiannually	52%
Quarterly	26%
Monthly	9%

Copyright © Cengage Learning®

STEPS TO CALCULATE LIFE INSURANCE PREMIUMS

STEP 1. Calculate the number of $1,000 of insurance desired by dividing the face value of the policy by $1,000. Round to the nearest whole $1,000.

$$\text{Number of } \$1,000 = \frac{\text{Face value of policy}}{\$1,000}$$

STEP 2. Locate the appropriate premium rate per $1,000 from Table 19-1. Choose the rate based on the type of policy desired and the age and sex of the applicant.

STEP 3. Calculate annual premium by multiplying the number of $1,000 of insurance desired by the Table 19-1 rate.

Annual premium = Number of $1,000 × Rate per $1,000

STEP 4. For premiums other than annual, multiply the appropriate Table 19-2 premium factor by the annual premium.

Premium other than annual = Annual premium × Premium factor

EXAMPLE1 — CALCULATING LIFE INSURANCE PREMIUMS

Claudia Mercado is 24 years old. She is interested in purchasing a whole life insurance policy with a face value of $50,000. As her insurance agent, calculate the annual and monthly insurance premiums for this policy.

SOLUTIONSTRATEGY

Step 1. Number of $1,000 = $\dfrac{\text{Face value of policy}}{\$1,000} = \dfrac{50,000}{1,000} = 50$

Step 2. From Table 19-1, we find the premium per $1,000 for whole life insurance for a 24-year-old woman to be $13.92.

Step 3. Annual premium = Number of $1,000 × Rate per $1,000
Annual premium = 50 × 13.92 = $696

Step 4. Monthly premium = Annual premium × Monthly premium factor
Monthly premium = 696 × .09 = $62.64

TRYITEXERCISE 1

Gary Foster, age 26, wants to purchase a 10-year term insurance policy with a face value of $75,000. Calculate his annual and quarterly premiums. How much more will Gary pay per year if he chooses quarterly payments?

CHECK YOUR ANSWERS WITH THE SOLUTIONS ON PAGE 667.

CALCULATING THE VALUE OF VARIOUS NONFORFEITURE OPTIONS

19-2

Because all life insurance policies (except term) build up a **cash value** after the first two or three years, they should be viewed as being property with a value. Policyholders in effect own these properties and therefore have certain **ownership rights**. For example, policyholders, or policyowners, have the right to change beneficiaries, designate how the death benefits will be paid, borrow money against the policy, assign ownership to someone else, or cancel the policy.

Let's take a closer look at what happens when a policyowner decides to cancel a policy or allows it to terminate, or **lapse**, by failing to make the required premium payments within 31 days of the due date. The amount of cash value that has accumulated to that point is based on the size of the policy and the amount of time it has been in force. Most policies give the policyowner three choices, known as **nonforfeiture options**.

Option 1—Cash Value or Cash Surrender Option. Once a policy has accumulated cash value, the policyowner may choose to surrender (give up) the policy to the company and receive its cash value. At this point, the policy is terminated. If the insured wants to maintain the insurance coverage, the amount of the cash value may be borrowed and later repaid with interest.

Option 2—Reduced Paid-Up Insurance. The second option is that the available cash value is used to purchase a reduced level of paid-up insurance. This policy is of the same type as the original and continues for the life of the policyowner, with no further premiums due.

Option 3—Extended Term Insurance. With this option, the policyholder elects to use the cash value to purchase a term policy with the same face value as the original policy. The new policy will last for as long a time period as the cash value will purchase. When a policyowner simply stops paying on a policy and does not choose a nonforfeiture option, the insurance company automatically implements this extended term option.

Table 19-3 illustrates typical nonforfeiture options per $1,000 of face value for a policy issued to a woman at age 20.

cash value The amount of money that begins to build up in a permanent life insurance policy after the first two or three years.

ownership rights The rights of life insurance policyholders, including the right to change beneficiaries, designate how the death benefits will be paid, borrow money against the policy, assign ownership to someone else, or cancel the policy.

lapse To terminate. This is what happens when a policyholder fails to make the required premium payments on an insurance policy within 31 days of the due date.

nonforfeiture options The options available to the policyholder upon termination of a permanent life insurance policy with accumulated cash value; these include receiving the cash value, using the cash value to purchase a reduced paid-up insurance policy of the same type, or purchasing term insurance with the same face value as the original policy for as long a time period as the cash value will purchase.

TABLE 19-3 Nonforfeiture Options (per $1,000 of Face Value Issued to a Woman at Age 20)

End of Year	Whole Life Options					20-Payment Life Options					20-Year Endowment Options				
	1	2	3			1	2	3			1	2	3		
	Cash Value	Reduced Paid-Up Insurance	Extended Term			Cash Value	Reduced Paid-Up Insurance	Extended Term			Cash Value	Reduced Paid-Up Insurance	Extended Term		
			Years	Days				Years	Days				Years	Days	
3	$ 11	$ 25	2	17		$ 29	$ 90	4	217		$ 39	$ 97	7	132	
5	32	64	9	23		73	212	14	86		91	233	19	204	
7	54	99	13	142		101	367	23	152		186	381	26	310	
10	98	186	17	54		191	496	30	206		324	512	32	117	
15	157	314	21	218		322	789	34	142		647	794	37	350	
20	262	491	25	77		505	1,000	-Life-			1,000	1,000	-Life-		

STEPS TO CALCULATE THE VALUE OF VARIOUS NONFORFEITURE OPTIONS

STEP 1. Calculate the number of $1,000 of insurance by dividing the face value of the policy by $1,000.

STEP 2. *Option 1—Cash Value*. Locate the appropriate dollars per $1,000 in the Cash Value column of Table 19-3 and multiply this figure by the number of $1,000 of insurance.

Option 2—Reduced Paid-Up Insurance. Locate the appropriate dollars per $1,000 in the Reduced Paid-Up Insurance column of Table 19-3 and multiply this figure by the number of $1,000 of insurance.

Option 3—Extended Term. Locate the length of time of the new extended term policy in the Years and Days columns of Table 19-3.

EXAMPLE2 CALCULATING NONFORFEITURE OPTIONS

Tricia Lee purchased a $30,000 whole life insurance policy when she was 20 years old. She is now 35 years old and wants to investigate her nonforfeiture options. As her insurance agent, use Table 19-3 to calculate the value of Tricia's three options.

SOLUTIONSTRATEGY

Step 1. Number of $1,000 $= \dfrac{\text{Face value of policy}}{\$1,000} = \dfrac{30,000}{1,000} = 30$

Step 2. *Option 1—Cash Value*. From Table 19-3, we find that after being in force for 15 years, a whole life policy issued to a woman at age 20 has a cash value of $157 per $1,000 of insurance.

Number of $1,000 × Table value $= 30 × 157 = \underline{\$4,710}$

Tricia's cash value option is to receive $4,710 in cash from the company and have no further insurance coverage.

Option 2—Reduced Paid-Up Insurance. From Table 19-3, we find that after being in force for 15 years, a whole life policy issued to a woman at age 20 will have enough cash value to buy $314 in paid-up whole life insurance per $1,000 of face value.

Number of $1,000 × Table value $= 30 × 314 = \underline{\$9,420}$

Tricia's reduced paid-up insurance option is to receive a $9,420 whole life policy effective for her entire life with no further payments.

Option 3—Extended Term Insurance. From Table 19-3, we find that after being in force for 15 years, a whole life policy issued to a woman at age 20 will have enough cash value to purchase $30,000 of term insurance for a period of <u>21 years, 218 days</u>.

Dollars AND Sense

It is important to check your insurance coverage periodically or whenever your situation changes to be sure it meets your current needs.

Some changes that require insurance review might include increased income, change in marital status, or change in family size.

Many insurable assets are tied to inflation and therefore require periodic increases.

- Life insurance—Cost of living increases such as food, clothing, and transportation
- Property insurance—Rising real estate values and cost of replacement materials
- Health care insurance—Increases in physician, hospital, and other medical-related costs

►TRYITEXERCISE 2

Virginia Bennett purchased a $100,000 20-payment life insurance policy when she was 20 years old. She is now 30 years old and wants to investigate her nonforfeiture options. As her insurance agent, use Table 19-3 to determine the value of Virginia's three options.

CHECK YOUR ANSWERS WITH THE SOLUTIONS ON PAGE 667.

CALCULATING THE AMOUNT OF LIFE INSURANCE NEEDED TO COVER DEPENDENTS' INCOME SHORTFALL

19-3

Evaluating your life insurance needs is a fundamental part of sound financial planning. The amount of insurance and type of policy you should purchase are much less obvious. Life insurance is needed if you run a household, support a family, have a mortgage or other major debts, or expect children to attend college. Insurance should be used to fill the financial gap a family may incur by the death or disability of the insured.

One so-called rule of thumb is that you carry between seven and ten times your annual income depending on your lifestyle, number of dependents, and other sources of income. Another estimator of the amount of insurance to purchase is based on a family's additional income requirements needed in the event of the death of the insured. These additional requirements are known as the **income shortfall**.

Let's say, for example, that a family has $30,000 in living expenses per year. If after the death of the insured the family's total income decreases to only $20,000, the income shortfall would be $10,000 ($30,000 – $20,000). The theory is to purchase enough life insurance so that the face value of the policy, collected by the family on the death of the insured, can be invested at the prevailing interest rate to generate the additional income needed to overcome the $10,000 shortfall. When prevailing interest rates are low, large amounts of insurance are needed to cover the shortfall. As interest rates rise, less insurance is needed.

Income shortfall The difference between the total living expenses and the total income of a family in the event of the death of the insured; used as an indicator of how much life insurance to purchase.

STEPS TO CALCULATE INSURANCE NEEDED TO COVER DEPENDENTS' INCOME SHORTFALL

STEP 1. Determine the dependents' total annual living expenses, including mortgages.

STEP 2. Determine the dependents' total annual sources of income, including salaries, investments, and social security.

STEP 3. Subtract the income from the living expenses to find the income shortfall.

Income shortfall = Total living expenses − Total income

STEP 4. Calculate the insurance needed to cover the shortfall by dividing the shortfall by the prevailing interest rate (round to the nearest $1,000).

$$\text{Insurance needed} = \frac{\text{Income shortfall}}{\text{Prevailing interest rate}}$$

EXAMPLE3 CALCULATING AMOUNT OF INSURANCE NEEDED

With a prevailing interest rate of 6%, how much life insurance is required to cover dependents' income shortfall if their living expenses amount to $48,000 per year and their total income sources amount to $33,000 per year?

►SOLUTIONSTRATEGY

Step 1. Living expenses per year are $48,000 (given).

Step 2. Dependents' total income is $33,000 (given).

Step 3. Income shortfall = Total expenses − Total income

Income shortfall = 48,000 − 33,000 = $15,000

Step 4. Insurance needed = $\dfrac{\text{Shortfall}}{\text{Prevailing rate}}$ = $\dfrac{15,000}{.06}$ = $250,000

▶ TRYITEXERCISE 3

Norm Jaffe is evaluating his life insurance needs. His family's total living expenses are $54,000 per year. Kate, his wife, earns $38,000 per year in salary and receives another $5,000 per year from an endowment fund. If the prevailing interest rate is currently 5%, how much life insurance should Norm purchase to cover his dependents' income shortfall?

CHECK YOUR ANSWER WITH THE SOLUTION ON PAGE 667.

SECTION I — 19 — REVIEW EXERCISES

Calculate the annual, semiannual, quarterly, and monthly premiums for the following life insurance policies.

	Face Value of Policy	Sex and Age of Insured	Type of Policy	Annual Premium	Semiannual Premium	Quarterly Premium	Monthly Premium
1.	$ 5,000	Male—24	Whole Life	$79.50	$41.34	$20.67	$7.16
2.	10,000	Female—35	10-Year Term				
3.	25,000	Male—19	20-Year Endowment				
4.	75,000	Male—50	20-Payment Life				
5.	100,000	Female—29	5-Year Term				
6.	40,000	Male—35	Whole Life				
7.	35,000	Male—30	20-Payment Life				
8.	250,000	Female—45	20-Year Endowment				

Calculate the value of the nonforfeiture options for the following life insurance policies.

	Face Value of Policy	Years in Force	Type of Policy	Cash Value	Reduced Paid-Up Insurance	Extended Term Years	Extended Term Days
9.	$ 50,000	10	Whole Life	$4,900	$9,300	17	54
10.	250,000	7	20-Year Endowment				
11.	35,000	15	Whole Life				
12.	100,000	3	20-Payment Life				
13.	25,000	5	20-Year Endowment				
14.	75,000	7	20-Payment Life				

15. Leroy Kirk is 35 years old and is interested in purchasing a 20-year endowment insurance policy with a face value of $120,000.

  a. Calculate the annual premium for this policy.

  b. Calculate the semiannual premium.

16. Rene Boyer, age 27, wants to purchase a 5-year term insurance policy with a face value of $25,000. As her insurance agent, answer the following questions:

    a. What is the annual premium for this policy?

    b. What is the monthly premium?

    c. How much more will Rene pay per year if she chooses monthly payments?

17. Carmen Gutierrez purchased a $75,000, 20-payment life insurance policy when she was 20 years old. She is now 30 years old and wants to investigate her nonforfeiture options. As her insurance agent, calculate the value of Carmen's three options.

18. Alex Baron is evaluating his life insurance needs. His family's total living expenses are $39,800 per year. Carol, his wife, earns $23,000 per year in salary and receives an additional $4,000 per year in municipal bond interest. If the prevailing interest rate is currently 2.5%, how much life insurance should Alex purchase to cover his dependents' income shortfall?

    Total living expenses = $39,800

    Total income = 23,000 + 4,000 = $27,000

    Income shortfall = 39,800 − 27,000 = $12,800

    $$\frac{\text{Income shortfall}}{\text{Prevailing interest rate}} = \frac{12,800}{.025} = \$512,000 \text{ Insurance needed}$$

19. Richard Ryan is evaluating his life insurance needs. His family's total living expenses are $37,500 per year. Olga, his wife, earns $14,900 per year in salary and receives another $3,500 annually in disability benefits from an insurance settlement for an accident. If the prevailing interest rate is $7\frac{1}{2}\%$, how much life insurance should Richard purchase to cover his dependents' income shortfall? Round to the nearest $1,000.

BUSINESS DECISION: THE CONSULTATION

20. Tina Parker, a single mother, is 20 years old. She has called on you for an insurance consultation. Her objective is to purchase life insurance protection for the next 10 years while her children are growing up. Tina tells you that she can afford about $250 per year for insurance premiums. You have suggested either a 10-year term policy or a whole life policy.

    a. Rounded to the nearest thousand, how much insurance coverage can Tina purchase under each policy? *Hint*: Divide her annual premium allowance by the rate per $1,000 for each policy.

b. If she should die in the next 10 years, how much more will her children receive under the term insurance?

c. If she should live beyond the 10th year, what are her nonforfeiture options with the whole life policy?

19

PROPERTY INSURANCE

19-4 UNDERSTANDING PROPERTY INSURANCE AND CALCULATING TYPICAL FIRE INSURANCE PREMIUMS

property insurance Insurance protection for the financial losses that may occur to business' and homeowner's property from such perils as fire, lightning, wind, water, negligence, burglary, and vandalism.

Businesses and homeowners alike need insurance protection for the financial losses that may occur to their property from such perils as fire, lightning, wind, water, negligence, burglary, and vandalism. Although the probability that a particular peril will occur is small, no homeowner or business can afford the risk of not having **property insurance**. Most mortgage lenders, in fact, require that sufficient property insurance be purchased by the borrower as a condition for obtaining a mortgage.

EXHIBIT 19-2 The Top Ten Most Expensive and Least Expensive States for Homeowners Insurance

Rank	Most expensive states	Homeowners average premium	Rank	Least expensive states	Homeowners average premium
1	Texas	$1,560	1	Idaho	$500
2	Louisiana	1,546	2	Oregon	535
3	Florida	1,544	3	Utah	558
4	Oklahoma	1,246	4	Wisconsin	563
5	Mississippi	1,217	5	Washington	595
6	Rhode Island	1,092	6	Ohio	614
7	Kansas	1,066	7	Delaware	636
8	District of Columbia	1,065	8	Arizona	666
9	Connecticut	1,052	9	Maine	676
10	Alabama	1,050	10	South Dakota	678

Source: ©2012 National Association of Insurance Commissioners (NAIC).

In addition to the items listed above, most property insurance policies today have provisions for liability coverage, medical expenses, and additional expenses that may be incurred while the damaged property is being repaired. For example, a business may have to move to a temporary location during reconstruction or a family may have to stay in an apartment or a motel while their house is being repaired. Insurance companies offer similar policies to meet the needs of apartment and home renters as well as condominium owners.

In this section, we focus our attention on fire insurance and how these premiums are determined. Fire insurance rates are quoted as an amount per $100 of insurance coverage purchased. Rates are separated into two categories: (1) the structure or building itself and (2) the contents in the building.

A *building's* fire insurance rates are determined by a number of important factors:

* The *dollar amount* of insurance purchased on the property
* The *location of the property*—city, suburbs, and rural areas
* The *proximity* and *quality* of fire protection available
* The *type of construction* materials used—masonry (brick) or wood (frame)

The *contents* portion of the fire insurance rate is based on the following:

* The *dollar amount* or value of the contents
* The *flammability* of the contents

From this rate structure, we can see that a building made of concrete, bricks, and steel that is located 2 or 3 miles from a fire station would have a considerably lower rate than a building of the same value with wood frame construction located in a rural area 12 miles from the nearest fire-fighting equipment. Or for that matter, a warehouse filled with explosive chemicals would cost more to insure than the same warehouse filled with Coca-Cola.

Table 19-4 illustrates typical annual fire insurance premiums. Note that the rates are per $100 of insurance coverage. The building and contents are listed separately and divided by the structural class of the building and the location (area rating).

© Jerry Sharp/Shutterstock.com

Most businesses and homeowners carry special insurance policies to protect against loss due to fire and other perils. According to the Insurance Information Institute, the average annual homeowner's insurance expenditure was estimated at $879 in 2010.

STEPS TO CALCULATE TYPICAL FIRE INSURANCE PREMIUMS

STEP 1. From Table 19-4, locate the appropriate rate based on *structural class* and *area rating* for both the building and the contents.

STEP 2. Calculate the number of $100 of insurance coverage desired for both the building and the contents by dividing the amount of coverage for each by $100.

STEP 3. Multiply the number of $100 for both the building and contents by the rates from Step 1 to find the annual premium for each.

STEP 4. Add the annual premiums for the building and the contents to find the total annual premium.

Total annual fire premium = Building premium + Contents premium

TABLE 19-4 Annual Fire Insurance Premiums (per $100 of Face Value)

Area Rating	Structural Classification							
	A		B		C		D	
	Building	Contents	Building	Contents	Building	Contents	Building	Contents
1	$.21	$.24	$.32	$ .37	$ .38	$ .42	$ .44	$ .48
2	.38	.42	.39	.48	.43	.51	.57	.69
3	.44	.51	.55	.66	.69	.77	.76	.85
4	.59	.68	.76	.83	.87	1.04	.98	1.27
5	.64	.73	.92	1.09	1.08	1.13	1.39	1.43

EXAMPLE4 CALCULATING FIRE INSURANCE PREMIUMS

What is the total annual fire insurance premium on a building valued at $200,000 with structural classification B and area rating 4 and contents valued at $40,000?

SOLUTIONSTRATEGY

Step 1. From Table 19-4, we find the following rates for structural class B and area rating 4:

$$\text{Building—\$.76 per \$100 of coverage}$$
$$\text{Contents—\$.83 per \$100 of coverage}$$

Step 2. Number of $100 of coverage:

$$\text{Building} = \frac{\text{Amount of coverage}}{\$100} = \frac{200,000}{100} = 2,000$$

$$\text{Contents} = \frac{\text{Amount of coverage}}{\$100} = \frac{40,000}{100} = 400$$

Step 3. Annual fire insurance premiums:

$$\text{Building} = \text{Number of \$100} \times \text{Table rate} = 2,000 \times .76 = \underline{\$1,520}$$
$$\text{Contents} = \text{Number of \$100} \times \text{Table rate} = 400 \times .83 = \underline{\$332}$$

Step 4. Total annual fire premium = Building premium + Contents premium
Total annual fire premium = 1,520 + 332 = $\underline{\$1,852}$

▶TRYITEXERCISE 4

You are the insurance agent for Diamond Enterprises, Inc. The owner, Ed Diamond, would like you to give him a quote on the total annual premium for a property insurance policy on a new warehouse in the amount of $420,000 and contents valued at $685,000. The warehouse is structural classification A and area rating 2.

CHECK YOUR ANSWER WITH THE SOLUTION ON PAGE 667.

19-5 CALCULATING PREMIUMS FOR SHORT-TERM POLICIES AND THE REFUNDS DUE ON CANCELED POLICIES

short-term policies Insurance policies for less than one year.

From time to time, businesses and individuals cancel insurance policies or require **short-term policies** of less than one year. For example, a family might sell their home two months after paying the annual premium or a business may require coverage for a shipment of merchandise that will be sold in a few months. When a policy is canceled by the insured or is written for less than one year, the premium charged is known as the **short-rate**.

short-rate The premium charged when a policy is canceled by the insured or is written for less than one year.

SHORT-RATE REFUND

Table 19-5 illustrates typical short-term policy rate factors. These rate factors should be used to calculate the premiums and refunds for short-term policies canceled by the insured. Note that these rate factors are a percentage of the annual premium.

STEPS TO CALCULATE SHORT-RATE REFUNDS—POLICIES CANCELED BY INSURED

STEP 1. Calculate the short-term premium using the short-rate from Table 19-5.

Short-rate premium = Annual premium × Short-rate

STEP 2. Calculate the short-rate refund by subtracting the short-rate premium from the annual premium.

Short-rate refund = Annual premium − Short-rate premium

TABLE 19-5 Property Insurance Short-Rate Schedule

Time Policy Is in Force	Percent of Annual Premium	Time Policy Is in Force (months)	Percent of Annual Premium
5 days	8	4	50
10 days	10	5	60
15 days	14	6	70
20 days	16	7	75
25 days	18	8	80
		9	85
1 month	20	10	90
2 months	30	11	95
3 months	40	12	100

EXAMPLE5 CALCULATING SHORT-RATE RETURNS

A property insurance policy has an annual premium of $500. What is the short-rate refund if the policy is canceled by the insured after 3 months?

SOLUTIONSTRATEGY

Step 1. Short-rate premium = Annual premium × Short-rate
Short-rate premium = 500 × 40% = $200

Step 2. Short-rate refund = Annual premium − Short-rate premium
Short-rate refund = 500 − 200 = $300

TRYITEXERCISE 5

A property insurance policy has an annual premium of $850. What is the short-rate refund if the policy is canceled by the insured after 8 months?

CHECK YOUR ANSWER WITH THE SOLUTION ON PAGE 667.

REGULAR REFUND

When a policy is canceled by the insurance company rather than the insured, the company must refund the entire unused portion of the premium. This short-term refund calculation is based on the fraction of a year the policy was in force and is known as a regular refund.

 STEPS TO CALCULATE REGULAR REFUNDS—POLICIES CANCELED BY COMPANY

STEP 1. Calculate the premium for the period of time the policy was in force.

$$\text{Annual premium} \times \frac{\text{Days policy in force}}{365}$$

or

$$\text{Annual premium} \times \frac{\text{Months policy in force}}{12}$$

STEP 2. Calculate refund by subtracting premium for period in force from the annual premium.

Regular refund = Annual premium − Premium for period

IN THE Business World

In addition to homeowners, insurance companies offer similar policies to meet the needs of apartment and home renters as well as condominium owners.

- *Renter's insurance*—Insurance that covers the renter's personal property and liability. The property owner pays the insurance for the building.

- *Condominium insurance*—Insurance that covers the interior walls, wiring, and contents of the condominium.

EXAMPLE6 CALCULATING REGULAR REFUNDS

A property insurance policy has an annual premium of $500. What is the regular refund if the policy is canceled by the insurance company after 3 months?

SOLUTIONSTRATEGY

Step 1. Premium for period = Annual premium $\times \dfrac{\text{Months policy in force}}{12}$

Premium for period = $500 \times \dfrac{3}{12} = \underline{\$125}$

Step 2. Regular refund = Annual premium − Premium for period
Regular refund = $500 - 125 = \underline{\underline{\$375}}$

TRYITEXERCISE 6

A property insurance policy has an annual premium of $850. What is the regular refund if the policy is canceled by the insurance company after 8 months?

CHECK YOUR ANSWER WITH THE SOLUTION ON PAGE 667.

19-6 UNDERSTANDING COINSURANCE AND COMPUTING COMPENSATION DUE IN THE EVENT OF A LOSS

coinsurance clause A clause in a property insurance policy stipulating the minimum amount of coverage required for a claim to be paid in full. This requirement is stated as a percent of the replacement value of the property.

Knowing that most fires do not totally destroy the insured property, many businesses, as a cost-saving measure, insure their buildings and contents for less than the full value. To protect themselves from having more claims than premiums collected, insurance companies write a **coinsurance clause** into most business policies. This clause stipulates the minimum amount of coverage required for a claim to be paid in full. The coinsurance minimum is stated as a percent of the replacement value of the property and is usually between 70% and 90%.

Here is an example of how coinsurance works. Let's say that a building has a replacement value of $100,000. If the insurance policy has an 80% coinsurance clause, the building must be insured for $80,000 (80% of the $100,000) to be fully covered for any claim up to the face value of the policy. Any coverage less than the required 80% would be paid out in proportion to the coverage ratio. The **coverage ratio** is a ratio of the amount of insurance carried by the insured to the amount of insurance required by the insurance company.

coverage ratio A ratio of the amount of insurance carried by the insured to the amount of insurance required according to the coinsurance clause of the insurance policy.

$$\text{Coverage ratio} = \frac{\textbf{Insurance carried}}{\textbf{Insurance required}}$$

If, for example, the owner had purchased only $40,000 rather than the required $80,000, the insurance company would be obligated to pay only half, or 50%, of any claim. This is because the ratio of insurance carried to insurance required was 50%.

$$\text{Coverage ratio} = \frac{40,000}{80,000} = \frac{1}{2} = 50\%$$

STEPS TO CALCULATE AMOUNT OF LOSS TO BE PAID WITH A COINSURANCE CLAUSE

STEP 1. Determine the amount of insurance required by the coinsurance clause.

Insurance required = Replacement value of property × Coinsurance percent

STEP 2. Calculate the amount of the loss to be paid by the insurance company by multiplying the coverage ratio by the amount of the loss.

$$\textbf{Amount of loss paid by insurance} = \frac{\textbf{Insurance carried}}{\textbf{Insurance required}} \times \textbf{Amount of the loss}$$

EXAMPLE7 CALCULATING INSURANCE LOSS PAYOUT

The Tradewinds Corporation had property valued at $500,000 and insured for $300,000. If the fire insurance policy contained an 80% coinsurance clause, how much would be paid by the insurance company in the event of a $100,000 fire?

▶SOLUTIONSTRATEGY

Step 1. Insurance required = Value of the property × Coinsurance percent

Insurance required = $500,000 \times .80 = \$400,000$

Step 2. Amount of loss paid by insurance $= \dfrac{\text{Insurance carried}}{\text{Insurance required}} \times$ Amount of loss

Amount of loss paid by insurance $= \dfrac{300,000}{400,000} \times 100,000 = \underline{\$75,000}$

▶TRYITEXERCISE 7

Bravo Manufacturing, Inc., had property valued at $850,000 and insured for $400,000. If the fire insurance policy contained a 70% coinsurance clause, how much would be paid by the insurance company in the event of a $325,000 fire?

CHECK YOUR ANSWER WITH THE SOLUTION ON PAGE 667.

DETERMINING EACH COMPANY'S SHARE OF A LOSS WHEN LIABILITY IS DIVIDED AMONG MULTIPLE CARRIERS

19-7

Sometimes businesses are covered by fire insurance policies from more than one company at the same time, which is known as having **multiple carriers**. This situation occurs because one insurance company is unwilling or unable to carry the entire liability of a particular property or because additional coverage was purchased from different insurance companies over a period of time as the business expanded and became more valuable.

Assuming that all coinsurance clause requirements have been met, when a claim is made against multiple carriers, each carrier is responsible for its portion of the total coverage carried. To calculate that portion, we divide the amount of each company's policy by the total insurance carried. This portion is expressed as a percent of the total coverage.

For example, if an insurance company was one of multiple carriers and had a $30,000 fire policy written on a business that had a total of $200,000 in coverage, that insurance company would be responsible for $\dfrac{30,000}{200,000}$, or 15%, of any loss.

multiple carriers A situation in which a business is covered by fire insurance policies from more than one company at the same time.

STEPS TO DETERMINE EACH COMPANY'S SHARE OF A LOSS WHEN LIABILITY IS SHARED AMONG MULTIPLE CARRIERS

STEP 1. Calculate each carrier's portion by dividing the amount of each policy by the total insurance carried.

$$\text{Carrier's percent of total coverage} = \frac{\textbf{Amount of carrier's policy}}{\textbf{Total amount of insurance}}$$

STEP 2. Determine each carrier's share of a loss by multiplying the amount of the loss by each carrier's percent of the total coverage.

Carrier's share of loss = Amount of loss × Carrier's percent of total coverage

EXAMPLE8 CALCULATING MULTI-CARRIER PAYOUTS

Dynaco Development Corp. had multiple carrier fire insurance coverage in the amount of $400,000 as follows.

Travelers:	$80,000	policy
State Farm:	$120,000	policy
Allstate:	$200,000	policy
	$400,000	total coverage

Assuming that all coinsurance clause stipulations have been met, how much would each carrier be responsible for in the event of a $50,000 fire?

►SOLUTIONSTRATEGY

Step 1. Carrier's percent of total coverage $= \dfrac{\text{Amount of carrier's policy}}{\text{Total amount of insurance}}$

$$\text{Travelers} = \frac{80,000}{400,000} = \underline{20\%}$$

$$\text{State Farm} = \frac{120,000}{400,000} = \underline{30\%}$$

$$\text{Allstate} = \frac{200,000}{400,000} = \underline{50\%}$$

Step 2. Carrier's share of loss $=$ Amount of loss $\times$ Carrier's percent of total coverage

Travelers Share $= 50,000 \times .20 = \underline{\$10,000}$

State Farm Share $= 50,000 \times .30 = \underline{\$15,000}$

Allstate Share $= 50,000 \times .50 = \underline{\$25,000}$

►TRYITEXERCISE 8

Savoy International had multiple carrier fire insurance coverage in the amount of $125,000 as follows.

Aetna:	$20,000	policy
USF&G:	$45,000	policy
John Hancock:	$60,000	policy
	$125,000	total coverage

Assuming that all coinsurance clause stipulations have been met, how much would each carrier be responsible for in the event of a $16,800 fire?

CHECK YOUR ANSWERS WITH THE SOLUTIONS ON PAGE 667.

SECTION II 19 REVIEW EXERCISES

Calculate the building, contents, and total property insurance premiums for the following policies.

	Area Rating	Structural Class	Building Value	Building Premium	Contents Value	Contents Premium	Total Premium
1.	5	D	$425,000	$5,907.50	$70,000	$1,001.00	$6,908.50
2.	4	B	$88,000	_____	$21,000	_____	_____
3.	2	C	$124,000	_____	$35,000	_____	_____
4.	1	A	$215,000	_____	$29,000	_____	_____
5.	5	D	$518,000	_____	$90,000	_____	_____
6.	3	C	$309,000	_____	$57,000	_____	

Calculate the short-term premium and refund for each of the following policies.

	Annual Premium	Canceled After	Canceled By	Short-Term Premium	Refund
7.	$750	2 months	insured	$225.00	$525.00
8.	$390	5 months	insurance company	$162.50	$227.50
9.	$450	3 months	insurance company		
10.	$560	20 days	insured		
11.	$1,280	9 months	insured		
12.	$322	5 months	insurance company		
13.	$630	5 days	insured		

Calculate the amount to be paid by the insurance company for each of the following claims.

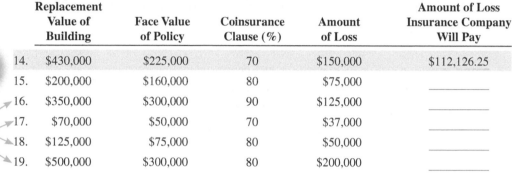

	Replacement Value of Building	Face Value of Policy	Coinsurance Clause (%)	Amount of Loss	Amount of Loss Insurance Company Will Pay
14.	$430,000	$225,000	70	$150,000	$112,126.25
15.	$200,000	$160,000	80	$75,000	
16.	$350,000	$300,000	90	$125,000	
17.	$70,000	$50,000	70	$37,000	
18.	$125,000	$75,000	80	$50,000	
19.	$500,000	$300,000	80	$200,000	

20. You are the insurance agent for Castle Mountain Furniture, Inc. The owner, Craig Ferguson, would like you to give him a quote on the total annual premium for property insurance on a new production facility in the amount of $1,640,000 and equipment and contents valued at $955,000. The building is structural classification B and area rating 4.

21. A property insurance policy has an annual premium of $1,350. What is the short-rate refund if the policy is canceled by the insured after 9 months?

22. Insignia Enterprises has a property insurance policy with an annual premium of $1,320. In recent months, Insignia has filed four different claims against the policy: a fire, two burglaries, and a vandalism incident. The insurance company has elected to cancel the policy, which has been in effect for 310 days. What is the regular refund due to Insignia?

23. Hi-Volt Electronics had multiple carrier fire insurance coverage in the amount of $500,000, as follows:

$$\begin{array}{rl} \text{Aetna:} & \$300,000 \quad \text{policy} \\ \text{State Farm:} & \$125,000 \quad \text{policy} \\ \text{Liberty Mutual:} & \underline{\$75,000} \quad \text{policy} \\ & \$500,000 \quad \text{total coverage} \end{array}$$

Assuming that all coinsurance clause stipulations have been met, how much would each carrier be responsible for in the event of a $95,000 fire?

BUSINESS DECISION: BUSINESS INTERRUPTION INSURANCE

24. As the owner of a successful business, you have just purchased an additional type of property insurance coverage known as *business interruption insurance*. This insurance protects the profits that a company would have earned had there been no problem. Business interruption insurance covers damages caused by all types of perils, such as fires, tornadoes, hurricanes, lightning, or any other disaster except floods and earthquakes.

This insurance pays for "economic" losses incurred when business operations suddenly cease. These include loss of income due to the interruption and additional expenses (e.g., leases; relocation to temporary facilities; overtime to keep up with production demands; recompiling of business, financial, and legal records; and even the salaries of key employees).

Your coverage provides insurance reimbursement for 80% of any losses. Your company pays the other 20%. The annual premium is 2% of the income and extra expenses that you insure.

a. If you have purchased coverage amounting to $20,000 per month, what is the amount of your annual premium?

b. If a tornado put your company out of business for $5\frac{1}{2}$ months, what would be the amount of the insurance reimbursement for your economic loss?

© Monkey Business Images/Shutterstock.com

Home-Based Business For those running a business from home, a typical homeowner's policy is not enough because it provides only $2,500 in coverage for business equipment. The insurance industry has recently created "in-home business" insurance policies. For about $200 a year, you can insure your business property for $10,000. General liability coverage is included in the policy.

For an additional premium, a business owner can purchase $300,000 to $1 million in liability coverage. The policy also covers lost income and expenses such as payroll for up to one year if damage occurs to the house and the business is shut down.

SECTION III | **19** MOTOR VEHICLE INSURANCE

19-8 UNDERSTANDING MOTOR VEHICLE INSURANCE AND CALCULATING TYPICAL PREMIUMS

motor vehicle insurance Insurance protection for the financial losses that may be incurred due to a motor vehicle accident or damage caused by fire, vandalism, or other perils.

liability A portion of motor vehicle insurance that includes payment for bodily injury to other persons and damages to the property of others resulting from the insured's negligence.

collision A portion of motor vehicle insurance that covers damage sustained by the insured's vehicle in an accident.

comprehensive Insurance coverage that protects the insured's vehicle for damage caused by fire, wind, water, theft, vandalism, and other perils not caused by accident.

With the steadily increasing costs of automobile and truck repairs and replacement, as well as all forms of medical services, **motor vehicle insurance** today is an absolute necessity! In fact, most states require a minimum amount of insurance before a vehicle may be registered.

Motor vehicle insurance rates, regulations, and requirements vary widely from state to state, but the basic structure is the same. Vehicle insurance is divided into three main categories: **liability**, **collision**, and **comprehensive**.

Liability.   This category includes (1) payment for bodily injury to other persons resulting from the insured's negligence and (2) damages to the property of others resulting from the insured's negligence. This property may be other vehicles damaged in the accident or other objects such as fences, landscaping, or buildings.

Collision.   This category covers damage sustained by the insured's vehicle in an accident. As a premium reduction measure, collision coverage is often sold with a **deductible** amount, for example, $250 deductible. This means that the insured pays the first $250 in damages for each occurrence and the insurance company pays the amount over $250. As the deductible amount increases, the premium for the insurance decreases.

■ **DatabankUSA**

Got You Covered

State rankings of car insurance rates

Louisiana $2,699	Texas $1,545	
Michigan $2,520	Arkansas $1,545	
Georgia $2,155	Maryland $1,528	Nevada $1,341
Oklahoma $2,074	National average $1,510	Virginia $1,322
Washington, D.C. $2,006	North Dakota $1,501	Illinois $1,322
Montana $1,914	Wyoming $1,496	South Carolina $1,288
California $1,819	Alaska $1,455	Colorado $1,271
West Virginia $1,816	Utah $1,438	Wisconsin $1,228
Rhode Island $1,735	Kansas $1,435	Arizona $1,227
Kentucky $1,725	Minnesota $1,432	Washington $1,226
Connecticut $1,723	New Mexico $1,431	Indiana $1,183
New Jersey $1,697	Tennessee $1,408	Vermont $1,176
Alabama $1,667	South Dakota $1,397	Idaho $1,133
Missouri $1,638	Oregon $1,387	New Hampshire $1,112
Massachusetts $1,625	Nebraska $1,384	Ohio $1,106
Pennsylvania $1,604	New York $1,369	North Carolina $1,085
Delaware $1,586	Florida $1,364	Iowa $1,028
Hawaii $1,583	Mississippi $1,345	Maine $934

Source: Insure.com.

*Dollar figures shown are an average of insurance rates for more than 750 vehicles in the 2013 model year.

Least and Most Expensive Cars to Insure

In 2013, the least expensive car to insure was the Ford Edge SE (averaging $1,128 per year) and the most expensive ("non-exotic") car to insure was the Mercedes-Benz CL600 (averaging $3,357 per year).

Source: Based on *The New York Times*, March 18, 2013

Comprehensive. This insurance coverage protects the insured's vehicle for damage caused by fire, wind, water, theft, vandalism, and other perils not caused by an accident.

Most insurance companies also offer policyholders the option of purchasing policy extras such as uninsured motorist's protection and coverage while driving a rented or borrowed car. Some policies even offer to pay towing expenses in the event of a breakdown or cover the cost for a rental car while the insured's vehicle is being repaired after an accident.

Liability rates are based on three primary factors: *who* is driving the vehicle, *where* the vehicle is being driven, and the *amount* of insurance coverage desired. Table 19-6 illustrates typical annual liability premiums for bodily injury and property damage. Note that the rates are listed by driver classification (age, sex, and marital status of the driver), territory (metropolitan area, suburb, small town, rural or farm area), and amount (in thousands of dollars).

Motor vehicle liability coverage is typically stated in a three-number format, such as 50/100/50, with the numbers given in thousands of dollars. The first two numbers, 50/100, refer to the bodily injury portion and means the policy will pay up to $50,000 for bodily injury caused by the insured's vehicle to any one person, with $100,000 maximum per accident regardless of the number of persons injured. The third number, 50 ($50,000), represents the maximum property damage benefits to be paid per single accident.

deductible A premium reduction measure in collision insurance whereby the insured pays a stipulated amount of the damage first, the deductible, and the insurance company pays any amount over that; common deductibles are $100, $250, $500, and $1,000.

TABLE 19-6 Motor Vehicle Liability Insurance Annual Premiums—Bodily Injury and Property Damage Rates

Territory	Driver Class	Bodily Injury Coverage ($000)					Property Damage Coverage ($000)				
		10/20	15/30	25/50	50/100	100/300	5	10	25	50	100
1	1	$61	$73	$88	$92	$113	$46	$49	$53	$58	$64
	2	63	75	81	94	116	48	51	55	61	66
	3	65	78	84	98	118	52	54	58	63	69
	4	69	81	86	101	121	54	56	60	65	71
2	1	66	75	83	93	114	56	63	68	73	77
	2	69	77	88	98	117	58	64	70	75	79
	3	75	82	92	104	119	59	66	71	76	82
	4	78	86	95	109	122	62	67	73	78	84
3	1	73	77	84	95	116	64	65	72	76	81
	2	78	83	86	99	119	66	69	74	80	83
	3	84	88	92	103	124	70	73	77	82	85
	4	87	93	95	106	128	72	78	81	85	89
4	1	77	81	86	99	118	76	78	83	88	92
	2	81	86	93	103	121	79	83	87	91	95
	3	87	92	100	106	126	80	84	88	93	97
	4	90	94	103	111	132	84	86	91	94	100

Table 19-7 illustrates typical collision and comprehensive premiums. Note that these rates are listed according to model class (type of vehicle—compact, luxury, truck, or van), vehicle age, territory (where driven), and the amount of the deductible.

TABLE 19-7 Motor Vehicle Insurance Annual Premiums—Collision and Comprehensive Rates

		Territories 1 & 2				Territories 3 & 4			
		Collision		Comprehensive		Collision		Comprehensive	
Model Class	Vehicle Age	$250 Deductible	$500 Deductible	Full Coverage	$100 Deductible	$250 Deductible	$500 Deductible	Full Coverage	$100 Deductible
A–G	0–1	$89	$81	$63	$59	$95	$88	$67	$61
	2–3	87	79	60	57	93	84	63	58
	4–5	86	77	58	54	89	81	60	57
	6+	84	76	55	50	86	78	57	52
H–L	0–1	96	92	78	71	104	95	83	75
	2–3	93	89	76	68	101	90	80	72
	4–5	89	85	74	66	96	87	78	68
	6+	86	81	70	64	92	84	74	66
M–R	0–1	108	104	86	83	112	106	91	88
	2–3	104	101	83	79	109	104	88	82
	4–5	100	98	79	75	104	101	84	77
	6+	94	90	75	71	100	96	80	74
S–Z	0–1	120	115	111	108	124	116	119	113
	2–3	116	112	106	104	121	114	115	109
	4–5	111	107	101	99	116	110	111	106
	6+	108	103	98	96	111	107	108	101

rating factors Multiples of the base rates for motor vehicles; used by insurance companies to adjust premiums upward (factors greater than 1) or downward (factors less than 1) depending on the amount of risk involved in the coverage.

Insurance companies often adjust premiums upward or downward by the use of **rating factors**, which are multiples of the base rates found in the tables. For example, if a vehicle is used for business purposes, the risk of an accident is increased; therefore, a rating factor of, say, 1.5 might be applied to the base rate to adjust for this risk. A $200 base-rate premium would increase to $300, $200 times the rating factor of 1.5. However, a vehicle driven less than 3 miles to work each way would have less chance of having an accident and might have a rating factor of .9 to lower the rate.

STEPS TO CALCULATE TYPICAL MOTOR VEHICLE INSURANCE PREMIUMS

STEP 1. Use Table 19-6 to find the appropriate base premiums for bodily injury and property damage.

STEP 2. Use Table 19-7 to find the appropriate base premiums for collision and comprehensive.

STEP 3. Add all the individual premiums to find the total base premium.

STEP 4. Multiply the total base premium by the rating factor, if any.

Total annual premium = Total base premium × Rating factor

EXAMPLE9 CALCULATING MOTOR VEHICLE PREMIUMS

Michelle Hiland wants to purchase a motor vehicle insurance policy with bodily injury and property damage coverage in the amounts of 25/50/25. In addition, she wants collision coverage with $500 deductible and comprehensive with no deductible. Michelle is in driver classification 3 and lives in territory 1. Her vehicle, a Toyota Prius, is in model class P and is 3 years old. Because she has taken driver training classes, Michelle qualifies for a .95 rating factor. As Michelle's insurance agent, calculate her total annual premium.

▶SOLUTIONSTRATEGY

Step 1. From Table 19-6, we find the bodily injury premium to be $84 and the property damage premium to be $58.

Step 2. From Table 19-7, we find collision to be $101 and comprehensive to be $83.

Step 3. Total base premium = Bodily injury + Property damage + Collision + Comprehensive
Total base premium = 84 + 58 + 101 + 83 = $326

Step 4. Total annual premium = Total base premium × Rating factor
Total annual premium = 326 × .95 = $309.70

▶TRYITEXERCISE 9

Jeff Wasserman, owner of High Performance Racing Equipment, wants to purchase truck insurance with bodily injury and property damage coverage in the amounts of 100/300/100. Jeff also wants $250 deductible collision and $100 deductible comprehensive. He is in driver classification 4 and lives in territory 3. His vehicle, a Ford F-150, is in model class F and is 4 years old. Because Jeff uses his truck to make trackside calls and haul cars to his shop, the insurance company has assigned a 2.3 rating factor to his policy. What is Jeff's total annual premium?

CHECK YOUR ANSWER WITH THE SOLUTION ON PAGE 667.

IN THE Business World

Many insurance companies give money-saving *rating factor* discounts to students who have good grade point averages, usually over 3.0 out of 4.0, or safe-driving records—without tickets or accidents.

COMPUTING THE COMPENSATION DUE FOLLOWING AN ACCIDENT

19-9

When the insured is involved in a motor vehicle accident in which he or she is at fault, his or her insurance company must pay out the claims resulting from that accident. Any amounts of bodily injury or property damage that exceed the limits of the policy coverage are the responsibility of the insured.

EXAMPLE10 CALCULATING ACCIDENT COMPENSATION

Bill Strickland has motor vehicle insurance in the following amounts: liability, 15/30/5; $500 deductible collision; and $100 deductible comprehensive. Recently, Bill was at fault in an accident in which his van hit a car stopped at a traffic light. Two individuals in the other vehicle, Angel and Martha Diaz, were injured. Angel's bodily injuries amounted to $6,300, whereas Martha's more serious injuries totaled $18,400. In addition, their car sustained $6,250 in damages. Although Bill was not physically injured, the damage to his van amounted to $4,788.

a. How much will the insurance company have to pay and to whom?
b. What part of the settlement will be Bill's responsibility?

▶SOLUTIONSTRATEGY

Liability Portion:

Bill's liability coverage is limited to $15,000 per person. The insurance company will pay the $6,300 for Angel's injuries; however, Bill is responsible for Martha's expenses above the limit.

$18,400	Martha's medical expenses
−15,000	Insurance limit—bodily injury
$3,400	Bill's responsibility

Property Damage Portion:

The property damage limit of $5,000 is not sufficient to cover the damage to Angel's car. Bill will have to pay the portion above the limit.

$6,250	Angel's car repairs
−5,000	Insurance limit—property damage
$1,250	Bill's responsibility

The damage to Bill's van will be paid by the insurance company, except for the $500 deductible.

$4,788	Bill's van repairs
−500	Deductible
$4,288	Insurance company responsibility

▶ TRYITEXERCISE 10

Jody Burnett has automobile liability insurance in the amount of 25/50/10 and carries $250 deductible collision and full-coverage comprehensive. Recently, Jody was at fault in an accident in which her Nissan went out of control on a rainy day and hit two cars, a fence, and the side of a house. The first car, a Lexus, had $8,240 in damages. The second car, a Ford Taurus, sustained damages of $2,540. The repairs to Jody's car amounted to $3,542. In addition, the fence repairs came to $880 and the house damages were estimated at $5,320.

a. How much will the insurance company have to pay and to whom?

b. What part of the settlement will be Jody's responsibility?

CHECK YOUR ANSWERS WITH THE SOLUTIONS ON PAGE 667.

SECTION III 19 REVIEW EXERCISES

As an insurance agent, calculate the annual premium for the following clients.

Name	Territory	Driver Class	Bodily Injury	Property Damage	Model Class	Vehicle Age	Comprehensive Deductible	Collision Deductible	Rating Factor	Annual Premium
1. Schwartz	2	4	50/100	25	J	3	$100	$250	None	$343.00
2. Mager	1	2	10/20	10	R	1	Full Coverage	$500	1.5	
3. Almas	3	1	25/50	5	U	5	Full Coverage	$250	3.0	
4. Denner	2	3	100/300	25	C	4	$100	$250	None	
5. Nadler	4	2	50/100	100	H	2	Full Coverage	$500	1.7	
6. Manners	1	4	15/30	50	M	3	$100	$250	2.5	
7. Hale	2	1	10/20	10	Q	6	$100	$250	3.9	
8. Coll	3	3	100/300	100	Z	1	Full Coverage	$500	None	

 9. Rick Clinton wants to purchase an automobile insurance policy with bodily injury and property damage coverage in the amounts of 50/100/50. In addition, he wants collision coverage with $250 deductible and comprehensive with no deductible. Rick is in driver classification 4 and lives in territory 3. His vehicle, a Buick Regal, is in model class B and is 1 year old. Rick has had two accidents and one ticket in the past 12 months and is therefore considered to be a high risk. Consequently, the insurance company has assigned a rating factor of 4.0 to his policy. As Rick's automobile insurance agent, calculate the total annual premium for his policy.

 10. Howard Marshall's Corvette was hit by a palm tree during a hurricane. The damage was estimated at $1,544. If Howard carried $250 deductible collision and $100 deductible comprehensive, how much of the damages does the insurance company have to pay?

11. Ben Hoffman has motor vehicle liability insurance in the amount of 50/100/50 and carries $250 deductible collision coverage and full-coverage comprehensive. Recently, he was at fault in an accident in which his camper hit a bus. Five individuals were injured on the bus and were awarded the following settlements by the courts: Hart, $13,500; Black, $11,700; Garner, $4,140; Williams, $57,800; and Morgan, $3,590. The damage to the bus was $12,230, and Ben's camper sustained $3,780 in damages.

   a. How much will the insurance company have to pay and to whom?

   b. What part of the settlement will be Ben's responsibility?

BUSINESS DECISION: INSURING THE FLEET

12. The Flamingo Cab Company of Cougar Creek is interested in purchasing $250 deductible collision insurance and full-coverage comprehensive insurance to cover its fleet of 10 taxicabs. As a requirement for the job, all drivers already carry their own liability coverage in the amount of 100/300/100. Cougar Creek is rated as territory 2. Five of the cabs are 4-year-old Checker Towncars, model class Y. Three of them are 2-year-old Chrysler station wagons, model class R. The remaining two are new Buick sedans, model class C. Because the vehicles are on the road almost 24 hours a day, they are considered to be very high risk and carry a rating factor of 5.2. They are, however, subject to an 18% multi-vehicle fleet discount.

   a. As the insurance agent for Flamingo Cabs, calculate the total annual premium for the fleet.

   b. When the owner saw your rate quote, he exclaimed, "Too expensive! How can I save some money on this insurance?" At that point, you suggested changing the coverage to $500 deductible collision and $100 deductible comprehensive. How much can you save Flamingo by using the new coverage?

CHAPTER
19

CHAPTER FORMULAS

Life Insurance

$$\text{Number of } \$1,000 = \frac{\text{Face value of policy}}{1,000}$$

$$\text{Annual premium} = \text{Number of } \$1,000 \times \text{Rate per } \$1,000$$

$$\text{Premium other than annual} = \text{Annual premium} \times \text{Premium factor}$$

$$\text{Income shortfall} = \text{Total living expenses} - \text{Total income}$$

$$\text{Insurance needed} = \frac{\text{Income shortfall}}{\text{Prevailing interest rate}}$$

Property Insurance

$$\text{Total annual fire premium} = \text{Building premium} + \text{Contents premium}$$

$$\text{Short-rate premium} = \text{Annual premium} \times \text{Short-rate}$$

$$\text{Short-rate refund} = \text{Annual premium} - \text{Short-rate premium}$$

$$\text{Regular refund} = \text{Annual premium} - \text{Premium for period}$$

$$\text{Coverage ratio} = \frac{\text{Insurance carried}}{\text{Insurance required}}$$

$$\text{Insurance required} = \text{Replacement value of property} \times \text{Coinsurance percent}$$

$$\text{Amount of loss paid by insurance} = \frac{\text{Insurance carried}}{\text{Insurance required}} \times \text{Amount of loss}$$

$$\text{Carrier's percent of total coverage} = \frac{\text{Amount of carrier's policy}}{\text{Total amount of insurance}}$$

$$\text{Carrier's share of loss} = \text{Amount of loss} \times \text{Carrier's percent of total coverage}$$

CHAPTER SUMMARY

Section I: Life Insurance

Topic	Important Concepts	Illustrative Examples
Understanding Life Insurance and Calculating Typical Premiums for Various Types of Policies **Performance Objective 19-1, Page 642**	Life insurance guarantees a specified sum of money to the surviving beneficiaries upon the death of the insured. It is purchased in increments of $1,000. Calculating premiums: 1. Calculate the number of $1,000 of insurance desired by dividing the face value of the policy by $1,000. 2. Locate the appropriate premium rate per $1,000 in Table 19-1. 3. Calculate the total annual premium by multiplying the number of $1,000 by the Table 19-1 rate. 4. For premiums other than annual, multiply the annual premium by the appropriate Table 19-2 premium factor.	Chelsea Anderson is 20 years old. She is interested in purchasing a 20-payment life insurance policy with a face value of $25,000. Calculate her annual and monthly premium. $\text{Number of } \$1,000 = \dfrac{25,000}{1,000} = 25$ Table 19-1 rate = $21.50 Annual premium = $25 \times 21.50 = \underline{\$537.50}$ Monthly premium = $537.50 \times 9\% = \underline{\$48.38}$

Section I (continued)

Topic	Important Concepts	Illustrative Examples
Calculating the Value of Various Nonforfeiture Options **Performance Objective 19-2, Page 645**	Life insurance policies with accumulated cash value may be converted to one of three nonforfeiture options. Use Table 19-3 and the number of $1,000 of insurance to determine the value of each option. Option 1—Take the cash value of the policy and cancel the insurance coverage. Option 2—Reduced, paid-up amount of the same insurance. Option 3—Term policy for a certain number of years and days, with the same face value as the original policy.	Betty Price, 30 years old, purchased a $50,000 whole life insurance policy at age 20. What is the value of her nonforfeiture options? Number of $1,000 = $\dfrac{50,000}{1,000}$ = 50 Option 1: 50 × $98 = $\underline{\$4,900\ Cash}$ Option 2: 50 × $186 = $\underline{\$9,300\ Reduced\ Paid\text{-}Up\ Insurance}$ Option 3: $\underline{17\ years,\ 54\ days\ Term\ Policy}$
Calculating the Amount of Life Insurance Needed to Cover Dependents' Income Shortfall **Performance Objective 19-3, Page 647**	When one of the wage earners in a household dies, the annual living expenses of the dependents may exceed the annual income. This difference is known as the income shortfall. To calculate the amount of insurance needed to cover the shortfall, use Insurance needed = $\dfrac{\text{Income shortfall}}{\text{Prevailing interest rate}}$	With a prevailing interest rate of 5%, how much life insurance will be needed to cover dependents' income shortfall if the annual living expenses amount to $37,600 and the total income is $21,200? Income shortfall = 37,600 − 21,200 = $\underline{\$16,400}$ Insurance needed at 5% = $\dfrac{16,400}{.05}$ = $\underline{\$328,000}$

Section II: Property Insurance

Topic	Important Concepts	Illustrative Examples
Understanding Property Insurance and Calculating Typical Fire Insurance Premiums **Performance Objective 19-4, Page 650**	Fire insurance premiums are based on type of construction, location of the property, and availability of fire protection. Fire insurance premiums are quoted per $100 of coverage, with buildings and contents listed separately. Use Table 19-4 to calculate fire insurance premiums: **Premium = Number of $100 × Table rate**	What is the total annual fire insurance premium on a building valued at $120,000 with structural class C and area rating 3 and contents valued at $400,000? Building: 1,200 × .69 = $828 Contents: 4,000 × .77 = $\underline{\$3,080}$ Total annual fire premium = 828 + 3,080 = $\underline{\$3,908}$

Calculating Premiums for Short-Term Policies and the Refunds Due on Canceled Policies
 	
Performance Objective 19-5, Page 652
	Fire policies for less than 1 year are known as short-rate. Use Table 19-5 for these policies.
	
	a. Short-rate refund
	(Policy canceled by insured):
	
	Short-rate premium =
	  Annual premium × Table factor
	Short-rate refund =
	  Annual premium − Short-rate premium
	
	b. Regular refund
	(Policy canceled by insurance company):
	
	Premium for time in force =
	  Annual premium × $\dfrac{\text{Months in force}}{12}$
	Regular refund = Annual premium −
	  Premium for time in force
		The Evergreen Company has property insurance with State Farm. The annual premium is $3,000.
		
		a. If Evergreen cancels the policy after 2 months, what is the short-rate refund?
		
		b. If State Farm cancels the policy after 2 months, what is the regular refund?
		
		a. Short-rate refund
		Short-rate premium = 3,000 × 30% = $\underline{\$900}$
		
		Short-rate refund = 3,000 − 900 = $\underline{\$2,100}$
		
		b. Regular refund
		
		Time in force premium = 3,000 × $\dfrac{2}{12}$ = $\underline{\$500}$
		
		Regular refund = 3,000 − 500 = $\underline{\$2,500}$

Understanding Coinsurance and Computing Compensation Due in the Event of a Loss
 	
Performance Objective 19-6, Page 654
	A coinsurance clause stipulates the minimum amount of coverage required for a claim to be paid in full. If less than the coinsurance requirement is carried, the payout is proportionately less.
	
	Amount of insurance required
	  = Replacement value × Coinsurance %
	
	Amount of loss paid =
	  $\dfrac{\text{Insurance carried}}{\text{Insurance required}}$ × Amount of loss
		Metro Holdings, Inc., has a $150,000 fire insurance policy on a property valued at $250,000. If the policy has an 80% coinsurance clause, how much would be paid in the event of a $50,000 fire?
		
		Insurance required = 250,000 × 80% = $200,000
		
		Amount of loss paid =
		$\dfrac{150,000}{200,000}$ × 50,000 = $\underline{\$37,500}$

Section II (continued)

Topic	Important Concepts	Illustrative Examples
Determining Each Company's Share of a Loss When Liability Is Divided among Multiple Carriers **Performance Objective 19-7, Page 655**	When more than one insurance company covers a piece of property, the property has multiple carriers. In the event of a claim, each company is responsible for its portion of the total insurance carried. Carrier's % of total $= \dfrac{\text{Amount of carrier's policy}}{\text{Total insurance}}$ Carrier's share = Amount of loss × Carrier's %	Lorenzo's Italian Market has multiple carrier fire insurance on its property as follows: Southwest Mutual .... $300,000 Travelers .... 100,000 　　　　　　Total .... $400,000 Assuming that all coinsurance requirements have been met, how much will each carrier be responsible for in the event of a $20,000 fire? Southwest Mutual: $\dfrac{300{,}000}{400{,}000} \times 20{,}000 = \$15{,}000$ Travelers: $\dfrac{100{,}000}{400{,}000} \times 20{,}000 = \$5{,}000$

Section III: Motor Vehicle Insurance

Topic	Important Concepts	Illustrative Examples
Understanding Motor Vehicle Insurance and Calculating Typical Premiums **Performance Objective 19-8, Page 658**	Motor vehicle insurance is divided into three main categories: Liability—Covers bodily injury and property damage to others. Use Table 19-6 for these rates. Collision—Covers damage to the insured's vehicle from an auto accident. Use Table 19-7. Comprehensive—Covers damage to the insured's vehicle from fire, wind, water, vandalism, theft, and so on. Use Table 19-7. Rates may be adjusted up or down by multiplying the total table rate by a rating factor.	Casey Roberts wants auto liability coverage of 25/50/25, $250 deductible collision, and $100 deductible comprehensive. She is in driver class 2 and lives in territory 3. Her vehicle, a new SL 500, is in model class L and has a sports car rating factor of 1.7. What is Casey's total auto premium? $86　Bodily injury　　Table 19-6 　74　Property damage　Table 19-6 104　Collision　　　　Table 19-7 + 75　Comprehensive　Table 19-7 $339　Total base × 1.7　Rating factor $576.30　Total premium
Computing the Compensation Due Following an Accident **Performance Objective 19-9, Page 661**	When the policyholder is at fault in an accident, his or her insurance company is responsible for all settlements up to the limits and deductibles of the policy. Any settlement amounts greater than the policy coverage are the responsibility of the insured.	Warner Bouton has auto liability coverage of 50/100/50, no deductible comprehensive, and $250 deductible collision. Recently, Warner ran a red light and broadsided Sylvia Norton's car. 　In the court settlement, Sylvia was awarded $75,000 for bodily injury and $14,500 in property damages. Warner's car sustained $7,500 in damages. How much is the insurance company responsible for paying? 　How much of the settlement is Warner's responsibility? Liability: 　Warner's policy limit for bodily injury liability is $50,000. $75,000　Court settlement −50,000　Paid by insurance $25,000　Paid by Warner The policy limit for property damage is $50,000; therefore, the insurance company will pay the full $14,500. Collision: $7,500　Collision damage − 250　Deductible $7,250　Paid by insurance

TRY IT: EXERCISE SOLUTIONS FOR CHAPTER 19

1. Number of $1,000 = $\dfrac{\text{Face value of policy}}{1,000}$

Number of $1,000 = $\dfrac{75,000}{1000} = 75$

Table 19-1 rate = $4.92 per $1,000

Annual premium = Number of $1,000 × Rate per $1,000
Annual premium = 75 × 4.92 = $369

Quarterly premium = Annual premium × Quarterly factor
Quarterly premium = 369 × .26 = $95.94

Total payment = Quarterly payment × 4 payments
Total payment = 95.94 × 4 = $383.76
Jason will pay $14.76 (383.76 − 369) more if paid quarterly.

2. Number of $1,000 = $\dfrac{\text{Face value of policy}}{1,000} = \dfrac{100,000}{1,000} = 100$

Option 1:
Cash Value = 100 × 191 = $19,100

Option 2:
Reduced Paid-Up Insurance = 100 × 496 = $49,600

Option 3:
Extended Term Insurance = 30 years, 206 days

3. Total income = 38,000 + 5,000 = $43,000

Income shortfall = Total expenses − Total income
Income shortfall = 54,000 − 43,000 = $11,000

Insurance needed = $\dfrac{\text{Shortfall}}{\text{Prevailing rate}}$

Insurance needed = $\dfrac{11,000}{.05}$ = $220,000

4. From Table 19-4
  Building: .38
  Contents: .42

Building = $\dfrac{\text{Amount of coverage}}{100} = \dfrac{420,000}{100} = 4,200$

Contents = $\dfrac{\text{Amount of coverage}}{100} = \dfrac{685,000}{100} = 6,850$

Building = Number of $100 × Rate = 4,200 × .38 = $1,596
Contents = Number of $100 × Rate = 6,850 × .42 = $2,877

Total premium = Building + Contents
Total premium = 1,596 + 2,877 = $4,473

5. From Table 19-5, 8 months = 80%
Short-rate premium = Annual premium × Short-rate
Short-rate premium = 850 × .8 = $680
Short-rate refund = Annual premium − Short-rate premium
Short-rate refund = 850 − 680 = $170

6. Premium for period = Annual premium × $\dfrac{\text{Months in force}}{12}$

Premium for period = $850 \times \dfrac{8}{12}$ = $566.67

Regular refund = Annual premium − Premium for period
Regular refund = 850.00 − 566.67 = $283.33

7. Insurance required = Value of property × Coinsurance percent
Insurance required = 850,000 × .7 = $595,000

Amount of loss paid = $\dfrac{\text{Insurance carried}}{\text{Insurance required}}$ × Loss

Amount of loss paid = $\dfrac{400,000}{595,000}$ × 325,000 = $218,487.40

8. Carrier's percent of total = $\dfrac{\text{Amount of carrier's policy}}{\text{Total amount of insurance}}$

Aetna = $\dfrac{20,000}{125,000} = 16\%$

USF&G = $\dfrac{45,000}{125,000} = 36\%$

John Hancock = $\dfrac{60,000}{125,000} = 48\%$

Carrier's share of loss = Amount of loss × Carrier's percent
  Aetna = 16,800 × .16 = $2,688
  SF&G = 16,800 × .36 = $6,048
John Hancock = 16,800 × .48 = $8,064

9. Base premium = Bodily injury + Property damage + Collision + Comprehensive
Base premium = 128 + 89 + 89 + 57 = $363
Total annual premium = Base premium × Rating factor
Total annual premium = 363 × 2.3 = $834.90

10.

	a. Insurance Pays	
$10,000	Property damage	
+ 3,292	Jody's car *less* deductible	
$13,292	Total insurance responsibility	

	b. Jody Pays	
$8,240	Lexus	
2,540	Taurus	
880	Fence	
+ 5,320	House	
16,980	Total property damage	
−10,000	Insurance	
$6,980	Jody's portion	
+ 250	Collision deductible	
$7,230	Jody's responsibility	

CONCEPT REVIEW

1. A mechanism for reducing financial risk and spreading financial loss due to unexpected events is known as _____. The document stipulating the terms of this agreement is known as a(n) _____. (19-1)

2. The amount of protection provided by an insurance policy is known as the _____ value. The amount paid to purchase the protection is known as the _____. The _____ is the person or institution to whom the proceeds of the policy are paid in the event that a loss occurs. (19-1)

3. Name the two major categories of life insurance. (19-1)

4. The _____ factor is a small surcharge added to the cost of insurance policies when the insured chooses to pay the premiums more frequently than annually. (19-1)

5. The options available to a policyholder upon termination of a permanent life insurance policy with accumulated cash value are known as the _____ options. List these three options. (19-2)

6. The difference between the total living expenses and the total income of a family in the event of the death of the insured is known as the income _____ . Write the formula used to calculate the amount of life insurance needed to cover this difference. (19-3)

7. List four perils covered by property insurance. (19-4)

8. List the four factors used to determine the fire insurance rates on a building. (19-4)

9. The premium charged when a policy is canceled by the insured or is written for less than one year is known as the _____. (19-5)

10. The clause in a property insurance policy stipulating the minimum amount of coverage required for a claim to be paid in full is known as the _____ clause. (19-6)

11. Write the coverage ratio formula used in calculating property insurance rates. (19-6)

12. A situation in which a business is covered by fire insurance policies from more than one company at the same time is known as _____ carriers. (19-7)

13. In motor vehicle insurance, _____ covers bodily injury to other persons and damages to the property of others resulting from the insured's negligence; _____ covers accident damage to the insured's vehicle; and _____ covers the insured's vehicle for damage caused by fire, wind, water, theft, vandalism, and other perils. (19-8, 19-9)

14. In motor vehicle insurance, companies often use _____ factors to adjust premiums upward or downward depending on the amount of the risk involved in the coverage. (19-8, 19-9)

ASSESSMENT TEST

Calculate the annual, semiannual, quarterly, and monthly premiums for the following life insurance policies.

	Face Value of Policy	Sex and Age of Insured	Type of Policy	Annual Premium	Semiannual Premium	Quarterly Premium	Monthly Premium
1.	$80,000	Male, 29	20-Payment Life	_____	_____	_____	_____
2.	$55,000	Female, 21	20-Year Endowment	_____	_____	_____	_____
3.	$38,000	Female, 40	5-Year Term	_____	_____	_____	_____
4.	$175,000	Male, 30	Whole Life	_____	_____	_____	_____

EXCEL 2

Calculate the value of the nonforfeiture options for the following life insurance policies.

	Face Value of Policy	Years in Force	Type of Policy	Cash Value	Reduced Paid-Up Insurance	Extended Term Years	Extended Term Days
5.	$130,000	15	Whole Life	_____	_____	_____	_____
6.	$60,000	5	20-Payment Life	_____	_____	_____	_____

7. Tommy Cook is 19 years old and is interested in purchasing a whole life insurance policy with a face value of $80,000.

   a. Calculate the annual insurance premium for this policy.

   b. Calculate the monthly insurance premiums.

   c. How much more will Tommy pay per year if he chooses monthly payments?

8. Mary Hall purchased a $45,000 20-year endowment life insurance policy when she was 20 years old. She is now 35 years old and wants to look into her nonforfeiture options. As her insurance agent, calculate the value of Mary's three options.

   a. Option 1   **b.** Option 2

   c. Option 3

9. Joe Moutran is evaluating his life insurance needs. His family's total annual living expenses are $54,500. Gloria, his wife, earns a salary of $28,900 per year. If the prevailing interest rate is 4%, how much life insurance should Joe purchase to cover his dependents' income shortfall in the event of his death?

Calculate the building, contents, and total property insurance premiums for the following property insurance policies.

	Area Rating	Structural Class	Building Value	Building Premium	Contents Value	Contents Premium	Total Premium
10.	4	B	$47,000	_____	$93,000	_____	_____
11.	2	A	$125,000	_____	$160,000	_____	_____
12.	3	C	$980,000	_____	$1,500,000	_____	_____

Calculate the short-term premium and refund for the following policies.

	Annual Premium	Canceled After	Canceled By	Short-Term Premium	Refund
13.	$260	8 months	insurance company	_____	_____
14.	$720	15 days	insured	_____	_____

Calculate the amount to be paid by the insurance company for each of the following claims.

	Replacement Value of Building	Face Value of Policy	Coinsurance Clause (%)	Amount of Loss	Amount of Loss Insurance Company Will Pay
15.	$260,000	$105,000	80	$12,000	_____
16.	$490,000	$450,000	90	$80,000	_____

17. You are the insurance agent for Fandango Fashions, a company that imports men's and women's clothing from Europe and the Far East. The owner, Ron Harris, wants you to give him a quote on the total annual premium for property insurance on a new warehouse and showroom facility in the amount of $320,000. The building is structural classification B and area rating 4. In addition, Ron will require contents insurance in the amount of $1,200,000. What is the amount of the quote you will give Ron for the total annual premium?

CHAPTER 19

18. "Movers of the Stars" has been contracted by Premier Events, Inc., to transport the stage and sound equipment for a 4-month tour by Lady Gaga. The moving company purchased property insurance to cover this valuable equipment for an annual premium of $12,500. What is the short-rate premium due for this coverage?

19. La Belle Beauty Supply had property valued at $750,000 and insured for $600,000. The fire insurance policy contained an 80% coinsurance clause. One evening an electrical short circuit caused a $153,000 fire. How much of the damages will be paid by the insurance company?

20. Pinnacle Manufacturing has multiple carrier fire insurance coverage on its plant and equipment in the amount of $2,960,000 as follows:

Kemper	$1,350,000	policy
Metropolitan	921,000	policy
The Hartford	689,000	policy
	$2,960,000	total coverage

Assuming that all coinsurance clause stipulations have been met, how much would each carrier be responsible for in the event of a $430,000 fire? Round to the nearest whole percent before using them in your final calculations.

a. Kemper   b. Metropolitan   c. The Hartford

As an insurance agent, calculate the annual premium for the following clients.

	Name	Territory	Driver Class	Bodily Injury	Property Damage	Model Class	Vehicle Age	Comprehensive Deductible	Collision Deductible	Rating Factor	Annual Premium
21.	Reeves	3	2	50/100	25	X	1	$100	$500	0.9	_____
22.	Chang	1	1	10/20	5	Q	4	Full Cov.	$250	2.2	_____
23.	Lerner	2	4	100/300	100	F	7	$100	$500	1.7	_____

24. Karen Doyle wants to purchase an automobile insurance policy with bodily injury and property damage coverage in the amounts of 25/50/25. In addition, she wants collision coverage with $250 deductible and comprehensive with $100 deductible. Karen is in driver classification 2 and lives in territory 3. Her vehicle, a new Ford Mustang, is in model class B. Because the car has an airbag, an alarm, and antilock brakes, the insurance company has assigned a rating factor of .95 to the policy. As her auto insurance agent, calculate Karen's total annual premium.

25. Sid King has automobile liability insurance in the amount of 50/100/50. He also carries $250 deductible collision and full comprehensive coverage. Recently, he was at fault in an accident in which his car went out of control in the rain and struck four pedestrians. In an out-of-court settlement, they were awarded the following: Goya, $45,000; Truman, $68,000; Copeland, $16,000; and Kelly, $11,000. Damage to Sid's car amounted to $3,900.

a. How much will the insurance company pay and to whom?

b. What part of the settlement will be Sid's responsibility?

How crashes affect auto premiums
Average annual auto insurance premiums rise with each at-fault traffic accident:

No accidents $1,387
One $1,689
Two $2,041
Three $2,348
Four $2,806

Source: Insurance.com study
By Ann Carey and Keith Simmons, *USA Today*

BUSINESS DECISION: GROUP INSURANCE

CHAPTER 19

26. Many employers purchase group insurance on behalf of their employees. Under a group insurance plan, a master contract issued to the company provides life insurance, health insurance, or both for the employees who choose to participate. Most plans also provide coverage for dependents of employees. The two major benefits of group plans are lower premiums than individual insurance of the same coverage and no medical exams.

You are the owner of Imperial Products, Inc., a small manufacturing company with 250 employees. The company has just instituted a group health insurance plan for employees. Under the plan, the employees pay 30% of the premium and the company pays 70%. The insurance company reimburses 80% of all medical expenses over the deductible. The annual rates and deductibles from the insurance company are as follows:

	Annual Premium	Deductible
Employee with no dependents	$1,200	$300
Employee with one dependent	$1,400	$500
Employee with multiple dependents	$1,800	$800

a. If all 250 employees opt for the group health plan, what is the annual cost to the company assuming the following: 100 employees have no dependents, 80 employees have one dependent, and 70 employees have multiple dependents?

b. If your employees are paid biweekly, how much should be deducted from each paycheck for each of the three categories?

c. If Mert Wetstein, one of the employees, chooses the multiple dependent option and has a total of $3,400 in medical bills for the year, how much will be reimbursed by the insurance company?

COLLABORATIVE LEARNING ACTIVITY

Insurance for Sweetie Pie

As a team, you and your partners are going to start a hypothetical company called The Sweetie Pie Bakery, a company that makes and distributes pies, cakes, cookies, and doughnuts to restaurants and food stores in your area.

The company will have property and a building valued at $300,000, baking and production-line equipment valued at $400,000, office equipment and fixtures worth $200,000, and four delivery trucks valued at $45,000 each. The expected revenue is $50,000 per month. There will be 18 employees and 4 partners, including you.

Each team member is to consult with a different insurance agent to put together a "package" of business insurance coverage for Sweetie Pie, including property insurance, liability insurance, and business interruption insurance.

In addition, look into a health insurance program for the partners and the employees, as well as $500,000 "key man" life insurance for each partner.

a. Compare and contrast the various insurance packages quoted for Sweetie Pie.
b. Which insurance company came up with the best package? Why?
c. What other types of coverage did the insurance agents recommend?

PERFORMANCE OBJECTIVES

SECTION I **21** DATA INTERPRETATION AND PRESENTATION

INFORMATION, THE NAME OF THE GAME!

Statistical ideas and methods are used in almost every aspect of human activity, from the natural sciences to the social sciences. Statistics has special applications in such areas as medicine, psychology, education, engineering, and agriculture. In business, statistical methods are applied extensively in production, marketing, finance, and accounting.

Business statistics is the systematic process of collecting, interpreting, and presenting numerical data about business situations. In business, statistics is organized into two categories: descriptive statistics and statistical inference. **Descriptive statistics** deals with tabular, graphical, or numerical methods for organizing and summarizing information. Whereas **statistical inference** is the process of arriving at conclusions, predictions, forecasts, or estimates based on a sample drawn from the population of all data under consideration. For example, a company may contact a randomly selected sample of 250 customers and ask their opinion of a possible new product. From this sample, the company will try to infer information about the opinions of the entire population of prospective customers. In this chapter, we will concentrate on various types of descriptive statistical methods.

Business statistics starts with the collection of raw data concerning a particular business situation or question. For example, if management wants the next annual report to present a comparison chart of company sales and profit figures with current industry trends, two types of information are required. First are the company records of sales and profits. These data would be readily available from *internal* company sources. Most large corporations today use a vast array of computer systems to collect and store incredible amounts of information relating to all aspects of business activity. Management information systems are then used to deliver these data, upon request, in an electronic instant.

Information gathered from sources outside the firm, such as current industry statistics, is known as *external* data and is readily available from a variety of private and government publications. The federal government is by far the largest researcher and publisher of business data. The Departments of Commerce and Labor periodically publish information relating to all aspects of the economy and the country. Some of these publications are the *Statistical Abstract of the United States, Survey of Current Business, Monthly Labor Review, Federal Reserve Bulletin, Census of the United States*, and *Census of Business*.

Private statistical services such as Moody's Investors Service and Standard and Poor's offer a wealth of information for business decision making. Other private sources are periodicals such as the *Wall Street Journal, Fortune, Business Week, Forbes*, and *Money*, as well as hundreds of industry and trade publications, and websites.

Numerical data form the raw material on which analyses, forecasts, and managerial plans are based. In business, tables and charts are used extensively to summarize and display data in a clear and concise manner. In this section, you learn to read, interpret, and construct information from tables and charts.

business statistics The systematic process of collecting, interpreting, and presenting numerical data about business situations.

descriptive statistics Statistical procedures that deal with tabular, graphical, or numerical methods for organizing and summarizing information.

statistical inference The process of arriving at conclusions, predictions, forecasts, or estimates based on a sample drawn from the population of all data under consideration.

21-1 READING AND INTERPRETING INFORMATION FROM A TABLE

table A collection of related data arranged for ease of reference or comparison, usually in parallel columns with meaningful titles.

A **table** is a collection of related data arranged for ease of reference or comparison, usually in parallel columns with meaningful titles. Tables are a very useful tool in summarizing statistical data and are found everywhere in business. Once the data have been obtained from the table, they can be compared with other data by arithmetic or percentage analysis.

STEPS TO READING A TABLE

STEP 1. Scan the titles above the columns for the category of information being sought.

STEP 2. Look down the column for the specific fact required.

Table 21-1 shows the sales figures in dollars for Magnum Enterprises over a six-month period. Magnum manufactures and sells standard and deluxe computer components. Note that the table is divided into columns representing sales per month of each product type by territory.

TABLE 21-1 Magnum Enterprises Six-Month Sales Report

	January		February		March		April		May		June	
	Standard	**Deluxe**	**Standard**	**Deluxe**	**Standard**	**Deluxe**	**Standard**	**Deluxe**	**Standard**	**Deluxe**	**Standard**	**Deluxe**
Northwest	$123,200	$86,400	$115,800	$73,700	$133,400	$91,100	$136,700	$92,600	$112,900	$65,300	$135,000	$78,400
Northeast	$214,700	$121,300	$228,400	$133,100	$246,600	$164,800	$239,000	$153,200	$266,100	$185,000	$279,300	$190,100
Southwest	$88,300	$51,000	$72,100	$45,700	$97,700	$58,300	$104,000	$67,800	$125,000	$78,300	$130,400	$74,500
Southeast	$143,200	$88,700	$149,900	$91,300	$158,400	$94,500	$127,700	$70,300	$145,700	$79,400	$162,000	$88,600

Magnum Enterprises Six-Month Sales Report

EXAMPLE1 READING A TABLE

Use Table 21-1 to answer the following questions about Magnum Enterprises.

a. What were the sales of deluxe units in April in the Northeast?

b. What were the sales of standard units in May in the Southwest?

c. What were the total sales for February and March in the Southeast?

d. What months showed a decrease in sales of deluxe units in the Northwest?

e. How much more standard sales were there company-wide in June than in January?

f. What percent of the total sales in March were deluxe?

SOLUTIONSTRATEGY

Questions a, b, and d can be answered by inspection. Questions c, e, and f require numerical or percentage calculations.

a. Deluxe unit sales in April in the Northeast = $153,200

b. Standard unit sales in May in the Southwest = $125,000

c. Total sales in February and March in the Southeast:

$$149,900 + 91,300 + 158,400 + 94,500 = \$494,100$$

d. Decrease in sales of deluxe units in the Northwest occurred in February and May.

e. Standard sales in January = $569,400

Standard sales in June = $706,700

$$706,700 - 569,400 = \$137,300 \text{ more in June}$$

f. To solve this problem, we use the percentage formula Rate = Portion ÷ Base. In this case, the rate is the unknown, the total sales in March is the base, and the deluxe sales in March is the portion.

$$\text{Rate} = \frac{408,700}{1,044,800} = .3911 = 39.1\%$$

TRYITEXERCISE 1

Use Table 21-1 to answer the following questions about Magnum Enterprises.

a. What were the sales of standard units in February in the Northeast?

b. What were the sales of deluxe units in April in the Southeast?

c. What were the total sales for May and June in the Northwest?

d. What months showed an increase in sales of standard units in the Southwest?

e. How much more deluxe sales were there company-wide in May than in April?

f. What percent of the total sales in the Northwest were standard?

CHECK YOUR ANSWERS WITH THE SOLUTIONS ON PAGE 749.

21-2 READING AND CONSTRUCTING A LINE CHART

line chart A series of data points on a grid that are continuously connected by straight lines and that display a picture of selected data changing over a period of time.

x-axis The horizontal axis of a chart usually used to measure units of time such as days, weeks, months, or years.

y-axis The vertical axis of a chart usually used to measure the quantity or magnitude of something, such as sales dollars or production units. The y-axis is frequently used to measure the percentage of something.

Charts are used to display a picture of the relationships among selected data. A **line chart** shows data changing over a period of time. A single glance at a line chart gives the viewer a general idea of the direction, or trend, of the data: up, down, or up and down.

The horizontal axis, or *x*-axis, is used to measure units of time, such as days, weeks, months, or years, whereas the vertical axis, or *y*-axis, depicts magnitude, such as sales dollars or production units. Frequently, the y-axis is used to measure the percentage of something.

Line charts are actually a series of data points on a grid that are continuously connected by straight lines. They may contain a single line, representing the change of one variable such as interest rates, or they may contain multiple lines, representing the change of interrelated variables such as interest rates and stock prices or sales and profits.

IN THE Business World

Frequently, the word *graph* is used instead of *chart*. Graph is short for *graphic formula*—that is, a means of providing information graphically rather than in words. *Graph* is from the Greek *graphein*, meaning to draw.

STEPS FOR READING A LINE CHART

STEP 1. Scan either the *x*- or *y*-axis for the known variable: *x* for time, *y* for amount.

STEP 2. Draw a perpendicular line from that axis to the point where it intersects the chart.

STEP 3. Draw a line from that point perpendicular to the opposite axis.

STEP 4. The value of the other variable is read where the line intersects the opposite axis.

Exhibits 21-1 and 21-2 are an example of a single- and multiple-line chart, respectively.

EXHIBIT 21-1
Single-Line Chart

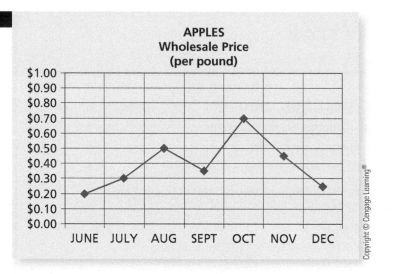

IN THE Business World

Tables illustrate specific data better than line charts do; however, line charts show relationships among data more clearly.

Frequently, in business presentations, tables and charts are used together, with the chart used to clarify or reinforce facts presented in the table.

EXHIBIT 21-2
Multiple-Line Chart

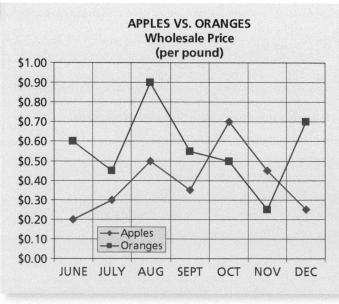

EXAMPLE 2   READING A LINE CHART

Use Exhibits 21-1 and 21-2 to answer the following questions.

a. In which month was the price of apples highest?

b. In which month was the price of apples higher—August or November?

c. How much lower was the price of apples in June compared with September?

d. Which fruit had a higher price in November—apples or oranges?

e. In which months was the price of apples higher than the price of oranges?

f. In August, how much lower was the price of apples than the price of oranges?

SOLUTIONSTRATEGY

a. In Exhibit 21-1, by inspection, we find the high point on the graph. This corresponds to October on the *x*-axis.

b. In Exhibit 21-1, look vertically from the *x*-axis at August ($0.50) and November ($0.45) to find that August had the higher price.

c. In Exhibit 21-1, find the values for June ($0.20) and September ($0.35) and then calculate the difference—$0.15 ($0.35 – $0.20).

d. In Exhibit 21-2, from November on the *x*-axis, look vertically to both lines to find that apples had the higher price.

e. In Exhibit 21-2, by inspection, we find that apples had a higher price in October and November.

f. In Exhibit 21-2, locate the August price for both apples ($0.50) and oranges ($0.90). Then calculate the difference between the two prices: $0.40 ($0.90 – $0.50).

TRYITEXERCISE 2

Use Exhibits 21-1 and 21-2 to answer the following questions.

a. In which month was the price of apples lowest?

b. In which month was the price of apples higher—July or December?

c. How much lower was the price of apples in November compared with August?

d. Which fruit had a lower price in July—apples or oranges?

e. In which months was the price of oranges higher than the price of apples?

f. In which month was the price differential between apples and oranges the greatest? How much?

CHECK YOUR ANSWERS WITH THE SOLUTIONS ON PAGE 750.

STEPS TO CONSTRUCT A LINE CHART

STEP 1. Evenly space and label the time variable on the *x*-axis.

STEP 2. Evenly space and label the amount variable on the *y*-axis.

STEP 3. Show each data point by placing a dot above the time period and across from the corresponding amount.

STEP 4. Connect the plotted points with straight lines to form the chart.

STEP 5. When multiple lines are displayed, they should be labeled or differentiated by various colors or line patterns.

EXAMPLE3   CONSTRUCTING A LINE CHART

You are the manager of Handy Hardware Stores, Inc. The company has one store in Centerville and one in Carson City. The following table shows the monthly sales figures in thousands of dollars for each store last year. From this information, construct a line chart of the total sales for each month.

Handy Hardware: Monthly Sales Report ($1,000s)

	Jan.	Feb.	Mar.	Apr.	May	June	July	Aug.	Sept.	Oct.	Nov.	Dec.
Centerville	16	18	24	21	15	13	17	18	16	23	24	20
Carson City	8	11	14	12	10	16	13	13	9	13	14	17
Total	24	29	38	33	25	29	30	31	25	36	38	37

►SOLUTIONSTRATEGY

For this chart, show the months on the *x*-axis and the sales on the *y*-axis. Use a range of 0 to 40 on the *y*-axis. Plot each month with a dot and connect all the dots with straight lines.

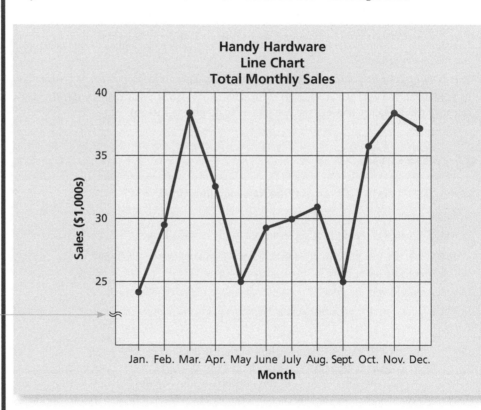

Learning Tip

Sometimes the *x*- or *y*-axis of a chart is "shortened" to better display the required scale. A pair of wavy lines (≈) intersecting the axis are used to indicate when this occurs.

►TRYITEXERCISE 3

The following data represent the audience statistics for a circus that performed in your town last week. Use the grid on the next page to draw a line chart of the total attendance for each day.

Circus Attendance

	Monday	Tuesday	Wednesday	Thursday	Friday	Saturday	Sunday
Adults	2,300	2,100	1,900	2,200	2,400	2,700	2,600
Children	3,300	2,600	2,400	1,900	2,700	3,100	3,600
Total	5,600	4,700	4,300	4,100	5,100	5,800	6,200

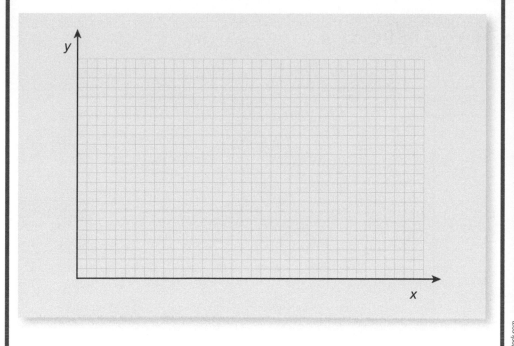

CHECK YOUR CHART WITH THE SOLUTION ON PAGE 750.

Statistical information is recorded and used in many different ways at sporting events, including measuring attendance and athletic performance.

EXAMPLE4   CONSTRUCTING A MULTIPLE-LINE CHART

From the Handy Hardware table on page 716, construct a multiple-line chart of the monthly sales for each of the stores. Show the Centerville store with a solid line and the Carson City store with a dashed line.

SOLUTIONSTRATEGY

As in the last example, the *x*-axis, time, will be months. The *y*-axis should range from 0 to 25 to include all the data.

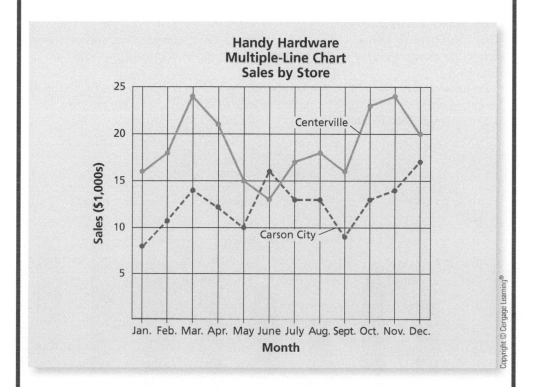

▶TRYITEXERCISE 4

From the Circus Attendance table on page 716, draw a multiple-line chart showing the number of adults and children attending the circus last week. Use a solid line for the adults and a dashed line for the children.

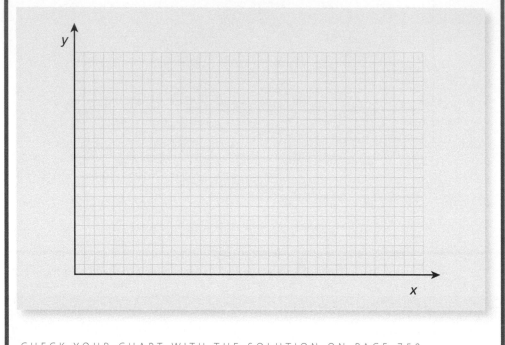

CHECK YOUR CHART WITH THE SOLUTION ON PAGE 750.

21-3 READING AND CONSTRUCTING A BAR CHART

bar charts Graphical presentations that represent quantities or percentages by the length of horizontal or vertical bars. These charts may or may not be based on the movement of time.

standard bar charts Bar charts that illustrate increases or decreases in magnitude of one variable.

comparative bar charts Bar charts used to illustrate the relationship between two or more similar variables.

Bar charts represent quantities or percentages by the length of horizontal or vertical bars. As with line charts, bar charts often illustrate increases or decreases in magnitude of a certain variable or the relationship between similar variables. Bar charts may or may not be based on the movement of time.

Bar charts are divided into three categories: standard, comparative, and component. **Standard bar charts** are used to illustrate the change in magnitude of one variable. (See Exhibit 21-3.)

Comparative bar charts are used to illustrate two or more related variables. The bars representing each variable should be shaded or colored differently to make the chart easy to read and interpret. (See Exhibit 21-4.)

EXHIBIT 21-3

Standard Bar Chart

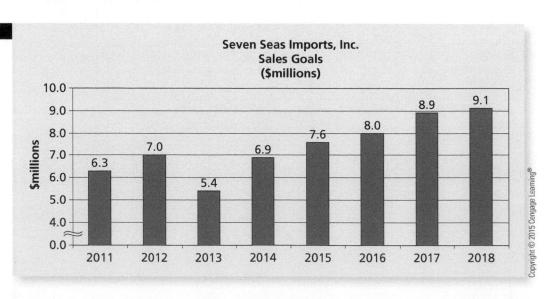

EXHIBIT 21-4 Comparative Bar Chart

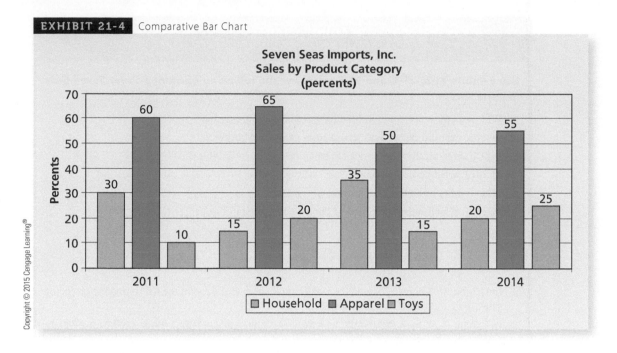

Component bar charts are used to illustrate parts of something that add to a total. Each bar is divided into the components that are stacked on top of each other and shaded or colored differently. (See Exhibit 21-5.)

component bar charts Bar charts used to illustrate the parts of something that add to a total; each bar is divided into the components stacked on top of each other and shaded or colored differently.

EXHIBIT 21-5

Component Bar Chart

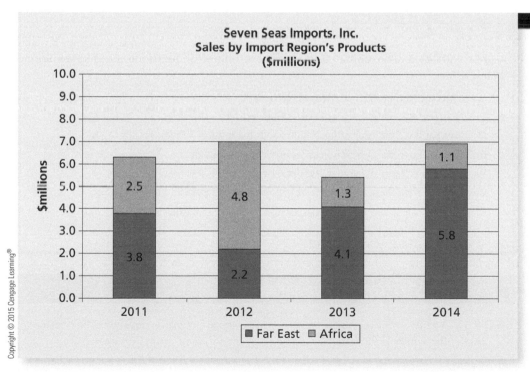

STEPS FOR READING A BAR CHART

STEP 1. Scan the *x*- or *y*-axis for a known variable.

STEP 2. Read the answer on the opposite axis directly across from the top of the appropriate bar.

EXAMPLE5   READING A BAR CHART

Use Exhibits 21-3, 21-4, and 21-5 to answer the following questions about Seven Seas Imports, Inc.

a. What was the sales goal for 2014 for Seven Seas Imports, Inc.

b. In what year did Seven Seas have a sales goal of $8.0 million?

c. Which three product categories are being compared in Exhibit 21-4?

d. In 2012, what percent of Seven Seas' sales were toys?

e. What are the two import regions for Seven Seas?

f. In 2011, which import regions had the greatest amount of sales?

SOLUTIONSTRATEGY

a. In Exhibit 21-3, locate 2014 on the *x*-axis and scan up to the top of the bar to find the projected sales, $6.9 million.

b. In Exhibit 21-3, locate $8.0 million on the *y*-axis and scan right until you reach the top of a bar. Look down to the *x*-axis for the answer, 2016.

c. In Exhibit 21-4, by inspection, we find the three product categories in the legend: household, apparel, and toys.

d. In Exhibit 21-4, locate 2012 on the *x*-axis. Then locate the "Toys" bar as indicated by the orange color to find the answer, 20%.

e. In Exhibit 21-5, by inspection, we find the two import regions: Far East and Africa.

f. In Exhibit 21-5, locate 2011 on the *x*-axis. Scan the bar to find that the greatest amount of sales were goods from the Far East as indicated by a larger portion of the bar represented by the dark purple color.

TRYITEXERCISE 5

Use Exhibits 21-3, 21-4, and 21-5 to answer the following questions about Seven Seas Imports, Inc.

a. What was the sales goal in 2012 for Seven Seas?

b. In which year was the sales goal lowest? How much?

c. In what year were the sales of household goods the lowest? What percent?

d. In 2014, what percent of Seven Seas' sales were from apparel?

e. Explain what is being illustrated in Exhibit 21-5.

f. In what year were the sales of Far East imports less than African imports?

CHECK YOUR ANSWERS WITH THE SOLUTIONS ON PAGE 751.

STEPS TO CONSTRUCT A BAR CHART

STEP 1. Evenly space and label the *x*-axis. The space between bars should be one-half the width of the bars.

STEP 2. Evenly space and label the *y*-axis. Be sure to include the full range of values needed to represent the variable. The lowest values should start at the bottom of the *y*-axis and increase upward.

STEP 3. Draw each bar up from the *x*-axis to the point opposite the *y*-axis that corresponds to its value.

STEP 4. For comparative and component bar charts, differentiate the bars by color or shading pattern. For complex presentations, provide a key or legend that shows which pattern or color represents each variable. This will help the reader interpret the chart.

Learning Tip

The steps shown here are used to construct charts with *vertical* bars. For charts with *horizontal* bars, lay out the bars on the *y*-axis and the magnitude variable on the *x*-axis.

EXAMPLE6 CONSTRUCTING A STANDARD BAR CHART

From the Handy Hardware sales report table on page 716, construct a standard bar chart of total sales for January through June.

SOLUTIONSTRATEGY

For this chart, the time variable, January through June, is shown on the *x*-axis. A range of 0 to 40 is used on the *y*-axis.

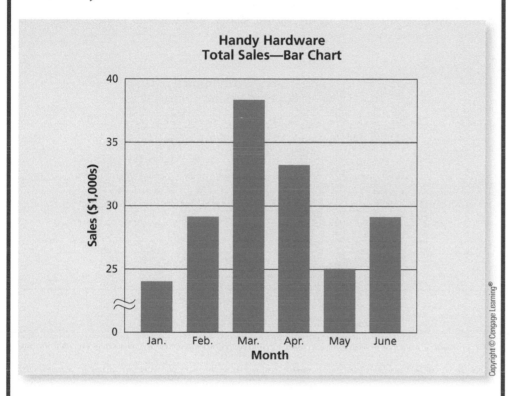

TRYITEXERCISE 6

From the table for Circus Attendance on page 716, use the following grid to construct a standard bar chart of the total attendance for each day.

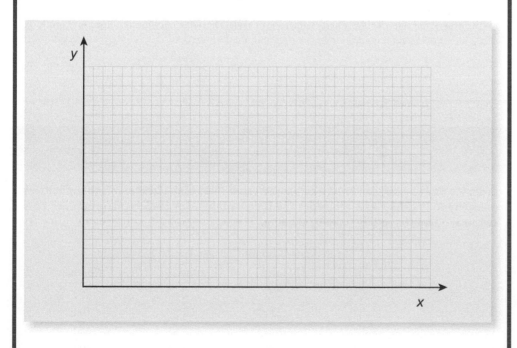

CHECK YOUR CHART WITH THE SOLUTION ON PAGE 751.

EXAMPLE7　CONSTRUCTING A COMPONENT BAR CHART

From the table for Circus Attendance on page 716, construct a component bar chart that displays the number of adults and children as components of each day's total audience. Plot the number of adults at the bottom of the bars in blue shading and the number of children stacked above the adults in green shading.

▶ SOLUTIONSTRATEGY

For this chart, the time variable, Monday through Sunday, is shown on the *x*-axis. A range of 0 to 7,000 is used on the *y*-axis.

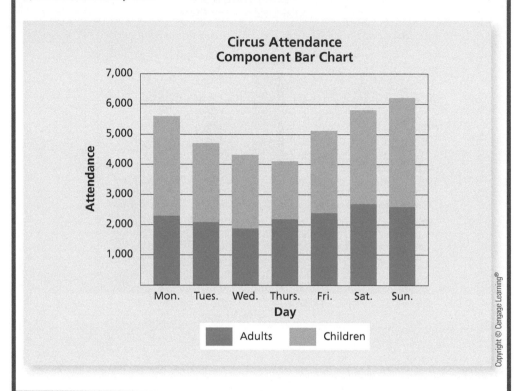

▶ TRYITEXERCISE 7

Refer to the Handy Hardware sales report on page 716. Use a separate sheet of graph paper to construct a component bar chart that displays the Centerville and the Carson City stores as components of the total monthly sales for July through December.

CHECK YOUR CHART WITH THE SOLUTION ON PAGE 751.

EXAMPLE8　CONSTRUCTING A COMPARATIVE BAR CHART

From the table below, construct a comparative bar chart of the freshman and sophomore enrollment. Let the *x*-axis represent the time variable. For each term, group the bars together and differentiate them by shading.

Interstate Business College: Annual Enrollment				
	Fall	Winter	Spring	Summer
Freshmen	1,800	1,400	1,350	850
Sophomores	1,200	1,200	1,150	700
Juniors	1,200	1,100	750	650
Seniors	850	700	500	400

Dollars AND Sense

Business presentation programs have replaced the use of pamphlets, handouts, flip charts, slides, and overhead transparencies with beautifully narrated presentations. These presentations use digital photography, high-definition video, and animated slide shows stored electronically on a computer. The content is delivered to a screen via a projector or is networked to an unlimited number of computers.

These programs can be used to enhance your business presentations. Some of the top presentation programs are PowerPoint with PowerPlugs, Flash, and Apple Keynote.

►SOLUTIONSTRATEGY

This chart is constructed the same way as the standard bar chart except that the variables being compared are drawn side by side. The space between the bars is one-half the width of each bar. The y-axis ranges from 0 to 2,000 students. Note that the bars are shaded to differentiate the variables and that an explanation key is provided.

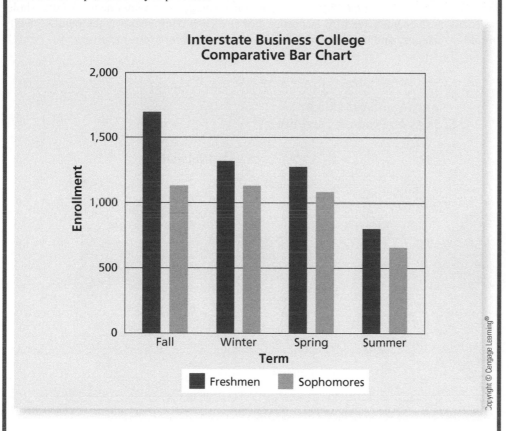

►TRYITEXERCISE 8

From the Interstate Business College enrollment figures in the table on page 722, construct a comparative bar chart of the junior and senior enrollment. Let the x-axis represent the time variable. For each term, group the bars together and differentiate them by shading.

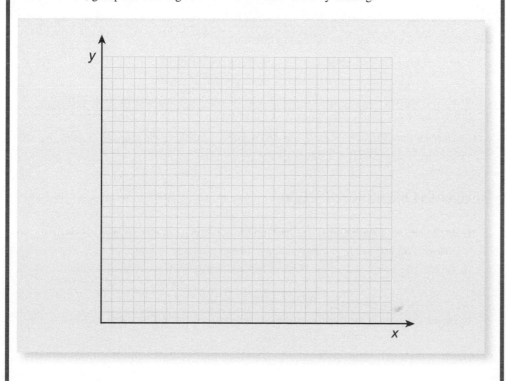

CHECK YOUR CHART WITH THE SOLUTION ON PAGE 751.

21-4   READING AND CONSTRUCTING A PIE CHART

pie chart A circle divided into sections that are usually expressed in percentage form and that represent the component parts of a whole.

The **pie chart** is a circle divided into sections representing the component parts of a whole. The whole, 100%, is the circle; the parts are the wedge-shaped sections of the circle. When this type of chart is used, the data are usually converted to percentages. The size of each section of the circle is determined by the portion or percentage each component is of the whole. Pie charts are generally read by inspection because each component of the data is clearly labeled by category and percent. Exhibit 21-6 illustrates examples of pie charts.

EXHIBIT 21-6 Pie Charts

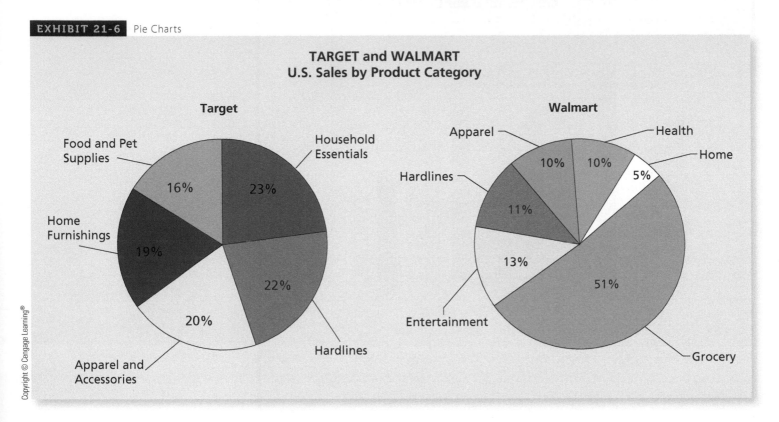

EXAMPLE9   READING A PIE CHART

Use Exhibit 21-6 to answer the following questions.

a. What percent of Target's sales were from food and pet supplies?

b. At Walmart, which two categories had the same percent of sales?

c. What percent were the combined sales of hardlines and household essentials at Target?

d. At Walmart, what category represented 5% of sales?

e. Considering that Target's revenue was $63.4 billion, calculate the amount of sales that the home furnishings category generated. (Round to the nearest billion.)

▶ SOLUTIONSTRATEGY

a. By inspection, we find that food and pet supplies at Target amounted to 16% of sales.

b. At Walmart, apparel and health products had the same amount of sales.

c. At Target, the combined sales of hardlines and household essentials amounted to 45% (22% + 23%).

d. The home category represented 5% of sales at Walmart.

e. At Target, the sales in the home furnishings category were $12 (19% × $63.4).

▶TRYITEXERCISE 9

Use Exhibit 21-6 to answer the following questions.

a. What percent of Walmart's sales were from entertainment?

b. At Target, which category had the highest percent of sales? What percent?

c. What were the combined sales in percent of the hardlines and home categories at Walmart?

d. At Target, what category represented 22% of sales?

e. Considering that Walmart's sales amounted to $405 billion, how much was generated by the grocery category? (Round to the nearest billion.)

CHECK YOUR ANSWERS WITH THE SOLUTIONS ON PAGE 752.

STEPS **TO CONSTRUCT A PIE CHART**

STEP 1. Convert the amount of each component to a percent by using the percentage formula Rate = Portion ÷ Base. Let the portion be the amount of each component and the base the total amount.

STEP 2. Because a full circle is made up of 360° representing 100%, multiply each component's percent (decimal form) by 360° to determine how many degrees each component's slice will be. Round to the nearest whole degree.

STEP 3. Draw a circle with a compass and mark the center.

STEP 4. Using a protractor, mark off the number of degrees on the circle that represents each component.

STEP 5. Connect each point on the circle to the center using a straight line to form a segment, or slice, for each component.

STEP 6. Label the segments clearly by name, color, or shading.

EXAMPLE10 CONSTRUCTING A PIE CHART

Cycle World sold the following bicycles last week: 30 racing bikes, 20 off-road bikes, 15 standard bikes, and 15 tricycles. Construct a pie chart showing the sales breakdown for the shop.

▶SOLUTIONSTRATEGY

For this chart, we must convert the component amounts to percents and then multiply the decimal form of the percents by 360° as follows:

$$\text{Racing bikes:} \quad \frac{30}{80} = .375 = 37.5\% \qquad .375 \times 360 = 135$$

$$\text{Off-road bikes:} \quad \frac{20}{80} = .25 = 25\% \qquad .25 \times 360 = 90$$

$$\text{Standard bikes:} \quad \frac{15}{80} = .1875 = 18.75\% \qquad .1875 \times 360 = 67.5$$

$$\text{Tricycles:} \quad \frac{15}{80} = .1875 = 18.75\% \qquad .1875 \times 360 = 67.5$$

Now draw a circle and use a protractor to mark the degree points of each component. Connect the points to the center of the circle to form the segments and label each segment appropriately. The completed chart follows.

Learning Tip

Although a full circle has exactly 360°, sometimes the total of the degrees from each slice may be slightly higher or lower than 360° because of rounding.

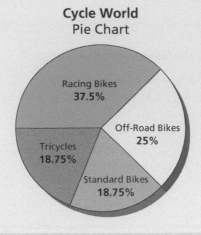

Cycle World
Pie Chart

Racing Bikes
37.5%

Off-Road Bikes
25%

Tricycles
18.75%

Standard Bikes
18.75%

TRYITEXERCISE 10

From the Interstate Business College enrollment figures in the table on page 722, construct a pie chart illustrating the winter term enrollment.

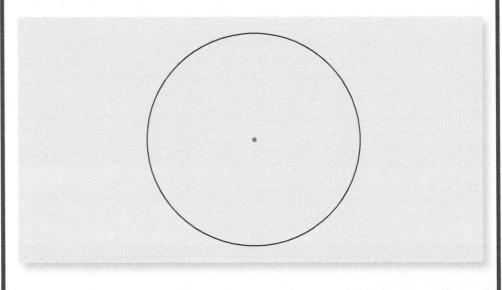

CHECK YOUR CHART WITH THE SOLUTION ON PAGE 752.

SECTION I   21   REVIEW EXERCISES

1. Use the line chart "Widget Sales 2007–2014" to answer the following questions.

   a. What was the amount of widget sales in 2007?

   <u>$0.2 billion</u>

   b. In what year did widget sales reach $0.8 billion?

   <u>2012</u>

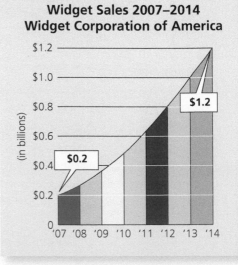

Widget Sales 2007–2014
Widget Corporation of America

(in billions)

$1.2
$1.0
$0.8
$0.6
$0.4
$0.2
0

$1.2
$0.2

'07 '08 '09 '10 '11 '12 '13 '14

c. What does this line graph represent?

d. What variables are represented on the *x*-axis and the *y*-axis?

e. What was the amount of widget sales in 2013?

f. In which year did sales reach $0.6 billion?

g. Calculate how much greater widget sales were in 2014 compared with 2007.

As the sales manager for Magnum Enterprises, you have been asked by the president to prepare the following charts for the shareholders' meeting next week. Use the six-month sales report, Table 21-1 on page 713, as the database for these charts. Calculate totals as required.

2. Single-line chart of the total company sales per month

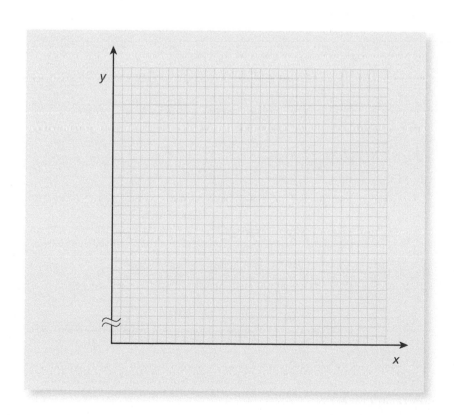

3. Multiple-line chart of the total sales per month of each model, standard and deluxe

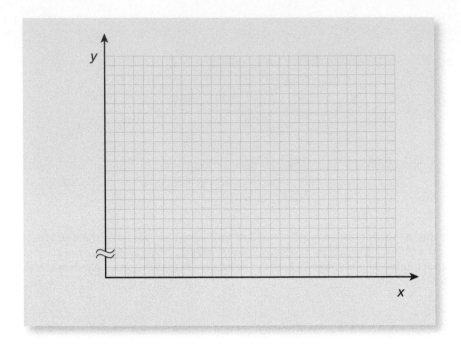

4. Standard bar chart of the deluxe sales per month in the Southeast territory

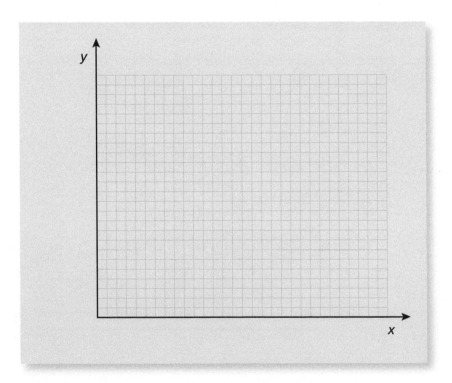

5. Component bar chart of the standard and deluxe model sales as components of total monthly sales in the Northeast territory

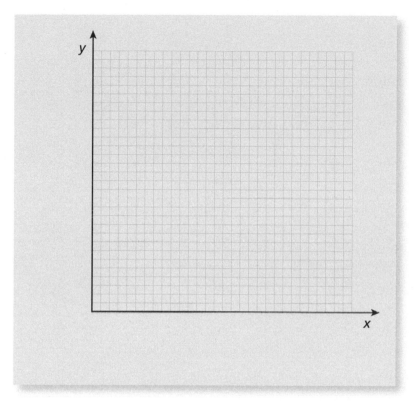

6. Comparative bar chart of the standard and deluxe model sales per month in the Northwest terrItory

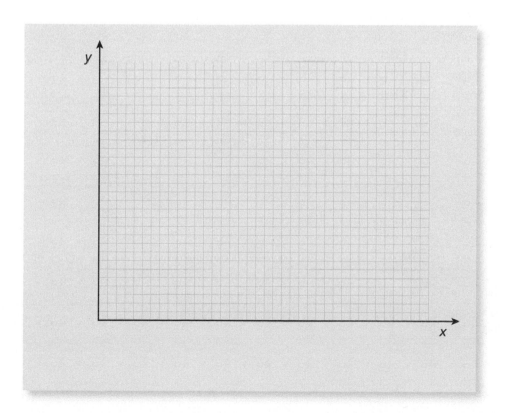

7. Pie chart of the total six-month sales of the four territories

BUSINESS DECISION: CHOOSING A CHART

8. You have been asked to prepare a chart of stock prices for the upcoming semiannual stockholders' meeting for Magnum Enterprises. The following table shows Magnum's stock prices on the first day of each month. Choose and prepare a chart that best illustrates this information.

Month	Stock Price
January	$35.50
February	$32.75
March	$37.25
April	$38.50
May	$40.25
June	$39.75

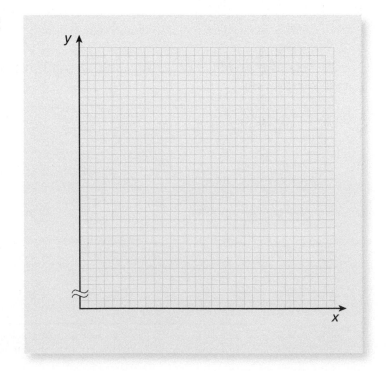

"So, with just a few extra lines and a splash of color, our dismal earnings become a lovely mountain scene."

© 2001–2009 Mark Anderson

MEASURES OF CENTRAL TENDENCY AND DISPERSION—UNGROUPED DATA

21

SECTION II

A numerical average is a value that is representative of a whole set of values. In business, managers use averages extensively to describe or represent a variety of situations. Imagine a payroll director being asked to describe the hourly wages of his 650 factory workers. On the one extreme, he might produce a list of his 650 workers along with their hourly wages. This action answers the question, but it provides too much information. A more appropriate response might be to calculate the average hourly wage and report that "$9.75 was the average hourly wage of the workers."

Because an average is numerically located in the range of values it represents, averages are often referred to as **measures of central tendency**. In this section, we study the three most commonly used measures of central tendency in business statistics: the arithmetic mean, the median, and the mode. In this section, we also study a measure of dispersion known as the range.

measure of central tendency A numerical value that is representative of a whole set of values.

CALCULATING THE ARITHMETIC MEAN OF UNGROUPED DATA

21-5

The **arithmetic mean** corresponds to the generally accepted meaning of the word *average*. It is customary to abbreviate the term *arithmetic mean* and refer to this average simply as the **mean**.

mean, or **arithmetic mean** The sum of the values of a set of data divided by the number of values in that set.

STEPS TO CALCULATE THE ARITHMETIC MEAN OF UNGROUPED DATA

STEP 1. Find the sum of all the values in the data set.

STEP 2. Divide the sum in Step 1 by the number of values in the set.

$$\text{Mean of ungrouped data} = \frac{\text{Sum of values}}{\text{Number of values}}$$

EXAMPLE 11 CALCULATING THE MEAN

WorldWide Travel had daily sales of $4,635 on Monday, $3,655 on Tuesday, $3,506 on Wednesday, $2,870 on Thursday, $4,309 on Friday, and $5,475 on Saturday. What is the mean sales per day?

SOLUTION STRATEGY

To calculate the mean (average sales per day), we find the sum of the values (sales per day) and divide this sum by the number of values (6 days).

$$\text{Mean of ungrouped data} = \frac{\text{Sum of values}}{\text{Number of values}}$$

$$\text{Mean} = \frac{4,635 + 3,655 + 3,506 + 2,870 + 4,309 + 5,475}{6} = \frac{24,450}{6} = \$4,075$$

TRY IT EXERCISE 11

The attendance figures for a series of management seminars were as follows: 432, 247, 661, 418, and 512. What was the mean number of individuals attending per seminar?

CHECK YOUR ANSWER WITH THE SOLUTION ON PAGE 752.

IN THE Business World

The word *average* is derived from maritime laws dating back to the 16th century. When a cargo vessel was in danger of sinking during a storm at sea, the heavy cargo was usually thrown overboard to save the ship. By law, the cost of the lost or damaged goods was equally divided among all the concerned parties. In French, this practice was known as *avarié*, which later became the English word *average*!

21-6 DETERMINING THE MEDIAN

median The *midpoint* value of a set of data when the numbers are ranked in ascending or descending order.

Another measure of central tendency—and a very useful way of describing a large quantity of data—is the median. The **median** of a set of numbers is the *midpoint* value when the numbers are ranked in ascending or descending order. Compared to the mean, the median is a more useful measure of central tendency when one or more of the values of the set is significantly higher or lower than the rest of the set. For example, if the ages of five individuals in a group are 22, 26, 27, 31, and 69, the mean of this set is 35. However, the median is 27, a value that better describes the set.

When there is an odd number of values in the set, the middle value is the median. For example, in a set of seven ranked values, the fourth value is the midpoint. There are three values greater than and three values less than the median.

When there is an even number of values in the set, the median is the mean of the two middle values. For example, in a set with 10 values, the median is the mean of the fifth and the sixth value.

STEPS TO DETERMINE THE MEDIAN

STEP 1. Rank the numbers in ascending or descending order.

STEP 2a. For an *odd number* of values, the median is the middle value.

STEP 2b. For an *even number* of values, the median is the mean of the two middle values.

EXAMPLE 12   DETERMINING THE MEDIAN

Determine the median for the following set of values:

$$2 \quad 8 \quad 5 \quad 13 \quad 11 \quad 6 \quad 9 \quad 15 \quad 4$$

SOLUTION STRATEGY

Step 1. Rank the data in ascending order as follows:

$$2 \quad 4 \quad 5 \quad 6 \quad 8 \quad 9 \quad 11 \quad 13 \quad 15$$

Step 2. Because the number of values in this set is *odd* (nine), there are four values less than and four values greater than the median. Therefore, the median is the fifth value, 8.

TRY IT EXERCISE 12

Determine the median for the following set of values:

$$4,589 \quad 6,558 \quad 4,237 \quad 2,430 \quad 3,619 \quad 5,840 \quad 1,220$$

CHECK YOUR ANSWER WITH THE SOLUTION ON PAGE 752.

EXAMPLE 13   DETERMINING THE MEDIAN

A runner preparing for the Marine Corps Marathon in Washington, D.C., had training runs of 5, 9, 23, 6, 7, and 5 miles. Find the median of these values.

© Cengage Learning

▶ SOLUTIONSTRATEGY

Step 1. Rank the data in ascending order:

$$5 \quad 5 \quad 6 \quad 7 \quad 9 \quad 23$$

Step 2. Because the number of values in this set is *even* (six), the median is the mean of the third and the fourth values, 6 and 7.

$$\text{Median} = \frac{6+7}{2} = \frac{13}{2} = \underline{6.5 \text{ miles}}$$

▶ TRYITEXERCISE 13

Determine the median for the following set of values representing the number of plants sold at Exotic Gardens in the past 10 days.

$$12 \quad 33 \quad 42 \quad 13 \quad 79 \quad 29 \quad 101 \quad 54 \quad 76 \quad 81$$

CHECK YOUR ANSWER WITH THE SOLUTION ON PAGE 752.

DETERMINING THE MODE

21-7

The **mode** is the third measure of central tendency that we consider. It is the value or values in a set that occur *most often*. It is possible for a set of data to have more than one mode or no mode at all.

mode The value or values in a set of data that occur *most often*.

STEPS TO DETERMINE THE MODE

STEP 1. Count the number of times each value in a set occurs.

STEP 2a. If one value occurs more times than any other, it is the mode.

STEP 2b. If two or more values occur more times than any other, they are all modes of the set.

STEP 2c. If all values occur the same number of times, there is no mode.

One common business application of the mode is in merchandising, where it is used to keep track of the most frequently purchased goods, as in the following example. Note that the mean and median of this set of data would provide little useful information regarding sales.

EXAMPLE14 DETERMINING THE MODE

Find the mode of the following set of values representing the wattage of lightbulbs sold at a Home Depot yesterday.

$$25 \quad 25 \quad 60 \quad 60 \quad 60 \quad 75 \quad 75 \quad 75 \quad 75 \quad 100 \quad 100 \quad 150$$

▶ SOLUTIONSTRATEGY

From these data, we see that the mode is <u>75 watts</u> because the value 75 occurs most often. This would indicate to the retailer that 75-watt bulbs were purchased most frequently.

▶ TRYITEXERCISE 14

Calculate the mode of the following set of values representing the size, in gallons, of fish tanks sold at Aquarium Adventures.

$$10 \quad 10 \quad 20 \quad 10 \quad 55 \quad 20 \quad 10 \quad 65 \quad 85 \quad 20 \quad 10 \quad 20 \quad 55 \quad 10 \quad 125 \quad 55 \quad 10 \quad 20$$

CHECK YOUR ANSWER WITH THE SOLUTION ON PAGE 752.

IN THE Business World

The *mode* is used extensively in marketing research to measure the most frequent responses on survey questions. In advertising, the mode translates into persuasive headlines, "4 Out of 5 Doctors Recommend. ..."

21-8   Determining the Range

range The difference between the lowest and the highest values in a data set; used as a measure of *dispersion*.

Although it does not measure central tendency as the mean, median, and mode do, the range is another useful measure in statistics. The **range** is a measure of *dispersion*; it is the difference between the lowest and the highest values in a data set. It is used to measure the scope, or broadness of a set of data. A small range indicates that the data in a set are narrow in scope; the values are close to each other. A large range indicates that the data in a set are wide in scope; the values are spread far apart.

STEPS TO DETERMINE THE RANGE

STEP 1. Locate the highest and lowest values in a set of numbers.

STEP 2. Subtract the lowest from the highest to get the range.

$$\text{Range} = \text{Highest value} - \text{Lowest value}$$

EXAMPLE15   DETERMINING THE RANGE

Determine the range of the following shirt prices at Styline Men's Shop.

$37.95 $15.75 $24.75 $18.50 $33.75 $42.50 $14.95 $27.95 $19.95

▶SOLUTIONSTRATEGY

To determine the range of shirt prices, subtract the lowest price from the highest price:

$$\text{Range} = \text{Highest value} - \text{Lowest value} = 42.50 - 14.95 = \underline{\$27.55}$$

Note that the range for shirts, $27.55, is relatively large. It might be said that customers shopping in this shirt department have a wide range of prices from which to choose.

▶TRYITEXERCISE 15

Determine the range of the following temperature readings from the oven at Bon Appétit Bakery.

367°   351°   349°   362°   366°   358°   369°   355°   354°

CHECK YOUR ANSWER WITH THE SOLUTION ON PAGE 752.

SECTION II   21   REVIEW EXERCISES

Calculate the mean of the following sets of values. Round to the nearest tenth when applicable.

1. 5   7   21   46   35   2   19   7

$$\frac{5 + 7 + 21 + 46 + 35 + 2 + 19 + 7}{8} = \frac{142}{8} = \underline{\underline{17.8}}$$

2. 4   6   1   8   9   2   3   5   5   6   8   9   10

3. 324   553   179   213   423   336   190   440   382   111   329   111   397

4. .87   .32   1.43   2.3   5.4   3.25   .5

Determine the median of the following sets of values. Round to the nearest tenth when applicable.

5. 4   18   8   5   16   3   9   30   12

   3   4   5   8   (9)   12   16   18   30

   9 is the median.

6. 56   34   28   60   48   55

   28   34   (48   55)   56   60

$$\frac{48 + 55}{2} = \frac{103}{2} = 51.5$$

7. 57   38   29   82   71   90   11   94   26   18   18

8. $2.50 $3.25 $4.35 $1.22 $1.67 $4.59

9. 35%   51%   50%   23%   18%   67%   44%   52%

Determine the mode of the following sets of values.

10. 8   3   5   6   3   7   2   1   8   2   4   3   6   2

    8 × 2   (3 × 3)   5 × 1   6 × 2   7 × 1   (2 × 3)   1 × 1   4 × 1

    Both 3 and 2 are modes in this set.

11. 21   57   46   21   34   76   43   68   21   76   18   12

12. $1,200 $7,300 $4,500 $3,450 $1,675

13. 4   9   3   5   4   7   1   9   9   4   7   1   8   1   4   6   7   4   6   9   9   2

Determine the range of the following sets of values.

14. 184   237   256   359   36   71

    Highest   359

    Lowest − 36

    Range   323

15. 12 42 54 28 112 76 95 27 36 11 96 109 210

16. $2.35 $4.16 $3.42 $1.29 $.89 $4.55   17. 1,099 887 1,659 1,217 2,969 790

Ice Cream According to the U.S. Department of Agriculture (USDA), U.S. production of ice cream and related frozen desserts, one of the U.S. food industry's largest sectors, amounted to more than 1.4 billion gallons in a recent year. That translates to more than 21 pounds per person.

Dairy Queen, one of the largest soft serve ice cream franchises in the world, has reported more than 5,700 stores in 19 countries, including 652 locations outside the United States and Canada.

18. The following numbers represent the gallons of chocolate fudge syrup used per month by a Dairy Queen to make hot fudge sundaes.

Jan.—225	Feb.—254	March—327	April—370	May—425	June—435
July—446	Aug.—425	Sept.—359	Oct.—302	Nov.—270	Dec.—241

a. What is the mean of this set of data?

b. What is the median of this set of data?

c. What is the mode of this set of data?

d. What is the range of this set of data?

19. You are the owner of The Dependable Delivery Service. Your company has four vehicles: a large and a small van and a large and a small truck. The following set of data represents the number of packages delivered last week.

	Monday	Tuesday	Wednesday	Thursday	Friday
Small Van	67	86	94	101	86
Large Van	142	137	153	165	106
Small Truck	225	202	288	311	290
Large Truck	322	290	360	348	339

a. What is the mean number of packages delivered for each van?

b. What is the median number of packages delivered for each truck?

c. What is the mean number of packages delivered on Monday?

d. What is the median number of packages delivered on Thursday?

e. What is the mode of all the packages delivered during the week?

f. What is the range of all the packages delivered during the week?

BUSINESS DECISION: INTERPRETING THE NUMBERS

20. You are the manager of a production plant that makes computer hard drives for Digital Storage Corporation. Last week your plant had the following production numbers during a 6-day production run:

2,300　2,430　2,018　2,540　2,675　4,800

a. What is the mean, median, mode, and range of this set of production data?

b. Which measure best describes the production at your plant? Why?

FREQUENCY DISTRIBUTIONS—GROUPED DATA　　　　**21**　　SECTION III

In the previous section, the values in the sets are listed individually and are known as **ungrouped data**. Frequently, business statistics deals with hundreds, even thousands, of values in a set. In dealing with such a large number of values, it is often easier to represent the data by dividing the values into equal-size groups known as classes, creating **grouped data**.

The number of values in each class is called the **frequency**, with the resulting chart called a **frequency distribution** or **frequency table**. The purpose of a frequency distribution is to organize large amounts of data into a more compact form without changing the essential information contained in those values.

ungrouped data Data that have not been grouped into a distribution-type format.

grouped data Data that have been divided into equal-size groups known as classes. Frequently used to represent data when dealing with large amounts of values in a set.

frequency The number of values in each class of a frequency distribution.

CONSTRUCTING A FREQUENCY DISTRIBUTION　　　　**21-9**

STEPS TO CONSTRUCT A FREQUENCY DISTRIBUTION

STEP 1. Divide the data into equal-size classes. Be sure to use an extent that includes all values in the set.

STEP 2. Use tally marks to record the frequency of values in each class.

STEP 3. Rewrite the tally marks for each class numerically in a column labeled "Frequency (f)." The data are now grouped.

frequency distribution or **frequency table** The chart obtained by dividing data into equal-size classes; used to organize large amounts of data into a more compact form without changing the essential information contained in those values.

EXAMPLE16   CONSTRUCTING A FREQUENCY DISTRIBUTION

From the following ungrouped data representing the weight of packages shipped by Monarch Manufacturing this month, construct a frequency distribution using classes with an interval of 10 pounds each.

13   16   65   45   44   35   22   46   36   49   56   26
68   27   35   15   43   62   32   57   48   23   43   44

▶SOLUTIONSTRATEGY

First, we find the range of the data by subtracting the lowest value, 13, from the highest value, 68. This gives a range of 55 pounds. Second, by using 60 pounds as the extent for the classes of our frequency distribution, we include all values in the set. Class intervals of 10 pounds each allow for six equal classes.

Frequency Distribution for Monarch Manufacturing

Class (lb)	Tally	Frequency (f)
10 to 19	III	3
20 to 29	IIII	4
30 to 39	IIII	4
40 to 49	JHI III	8
50 to 59	II	2
60 to 69	III	3

▶TRYITEXERCISE 16

You are the manager of The Dress Code Boutique. From the following ungrouped data representing the dollar sales of each transaction at the store today, construct a frequency distribution using classes with an interval of $10 each.

14   19   55   47   44   39   22   71   35   49   64   22   88   78   16
88   37   29   71   74   62   54   59   18   93   49   74   26   66   75

CHECK YOUR ANSWER WITH THE SOLUTION ON PAGE 752.

21-10   CALCULATING THE MEAN OF GROUPED DATA

Just as with ungrouped data, we can calculate the arithmetic mean of grouped data in a frequency distribution. Keep in mind, however, that the means for grouped data are calculated by using the midpoints of each class rather than the actual values of the data and are therefore only approximations. Because the actual values of the data in each class of the distribution are lost, we must make the assumption that the midpoints of each class closely approximate the values in that class. In most cases, this is true because some class values fall below the midpoint and some above, thereby canceling the inaccuracy.

STEPS TO CALCULATE THE MEAN OF A FREQUENCY DISTRIBUTION

STEP 1. Add a column to the frequency distribution listing the midpoints of each class. Label it "Midpoints (m)."

STEP 2. In a column labeled "($f \times m$)," multiply the frequency for each class by the midpoint of that class.

STEP 3. Find the sum of the frequency column.

STEP 4. Find the sum of the ($f \times m$) column.

STEP 5. Find the mean by dividing the sum of the ($f \times m$) column by the sum of the frequency column.

$$\text{Mean of grouped data} = \frac{\text{Sum of (frequency} \times \text{midpoint)}}{\text{Sum of frequencies}}$$

EXAMPLE17 CALCULATING THE MEAN OF GROUPED DATA

Calculate the mean of the grouped data from the frequency distribution for Monarch Manufacturing in the previous example.

SOLUTIONSTRATEGY

Begin by attaching the Midpoint (m) and Frequency × Midpoint (f × m) columns to the frequency distribution as follows:

Frequency Distribution for Monarch Manufacturing

Class (lb)	Tally	Frequency (f)	Midpoint (m)	f × m
10 to 19	|||	3	14.5	43.5
20 to 29	||||	4	24.5	98.0
30 to 39	||||	4	34.5	138.0
40 to 49	||||| |||	8	44.5	356.0
50 to 59	||	2	54.5	109.0
60 to 69	|||	3	64.5	193.5
		24		938.0

After finding the sum of the "Frequency" and f × m columns, use these sums to calculate the mean of the grouped data:

$$\text{Mean of grouped data} = \frac{\text{Sum of (frequency} \times \text{midpoint)}}{\text{Sum of frequencies}} = \frac{938}{24} = 39.1 \text{ lb}$$

TRYITEXERCISE 17

From the frequency distribution prepared in Try It Exercise 16 for The Dress Code Boutique, calculate the mean of the grouped data.

CHECK YOUR ANSWER WITH THE SOLUTION ON PAGE 753.

PREPARING A HISTOGRAM OF A FREQUENCY DISTRIBUTION

21-11

A **histogram** is a special type of bar chart that is used in business to display the data from a frequency distribution. A histogram is drawn in the same way as a standard bar chart but without space between the bars.

histogram A special type of bar chart without space between the bars that is used to display the data from a frequency distribution.

STEPS TO PREPARE A HISTOGRAM OF A FREQUENCY DISTRIBUTION

STEP 1. Locate the classes of the frequency distribution adjacent to each other along the x-axis, increasing from left to right.

STEP 2. Evenly space the frequencies on the y-axis, increasing from bottom to top.

STEP 3. Plot the frequency for each class in the form of a rectangular bar whose top edge is opposite the frequency of that class on the y-axis.

EXAMPLE18 PREPARING A HISTOGRAM

Prepare a histogram from the Monarch Manufacturing frequency distribution above.

SOLUTIONSTRATEGY

On page 740 is the histogram prepared from the data in the Monarch Manufacturing frequency distribution. Note that the x-axis displays the adjacent classes and the y-axis displays their frequencies.

Learning Tip

Because a frequency distribution has classes whose numbers are continuous, the histogram bars depicting that distribution are made to look continuous by drawing them adjacent to each other—no space between them.

2. You are the sales manager of the Esquire Sportswear Company. Last week your 30 salespeople reported the following automobile mileage while making sales calls to retail stores around the state:

| 385 | 231 | 328 | 154 | 283 | 86 | 415 | 389 | 575 | 117 | 75 | 173 | 247 | 316 | 357 |
| 211 | 432 | 271 | 93 | 515 | 376 | 328 | 183 | 359 | 136 | 88 | 438 | 282 | 375 | 637 |

a. Group the data into seven classes of equal size (0–99, 100–199, 200–299, 300–399, etc.) and construct a frequency distribution of the mileage.

b. Calculate the mean of the grouped data by using 49.5, 149.5, 249.5, etc., as the midpoints.

c. Using the grid provided below, prepare a histogram of these data to illustrate your salespeoples' mileage graphically.

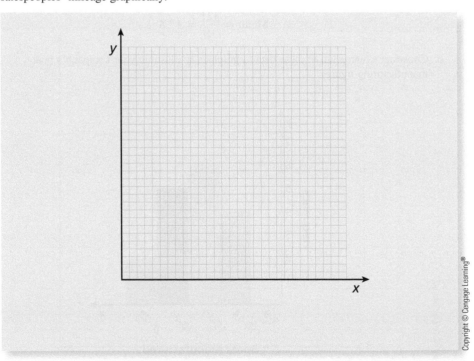

3. You are the owner of the Internet Café. As part of a marketing effort to increase the "average sale" per customer, you recently did a survey of the lunch-hour sales receipts for a busy Saturday. Following are the results of that survey.

$4.15	$5.60	$4.95	$6.70	$5.40	$7.15	$6.45	$8.25	$7.60	$6.25
$5.50	$4.90	$7.60	$6.40	$7.75	$5.25	$6.70	$8.45	$7.10	$8.80
$9.65	$8.40	$6.50	$5.25	$6.75	$8.50	$5.35	$6.80	$4.25	$9.95

a. Group the sales receipts into six classes of equal size ($4.00–$4.99, $5.00–$5.99, etc.) and construct a frequency distribution.

Many coffee establishments provide wireless Internet connections for their customers.

b. Calculate the mean of the grouped data.

c. Using the grid provided below, prepare a histogram of the sales receipts.

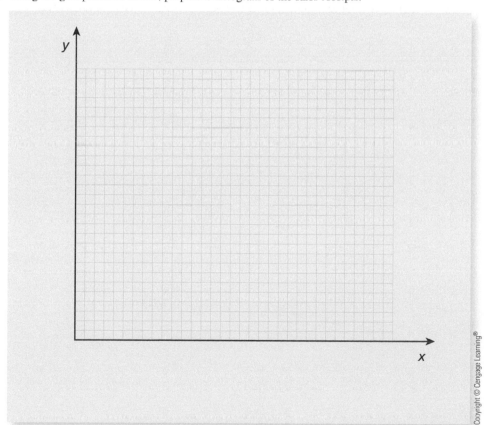

BUSINESS DECISION: RELATIVE FREQUENCY DISTRIBUTION

4. In business, percents are frequently used to represent the portion of observations falling within classes of a frequency distribution. A **relative frequency distribution** expresses the distribution as percents. To convert a frequency distribution to a relative frequency distribution, divide each of the class frequencies (portion) by the total number of observations (base). Remember, Rate = Portion ÷ Base.

   a. From the frequency distribution you constructed for the Internet Café in Exercise 3a, convert each class frequency to a relative class frequency, percents. Round your answers to tenths.

   b. What percent of the sales receipts were paid between $5.00 and $5.99?

   c. What percent of the sales receipts were $7.00 or more?

   d. What percent of the sales receipts were less than $8.00?

CHAPTER FORMULAS

Ungrouped Data

Mean of ungrouped data $= \dfrac{\text{Sum of values}}{\text{Number of values}}$

Median (odd number of values) = Middle value (Don't forget to rank scores first.)

Median (even number of values) = Mean of the middle two values (Don't forget to rank scores first.)

Mode = Value or values that occur most frequently

Range = Highest value − Lowest value

Grouped Data

Mean of grouped data $= \dfrac{\text{Sum of (frequency} \times \text{midpoint)}}{\text{Sum of frequencies}}$

CHAPTER SUMMARY

Section I: Data Interpretation and Presentation

Topic	Important Concepts	Illustrative Examples
Reading and Interpreting Information from a Table **Performance Objective 21-1, Page 712**	Tables are a collection of related data arranged for ease of reference or comparison, usually in parallel columns with meaningful titles. They are a very useful tool in summarizing statistical data and are found everywhere in business. Reading tables: 1. Scan the titles above the columns for the category of information being sought. 2. Look down the column for the specific fact required.	Apollo Auto Sales 90-Day Sales Report ($1,000s) |	April	May	June
---	---	---	---
Autos	56	61	64
Trucks	68	58	66
Parts	32	41	37
Total	156	160	167	
Reading and Constructing a Line Chart **Performance Objective 21-2, Page 714**	Charts are used to display a picture of the relationships among selected data. Line charts show changes occurring over a period of time. They are represented on a grid by a series of data points continuously connected by straight lines. Reading line charts: 1. Scan either the x- or y-axis for the known variable: x for time or y for amount. 2. Draw a perpendicular line from that axis to the point where it intersects the chart. 3. Draw a line from that point perpendicular to the opposite axis. 4. The value of the other variable occurs where the line intersects the opposite axis.	*Single-Line Chart* Copyright © Cengage Learning®

Section I (continued)

Topic	Important Concepts	Illustrative Examples
	Constructing line charts: 1. Evenly space and label the time variable on the *x*-axis. 2. Evenly space and label the amount variable on the *y*-axis. 3. Show each data point by placing a dot above the time period and across from the corresponding amount. 4. Connect the plotted points with straight lines to form the chart. 5. Lines should be differentiated by various line patterns or colors.	*Multiple-Line Chart* 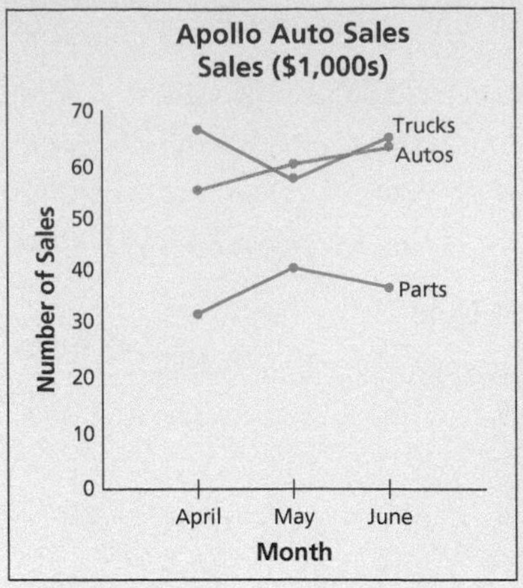 **Apollo Auto Sales** Sales ($1,000s) *(line chart showing Number of Sales vs. Month; lines for Trucks, Autos, and Parts across April, May, June)* Copyright © Cengage Learning®
Reading and Constructing a Bar Chart **Performance Objective 21-3, Page 718**	Bar charts represent data by the length of horizontal bars or vertical columns. As with line charts, bar charts often illustrate increases or decreases in magnitude of a certain variable or the relationship between similar variables. Comparative bar charts illustrate two or more related variables. In this chart, the bars of the related variables are drawn next to each other but do not touch. Component bar charts illustrate parts of something that add to a total. Each bar is divided into components stacked on top of each other and shaded or colored differently. Reading bar charts: 1. Scan the *x*- or *y*-axis for a known variable. 2. Read the answer on the opposite axis directly across from the top of the appropriate bar. Constructing bar charts: 1. Evenly space and label the *x*-axis. The space between bars should be one-half the width of the bars. 2. Evenly space and label the *y*-axis. 3. Draw each bar up from the *x*-axis to the point opposite the *y*-axis that corresponds to its value. 4. For comparative and component bar charts, differentiate the bars by color or shading pattern.	*Standard Bar Chart* 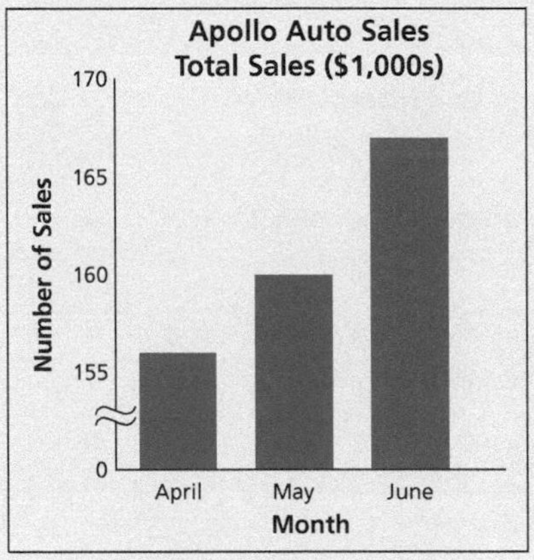 **Apollo Auto Sales** Total Sales ($1,000s) *(bar chart showing Number of Sales vs. Month for April, May, June)* Copyright © Cengage Learning® *Comparative Bar Chart* **Apollo Auto Sales** Sales ($1,000s) 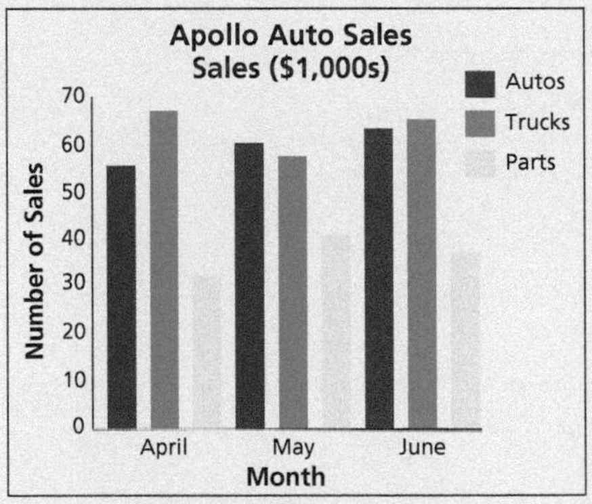 *(comparative bar chart showing Number of Sales vs. Month with bars for Autos, Trucks, Parts across April, May, June)* Copyright © Cengage Learning® *Component Bar Chart* 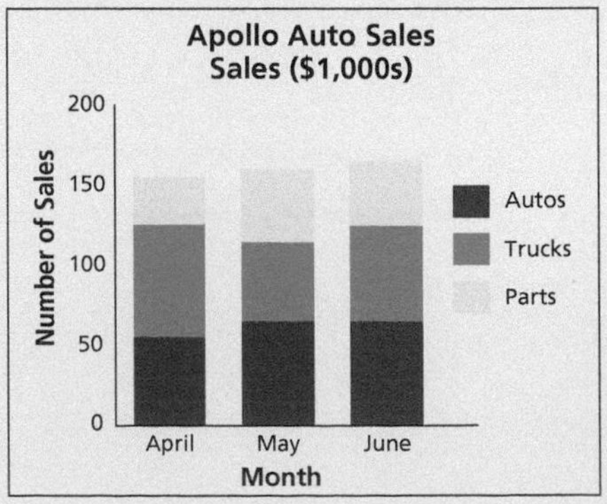 **Apollo Auto Sales** Sales ($1,000s) *(component bar chart showing Number of Sales vs. Month with stacked Autos, Trucks, Parts across April, May, June)* Copyright © Cengage Learning®

Section I (continued)

Topic	Important Concepts	Illustrative Examples
Reading and Constructing a Pie Chart **Performance Objective 21-4, Page 724**	The pie chart is a circle divided into sections representing the component parts of a whole, usually in percentage terms. Constructing pie charts: 1. Convert the amount of each component to a percent using the formula Rate = Portion ÷ Base. Let the percentage be the amount of each component and the base the total amount. 2. Because a full circle is made up of 360° representing 100%, multiply each component's percent (decimal form) by 360° to determine how many degrees each component's slice will be. Round to the nearest whole degree. 3. Draw a circle with a compass and mark the center. 4. Using a protractor, mark off the number of degrees on the circle that represents each component. 5. Connect each point on the circle with the center using a straight line to form a segment, or slice, for each component. 6. Label the segments clearly by name, color, or shading.	$\text{April} = \dfrac{156}{483} = .323 = 32.3\%$ $\text{April} = .323 \times 360° = 116°$ $\text{May} = \dfrac{160}{483} = .331 = 33.1\%$ $\text{May} = .331 \times 360° = 119°$ $\text{June} = \dfrac{167}{483} = .346 = 34.6\%$ $\text{June} = .346 \times 360° = 125°$ *Pie Chart* **Apollo Auto Sales** April 32.3% May 33.1% June 34.6% Copyright © Cengage Learning®

Section II: Measures of Central Tendency and Dispersion—Ungrouped Data

Topic	Important Concepts	Illustrative Examples
Calculating the Arithmetic Mean of Ungrouped Data **Performance Objective 21-5, Page 731**	A numerical average is a value that is representative of a whole set of values. The arithmetic mean corresponds to the generally accepted meaning of the word *average*. Computing the mean: 1. Find the sum of all the values in the set. 2. Divide by the number of values in the set. $$\text{Mean} = \frac{\text{Sum of values}}{\text{Number of values}}$$	If a grocery store had sales of $4,600 on Monday, $3,650 on Tuesday, and $3,500 on Wednesday, what is the mean sales for the 3 days? $$\text{Mean} = \frac{4,600 + 3,650 + 3,500}{3}$$ $$= \frac{11,750}{3} = \$3,916.67$$
Determining the Median **Performance Objective 21-6, Page 732**	Another measure of central tendency—and a very useful way of describing a large quantity of data—is the median. The median of a set of numbers is the *midpoint* value when the numbers are ranked in increasing or decreasing order. Determining the median: 1. Rank the numbers in increasing or decreasing order. 2a. For an *odd number* of values in the set, the median is the middle value. 2b. For an *even number* of values in the set, the median is the mean of the two middle values.	Find the median for the following set of values: 2 8 5 13 11 6 9 15 4 Rank the data as follows: 2 4 5 6 8 9 11 13 15 Because the number of values in the set is odd (nine), the median is the middle value, 8. Find the median for the following set of values: 56 34 87 12 45 49 Rank the data as follows: 12 34 45 49 56 87 Because the number of values in this set is even (six), the median is the mean of the third and the fourth values, 45 and 49. $$\text{Median} = \frac{45 + 49}{2} = \frac{94}{2} = 47$$

Section II (continued)

Topic	Important Concepts	Illustrative Examples
Determining the Mode **Performance Objective 21-7,** **Page 733**	The mode is the third measure of central tendency. It is the value or values in a set that occur most often. It is possible for a set of data to have more than one mode or no mode at all. Determining the mode: 1. Count the number of times each value in a set occurs. 2a. If one value occurs most often, it is the mode. 2b. If more than one value occurs the same number of times, all of the values are modes of the set. 2c. If all values occur only once, there is no mode.	Find the mode of the following set of values representing television screen sizes sold in a Best Buy store yesterday: 25 25 27 25 17 19 12 12 17 25 17 5 25 Because the value 25 occurs most often, the mode is 25 inches.
Determining the Range **Performance Objective 21-8,** **Page 734**	The range is a measure of dispersion equal to the difference between the lowest and the highest values in a set. It is used to measure the scope, or broadness, of a set of data. Determining the range: 1. Locate the highest and lowest values in a set of numbers. 2. Subtract these values to determine the range. Range = Highest value − Lowest value	Find the range of the following hard drive prices at CompUSA: 237 215 124 185 375 145 199 Highest = \$375 Lowest = \$124 Range = 375 − 124 = \$251

Section III: Frequency Distributions—Grouped Data

Topic	Important Concepts	Illustrative Examples
Constructing a Frequency Distribution **Performance Objective 21-9,** **Page 737**	Business statistics frequently deals with hundreds, even thousands, of values in a set. In dealing with large amounts of values, it is often easier to represent the data by dividing the values into equal-size groups known as classes, forming grouped data. The number of values in each class is called the frequency, with the resulting chart called a frequency distribution. Constructing a frequency distribution: 1. Divide the data into equal-size classes. Be sure to use a range that includes all values in the set. 2. Use tally marks to record the frequency of values in each class. 3. Rewrite the tally marks for each class numerically in a column labeled "Frequency (f)." The data are now grouped.	The following ungrouped data represent the number of sales calls made by the sales force of Northwest Supply Company last month. Construct a frequency distribution of these data using six equal classes with an interval of ten. 13 26 65 45 44 35 46 36 49 56 16 68 27 35 43 62 32 57 23 43 44 <table><tr><th>Class</th><th>Tally</th><th>Freq (f)</th></tr><tr><td>10 to 19</td><td>II</td><td>2</td></tr><tr><td>20 to 29</td><td>III</td><td>3</td></tr><tr><td>30 to 39</td><td>IIII</td><td>4</td></tr><tr><td>40 to 49</td><td>IIII II</td><td>7</td></tr><tr><td>50 to 59</td><td>II</td><td>2</td></tr><tr><td>60 to 69</td><td>III</td><td>3</td></tr></table>

Section III (continued)

Topic	Important Concepts	Illustrative Examples
Calculating the Mean of Grouped Data **Performance Objective 21-10, Page 738**	Calculating the mean of a frequency distribution: 1. Add a column to the frequency distribution listing the midpoints (m) of each class. 2. In a column labeled "($f \times m$)," multiply the frequency for each class by the midpoint of that class. 3. Find the sum of the frequency column. 4. Find the sum of the ($f \times m$) column. 5. Find the mean by dividing the sum of the ($f \times m$) column by the sum of the frequency column. $$\text{Mean} = \frac{\text{Sum of } (f \times m)}{\text{Sum of frequencies}}$$	Calculate the mean number of sales calls for Northwest Supply. The mean of the grouped data is computed by first attaching the Midpoint (m) and Frequency $\times$ Midpoint ($f \times m$) columns to the frequency distribution as follows: {| table |} $$\text{Mean} = \frac{854.5}{21} = 40.7 \text{ calls}$$

Illustrative Example table for Calculating the Mean of Grouped Data:

Class	Freq (f)	Midpt (m)	$f \times m$
10–19	2	14.5	29.0
20–29	3	24.5	73.5
30–39	4	34.5	138.0
40–49	7	44.5	311.5
50–59	2	54.5	109.0
60–69	3	64.5	193.5
	21		854.5

Topic	Important Concepts	Illustrative Examples
Preparing a Histogram of a Frequency Distribution **Performance Objective 21-11, Page 739**	A histogram is a special type of bar chart that is used in business to display the data from a frequency distribution. A histogram is drawn in the same way as a standard bar chart except there are no spaces between the bars. Constructing a histogram: 1. Locate the classes of the frequency distribution adjacent to each other along the x-axis, increasing from left to right. 2. Evenly space the frequencies on the y-axis, increasing from bottom to top. 3. Plot each class's frequency in the form of a rectangular bar whose top edge is opposite the frequency of that class on the y-axis.	*Histogram* Northwest Supply Sales Calls Histogram

Try It: EXERCISE SOLUTIONS FOR CHAPTER 21

1. **a.** Standard sales—February—Northeast = $228,400

b. Deluxe sales—April—Southeast = $70,300

c. Total sales—May and June—Northwest
May = 112,900 + 65,300 = 178,200
June = 135,000 + 78,400 = 213,400
Total $391,600

d. Months with increase in standard sales—Southwest
March, April, May, June

e. April—Deluxe = 92,600 + 153,200 + 67,800 + 70,300 = 383,900
May—Deluxe = 65,300 + 185,000 + 78,300 + 79,400 = 408,000
408,000 − 383,900 = $24,100

f. Northwest—Percent standard sales $= \dfrac{\text{Standard sales}}{\text{Total sales}}$

Northwest—Percent standard sales $= \dfrac{757,000}{1,244,500} = .6082 = 60.8\%$

CHAPTER 21

2. **a.** June

b. July

c. $0.05 ($0.50 – $0.45)

d. Apples

e. June, July, August, September, and December

f. December; $0.45 ($0.70 – $0.25)

3.

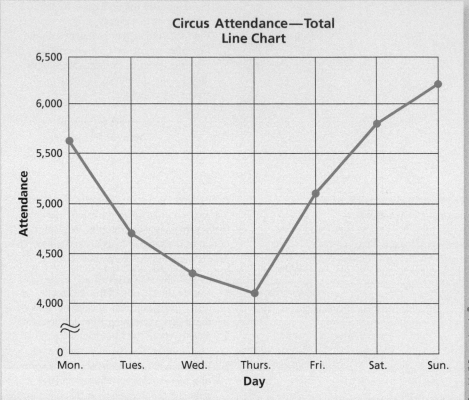

4.

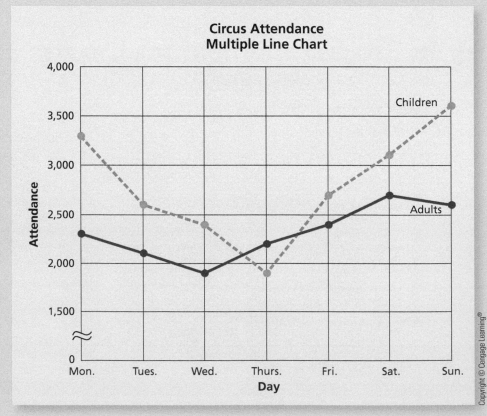

5. **a.** $7.0 million

    b. 2013; $5.4 million

    c. 2012; 15%

    d. 55%

    e. Exhibit 21-5 illustrates the annual sales breakdown of goods from each import region;
       Far East and Africa.

    f. 2012

6.

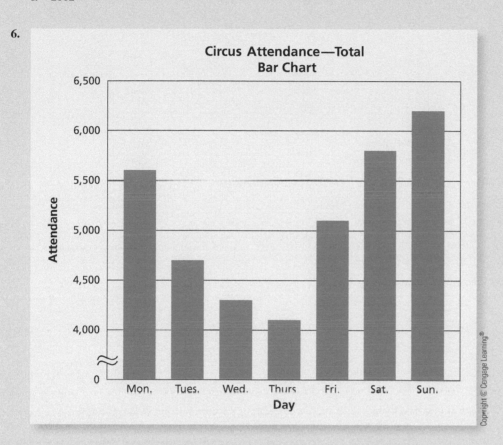

7.

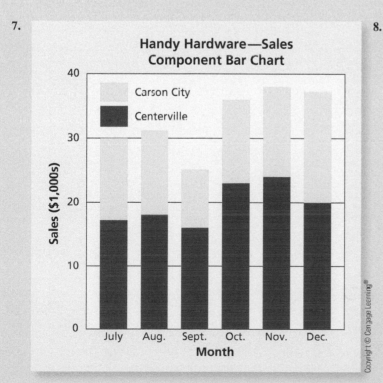

8.

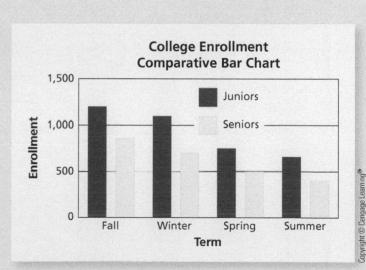

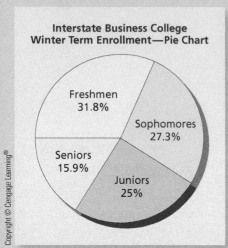

**Interstate Business College
Winter Term Enrollment—Pie Chart**

Freshmen
31.8%

Sophomores
27.3%

Seniors
15.9%

Juniors
25%

9. a. 13%

   b. Household essentials; 23%

   c. 16% (11% + 5%)

   d. Hardlines

   e. $207 billion (51% × $405 billion and then rounded to the nearest billion)

10. Freshmen $= \dfrac{1,400}{4,400} = .318 = \underline{\underline{31.8\%}}$ $.318 \times 360° = \underline{\underline{114°}}$

   Sophomores $= \dfrac{1,200}{4,400} = .273 = \underline{\underline{27.3\%}}$ $.273 \times 360° = \underline{\underline{98°}}$

   Juniors $= \dfrac{1,100}{4,400} = .25 \ \ = \underline{\underline{25\%}}$ $.25 \times 360° = \underline{\underline{90°}}$

   Seniors $= \dfrac{700}{4,400} = .159 = \underline{\underline{15.9\%}}$ $.159 \times 360° = \underline{\underline{57°}}$

11. Mean $= \dfrac{\text{Sum of values}}{\text{Number of values}}$

   Mean $= \dfrac{432 + 247 + 661 + 418 + 512}{5} = \dfrac{2,270}{5} = \underline{\underline{454}}$

12. Ranked in increasing order:

   1,220 2,430 3,619 $\boxed{4,237}$ 4,589 5,840 6,558

   Median is the middle value of the odd number of values = $\underline{4,237}$

13. Ranked in increasing order:

   12 13 29 33 42 54 76 79 81 101

   For even number of values, median is the mean of the two middle values.

   Median $= \dfrac{42 + 54}{2} = \dfrac{96}{2} = \underline{\underline{48}}$

14. $\underline{10} = 7$ $20 = 5$ $55 = 3$ $65 = 1$ $85 = 1$ $125 = 1$

   The mode of these values is $\underline{\underline{10}}$ because it occurred the most number of times, seven.

15. Range = Highest value – Lowest value

   Range = 369° – 349° = $\underline{\underline{20°}}$

16. *The Dress Code*

   Frequency Distribution

   $ Sales per transaction

Class ($)	Tally	Frequency
10–19	IIII	4
20–29	IIII	4
30–39	III	3
40–49	IIII	4
50–59	III	3
60–69	III	3
70–79	IIII I	6
80–89	II	2
90–99	I	1

17. *The Dress Code*

$ Sales per transaction

Class ($)	Tally	Freq (f)	Midpoint (m)	($f \times m$)
10–19	IIII	4	14.5	58.0
20–29	IIII	4	24.5	98.0
30–39	III	3	34.5	103.5
40–49	IIII	4	44.5	178.0
50–59	III	3	54.5	163.5
60–69	III	3	64.5	193.5
70–79	IIIII	6	74.5	447.0
80–89	II	2	84.5	169.0
90–99	I	1	94.5	94.5
		30		1,505.0

$$\text{Mean} = \frac{\text{Sum of } (f \times m)}{\text{Sum of frequencies}}$$

$$\text{Mean} = \frac{1,505}{30} = 50.166 = \underline{\underline{\$50.17}}$$

18.

**The Dress Code
Histogram**

Copyright © Cengage Learning®

CONCEPT REVIEW

1. The systematic process of collecting, interpreting, and presenting numerical data about business situations is known as business _____. (21-1)

2. Statistical procedures that deal with the collection, classification, summarization, and presentation of data are known as _____ statistics. The process of arriving at conclusions, predictions,

forecasts, or estimates based on a sample from a larger population is known as statistical _____. (21-1)

3. A collection of related data arranged for ease of reference or comparison, usually in parallel columns with meaningful titles, is known as a(n) _____. (21-1)

4. A(n) _____ chart is a series of data points on a grid that are continuously connected by straight lines that display a picture of change occurring over a period of time. (21-2)

5. The horizontal axis of a line chart is known as the _____ and is used to measure units of time; the vertical axis of a line chart is known as the _____ and is used to measure the quantity or magnitude of something. (21-2)

6. When a bar chart is used to illustrate the relationship between two or more similar variables, it is known as a(n) _____ bar chart. When a bar chart is used to illustrate the parts of something that add to a total, it is known as a(n) _____ bar chart. (21-3)

7. To construct a pie chart, we multiply each component's percent by _____ degrees to determine how many degrees of the circle each component's slice will be. (21-4)

8. A numerical value that is representative of a whole set of values is known as a(n) _____ . It is also known as the mean or the arithmetic mean. Write the formula for the mean of ungrouped data. (21-5)

9. The _____ is the midpoint value of a set of data that is listed in ascending or descending order. Write a formula for this midpoint value when there is an even number of values in the data set. (21-6)

10. The _____ is the value or values in a set of data that occur most often. (21-7)

11. The difference between the lowest and the highest values in a data set are known as the _____ . This useful statistic is a measure of _____. (21-8)

12. When dealing with large amounts of data in a set, it is often easier to represent the data by dividing the values into equal-size groups known as _____. The chart obtained by this procedure is known as a frequency _____ or frequency table. (21-9)

13. Write the formula for the mean of grouped data. (21-10)

14. A(n) _____ is a special type of bar chart without space between the bars that is used to display the data from a frequency distribution. (21-11)

ASSESSMENT TEST

1. The following data represent the monthly sales figures in thousands of dollars for the New York and California branches of Universal Corporation.

EXCEL 1

	April	May	June	July	August	September
New York	121	254	218	156	255	215
California	88	122	211	225	248	260

a. Construct a multiple-line chart depicting the monthly sales for the two branches. Show the New York branch as a solid line and the California branch as a dashed line.

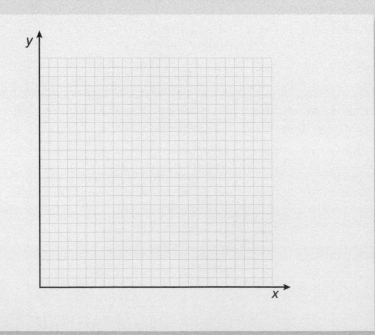

b. Construct a comparative bar chart for the same data. Highlight the bars for each branch differently.

2. Construct a pie chart from the following information compiled in a recent survey of the buying habits of children aged 8 to 17.

Category	Percentage
Clothing	35%
Fast food, snacks, candy	20%
Electronics products	15%
Entertainment	10%
School supplies	10%
Personal care	7%
Other	3%

3. Last month The Computer Connection sold $150,000 in desktop computers, $75,000 in notebook computers, $30,000 in software, $37,500 in printers, and $7,500 in accessories.

a. What percent of the total sales does each category of merchandise represent?

GO ONLINE FOR MORE ACTIVITIES www.cengagebrain.com

CHAPTER 21

b. Construct a pie chart showing the percentage breakdown of sales by merchandise category.

4. You have just been hired as the quality control manager for Pressure Point Manufacturing, a company producing fuel injection systems for General Motors, Ford, and Chrysler. Top management has requested a status report on the number of defective units produced each day. You decide to keep track of the number of defects each day for 30 days. Following are the results of your survey.

Pressure Point Manufacturing—Defects per day—Survey 1

11	13	17	13	15	9	14	11	13	15	11	10	14	12	15
19	15	13	17	9	20	13	14	18	16	15	14	17	18	13

a. Find the mean, median, mode, and range of these data for your report to top management.

After implementing your suggestions for improved quality on the production line, you decide to survey the defects for another 30 days with the following results:

Pressure Point Manufacturing—Defects per day—Survey 2

11	9	12	7	8	10	12	8	9	10	9	7	11	12	8
7	9	11	8	6	12	10	8	8	7	9	6	10	9	11

b. Find the mean, median, mode, and range of the new data.

c. If the company's cost to fix each defective unit is $75, use the *mean* of each survey to calculate the average cost per day for defects before and after your improvements.

d. Theoretically, how much will your improvements save the company in a 300-day production year?

e. Congratulations! The company has awarded you a bonus amounting to 15% of the first year's savings. How much is your bonus check?

5. You are the human resource director for Apollo Industries. Forty applicants for employment were given an assessment test in math and English with the following results:

$$
\begin{array}{cccccccccc}
87 & 67 & 81 & 83 & 94 & 72 & 84 & 68 & 33 & 56 \\
91 & 79 & 88 & 95 & 84 & 75 & 46 & 27 & 69 & 97 \\
69 & 57 & 66 & 81 & 87 & 19 & 76 & 54 & 78 & 91 \\
78 & 72 & 75 & 89 & 74 & 92 & 45 & 59 & 85 & 72
\end{array}
$$

a. What are the range and mode of these scores?

b. Group the data into nine classes of equal size (11–20, 21–30, etc.) and construct a frequency distribution.

c. Calculate the mean of the grouped data by using 15.5, 25.5, etc., as the midpoints.

d. If company policy is to consider only those who score *10 points higher or better* than the mean of the data, how many from this group are still being considered for the job?

e. Construct a histogram of the assessment test scores frequency distribution.

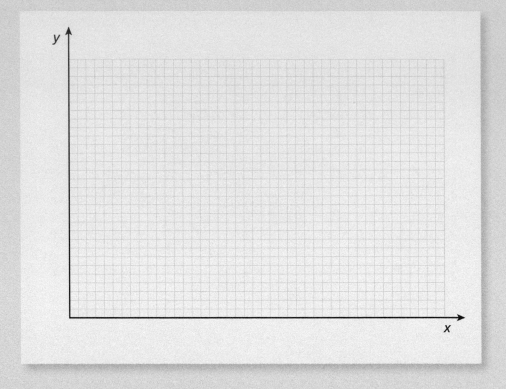

BUSINESS DECISION: BEAT THE MEAN BONUS!

6. You are the owner of The Green Machine, Inc., a car dealership specializing in pre-owned hybrid automobiles. You have a unique and motivating bonus plan for your salespeople that has worked well over the years.

Each quarter the mean number of cars sold is calculated. The first time a salesperson sells more cars than the mean, he or she earns a $100 bonus for each car *over the mean* in that quarter. If a salesperson exceeds the mean a second time in a year, the bonus increases to $150 per car for that quarter. If a salesperson exceeds the mean three times in one year, the bonus is $200 per car for that quarter. If anyone exceeds the mean all four quarters, the fourth-quarter bonus is $300 per car. Remember, the bonus is paid only for the number of cars over the mean.

Each year the program starts over again. All bonuses are paid once per year, in January, for the previous year. The following table represents the number of hybrid cars sold by your five salespeople for each quarter last year. Calculate the bonus each person should receive for last year.

	First Quarter	Second Quarter	Third Quarter	Fourth Quarter
Lugano	16	23	14	23
Gordon	12	20	16	25
Chen	15	13	26	19
Young	22	20	27	19
McIntosh	25	19	32	24

Jim West/Alamy

Tesla Hybrid The Tesla Roadster is the world's first massproduced, all-electric, high-performance sports car. According to the company, the Roadster boasts super car performance without super car emissions. The handbuilt, carbon fiber hybrid sets the mark for premium electric cars to come.

Engineered for efficiency, the zero-emissions Roadster can drive 245 miles per charge, maxes out at 125 mph, and doesn't require a single drop of gas. It plugs into almost any electric outlet anywhere in the world!

CHAPTER 21

COLLABORATIVE LEARNING ACTIVITY

Conducting a Marketing Research Survey

You and your team members have been hired to conduct a marketing research survey for a company that is interested in advertising its products to college students in your area. The company wants to know the news media preferences of the students at your school and specifically would like answers to the following questions:

- What radio station, if any, do you listen to for news in the morning?
- What local television news program, if any, do you watch in the evening?
- What newspaper, if any, do you read each day?
- What Internet sites, if any, do you access for news each week?

a. As a team, design a questionnaire for this research survey. For each media question, list all of the local choices, providing a place for easy check-off responses. Be sure to include "no preference" and "none of the above" as choices. For the Internet question, list the most popular news sites and include space for students to list other responses. In addition to the survey questions, design some easy check-off questions pertaining to demographics—for example, gender, age group, ethnic group, income range, and marital status.

b. Have each member of the research team personally interview between 25 and 30 students. Questionnaires can be handed out and then collected.

c. Tabulate the results of the surveys you conducted. As a team, total the results of each team member's surveys to arrive at the survey totals.

d. Convert the totals for each question to percents.

e. Calculate the mean, median, and mode for each demographic question that has numerical data.

f. Using different types of charts, prepare a visual presentation for the class by illustrating the results of the survey questions.

g. As a team, do you think the results of your survey are valid? Why or why not?

Business Math JOURNAL

BUSINESS, MATH, AND MORE ...

Census 2010 (the Last U.S. Census)

The Ultimate Survey

April 1, 2010, was Census Day in the United States. That was the official day of the full and complete count of the resident population, both legal and illegal. The decennial (every ten years) U.S. Census is mandated in the U.S. Constitution to apportion seats in the House of Representatives. In 2010, census numbers were also used to distribute more than $400 billion in federal aid to cities and states.

Census 2010 – By the Numbers

- **134 million** – Approximate number of total housing units in the United States that had to be contacted for the census via mail or in person to collect a form or determine whether a unit was vacant.
- **1.4 million** – Approximate total number of positions needed to conduct the 2010 Census.
- **3.8 million** – Approximate number of people recruited to fill positions for the 2010 Census operations between 2009 and 2010.
- **635,000** – Approximate number of positions hired for door-to-door follow-up phase in 2010.
- **$10 to $25** – The hourly pay rates established for door-to-door census takers, which were based on local prevailing competitive wages using Bureau of Labor Statistics data.
- **957 million** – Approximate number of total miles census takers traveled to obtain responses during door-to-door follow-up.
- **48 million** – Approximate number of total housing units in door-to-door follow-up.
- **3.4 million** – Approximate number of square feet of office space that was leased for the 12 Regional Census Centers and 494 Local Census Offices.
- **542 million** – Total pieces of mail sent through the U.S. Postal Service for Census 2010. If all the census forms were stacked, the pile would reach 29 miles, more than five times the height of Mount Everest.
- **10** – Number of tractor-trailer loads of mail that arrived daily at each processing center at the peak of the counting.
- **$44,000 and $7 billion** – The budget for the first census in 1790 was $44,000, or 1 cent per person counted. The 2010 Census budget was $7 billion, or $12.50 per person.
- **2082** – The year in which the 2010 Census' electronically stored page images will be opened to the public. By law, individual census records are kept confidential for 72 years before being released for genealogical research.

- **5 and $250,000** – The maximum number of years in prison and the maximum amount of the fine for a census worker who reveals personally identifiable information.
- **$20 and $5,000** In 1790, anyone not cooperating with a census taker was subject to a fine of $20. In 2010, failure to respond could have resulted in a $5,000 fine.

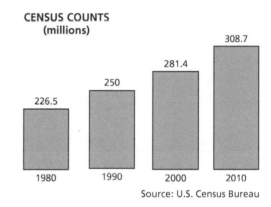

CENSUS COUNTS (millions)

1980	1990	2000	2010
226.5	250	281.4	308.7

Source: U.S. Census Bureau

Issues & Activities

1. Use the chart above to answer the following questions:
   a. Which census had the greatest percent increase from the previous census?
   b. If it is projected that the 2020 Census will count 13.8% more people than were counted in the 2010 Census, how many will be counted in 2020?
2. The 1960 Census form had 81 questions; the 2010 Census form had only 10 questions. What is the percent decrease in the number of questions from the 1960 form to the 2010 form?
3. In the 2000 Census final figures, the population was 281,421,906, there were 49.1% males and 50.9% females, the median age was 35.3 years, there were 105,480.101 households with 2.59 persons per household, the average family size was 3.14, and the homeownership rate was 66.2%.

   In teams, locate the final figures from the 2010 Census to compare and contrast the results with those of the 2000 Census. List your sources and visually report your findings to the class.

BrainTeaser—"The Missing Grade"

An absent-minded professor misplaced the business math test scores of his five students. However, he did remember that the mode of the five scores was 90, the median was 85, and the mean was 83. If the grades ranged from 0 to 100, what is the lowest possible grade from the missing set of scores?

See the end of Appendix A for the solution.

Answers to *Business Decisions* are not included.

1

Chapter 1: Whole Numbers

SECTION I

1. 22,938—Twenty-two thousand, nine hundred thirty-eight   **3.** 184—One hundred eighty-four   **5.** 2,433,590—Two million, four hundred thirty-three thousand, five hundred ninety   **7.** 183,622   **9.** $40,000,000,000   **11.** d   **13.** c   **15.** 1,760
17. 235,400   **19.** 8,000,000   **21.** 1,300,000,000   **23a.** Texas: eight thousand seven hundred ninety-seven megawatts, Iowa: three thousand, fifty-three megawatts
23b. Texas: 8,800 megawatts, Iowa: 3,100 megawatts

SECTION II

1. 91   **3.** 19,943   **5.** 37,648   **7.** 70,928   **9.** estimate 43,100—exact 41,844
11a. 7,000 Vehicles   **11b.** 6,935 Vehicles   **13.** $103,005 Grand Total
15. $1,627   **17.** 4,629   **19.** 278,091   **21.** $138   **23.** $139   **25.** 3,490,700
27. 378   **29a.** 43   **29b.** 22   **29c.** 94

SECTION III

1. 11,191   **3.** 294,300   **5.** 56,969,000   **7.** 13,110   **9.** estimate 100,000—exact 98,980   **11.** estimate 200—exact 187   **13.** $6,985,000   **15a.** $87   **15b.** $13
17. 128 R 20   **19.** 240   **21.** estimate 3—exact 3 R 5   **23.** estimate 578—exact 566 R 68   **25a.** 117   **25b.** 15   **27.** The Royale Hotel is more economical.
29a. $40,272   **29b.** $20,031   **29c.** $20,241

Assessment Test

1. 200,049—Two hundred thousand, forty-nine   **3.** 316,229   **5.** 18,300
7. 260,000   **9.** 99   **11.** 44 R 28   **13.** 22,258   **15.** 714   **17.** $12,763   **19a.** 19
19b. 25   **21a.** $11,340   **21b.** $36   **23.** $1,003   **25.** $49,260   **27.** $3,186
29. 15   **31.** $20

2

Chapter 2: Fractions

SECTION I

1. Mixed, Twenty-three and four-fifths   **3.** Improper, Fifteen-ninths   **5.** Mixed, Two and one-eighth   **7.** $3\frac{1}{3}$ **9.** $4\frac{4}{15}$ **11.** $1\frac{2}{31}$ **13.** $\frac{59}{5}$ **15.** $\frac{149}{8}$
17. $\frac{1,001}{4}$ **19.** $\frac{3}{4}$ **21.** $\frac{27}{115}$ **23.** $\frac{1}{8}$ **25.** $\frac{19}{65}$ **27.** $\frac{13}{16}$ **29.** $\frac{5}{18}$ **31.** $\frac{36}{48}$
33. $\frac{44}{64}$ **35.** $\frac{42}{98}$ **37.** $\frac{40}{64}$ **39.** $\frac{126}{182}$ **41.** $\frac{5}{11}$ **43a.** $\frac{1}{9}$ **43b.** $\frac{8}{9}$

SECTION II

1. 15   **3.** 12   **5.** 300   **7.** $1\frac{1}{3}$ **9.** $1\frac{7}{16}$ **11.** $1\frac{13}{20}$ **13.** $2\frac{3}{20}$ **15.** $11\frac{13}{24}$

17. $10\frac{17}{40}$ **19.** $10\frac{19}{30}$ **21.** $\frac{2}{3}$ **23.** $\frac{11}{18}$ **25.** $8\frac{4}{15}$ **27.** $26\frac{29}{45}$ **29.** $35\frac{13}{15}$

31. $21\frac{1}{8}$ **33.** $1\frac{13}{16}$

SECTION III

1. $\frac{8}{15}$ **3.** $\frac{2}{9}$ **5.** $\frac{10}{19}$ **7.** $2\frac{2}{5}$ **9.** $21\frac{13}{15}$ **11.** $\frac{1}{125}$ **13a.** $\frac{5}{8}$ **13b.** 2,750

15. $43\frac{15}{16}$ **17.** 15   **19.** $2\frac{2}{9}$ **21.** $1\frac{1}{15}$ **23.** $\frac{2}{5}$ **25.** $5\frac{17}{35}$ **27.** 19   **29.** $\frac{5}{14}$

31. 46   **33a.** 240   **33b.** 90   **35.** 185   **37.** 55   **39a.** $2\frac{17}{64}$ **39b.** 11

Assessment Test

1. Improper fraction, Eighteen-elevenths   **3.** Proper fraction, Thirteen-sixteenths

5. 25   **7.** $\frac{86}{9}$ **9.** $\frac{2}{5}$ **11.** $\frac{18}{78}$ **13.** $\frac{25}{36}$ **15.** $5\frac{1}{3}$ **17.** $4\frac{3}{10}$ **19.** $13\frac{1}{3}$ **21.** 69

23. $23\frac{5}{8}$ **25.** $10\frac{7}{16}$ **27a.** $588,000   **27b.** $49,000   **29a.** 275   **29b.** 495

31a. 99   **31b.** 22   **31c.** $6,605

Chapter 3: Decimals

3

SECTION I

1. Twenty-one hundredths   **3.** Ninety-two thousandths   **5.** Ninety-eight thousand, forty-five and forty-five thousandths   **7.** Nine hundred thirty-eight hundred-thousandths
9. Fifty-seven and one-half hundred-thousandths   **11.** .8   **13.** 67,309.04
15. 41.057 seconds, 41.183 seconds, 41.507 seconds   **17.** 0.448557 = 0.45
19. 0.9229388 = 0.9229   **21.** $688.75 = $689   **23.** 88.964 = 89.0   **25.** 1.344 = 1.34

SECTION II

1. 58.033   **3.** $45.27   **5.** 152.784494   **7.** 16.349   **9.** $.87
11. 116.278—One hundred sixteen and two hundred seventy-eight thousandths
13. 80.482   **15a.** $30.25   **15b.** $27.75   **17.** $11.14   **19a.** 900,000
19b. 11,800,000   **21.** 400.2129   **23.** 1,120,050   **25.** 15.152256   **27.** 33,090   **29.** .07
31. $2.72   **33.** 6   **35.** 217.39   **37a.** $2,480.98   **37b.** $15,590.00   **37c.** $230
39a. $250,000,000   **39b.** $2,640,000   **41a.** $2,104.32   **41b.** $920.06   **43.** $16
45a. 1,152   **45b.** $1,440   **45c.** 12-ounce size

SECTION III

1. $\frac{1}{8}$ **3.** $\frac{1}{125}$ **5.** $14\frac{41}{50}$ **7.** 5.67   **9.** 1.22   **11.** 58.43   **13.** 5   **15a.** 16
15b. $190.24   **17a.** $489.26   **17b.** 32.7¢   **19.** $2,520.50

Assessment Test

1. Sixty-one hundredths   **3.** One hundred nineteen dollars and eighty-five cents
5. Four hundred ninety-five ten-thousandths   **7.** 5.014   **9.** $16.57   **11.** 995.070
13. 4.7   **15.** $37.19   **17.** 7.7056   **19.** .736   **21.** .000192   **23.** .4   **25.** $20.06
27. $\frac{441}{10,000}$ **29.** 3.11   **31.** The box of 40 Blu-ray discs and box of 40 jewel cases is the better buy by $4.93.   **33.** $19.89   **35.** $9.25 Savings   **37.** $2,161.19 Remains
39a. 160   **39b.** $6.60

SECTION IV   **1.** $474.00, $15,326.00   **3.** $96.84, $2,324.16   **5.** $319.25, $8,802.19   **7.** $474.23, $870.37   **9.** $5,759.16, $1,472.92   **11.** May 8, June 22   **13.** 2% Feb. 8, 1% Feb. 18, Mar. 30   **15.** Jan. 10, Jan. 30   **17.** Oct. 23, Nov. 12   **19.** June 25, July 15   **21a.** April 27, May 27   **21b.** $21.24   **21c.** $1,148.76   **23a.** March 22   **23b.** April 11   **25a.** $32,931.08   **25b.** May 19

Assessment Test

1. Leisure Time Industries   **3.** 4387   **5.** $46.55   **7.** $2,558   **9.** $11,562.45   **11.** $1,485   **13.** 33.76%   **15.** Fancy Footwear   **17a.** .6052   **17b.** .3948   **19a.** April 24   **19b.** May 9   **19c.** May 15   **19d.** June 4   **21.** $14,563.80

---

8 Chapter 8: Markup and Markdown

SECTION I   **1.** $138.45, 85.7%   **3.** $6,944.80, 77.8%   **5.** $156.22, $93.73   **7.** $2,149.00, 159.2%   **9.** $.75, $1.33   **11.** $85.90   **13.** $195   **15a.** $4.19   **15b.** 71.7%   **17a.** $60.63   **17b.** 104.1%   **19.** $77.88   **21.** $1,029.41   **23.** $21.88

SECTION II   **1.** $115.00, 43.5%   **3.** $61.36, $136.36   **5.** 37.5%   **7.** $94.74, 133%, 57.1%   **9.** $9,468.74, $24,917.74, 61.3%   **11.** 60%   **13a.** $1.74   **13b.** 34.9%   **13c.** $2.09, 41.9%   **15.** $366.12   **17.** $125   **19.** 75.4%   **21a.** $30.49   **21b.** 141.8%   **21c.** 58.6%

SECTION III   **1.** $161.45, 15%   **3.** $1.68, 23.2%   **5.** $41.10, $16.44   **7.** $80.27, 30.7%   **9.** $559.96, $1,039.92   **11a.** $1,750   **11b.** 18.0%   **13a.** $.70   **13b.** 41.4%   **13c.** $1.39   **15.** $30   **17.** $6,018.75   **19.** $469.68   **21.** $233.99   **23a.** $65.00, 40.6%   **23b.** $85.00, 53.1%   **23c.** $396.25   **23d.** Answers will vary.

Assessment Test

1. $152.60   **3.** $18.58   **5.** $6.28, 52.9%   **7.** $15.95   **9a.** $778   **9b.** 21.3%   **11.** $216.06   **13a.** $56.25   **13b.** $64.68   **15a.** $2,499.99   **15b.** $1,000   **15c.** 60%   **15d.** 36%

---

9 Chapter 9: Payroll

SECTION I   **1.** $1,250.00, $625.00, $576.92, $288.46   **3.** $8,333.33, $4,166.67, $3,846.15, $1,923.08   **5.** $34,800, $2,900.00, $1,338.46, $669.23   **7.** $17,420, $1,451.67, $725.83, $670.00   **9.** $1,115.38   **11.** $1,329.23   **13.** 36, 0, $313.20, 0, $313.20   **15.** 48, 8, $290.00, $87.00, $377.00   **17.** $711.90   **19.** $320.25   **21.** $1,170.90   **23.** $5,790.40   **25.** $1,565   **27.** $352.66

SECTION II   **1.** $51.15 Social security, $11.96 Medicare   **3a.** $607.60 Social security, $142.10 Medicare   **3b.** December   **3c.** $365.80 Social security, $142.10 Medicare   **5.** $212.16, $49.62.   **7.** $291.40, $68.15   **9.** $28.40   **11.** $571.20   **13.** $157.24   **15.** $3,260.47 Paycheck   **17.** $114.53   **19.** $598.21

1a. $282.72 Total social security, $66.12 Total Medicare   **1b.** $3,675.36 Social security for the first quarter, $859.56 Medicare for the first quarter   **3.** $17,184.96
5. $5,282.40 Social security, $1,235.40 Medicare   **7a.** $378   **7b.** $42
9a. $347.76, $38.64   **11a.** $3,770.40   **11b.** 15%   **11c.** $196,060.80
13a. $23,699.70   **13b.** Form 1040-ES, *Quarterly Estimated Tax Voucher for Self-Employed Persons*

Assessment Test

1a. $67,200   **1b.** $2,584.62   **3.** $898.70   **5.** $656.25   **7.** $1,011.71   **9.** $6,963
11. $2,284.10   **13.** $44.95 Social security, $10.51 Medicare   **15a.** $2,008.47
15b. $2,151.77   **15c.** $2,454.41   **17.** $1,071.19   **19a.** $1,693.03 Social security, $395.95 Medicare   **19b.** $44,018.78 Social security, $10,294.70 Medicare
21a. $378   **21b.** $42   **23a.** $58,589.20   **23b.** 20.8%   **23c.** $3,046,638.40

Chapter 10: Simple Interest and Promissory Notes   10

1. $800.00   **3.** $8,250.00   **5.** $206.62   **7.** $1,602.74, $1,625.00   **9.** $1,839.79, $1,865.34   **11.** $15.16, $15.38   **13.** $60.82, $61.67   **15.** $882.88, $895.15
17. $12,852.00, $66,852.00   **19.** $2,362.50, $36,112.50   **21.** $22,929.60, $79,129.60
23. $1,770.00   **25.** $1,330,000.00   **27.** $155,043.00   **29.** 98   **31.** 289   **33.** 55
35. December 3   **37.** June 24   **39.** February 23   **41.** October 2   **43.** $62,005.48
45. $403.89   **47.** $14.97

1. $1,250   **3.** $50,000   **5.** $31,440   **7.** $26,000   **9.** 14   **11.** 12.8   **13.** 10.3
15. 158 days   **17.** 308 days   **19.** 180 days   **21.** 88 days   **23.** $13,063.16, $13,403.16
25. $2,390.63, $27,890.63   **27a.** 166 Days   **27b.** September 29   **29.** $10,000
31. 11.6%   **33.** $66,620.99   **35.** $12,370.68   **37a.** 12.5 Years   **37b.** 10 Years

1. $292.50, $4,207.50   **3.** $231.25, $1,618.75   **5.** $232.38, $7,567.62   **7.** 84, $171.50, $4,828.50   **9.** 100, $34.31, $1,265.69   **11.** $132.30, $2,567.70, 14.72   **13.** $107.14, $3,692.86, 7.46   **15.** $4,683.85, $52,816.15, 13.88   **17.** Jan. 31, $4,057.78, 12, $4,037.49
19. Aug. 8, $8,180, 34, $8,101.20   **21.** $195, $14,805, 5.27   **23.** $964, $79,036, 4.88
25. $2,075.00, $97,925.00, 4.24   **27.** 13.61%   **29a.** $484.62   **29b.** $149,515.38
29c. 4.21%

Assessment Test

1. $641.10   **3.** $672.93   **5.** $20,224.00   **7.** 107   **9.** Jan. 24   **11.** $11,666.67
13. 9.1   **15.** 72   **17.** 190, $13,960.00   **19.** 15.2, $2,795.00   **21.** Jan. 20, $20,088.54, $854,911.46   **23.** $10,544.72, $279,455.28, 12.35   **25.** Aug. 25, $5,642.31, 34, $5,569.30
27. $686.00, $27,314.00, 5.02   **29.** $99.37   **31.** 15.3%   **33.** $9,393.88
35a. $28,970.83   **35b.** November 12   **35c.** 13.46%   **37a.** $752   **37b.** $63,248
37c. 4.76%

11 Chapter 11: Compound Interest and Present Value

SECTION I

1. 3, 13   **3.** 24, 4   **5.** 16, 1.5   **7.** 3, 1   **9.** $10,406.04, $406.04   **11.** $2,524.95, $524.95   **13.** $13,950.66, $2,950.66   **15.** $95,776.50, $28,776.50   **17.** $450.86, $50.86   **19.** 1.43077, $18,600.01   **21.** 5.61652, $194,893.24   **23.** 8.71525, $8,715.25   **25.** $260.00, 13.00%   **27.** $82.43, 8.24%   **29a.** 6.14%   **29b.** $4,288.50   **31.** $16,174.20   **33.** 97 Sheep   **35.** $5,904.40, $904.40   **37.** $3,024.73, $224.73   **39.** $71,875

SECTION II

1. $4,633.08, $1,366.92   **3.** $437.43, $212.57   **5.** $3,680.50, $46,319.50   **7.** $6,107.07, $3,692.93   **9.** $235.48, $14.52   **11.** .20829, $2,499.48   **13.** .24200, $338.80   **15.** .26355, $28,990.50   **17a.** $2,549.58   **17b.** $950.42   **19.** $15,742,200   **21.** 47 Million songbirds   **23.** $3,466.02, $1,033.98   **25.** $15,643.55, $3,256.45   **27a.** $5,385   **27b.** $615

Assessment Test

1. $31,530.66, $17,530.66   **3.** $3,185.04, $185.04   **5.** 5.61652, $112,330.40   **7.** $1,078.06, 12.68%   **9.** $6,930.00, $143,070.00   **11.** $658.35, $241.65   **13.** .62027, $806.35   **15.** $81,392.40, $45,392.40   **17.** $17,150.85, $2,150.85   **19.** $92,727.70   **21a.** 12.55%   **21b.** $17,888.55   **23.** $48,545.40   **25a.** $37,243.34   **25b.** $14,243.34   **27.** 3.7 Million fleet miles   **29.** $25,910.82, $4,110.82   **31.** $11,218.11, $1,588.11   **33.** $77,380.73, $2,819.27   **35.** $2,263.80, $176.20   **37.** $97,129   **39.** $17,795

12 Chapter 12: Annuities

SECTION I

1. $18,639.29   **3.** $151,929.30   **5.** $51,722.22   **7.** $13,680.33   **9.** $100,226.90   **11.** $2,543.20   **13.** $2,956.72   **15.** $15,934.37   **17.** $36,848.56   **19.** $42,082.72   **21.** $83,581.92   **23a.** $8,101.04   **23b.** $28,442.52

SECTION II

1. $2,969.59   **3.** $27,096.86   **5.** $95,668.18   **7.** $16,819.32   **9.** $110,997.88   **11.** $9,025.15   **13.** $380,773   **15.** $7,900.87   **17.** $5,865.77   **19.** $6,696.93   **21.** $21,856.03   **23.** $100,490.79

SECTION III

1. $2,113.50   **3.** $55.82   **5.** $1,086.46   **7.** $336.36   **9.** $1,087.48   **11a.** $245,770.96   **11b.** $2,135,329.28   **13a.** $3,769.04   **13b.** $2,385.76   **15.** $12,802.39   **17.** $53.96   **19.** $3,756.68   **21.** $78.95   **23.** $169.11   **25a.** $13,787.95   **25b.** $172,723

Assessment Test

1. $121,687.44   **3.** $86,445.14   **5.** $42,646.92   **7.** $11,593.58   **9.** $993.02   **11.** $255.66   **13.** $20,345.57   **15.** $6,081.72   **17.** $368.62   **19.** $40,012.45   **21.** $7,639.68   **23.** $5,431.63   **25.** $69,840.21   **27.** $32,115.31   **29.** $5,913.62   **31.** $2,468.92   **33a.** $11,261.18   **33b.** $12,321.12   **35.** $1,454.65

Chapter 13: Consumer and Business Credit   13

1. 1.5%, $2.52, $335.90   **3.** 21%, $7.96, $544.32   **5.** .75%, $25.64, $2,573.14
7a. $1.20   **7b.** $259.13   **9.** $636.17, $11.13, $628.75   **11.** $817.08, $14.30, $684.76
13. $677.84   **15.** $158.51   **17a.** 12.4%   **17b.** 15.5%   **17c.** 14.65%   **17d.** 11%

1. $1,050.00, $582.00, $1,982.00   **3.** $10,800.00, $2,700.00, $14,700.00
5. $7,437.50, $2,082.34, $10,832.34   **7.** $15,000.00, $9,577.20, $29,577.20
9. $1,350.00, $270.00, $67.50   **11.** $15,450.00, $8,652.00, $502.13   **13.** $11,685.00,
$3,154.95, $412.22   **15.** $322.00, $14.00, 13%   **17.** $223.50, $12.02, 14.75%
19. $825.20, $12.60, 11.75%   **21.** $31.00, 11.25%   **23.** $4,940.00, 16.6%
25. $15,130.00, 14.71%   **27.** $29.97, $1,498.50, $135.39   **29.** $6.20, $111.60, $159.30
31. $13.82, $1,686.04, $578.59   **33.** 8, 36, 78, $\frac{36}{78}$ **35.** 15, 120, 300, 120/300
37. 40, 820, 1,176, 820/1,176   **39.** 120/300, $360.00, $2,077.50,   **41.** 78/1,176,
$219.94, $2,984.06   **43.** 55/465, $260.22, $4,139.78   **45a.** $1,709.10, $2,120.40,
$411.30   **45b.** $2,310.30   **47.** $68.75   **49a.** $729.52   **49b.** $8,329.52
51. $216.45, $63.19   **53a.** 300   **53b.** 465   **55a.** $504   **55b.** $152.25
55c. 14.64%, 14.75%   **55d.** $1,157.52

Assessment Test

1a. 1.33%   **1b.** $4.59   **1c.** $440.38   **3a.** $4.46, $724.12   **3b.** $724.12, $12.09,
$839.64   **3c.** $839.64, $14.02, $859.61   **5a.** $694.76   **5b.** $7.50   **5c.** $864.74
7a. $9,920   **7b.** $39,120   **9a.** $10,384   **9b.** 19.25%   **11a.** $66,300
11b. $4,646.67   **13a.** $14,144   **13b.** $1,428   **13c.** 11.75%   **13d.** $32,906.45
15a. $30,686.75   **15b.** $24,686.75   **15c.** $8,733.25   **15d.** $39,420   **15e.** 12.75%

Chapter 14: Mortgages   14

1. 80, 9.00, $720.00, $92,800.00   **3.** 130.9, 8.06, $1,055.05, $185,615.00   **5.** 96.8, 7.17,
$694.06, $153,061.60   **7.** 184.3, 8.58, $1,581.29, $100,332.20   **9.** $639.47, $821.39
11. $1,189.79, $1,601.21   **13.** $1,067.61, $1,458.78   **15a.** $1,736.46
15b. $275,328   **17a.** Fortune Bank, $115,950; Northern Trust Bank, $120,000
17b. Fortune Bank, $121,950; Northern Trust Bank, $120,000 (Better deal, $1,950 Less)
19a. 7.35%   **19b.** 12.35%   **21a.** 8.55%   **21b.** 14.75%

1. $89,025, $21,125   **3.** $112,960, $13,860   **5.** $63,700, 0   **7.** $930,300, $416,120
9. 14.32, 24.05   **11.** 26.04, 35.00   **13.** 27.01, 38.24   **15a.** Parker, Martin, and
Jameson   **15b.** Parker and Martin   **17.** 0   **19.** $19,200, No to the addition
21a. 25.75%   **21b.** 39.13%   **21c.** FHA   **21d.** $425.28

Assessment Test

1. 134.9, 7.56, $1,019.84, $171,052.00   **3.** Month 1 loan bal: $145,966.57, Month 2 loan
bal: $145,832.41, Month 3 loan bal: $145,697.53   **5.** $1,321, $1,596.67   **7.** $41,200,
$13,800   **9.** 24.30, 40.15   **11.** FHA, FHA and Conventional   **13a.** $4,269.20
13b. Month 1 loan bal: $519,089.13, Month 2 loan bal: $518,172.38   **13c.** $5,221.70
13d. $14,578.30   **15a.** $703,639.20, $651,744.00   **15b.** Foremost is better by $34,457.70
17a. $1,230.98   **17b.** $120,236   **17c.** $22,557.40   **17d.** $80,060   **19.** 0   **21a.** 27.86%
21b. 39.53%   **21c.** FHA

15 Chapter 15: Financial Statements and Ratios

SECTION I

1. $161,600   **3.** $29,000   **5.** $3,483,500   **7.** $2,406,200   **9.** $40,518, $22,620, $17,898
11. $4,309, $2,128, $2,755   **13.** Current Asset   **15.** Owner's Equity   **17.** Long-Term
Liability   **19.** Current Liability   **21.** Current Asset   **23.** Current Asset
25. Fixed Asset   **27.** Current Asset   **29.** Owner's Equity   **31.** Owner's Equity
33. Current Liability

35a.

Stargate Industries, Inc.
Balance Sheet
June 30, 2013

Assets

Current Assets		Percent*
Cash	$ 44,300	5.5%
Accounts Receivable	127,600	15.8
Merchandise Inventory	88,100	10.9
Prepaid Maintenance	4,100	.5
Office Supplies	4,000	.5
Total Current Assets	268,100	33.2
Property, Plant, and Equipment		
Land	154,000	19.0
Buildings	237,000	29.3
Fixtures	21,400	2.6
Vehicles	64,000	7.9
Computers	13,000	1.6
Total Property, Plant, and Equipment	489,400	60.4
Investments and Other Assets		
Investments	32,000	4.0
Goodwill	20,000	2.5
Total Assets	$809,500	100.0%

Liabilities and Stockholders' Equity

Current Liabilities		
Accounts Payable	55,700	6.9%
Salaries Payable	23,200	2.9
Notes Payable	38,000	4.7
Total Current Liabilities	116,900	14.5
Long-Term Liabilities		
Mortgage Payable	91,300	11.3
Debenture Bonds	165,000	20.4
Total Long-Term Liabilities	256,300	31.7
Total Liabilities	373,200	46.2
Stockholders' Equity		
Common Stock	350,000	43.2
Retained Earnings	86,300	10.7
Total Stockholders' Equity	436,300	53.9
Total Liabilities and Stockholders' Equity	$809,500	100.0%

*Percents may vary by .1 due to rounding.

35b.

Stargate Industries, Inc.
Comparative Balance Sheet
June 30, 2013 and 2014

Assets	2014	2013	Increase (Decrease) Amount	Increase (Decrease) Percent
Current Assets				
Cash	$ 40,200	$ 44,300	($4,100)	(9.3)%
Accounts Receivable	131,400	127,600	3,800	3.0
Merchandise Inventory	92,200	88,100	4,100	4.7
Prepaid Maintenance	3,700	4,100	(400)	(9.8)
Office Supplies	6,200	4,000	2,200	55.0
Total Current Assets	273,700	268,100	5,600	2.1
Property, Plant, and Equipment				
Land	154,000	154,000	0	0.0
Buildings	231,700	237,000	(5,300)	(2.2)
Fixtures	23,900	21,400	2,500	11.7
Vehicles	55,100	64,000	(8,900)	(13.9)
Computers	16,800	13,000	3,800	29.2
Total Property, Plant, and Equipment	481,500	489,400	7,900	1.6
Investments and Other Assets				
Investments	36,400	32,000	4,400	13.8
Goodwill	22,000	20,000	2,000	10.0
Total Assets	$813,600	$809,500	4,100	.5
Liabilities and Stockholders' Equity				
Current Liabilities				
Accounts Payable	51,800	55,700	(3,900)	(7.0)
Salaries Payable	25,100	23,200	1,900	8.2
Notes Payable	19,000	38,000	(19,000)	(50.0)
Total Current Liabilities	95,900	116,900	(21,000)	(18.0)
Long-Term Liabilities				
Mortgage Payable	88,900	91,300	(2,400)	(2.6)
Debenture Bonds	165,000	165,000	0	0.0
Total Long-Term Liabilities	253,900	256,300	(2,400)	(.9)
Total Liabilities	349,800	373,200	(23,400)	(6.3)
Stockholders' Equity				
Common Stock	350,000	350,000	0	0.0
Retained Earnings	113,800	86,300	27,500	31.9
Total Stockholders' Equity	463,800	436,300	27,500	6.3
Total Liabilities and Stockholders' Equity	$813,600	$809,500	4,100	.5

1. $565,700, $44,700   **3.** $306,850, $110,325   **5.** $880,000, $405,220   **7.** $154,560, $86,510   **9.** $20,561, $6,330, $3,461   **11.** $37,905, $12,975, $2,005   **13a.** $316,120 **13b.** $122,680   **13c.** $212,320   **13d.** $45,120

SECTION II

15a.

Sweets & Treats Candy Company, Inc.
Income Statement
For the year ended December 31, 2014

Revenue		
Gross Sales	$2,249,000	109.6%
Less: Sales Returns and Allowances	143,500	7.0
Sales Discounts	54,290	2.6
Net Sales	$2,051,210	100.0
Cost of Goods Sold		
Merchandise Inventory, Jan. 1	875,330	42.7
Net Purchases	546,920	26.7
Freight In	11,320	.6
Goods Available for Sale	1,433,570	69.9
Less: Merchandise Inventory, Dec. 31	716,090	34.9
Cost of Goods Sold	717,480	35.0
Gross Margin	1,333,730	65.0
Operating Expenses		
Salaries	319,800	15.6
Rent	213,100	10.4
Depreciation	51,200	2.5
Utilities	35,660	1.7
Advertising	249,600	12.2
Insurance	39,410	1.9
Administrative Expenses	91,700	4.5
Miscellaneous Expenses	107,500	5.2
Total Operating Expenses	1,107,970	54.0
Income before Taxes	225,760	11.0
Income Tax	38,450	1.9
Net Income	$ 187,310	9.1

15b.

Sweets & Treats Candy Company, Inc.
Comparative Income Statement
For the years ended December 31, 2014 and 2015

			Increase (Decrease)	
	2015	**2014**	**Amount**	**Percent**
Revenue				
Gross Sales	$2,125,000	$2,249,000	($124,000)	(5.5)%
Less: Sales Returns and Allowances	126,400	143,500	(17,100)	(11.9)
Sales Discounts	73,380	54,290	19,090	35.2
Net Sales	1,925,220	2,051,210	(125,990)	(6.1)
Cost of Goods Sold				
Merchandise Inventory, Jan. 1	716,090	875,330	(159,240)	(18.2)
Net Purchases	482,620	546,920	(64,300)	(11.8)
Freight In	9,220	11,320	(2,100)	(18.6)
Goods Available for Sale	1,207,930	1,433,570	(225,640)	(15.7)
Less: Merchandise Inventory, Dec. 31	584,550	716,090	(131,540)	(18.4)
Cost of Goods Sold	623,380	717,480	(94,100)	(13.1)
Gross Margin	1,301,840	1,333,730	(31,890)	(2.4)

Sweets & Treats Candy Company, Inc.
Comparative Income Statement
For the years ended December 31, 2014 and 2015

| | | | Increase (Decrease) | |
	2015	2014	Amount	Percent
Operating Expenses				
Salaries	340,900	319,800	21,100	7.0
Rent	215,000	213,100	1,900	.9
Depreciation	56,300	51,200	5,100	10.0
Utilities	29,690	35,660	(5,970)	(16.7)
Advertising	217,300	249,600	(32,300)	(13.0)
Insurance	39,410	39,410	0	0
Administrative Expenses	95,850	91,700	4,150	4.5
Miscellaneous Expenses	102,500	107,500	(5,000)	(4.7)
Total Operating Expenses	1,096,950	1,107,970	(11,020)	(1.0)
Income before Income Tax	204,890	225,760	(20,870)	(9.2)
Income Tax	44,530	38,450	6,080	15.8
Net Income	$ 160,360	$ 187,310	$ (26,950)	(14.4)

1. $318,000, 3.41:1   **3.** ($5,160), .74:1   **5.** $379,070, 1.45:1   **7.** $95,920, 1.29:1
9. $2,165, 1.73:1   **11.** 25 Days   **13a.** 32 Days   **13b.** 32, 16 Days faster than competition
15. $74,447.50, 6.6   **17.** $105,650, 6.2   **19.** .27:1   **21.** $865,000, .38:1, .62:1
23. $155,390, .70:1, 2.30:1   **25.** $226,000, $112,600, $113,400, 35.3, 17.7
27. $149,410, $50,210, 46.1, 15.5   **29.** 21.6   **31.** 8.2

SECTION III

33.

Hook, Line, and Sinker Fishing Supply
Trend Analysis

	2014	2013	2012	2011	2010
Net Sales	107.5	127.3	108.0	97.1	100.0
Net Income	124.3	128.5	99.4	104.2	100.0
Total Assets	109.7	107.4	105.0	97.7	100.0
Stockholders' Equity	105.9	120.3	106.4	94.5	100.0

Assessment Test

1. 4,412, 3,539, 873   **3.** 41,791, 15,818, 11,797

5a.

Uniflex Fabricators, Inc.
Balance Sheet
As of December 31, 2014

Assets		
Percent		
Current Assets	$132,500	52.2
Property, Plant, and Equipment	88,760	35.0
Investments and Other Assets	32,400	12.8
Total Assets	$253,660	100.0%

Uniflex Fabricators, Inc.
Balance Sheet
As of December 31, 2014

Liabilities		
Current Liabilities	51,150	20.2
Long-Term Liabilities	87,490	34.5
Total Liabilities	138,640	54.7
Owner's Equity		
Paul Provost, Equity	115,020	45.3
Total Liabilities and Owner's Equity	$253,660	100.0%

5b.
Uniflex Fabricators, Inc.
Comparative Balance Sheet
As of December 31, 2014 and 2015

			Increase (Decrease)	
	2015	**2014**	**Amount**	**Percent**
Assets				
Current Assets	$154,300	$132,500	$21,800	16.5
Property, Plant, and Equipment	124,650	88,760	35,890	40.4
Investments and Other Assets	20,000	32,400	(12,400)	(38.3)
Total Assets	$298,950	$253,660	45,290	17.9
Liabilities				
Current Liabilities	65,210	51,150	14,060	27.5
Long-Term Liabilities	83,800	87,490	(3,690)	(4.2)
Total Liabilities	149,010	138,640	10,370	7.5
Owner's Equity				
Paul Provost, Equity	149,940	115,020	34,920	30.4
Total Liabilities and Owner's Equity	$298,950	$253,660	45,290	17.9

7. $185,772

9a.
Woof & Meow Pet Supply
Income Statement
Third Quarter, 2014

Revenue		
Gross Sales	$224,400	106.8
Less: Sales Returns and Allowances	14,300	6.8
Net Sales	210,100	100.0
Cost of Goods sold		
Merchandise Inventory, July 1	165,000	78.5
Net Purchases	76,500	36.4
Goods Available for Sale	241,500	114.9
Less: Merchandise Inventory, Sept. 30	143,320	68.2
Cost of Goods Sold	98,180	46.7
Gross Margin	111,920	53.3
Operating Expenses	68,600	32.7

Woof & Meow Pet Supply
Income Statement
Third Quarter, 2014

Income before Taxes	43,320	20.6
Income Tax	8,790	4.2
Net Income	$ 34,530	16.4

9b.

Woof & Meow Pet Supply
Comparative Income Statement
Third and Fourth Quarters, 2014

	4th Qtr.	3rd Qtr.	Increase (Decrease) Amount	Increase (Decrease) Percent
Revenue				
Gross Sales	$218,200	$224,400	($6,200)	(2.8)
Less: Sales Returns and Allowances	9,500	14,300	(4,800)	(33.6)
Net Sales	208,700	210,100	1,400	.7
Cost of Goods Sold				
Merchandise Inventory, Beginning	143,320	165,000	(21,680)	(13.1)
Net Purchases	81,200	76,500	4,700	6.1
Goods Available for Sale	224,520	241,500	(16,980)	(7.0)
Less: Merchandise Inventory, Ending	125,300	143,320	(18,020)	(12.6)
Cost of Goods Sold	99,220	98,180	1,040	1.0
Gross Margin	109,480	111,920	(2,440)	(2.2)
Operating Expenses	77,300	68,600	8,700	12.7
Income before Income Tax	32,180	43,320	(11,140)	(25.7)
Income Tax	11,340	8,790	2,550	29.0
Net Income	$ 20,840	$ 34,530	(13,690)	(39.6)

11. $653,300   **13.** 1.51:1   **15.** 1.74 Times   **17.** 37.9%   **19.** 48.3%   **21.** 4.2%

23.

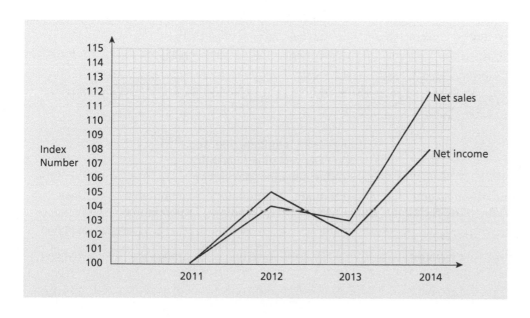

16 | Chapter 16: Inventory

SECTION I

1. 127, $16,531 **3.** 1,110, $1,798.30 **5a.** 600 **5b.** $86,230 **5c.** $24,765.20
5d. $23,380 **5e.** $24,001.24 **7.** $19,487 **9.** $43,030

SECTION II

1. $7,003 **3.** $187,738 **5.** $157,350 **7.** $61,716

SECTION III

1. $60,000, 8.3, $50,000.00 **3.** $486,500, 2.5, $342,857.00 **5.** $59,900, 4.3,
$49,692.00 **7.** $466,460, 2.8, Above **9a.** $58,400 **9b.** 4.2 Times **11a.** $77,650
11b. 5.9 Times **13a.** 4.8 Times **13b.** $134,309.09 **15a.** $38,150, 3.8 Times
15b. $29,591.84

Assessment Test

1. 81, $41,244 **3.** 454, $22,053.65 **5.** $178,159 **7.** $394,885 **9.** $153,500, 5,
$111,765 **11.** $81,780, 5.6, $73,226 **13a.** $173,200 **13b.** 2.5 Times
13c. $114,710.53

17 | Chapter 17: Depreciation

SECTION I

1. $45,650, $42,150, $4,215.00 **3.** $160,000, $140,000, $28,000.00 **5.** $125,250,
$111,750, $12,416.67 **7.** $470,000, $416,000, $52,000.00

9.
Fluffy Laundromat
Straight-Line Depreciation Schedule
Laundry Equipment

End of Year	Annual Depreciation	Accumulated Depreciation	Book Value
			(new) $57,970
1	$11,194	$11,194	46,776
2	11,194	22,388	35,582
3	11,194	33,582	24,388
4	11,194	44,776	13,194
5	11,194	55,970	2,000

11. 15, $\frac{5}{15}, \frac{13}{15}, \frac{1}{15}$ **13.** 55, $\frac{10}{15}, \frac{8}{55}, \frac{6}{55}$ **15.** 120, $\frac{15}{120}, \frac{13}{120}, \frac{11}{120}$

17.
Vanguard Manufacturing, Inc.
SYD Depreciation Schedule
Production-Line Machinery

End of Year	Total Depreciation	Depreciation Rate Fraction	Annual Depreciation	Accumulated Depreciation	Book Value
					(new) $445,000
1	$420,000	$\frac{6}{21}$	$120,000	$120,000	325,000
2	420,000	$\frac{5}{21}$	100,000	220,000	225,000

Vanguard Manufacturing, Inc.
SYD Depreciation Schedule
Production-Line Machinery

End of Year	Total Depreciation	Depreciation Rate Fraction	Annual Depreciation	Accumulated Depreciation	Book Value
3	420,000	$\frac{4}{21}$	80,000	300,000	145,000
4	420,000	$\frac{3}{21}$	60,000	360,000	85,000
5	420,000	$\frac{2}{21}$	40,000	400,000	45,000
6	420,000	$\frac{1}{21}$	20,000	420,000	25,000

19. 10.00, 15.00 **21.** 12.50, 18.75 **23.** 5.00, 10.00 **25.** $.122 **27.** .25 **29.** .166

31.
Thunderbird Manufacturing
Units-of-Production Depreciation Schedule
Stamping Machine

End of Year	Depreciation per Unit	Units Produced	Annual Depreciation	Accumulated Depreciation	Book Value
				(new)	$ 45,000
1	$.16	50,000	$ 8,000	$ 8,000	37,000
2	.16	70,000	11,200	19,200	25,800
3	.16	45,000	7,200	26,400	18,600
4	.16	66,000	10,560	36,960	8,040
5	.16	30,000	3,040*	40,000	5,000

*Maximum allowable to reach salvage value.

1a. $247,000 **1b.** $43,200.30 **3a.** $1,425,000 **3b.** $886,500 **5.** Commercial airplanes are in the 7-year property class. See Appendix B for schedule.
7a. $0.48 Per board foot **7b.** $375,360

Assessment Test

1. $5,864, $5,264, $877.33

3.
Oxford Manufacturing, Inc.
Straight-Line Depreciation Schedule
Manufacturing Equipment

End of Year	Annual Depreciation	Accumulated Depreciation	Book Value
		(new)	$652,000
1	$154,750	$154,750	497,250
2	154,750	309,500	342,500
3	154,750	464,250	187,750
4	154,750	619,000	33,000

5. 45, $\frac{8}{45}, \frac{6}{45}, \frac{4}{45}$ **7.** 12.5, 18.75

9.

Award Makers
150% Declining-Balance Depreciation Schedule
Computerized Engraving Machine

End of Year	Beginning Book Value	Depreciation Rate	Depreciation for the Year	Accumulated Depreciation	Ending Book Value
					(new) $33,800.00
1	$33,800.00	.3	$10,140.00	$10,140.00	23,660.00
2	23,660.00	.3	7,098.00	17,238.00	16,562.00
3	16,562.00	.3	4,968.60	22,206.60	11,593.40

11. .024   **13a.** $320,000

13b.

Stone Age Concrete, Inc.
MACRS Depreciation Schedule
Cement Manufacturing Equipment

End of Year	Original Basis (cost)	Cost Recovery Percentage	Cost Recovery (depreciation)	Accumulated Depreciation	Book Value
					(new) $320,000
1	$320,000	5.00	$16,000	$16,000	304,000
2	320,000	9.50	30,400	46,400	273,600
3	320,000	8.55	27,360	73,760	246,240
4	320,000	7.70	24,640	98,400	221,600
5	320,000	6.93	22,176	120,576	199,424

15a. $375,000   **15b.** $415,500

18 — Chapter 18: Taxes

SECTION I

1. $.59, $9.54   **3.** $.32, $5.20   **5.** $.65, $10.55   **7.** $100.80, $43.20, $1,584.00
9. $9.90, $22.00, $251.85   **11.** $17,847.98, $937.02   **13.** $12.10, $20.79, $221.89
15a. $44.91   **15b.** $1.80   **17a.** $1,392   **17b.** $740   **17c.** $19,532

SECTION II

1. $216,000, $8,856.00   **3.** $310,000, $5,347.50   **5.** $76,000, $2,614.40   **7.** $198,400,
$5,138.56   **9.** $106,440, $2,267.17   **11.** $264,033, $13,993.75   **13.** 4.65%, $4.65,
$46.50, 46.5   **15.** 5.89, $5.89, $58.90, 58.9   **17.** 1.55, $1.55, $15.50, 15.5
19a. $8,100,000   **19b.** $3,450,000 More

SECTION III

1. $32,180, $5,950, $3,800, $22,430   **3.** $43,910, $11,900, $7,600, $24,410
5. $6,780, $5,950, $3,800, $49,680   **7.** $4,080, $8,700, $11,400, $51,890
9. $29,907   **11.** $3,716   **13.** $5,574   **15.** $40,200   **17.** $66,242.27
19. $101,650.00   **21.** Refund $1,115   **23.** Owe $1,519   **25a.** $92,320
25b. $59,920   **25c.** $4,689   **25d.** $6,198 refund   **27.** $18,494.70, $70,460.30
29. $334,250,000.00, $620,750,000.00

Assessment Test

1. $1.17, $19.05   **3.** $6.62, $141.62   **5.** $1,184.63, $755.00, $19,489.63
7a. $25.42   **7b.** $471.30   **9a.** Sales tax per tire = $3.83, Total sales tax = $2,221.40
9b. Excise tax per tire = $7.50, Total excise tax = $4,350   **9c.** $55,871.40   **11.** $52,101,

$662.72   **13.** $82,615, $2,394.18   **15.** 1.65%, $1.65, $16.50, 16.5   **17a.** 0.07%
17b. $0.07 per $100   **17c.** $0.70 per $1,000   **17d.** 0.7 mills   **19.** $66,003, $11,900,
$11,400, $40,523   **21.** $42,527.36   **23.** $2,869   **25.** $59,217.75   **27.** Owe $228
29a. $36,150   **29b.** $22,600   **29c.** $1,194   **29d.** $2,706

Chapter 19: Insurance

SECTION I

1. $79.50, $41.34, $20.67, $7.16   **3.** $842.00, $437.84, $218.92, $75.78   **5.** $270.00,
$140.40, $70.20, $24.30   **7.** $1,125.25, $585.13, $292.57, $101.27   **9.** $4,900, $9,300,
17, 54   **11.** $5,495, $10,990, 21, 218   **13.** $2,275, $5,825, 19, 204   **15a.** $5,240.40
15b. $2,725.01   **17.** Option 1: $14,325 Cash value, Option 2: $37,200 Reduced paid-up
insurance, Option 3: 30 years, 206 days Extended term   **19.** $255,000 Insurance needed

SECTION II

1. $5,907.50, $1,001.00, $6,908.50   **3.** $533.20, $178.50, $711.70   **5.** $7,200.20,
$1,287.00, $8,487.20   **7.** $225.00, $525.00   **9.** $112.50, $337.50   **11.** $1,088.00,
$192.00   **13.** $50.40, $579.60   **15.** $75,000.00   **17.** $37,000.00   **19.** $150,000.00
21. $202.50   **23.** Aetna: $57,000, State Farm: $23,750, Liberty Mutual: $14,250

SECTION III

1. $343.00   **3.** $1,125.00   **5.** $625.60   **7.** $1,146.60   **9.** $1,412   **11a.** $98,690
11b. $8,050

Assessment Test

1. $2,521.60, $1,311.23, $655.62, $226.94   **3.** $148.20, $77.06, $38.53, $13.34
5. $20,410, $40,820, 21, 218   **7a.** $1,088   **7b.** 97.92   **7c.** $87.04   **9.** $640,000
11. $475.00, $672.00, $1,147.00   **13.** $173.33, $86.67   **15.** $6,057.69   **17.** $12,392
19. $153,000   **21.** $361.80   **23.** $564.40   **25a.** $103,650   **25b.** $40,250

Chapter 20: Investments

SECTION I

1. $6.00, $.50   **3.** $5.50, $.85   **5.** $8.00, $1.50   **7.** WMT, $51.02, up .06%
9. HPQ, $38.00, 13   **11.** $55.94, 2.94%, down 12.3%   **13.** 1.7%, 15   **15.** 1.4%, 23
17. $64.00, 13   **19.** $3,959.20, $4,910.40, $951.20   **21.** $6,585.15, $9,997.57,
$3,412.42   **23.** $29,723.41, $26,310.56, ($3,412.85)   **25.** $0.85 Per share
27a. $27,000,000   **27b.** $1.74 Per share   **29a.** $29,658.56   **29b.** $36,078.38
29c. $6,419.82

SECTION II

1. 8.000%, 107.250   **3.** MS.TJ, down 0.052   **5.** Citigroup   **7.** 4.600%, 4.521%
9. July 2014, A2/A/A+   **11.** $9.17, $876.67   **13.** $34.90, $7,959.20   **15.** $16.56,
$11,433.10   **17.** $28.33, $4,429.32   **19.** $8.13, $6,262.41   **21.** $66.25, 7.3%
23. $75.00, 6%   **25.** $53.75, 6.4%

SECTION III

1. PAAIX, $12.30   **3.** John Hancock Funds A, HiYMuBdA p, $8.30   **5.** John Hancock
Funds A, ClassicVal p, down 15.8%   **7.** GoldInst r, 17.7%   **9.** Fidelity Invest, down 8.5%
11. $.67, 3.8%   **13.** $0, 0%   **15.** $.55, 4.2%   **17.** $8.23, 526.316   **19.** $10.96,
2,281.022   **21.** $3,750, $4,260, $585, 15.6   **23.** $4,850, $6,120, $2,520, 52
25. $1,530, $1,880, $395, 25.8   **27.** $2.50   **29.** 43.3%

Assessment Test

1. 0, $.36　**3.** $15.00, $.09　**5.** 3M Company, 3,416,237 shares　**7.** McDonald's Corp., 18.50%　**9.** $2.09, 3.3　**11.** $8.98, $1.71　**13.** $15,665.20, $12,142.70, ($3,522.50)　**15.** $39,277.88, $44,975.31, $5,697.43　**17a.** $13,000,000　**17b.** $.71 Per share　**19a.** $4,472.28　**19b.** $3,346.85　**19c.** ($1,125.43) Loss　**21.** Baa/BBB/BBB+, 7.560%　**23.** NPGP.GL, TXU.LT　**25.** A2/A/A, down 0.052, 4.969%　**27.** $20.49, $4,074.95　**29.** $2.05, $9,410.50　**31.** $21.84, $4,969.20　**33.** $95.00, 9%　**35.** Vanguard Index, 500 Index, $96.95　**37.** $12.30, up 0.01　**39.** $.52, 5　**41.** $7.05, $6,410.256　**43.** $1,340, $1,180, ($85.00), (6.3)　**45.** $9,400, $12,820, $4,380, 46.6　**47.** $9.04　**49.** 33.6%

21 — Chapter 21: Business Statistics and Data Presentation

SECTION I

1a. $0.2 billion　**1b.** 2012　**1c.** widget sales in billions of dollars from 2007 to 2014
1d. x-axis = time from 2007 to 2014, y-axis = sales in billions of dollars
1e. $1.0 billion　**1f.** 2011　**1g.** $1 billion

3.

	Jan.	Feb.	Mar.	Apr.	May	June
Standard	$569,400	$566,200	$636,100	$607,400	$649,700	$706,700
Deluxe	$347,400	$343,800	$408,700	$383,900	$408,000	$431,600

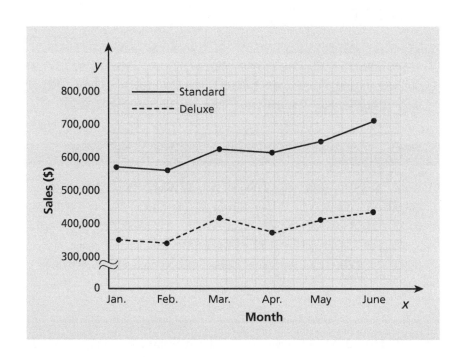

5.

	Jan.	Feb.	Mar.	Apr.	May	June
Standard	$214,700	$228,400	$246,600	$239,000	$266,100	$279,300
Deluxe	$121,300	$133,100	$164,800	$153,200	$185,000	$190,100
Total	$336,000	$361,500	$411,400	$392,200	$451,100	$469,400

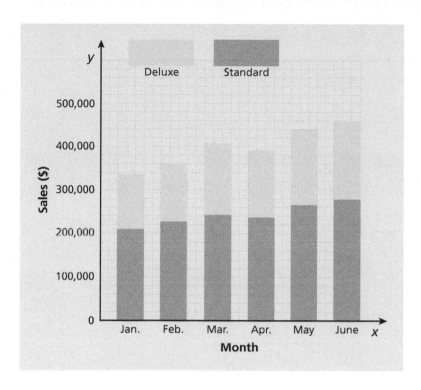

7.

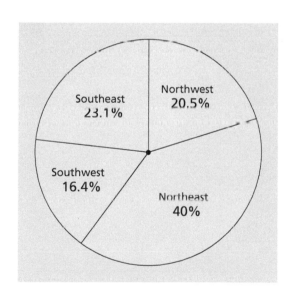

Northwest	$1,244,500	Northwest $\dfrac{1,244,500}{6,058,900} = 20.5\% \times 360 = 74°$
Northeast	2,421,600	
Southwest	993,100	Northeast $\dfrac{2,421,600}{6,058,900} = 40\% \times 360 = 144°$
Southeast	1,399,700	
Total sales	$6,058,900	Southwest $\dfrac{993,100}{6,058,900} = 16.4\% \times 360 = 59°$
		Southeast $\dfrac{1,399,700}{6,058,900} = 23.1\% \times 360 = \dfrac{83°}{360°}$

SECTION II   **1.** 17.8   **3.** 306.8   **5.** 9 is the median.   **7.** 38 is the median.   **9.** 47%   **11.** 21 is the mode in this set.   **13.** Both 4 and 9 are modes in this set.   **15.** 199   **17.** 2,179
19a. Small van = 86.8, Large van = 140.6   **19b.** Small truck = 288, Large truck = 339
19c. 189   **19d.** 238   **19e.** Both 86 and 290 are modes of this set of numbers.
19f. 293

SECTION III   **1a.**

Class	Tally	Frequency
5–9	I	1
10–14	IIII	4
15–19	IIII I	6
20–24	IIII	5
25–29	II	2

1b.

Class	Tally	Frequency (f)	Midpoint (m)	$f \times m$
5–9	I	1	7	7
10–14	IIII	4	12	48
15–19	IIII I	6	17	102
20–24	IIII	5	22	110
25–29	II	2	27	54
		18		321

$$\text{Mean} = \frac{321}{18} = \underline{\underline{17.8}}$$

1c.

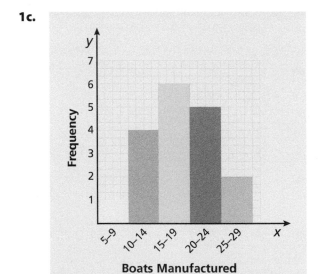

3a.

Class	Tally	Frequency
$4.00–4.99	IIII	4
$5.00–5.99	IIII I	6
$6.00–6.99	IIII III	8
$7.00–7.99	IIII	5
$8.00–8.99	IIII	5
$9.00–9.99	II	2

3b.

Class	Tally	Frequency (*f*)	Midpoint (*m*)	*f* × *m*
$4.00–4.99	IIII	4	4.495	17.980
$5.00–5.99	JHI I	6	5.495	32.970
$6.00–6.99	JHI III	8	6.495	51.960
$7.00–7.99	JHI	5	7.495	37.475
$8.00–8.99	JHI	5	8.495	42.475
$9.00–9.99	II	2	9.495	18.990
		30		201.850

$$\text{Mean} = \frac{201.85}{30} = \$6.73$$

3c.

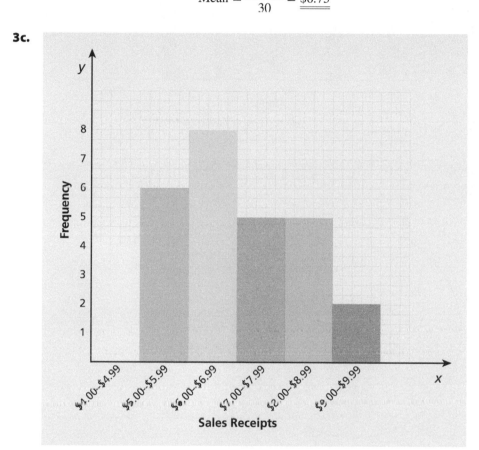

Sales Receipts

Assessment Test

1a.

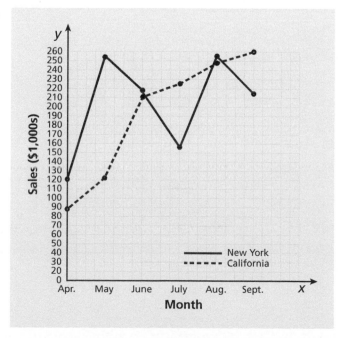

1b.

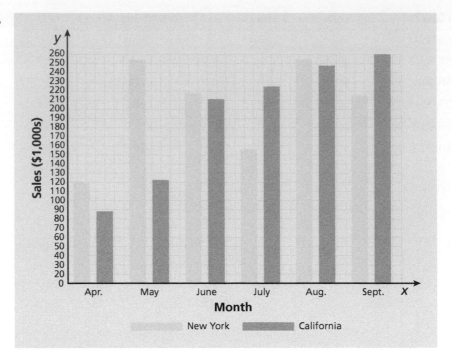

3a. Desktop computers: 50%, Notebook computers: 25%, Software: 10%, Printers: 12.5%, Accessories: 2.5%

3b.

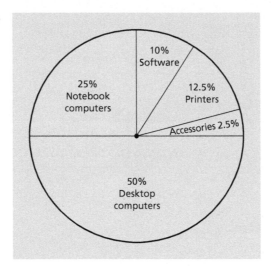

5a. Range: 78, Mode: 72

5b.

Class	Tally	Frequency
11–20	I	1
21–30	I	1
31–40	I	1
41–50	II	2
51–60	IIII	4
61–70	ЖІ	5
71–80	ЖІ ЖІ	10
81–90	ЖІ ЖІ	10
91–100	ЖІ I	6

5c.

Class	Tally	Frequency (f)	Midpoint (m)	$f \times m$
11–20	I	1	15.5	15.5
21–30	I	1	25.5	25.5
31–40	I	1	35.5	35.5
41–50	II	2	45.5	91.0
51–60	IIII	4	55.5	222.0
61–70	JHT	5	65.5	327.5
71–80	JHT JHT	10	75.5	755.0
81–90	JHT JHT	10	85.5	855.0
91–100	JHT I	6	95.5	573.0
		40		2,900.0

$$\text{Mean} = \frac{2,900}{40} = \underline{\underline{72.5}}$$

5d. 14

5e.

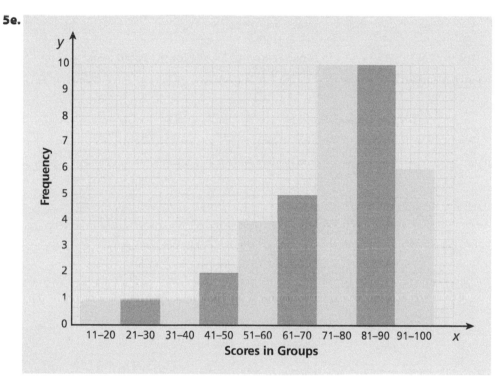

BUSINESS MATH JOURNAL

Brainteaser solutions

APPENDIX A

1. page 90   <u>A decimal point</u> 1.2

2. page 188   <u>20 nines</u>   Don't forget 90, 91, 92, 93, ... 99!

3. page 303   <u>24 days</u>

Let X = days worked
Let $(30 - X)$ = days not worked
$55X - 66(30 - X) = 924$
$X = 24$ Days

4. page 405   <u>866 miles high</u>

If 4 inches equals $1 million, then a foot equals
$3 million.
A mile equals $15.84 billion (5,280 ft × $3 million)

$$\$1 \text{ trillion} = \left(\frac{1,000}{15.84}\right) = 63.13 \text{ miles}$$

$13.72 \times 63.13 = 866.14 = 866$ miles

5. page 533   Assuming the clock displays AM and PM rather than a 24-hour display, the room will be <u>darkest at 1:11</u> and <u>brightest at 10:08</u>.

6. page 639 $60 million

Let X = Total taxes

$$X = \frac{1}{3}X + \frac{1}{4}X + \$25 \text{ million}$$

$$X = \frac{7}{12}X + \$25 \text{ million}$$

$$X - \frac{7}{12}X = \$25 \text{ million}$$

$$\frac{5}{12}X = \$25 \text{ million}$$

$$X = \$60 \text{ million}$$

7. page 761   66

The most common score (mode) was 90, so at least two scores were 90.
The middle score (median) was 85, so at least one score was 85.
The remaining two scores must be less than 85.
The mean was 83; therefore, the sum of all five test scores was 415 (5 × 83).
$415 - 2(90) - 85 = 150$
If one score was 84, the lowest possible score is 66 $(150 - 84)$.